LYLE PRICE GUIDE

CHINA

The publishers wish to express their sincere thanks to the following for their involvement and assistance in the production of this volume:

Editor	TONY CURTIS
Text By	EELIN McIVOR
Editorial	ANNETTE CURTIS
	DONNA RUTHERFORD
	JACQUELINE LEDDY
Art Production	CATRIONA DAY
	NICKY FAIRBURN
	DONNA CRUICKSHANK
Graphics	FRANK BURRELL
	JAMES BROWN
	EILEEN BURRELL

A CIP catalogue record for this book is available from the British Library.

ISBN 86248-140-6

Typeset by Word Power, Auchencrow, Berwickshire
Printed and bound in Great Britain by
Butler & Tanner Ltd, Frome and London

LYLE PRICE GUIDE

CHINA

TONY CURTIS

CONTENTS

Acknowledgements

AB Stockholms Auktionsverk, Box 16256, 103 25 Stockholm, Sweden
Abbots Auction Rooms, The Auction Rooms, Campsea Ash, Woodbridge, Suffolk
Abridge Auction Rooms, Market Place, Abridge, Essex RM4 1UA
Allen & Harris, St Johns Place, Whiteladies Road, Clifton, Bristol BS8 2ST
Jean Claude Anaf, Lyon Brotteaux, 13 bis place Jules Ferry, 69456 Lyon, France
Anderson & Garland, Marlborough House, Marlborough Crescent, Newcastle upon Tyne NE1 4EE
Antique Collectors Club & Co. Ltd, 5 Church Street, Woodbridge, Suffolk IP 12 1DS
Auction Team Köln, Postfach 50 11 68, D-5000 Köln 50 Germany
Auktionshause Arnold, Bleichstr. 42, 6000 Frankfurt a/M, Germany
Barber's Auctions, Woking, Surrey
Bearnes, Rainbow, Avenue Road, Torquay TQ2 5TG
Biddle & Webb, Ladywood Middleway, Birmingham B16 0PP
Bigwood, The Old School, Tiddington, Stratford upon Avon
Black Horse Agencies, Locke & England, 18 Guy Street, Leamington Spa
Boardman Fine Art Auctioneers, Station Road Corner, Haverhill, Suffolk CB9 0EY
Bonhams, Montpelier Street, Knightsbridge, London SW7 1HH
Bonhams Chelsea, 65–69 Lots Road, London SW10 0RN
Bonhams West Country, Dowell Street, Honiton, Devon
British Antique Exporters, School Close, Queen Elizabeth Avenue, Burgess Hill, Sussex
William H Brown, The Warner Auction Rooms, 16–18, Halford Street, Leicester LE1 1JB
Butterfield & Butterfield, 220 San Bruno Avenue, San Francisco CA 94103, USA
Butterfield & Butterfield, 7601 Sunset Boulevard, Los Angeles CA 90046, USA
Central Motor Auctions, Barfield House, Britannia Road, Morley, Leeds, LS27 0HN
H.C. Chapman & Son, The Auction Mart, North Street, Scarborough.
Christie's (International) SA, 8 place de la Taconnerie, 1204 Genève, Switzerland
Christie's Monaco, S.A.M, Park Palace 98000 Monte Carlo, Monaco
Christie's Scotland, 164–166 Bath Street Glasgow G2 4TG
Christie's South Kensington Ltd., 85 Old Brompton Road, London SW7 3LD
Christie's, 8 King Street, London SW1Y 6QT
Christie's East, 219 East 67th Street, New York, NY 10021, USA
Christie's, 502 Park Avenue, New York, NY 10022, USA
Christie's, Cornelis Schuytstraat 57, 1071 JG Amsterdam, Netherlands
Christie's SA Roma, 114 Piazza Navona, 00186 Rome, Italy
Christie's Swire, 1202 Alexandra House, 16–20 Chater Road, Hong Kong
Christie's Australia Pty Ltd., 1 Darling Street, South Yarra, Melbourne, Victoria 3141, Australia
A J Cobern, The Grosvenor Sales Rooms, 93b Eastbank Street, Southport PR8 1DG
Cooper Hirst Auctions, The Granary Saleroom, Victoria Road, Chelmsford, Essex CM2 6LH
Nic Costa/Brian Bates, 10 Madely Street, Tunstall
The Crested China Co., Station House, Driffield, E. Yorks YO25 7PY
Clifford Dann, 20/21 High Street, Lewes, Sussex
Julian Dawson, Lewes Auction Rooms, 56 High Street, Lewes BN7 1XE
Dee & Atkinson, The Exchange Saleroom, Driffield, Nth Humberside YO25 7LJ
Diamond Mills & Co., 117 Hamilton Road, Felixstowe, Suffolk
Dowell Lloyd & Co. Ltd, 118 Putney Bridge Road, London SW15 2NQ
Downer Ross, Charter House, 42 Avebury Boulevard, Central Milton Keynes MK9 2HS
Hy. Duke & Son, 40 South Street, Dorchester, Dorset
Du Mouchelles Art Galleries Co., 409 E. Jefferson Avenue, Detroit, Michigan 48226, USA
Duncan Vincent, 105 London Street, Reading RG1 4LF
Sala de Artes y Subastas Durán, Serrano 12, 28001 Madrid, Spain
Eldred's, Box 796, E. Dennis, MA 02641, USA
Ewbanks, Welbeck House, High Street, Guildford, Surrey, GU1 3JF
Fellows & Son, Augusta House, 19 Augusta Street, Hockley, Birmingham
Finarte, 20121 Milano, Piazzetta Bossi 4, Italy
John D Fleming & Co., 8 Fore Street, Dulverton, Somerset
G A Property Services, Canterbury Auction Galleries, Canterbury, Kent
Galerie Koller, Rämistr. 8, CH 8024 Zürich, Switzerland
Galerie Moderne, 3 rue du Parnasse, 1040 Bruxelles, Belgium
Geering & Colyer (Black Horse Agencies) Highgate, Hawkhurst, Kent
Glerum Auctioneers, Westeinde 12, 2512 HD's Gravenhage, Netherlands
The Goss and Crested China Co., 62 Murray Road, Horndean, Hants PO8 9JL
Graves Son & Pilcher, 71 Church Road, Hove, East Sussex, BN3 2GL
W R J Greenslade & Co., 13 Hammet Street, Taunton, Somerset, TA1 1RN
Peter Günnemann, Ehrenberg Str. 57, 2000 Hamburg 50, Germany
Halifax Property Services, 53 High Street, Tenterden, Kent
Halifax Property Services, 15 Cattle Market, Sandwich, Kent CT13 9AW
Hampton's Fine Art, 93 High Street, Godalming, Surrey
Hanseatisches Auktionshaus für Historica, Neuer Wall 57, 2000 Hamburg 36, Germany
Andrew Hartley Fine Arts, Victoria Hall, Little Lane, Ilkely

Hauswedell & Nolte, D-2000 Hamburg 13, Pöseldorfer Weg 1, Germany
Giles Haywood, The Auction House, St John's Road, Stourbridge, West Midlands, DY8 1EW
Heatheringtons Nationwide Anglia, The Amersham Auction Rooms, 125 Station Road, Amersham, Bucks
Muir Hewitt, Halifax Antiques Centre, Queens Road/Gibbet Street, Halifax HX1 4LR
Hobbs & Chambers, 'At the Sign of the Bell', Market Place, Cirencester, Glos
Hobbs Parker, Romney House, Ashford, Ashford, Kent
Hotel de Ventes Horta, 390 Chaussée de Waterloo (Ma Campagne), 1060 Bruxelles, Belgium
Jacobs & Hunt, Lavant Street, Petersfield, Hants. GU33 3EF
James of Norwich, 33 Timberhill, Norwich NR1 3LA
P Herholdt Jensens Auktioner, Rundforbivej 188, 2850 Nerum, Denmark
G A Key, Aylsham Saleroom, Palmers Lane, Aylsham, Norfolk, NR11 6EH
Kunsthaus am Museum, Drususgasse 1–5, 5000 Köln 1, Germany
Kunsthaus Lempertz, Neumarkt 3, 5000 Köln 1, Germany
Lambert & Foster (County Group), The Auction Sales Room, 102 High Street, Tenterden, Kent
W.H. Lane & Son, 64 Morrab Road, Penzance, Cornwall, TR18 2QT
Langlois Ltd., Westway Rooms, Don Street, St Helier, Channel Islands
Lawrence Butler Fine Art Salerooms, Marine Walk, Hythe, Kent, CT21 5AJ
Lawrence Fine Art, South Street, Crewkerne, Somerset TA18 8AB
Lawrence's Fine Art Auctioneers, Norfolk House, 80 High Street, Bletchingley, Surrey
David Lay, The Penzance Auction House, Alverton, Penzance, Cornwall TA18 4KE
Brian Loomes, Calf Haugh Farm, Pateley Bridge, North Yorks
Lots Road Chelsea Auction Galleries, 71 Lots Road, Chelsea, London SW10 0RN
R K Lucas & Son, Tithe Exchange, 9 Victoria Place, Haverfordwest, SA61 2JX
Duncan McAlpine, Stateside Comics plc, 125 East Barnet Road, London EN4 8RF
John Maxwell, 75 Hawthorn Street, Wilmslow, Cheshire
May & Son, 18 Bridge Street, Andover, Hants
Morphets, 4–6 Albert Street, Harrogate, North Yorks HG1 1JL
D M Nesbit & Co, 7 Clarendon Road, Southsea, Hants PO5 2ED
Onslow's, Metrostore, Townmead Road, London SW6 2RZ
Outhwaite & Litherland, Kingsley Galleries, Fontenoy Street, Liverpool, Merseyside L3 2BE
J R Parkinson Son & Hamer Auctions, The Auction Rooms, Rochdale, Bury, Lancs
Phillips Manchester, Trinity House, 114 Northenden Road, Sale, Manchester M33 3HD
Phillips Son & Neale SA, 10 rue des Chaudronniers, 1204 Genève, Switzerland
Phillips West Two, 10 Salem Road, London W2 4BL
Phillips, 11 Bayle Parade, Folkestone, Kent CT20 1SQ
Phillips, 49 London Road, Sevenoaks, Kent TN13 1UU
Phillips, 65 George Street, Edinburgh EH2 2JL
Phillips, Blenstock House, 7 Blenheim Street, New Bond Street, London W1Y 0AS
Phillips Marylebone, Hayes Place, Lisson Grove, London NW1 6UA
Phillips, New House, 150 Christleton Road, Chester CH3 5TD
Pinney's, 5627 Ferrier, Montreal, Quebec, Canada H4P 2M4
Pooley & Rogers, Regent Auction Rooms, Abbey Street, Penzance
Rennie's, 1 Agincourt Street, Monmouth
Riddetts, Richmond Hill, Bournemouth
Ritchie's, 429 Richmond Street East, Toronto, Canada M5A 1R1
Derek Roberts Antiques, 24–25 Shipbourne Road, Tonbridge, Kent TN10 3DN
Rogers de Rin, 79 Royal Hospital Road, London SW3 4HN
Russell, Baldwin & Bright, The Fine Art Saleroom, Ryelands Road, Leominster HR6 8JG
Sandoes Nationwide Anglia, Tabernacle Road, Wotton under Edge, Glos GL12 7EB
Schrager Auction Galleries, 2915 North Sherman Boulevard, Milwaukee, WI 53210, USA.
Selkirk's, 4166 Olive Street, St Louis, Missouri 63108, USA
Skinner Inc., Bolton Gallery, Route 117, Bolton MA, USA
Southgate Auction Rooms, Munro House, Cline Road, New Southgate, London N11.
Henry Spencer, 40 The Square, Retford, Notts. DN22 6DJ
G E Sworder & Son, Northgate End Salerooms, 15 Northgate End, Bishop Stortford, Herts
Taviner's of Bristol, Prewett Street, Redcliffe, Bristol BS1 6PB
Tennants, 27 Market Place, Leyburn, Yorkshire
Thomson Roddick & Laurie, 24 Lowther Street, Carlisle
Thomson Roddick & Laurie, 60 Whitesands, Dumfries
Venator & Hanstein, Cäcilienstr. 48, 5000 Köln 1, Germany
T Vennett Smith, 11 Nottingham Road, Gotham, Nottingham NG11 0HE
Duncan Vincent, 105 London Road, Reading RG1 4LF
Wallis & Wallis, West Street Auction Galleries, West Street, Lewes, E. Sussex BN7 2NJ
Ward & Morris, Stuart House, 18 Gloucester Road, Ross on Wye HR9 5BN
Warren & Wignall Ltd, The Mill, Earnshaw Bridge, Leyland Lane, Leyland PR5 3PH
Dominique Watine-Arnault, 11 rue François 1er, 75008 Paris, France
Wells Cundall Nationwide Anglia, Staffordshire House, 27 Flowergate, Whitby YO21 3AX
Woltons, 6 Whiting Street, Bury St Edmunds, Suffolk IP33 1PB
Woolley & Wallis, The Castle Auction Mart, Salisbury, Wilts SP1 3SU
Austin Wyatt Nationwide Anglia, Emsworth Road, Lymington, Hants SO41 9BL
Yesterday Child, 118 Islington High Street, London N11 8EG

CHINA

The word 'china' does not, surprisingly enough, come from the country of the same name, but from a Persian word which sounds like 'chini', and means porcelain. It was originally incorporated into English in the 17th century as 'cheney'.

If the term did not come from China, however, the product most certainly did, so it is perhaps inevitable that the word should have become adapted to conform.

The ceramics of China were the ideal to which every other country and civilisation aspired. From earliest times their influence had filtered west through Mesopotamia and the Middle East, reaching Europe in a diluted form when the Moorish armies conquered Spain in 711. They brought with them the secrets of what was to become known as Hispano-Moresque ware, by which the majolica of Italy was further inspired in the 15th and 16th centuries.

It was the Dutch East India company, however, which brought the first examples of real Chinese porcelain back from the East in the early years of the 17th century, and it would be difficult to overestimate the reaction when the new material burst upon Europe. Nothing like the brilliance of the blue, the sparkling white and the depth of the red and green of late Ming polychrome had ever been seen before, and at once everyone started trying to reproduce these hard, translucent, breathtaking pieces. Here again it was the Dutch who chalked up one of the earliest successes, with their blue and white delft ware.

It was not until the early years of the following century that Böttger discovered the secret of true porcelain for Augustus the Strong at Meissen, and from then on the stage was set for truly dazzling developments in Europe. It is interesting to note, however, how the influence of the original Chinese inspiration lingered on. Almost every 18th century factory produced its blue and white ware, while Chinese and oriental motifs remain a hugely popular decorative theme right to the present day.

The race to reproduce real porcelain had meant that china had become an enormous international status symbol and factories everywhere benefited from royal and aristocratic patronage, leading examples being Vincennes-Sèvres in France, Capodimonte in Italy, and of course, Meissen itself.

The enthusiasm was not confined to the rich and ruling classes, however, and factories were soon turning out pieces for the middle classes and finally the 'masses' as well.

It is this scale of production which helps to make china the vast, varied and fascinating collecting field it is today, for it is possible to make delightful collections of everything from famille verte to fairings, from Sèvres to Staffordshire, from Ming to mustard pots. There is something to appeal to the taste and pocket of everyone.

Nor is it necessary to go far into the distant past to begin a worthwhile collection. One of the most popular fields is Doulton figures, of which over 200 are in production today. Pieces by contemporary potters too, such as Hans Coper and Lucie Rie are now fetching huge sums, while those of their junior disciples are also attracting increasing attention. There are of course the stars, Meissen, Ming, Wedgwood etc., which are forever fixed in their firmament, but others are rising (and, occasionally, falling) all the time. Clarice Cliff, for example has enjoyed a period of unprecedented popularity of late, while such names as Poole and Moorcroft are becoming more and more sought after. (If embarking on a collection from a 'fashionable' field, it is worthwhile ensuring that it is one which you like for its own sake and not just for its potential investment value. That way, if fashions later change, you at least have something which it gives you pleasure to own. That, at the end of the day, must be the real criterion for the serious collector.)

This book is designed to assist the amateur and professional alike in distinguishing and determining the current value of a huge range of pieces. The examples have been carefully selected to provide a representative sample of each factory or potter's output, with a description and prices recently paid. It also contains short accounts of what is often the fascinating history of individual factories, together with useful hints on dating their output and identifying fakes. All in all, it provides an indispensable reference work for anyone interested in any branch of the china collecting field.

AMERICAN

Pottery has been a thriving American tradition from earliest times, and examples by native Americans are a prominent feature of every sale of Red Indian wares. Among the white settlers, the traditional pottery of the United States was redware, which was produced from the time of the earliest settlers in just about every town and village. It was only really supplanted by stoneware in the 19th century, due to persistent fears that the lead oxides which gave it its colour could be poisonous.

During the 19th century such firms as Norton and Fenton and the United States Pottery Co at Bennington had been turning out commercial wares, but, with the exception of the Chelsea Keramic Art Works, founded in 1866, art pottery as such did not exist in the US before 1879. The Centennial Exhibition of 1876 may possibly have acted as a touchstone for the development of a decorative pottery industry. In any case Ohio became a principal centre for the production of such wares, with six potteries opening in Cincinnati alone in the next ten years. Zanesville rapidly followed suit, with the Louwelsa, Roseville, and Owens works.

Scheier Pottery bowl, 1941, wide mouth on tapering cylindrical form, relief decorated with repeating figures, flowers, and the sun, 8¾in. diameter. (Skinner Inc.) £1,224

A Merrimac pottery decorated vase, Mass., circa 1893, 4in. diameter. (Skinner Inc.) £300

A Zuni pottery jar, decorated in brown and red on a white ground, 27cm. high. (Phillips) £1,200

Spongeware umbrella stand, late 19th/early 20th century, 21in. high. (Skinner Inc.) £266

Early 20th century pottery pitcher, New Hampshire, 8¼in. high. (Skinner Inc.) £125

A porcelain pitcher, by The Union Porcelain Works, Greenpoint, N.Y., designed by Karl Mueller, circa 1880, 9¼in. high. £1,750

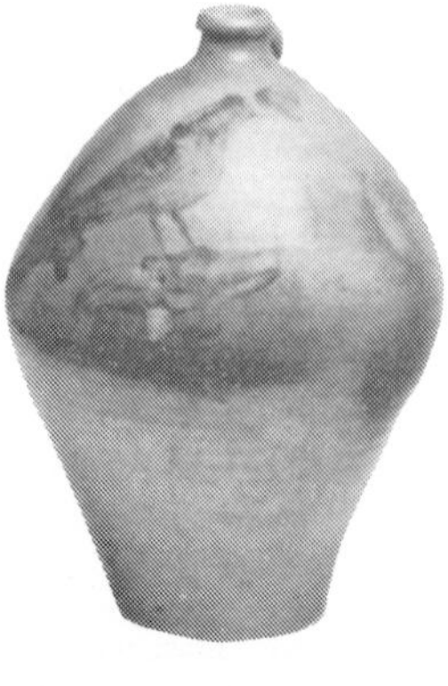

A cobalt decorated and incised jug, America, early 19th century, decorated with incised figure of standing bird, 15½in. high. (Skinner Inc.) £750

Porcelain pitcher, American China Manufactory, Philadelphia, circa 1830, each side decorated with floral bouquets, 9½in. high. (Skinner Inc.) £1,288

Rockingham glazed mantel ornament, possibly midwestern United States, 19th century, in the form of a recumbent lion, 15in. wide. (Skinner Inc.) £503

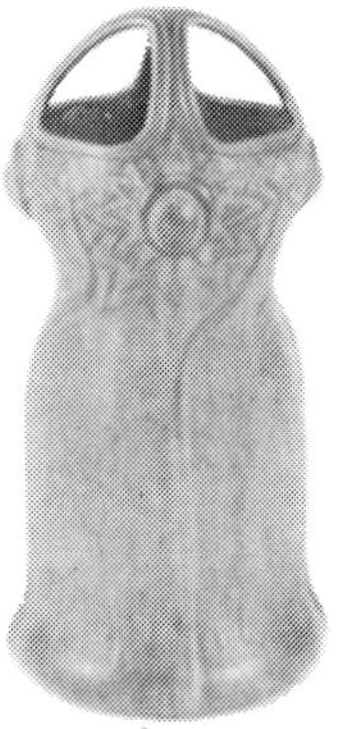

An Art Pottery matt green umbrella stand, early 20th century, the domed top with triangular cut-outs, unsigned, 26½in. high. (Skinner Inc.) £250

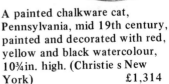

Grotesque pottery jug, America, late 19th/early 20th century, carved into a devil-like mask, 19in. high. (Skinner Inc.) £387

A five-piece Picard China Co. porcelain breakfast set, decorated with the 'Aura Argenta Linear' design, artist signed by Adolph Richter, circa 1910-30. (Skinner Inc.) £350

A painted chalkware cat, Pennsylvania, mid 19th century, painted and decorated with red, yellow and black watercolour, 10¾in. high. (Christie s New York) £1,314

Important Union porcelain Heathen-Chinee pitcher, Greenpoint, New York, 1876, the relief of Bill Nye, knife in hand, attacking Ah Sin for cheating at cards, 9⅝in. high. (Skinner Inc.) £1,998

Vance faience vase with moulded mermaid decoration, Ohio, circa 1905, with repeating figures and fish (some chips and roughness), 12½in. high. (Skinner Inc.) £184

Vance/Avon faience pottery water pitcher, Tiltonville, Ohio, circa 1902, moulded relief decoration of hunt scene and grapes, 12½in. high. (Skinner Inc.) £111

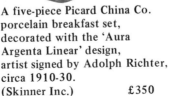

Porcelain group of colibri among hibiscus by Edward Boehm, 33cm. high.
(Duran) £276

Important Union porcelain Liberty cup and saucer, Greenpoint, New York, circa 1880, white moulded body with Justice on the one side and Hermes on the other, 4in. high.
(Skinner Inc.) £1,404

An Albany porcelain group of a kingfisher among reeds by David Burnham Smith, 39.5cm. high.
(Duran) £243

A sepia Fitzhugh-pattern part dinner service, circa 1800, each piece painted at the centre with a flower within radiating panels of animals and trellis pattern and surrounded by four clusters of fruit, flowers and scholar's utensils, all below a band of birds perched in branches and butterflies at the rim, 40 pieces. (Christie's) £5,000

A six-gallon salt-glazed and decorated stoneware churn, *Hubbell & Chesebro, Geddes, N.Y., 1867–1884*, cylindrical with everted neck and applied lug handles, 19½in. high.
(Christie's) £505

A pair of plates from the Dewitt Clinton part dinner service, circa 1805, 8⅞in. diameter.
(Christie's) £1,200

Important pottery vase, by Fritz Wilhelm Albert (1865-1940), circa 1906, 14½in. high.
(Skinner) £14,000

AMPHORA

The Amphora Porzellanfabrik was established at Turn-Teplitz in Bohemia to make earthenware and porcelain. Much of their porcelain figure output was exported.

The mark consists of three stars in a burst of rays over *RSK* (for the proprietors Reissner & Kessel).

ANSBACH

Forty years after faience production began, in 1758, Johann Friedrich Kaendler, who was possibly a relative of the Meissen modeller, helped the then margrave Alexander of Brandenburg to establish a porcelain factory at Ansbach, which continued in production until 1860.

Their wares show little originality and tended to follow Meissen, Nymphenburg and particularly Berlin styles pretty slavishly. The figures in particular closely resemble those produced at Berlin, though Ansbach pieces can be distinguished by their lightweight, elongated bodies and half-closed eyes painted in red. Groups were also made based on plays written by the margrave's wife, and show lovers, hunters or allegories set against architectural arbours.

Marks, where they exist, show the shield of the Arms of Ansbach, impressed, showing a stream with three fishes. Tablewares are sometimes marked with an *A*, sometimes with a shield or the Prussian eagle.

An Amphora polychrome painted porcelain group, modelled as a young woman, being presented with a casket from a small boy, 13in. high. (Christie's S. Ken) £165

An Amphora oviform earthenware jardinière, painted with geese walking in a wooded landscape, 8½in. high. (Christie's S. Ken) £330

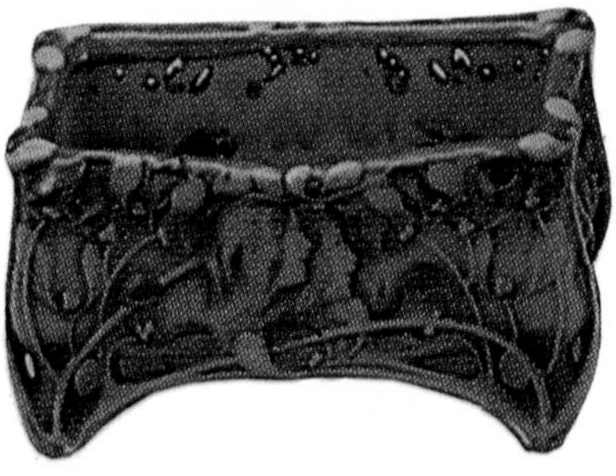

An Amphora ceramic planter, the exterior moulded and pierced in relief with mistletoe on curvilinear stems, enclosing maidens' heads, painted in green, sepia and gilt, 8¼in. wide. (Christie's) £209

An Amphora polychrome-painted pottery group modelled as a Bedouin tribesman astride a camel, 19in. high. (Christie's S. Ken) £209

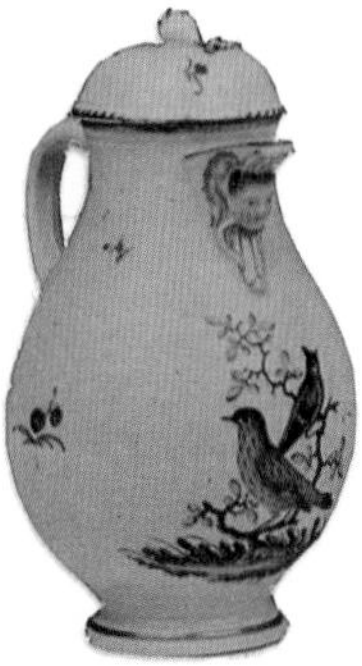

An Ansbach baluster coffee-pot and a cover, painted with two birds perched in branches flanked by scattered sprigs of puce flowers, circa 1770, 18.5cm. high overall. (Christie's) £935

An Ansbach arched rectangular tea-caddy and cover painted with men fishing from a rock and in a boat before a village and distant mountains, circa 1775, 12.5cm. high. (Christie's) £1,320

ARITA

Porcelain first appeared in Japan when the discovery of kaolin nearby in 1616 led to the establishment of a ceramic centre in Saga prefecture, Hizen, which came to be known as Arita. Early Arita was painted in greyish underglaze blue and primitive red and green enamels. Enamelled and blue and white wares with panelled decoration in the later Ming style were brought to the West by the Dutch from the 17th century onwards, often through the port of Imari. Kakiemon and Nabeshima wares were also made at Arita, and production continues there to the present day.

A pair of Arita blue and white candlesticks, the bell shaped lower sections decorated with buildings in a forested landscape, late 18th/early 19th century, 25cm. high. (Christie's) £770

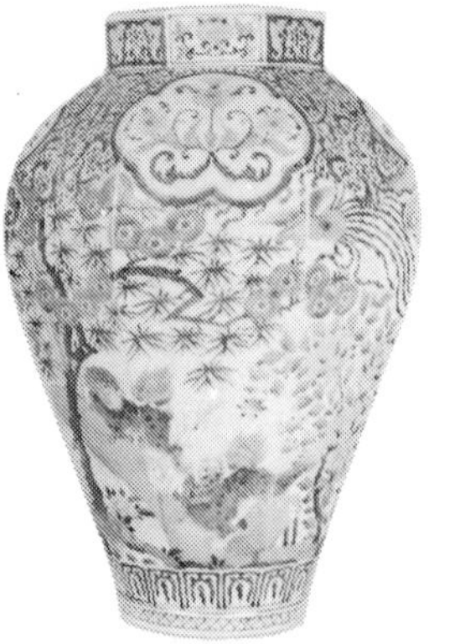

A large Arita blue and white octagonal vase decorated with karashishi prowling beneath bamboo, pine and peony with ho-o birds hovering above, late 17th century, 60cm. high. (Christie's) £3,850

A fine Arita blue and white charger, the central roundel containing a vase of cascading peony sprays on a veranda, Genroku period, 55cm. diam. (Christie's) £4,400

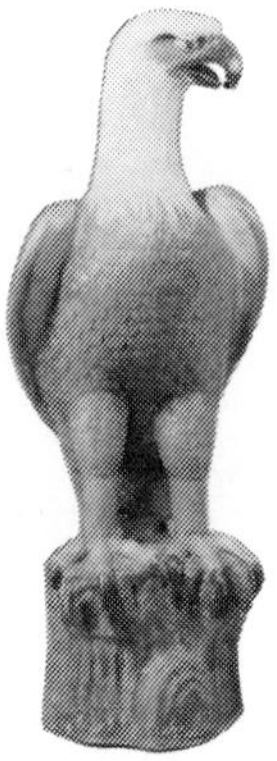

A Japanese Arita life-size model of an eagle, the biscuit body painted in colours, circa 1700, 59cm. high. (Christie's) £19,800

A rare Arita blue and white shallow dish, the wide everted rim with stylised lotus and scrolling foliage, late 17th century, 24.7cm. diam. (Christie's) £5,280

Late 17th century Arita blue and white ewer with loop handle, 24cm. high. (Christie's) £550

A fine pair of Arita blue and white oviform jars and covers, Genroku period, 88cm. high, wood stands. (Christie's) £6,600

A handsome Arita model of a seated dog, decorated in iron-red, brown and black enamels and gilt, its mouth agape, late 17th century, 40cm. high. (Christie's) £35,200

ARITA

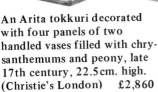

An Arita tokkuri decorated with four panels of two handled vases filled with chrysanthemums and peony, late 17th century, 22.5cm. high. (Christie's London) £2,860

A pair of Arita blue and white rectangular sake bottles, the sides decorated with sprays of tree peony among rockwork, late 17th century, 13.5cm. high. (Christie's) £2200

A fine Arita blue and white hexagonal vase decorated with a ho-o bird perched on rockwork amongst peonies, chrysanthemums and other flowers, late 17th century, 61.5cm. high.(Christie's London) £99,000

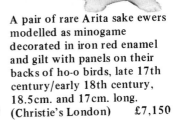

A pair of rare and important Arita seated kirin enamelled in the Kakiemon style, with stylised fur markings (both with some restoration), late 17th century, 24cm. high. (Christie's London) £55,000

A rare Arita model of a seated horse following a Dutch delft original, its saddle cloth with flowers and foliage (ears slightly damaged), circa 1700, 18cm. long. (Christie's London) £8,250

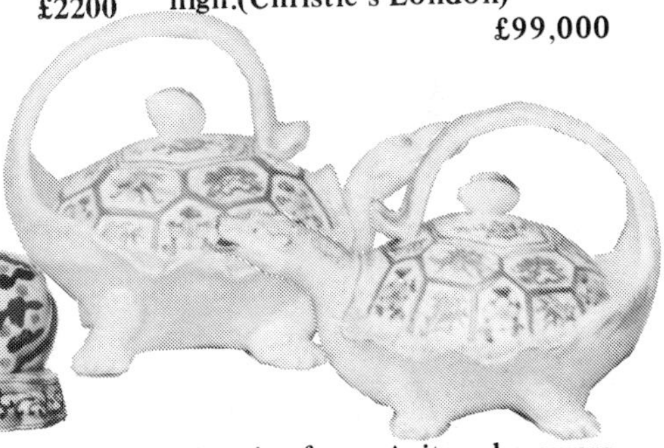

A pair of rare Arita sake ewers modelled as minogame decorated in iron red enamel and gilt with panels on their backs of ho-o birds, late 17th century/early 18th century, 18.5cm. and 17cm. long. (Christie's London) £7,150

A pair of Arita blue and white trumpet shaped vases decorated with a continuous landscape with two figures walking across a bridge, late 17th century, 41cm. high. (Christie's London) £7,150

An Arita shallow dish modelled in the form of an uchiwa with a cloud shaped panel depicting a scholar and attendants, early 18th century, 19cm. long. (Christie's London) £2,420

An Arita blue and white oviform vase decorated with a continuous landscape of pavilions and other buildings amongst a rocky outcrop, late 17th century, 26.75cm. high. (Christie's London) £3,300

An Arita blue and white foliate-rimmed bowl, the interior with two panels obtruding onto a ground of flowers and foliage, fuku mark, early 19th century, 36.3cm. diameter.
(Christie's) £2,200

An Arita lobed teapot and domed cover decorated in iron-red, green, yellow, aubergine, black and gilt with ho-o perched among scrolling flowers and foliage, late 17th century, 13cm. high.
(Christie's) £6,600

An Arita blue and white leaf-shaped dish, the interior with sprays of chrysanthemum on swirling waters, all on a ground of massed geometrical patterns, late 17th century, 10.9cm. long.
(Christie's) £1,800

An 18th century Japanese Arita Imari ewer of octagonal form decorated with outdoor scenes.
(Hotel de Ventes Horta) £9,434

A pair of boldly modelled Arita cockerels decorated in iron-red, green, blue-black enamels and gilt with underglaze blue, late 17th/early 18th century, 33cm. high.
(Christie's) £16,500

An Arita blue and white ewer decorated with birds and butterflies among flowers, foliage and rocks, the shoulder and neck decorated with bands of floral, foliate and geometric patterns, late 17th century, 22.3cm. high.(Christie's) £1,200

A pair of Arita Kakiemon style hexagonal jars, the sides with flowering saplings issuing from rocks below a band to the shoulder of stylised leaves, late 17th century, 27.5cm. high.
(Christie's) £9,900

An Arita blue and white charger, the central roundel with a jardinière of peonies and leaves on a terrace, the rim with six shaped rectangular panels, late 17th century, 54.5cm. diameter.
(Christie's) £5,500

A pair of Arita models of dogs decorated in iron-red, black enamels and gilt with irregular piebald, each seated with its mouth agape, late 17th/early 18th century, each approx. 41cm. high.
(Christie's) £71,500

An Arita blue and white irregularly shaped shallow dish, the interior with a design of two rabbits leaping near waves, chocolate rim, ring foot, late 17th century, 15.8cm. long.
(Christie's) £3,850

An Arita blue and white ewer with loop handle, the ovoid body decorated with figures in a garden, birds flying overhead, late 17th century, 16.1cm. high.
(Christie's) £1,210

An Arita blue and white rounded octagonal teapot and cover with two shaped panels depicting scenes from O.R. Dapper on a ground of stylised flowers and foliage, circa 1700, 26.7cm. long.
(Christie's) £7,700

A large Arita blue and white octagonal vase decorated in iron-red and green enamels and blue and black enamels in the kakiemon manner, late 17th/ early 18th century, 43.3cm. high.
(Christie's) £6,050

A pair of Arita blue and white foliate-rimmed armorial dishes, the centre with a coat-of-arms surrounded by stylised mantling, 18th century, 22.6cm. wide.
(Christie's) £3,850

An Arita blue and white bottle vase with slightly everted neck, the body with a cherry tree in blossom, the neck with collar and band of lozenge diaper, circa 1700, 21.5cm. high.
(Christie's) £2,750

An Arita blue and white dish, the central roundel containing a pair of herons before rocks under a weeping willow, late 17th century, 30cm. diameter.
(Christie's) £3,000

A pair of Arita blue and white baluster tankards with three shaped panels, silver mounts inset with a half-crown of Charles II, circa 1700, 19.7cm. high.
(Christie's) £8,250

An Arita blue and white charger with a central roundel containing four flowerheads issuing from a single foliate spray, late 17th/early 18th century, 45.6cm. diameter.
(Christie's) £6,050

ASHSTEAD POTTERY

The Ashstead Pottery was established in 1923 by Sir Laurence and Lady Weaver to give employment to disabled ex-servicemen. It produced tableware, nursery novelties and figures, at first in white glazed earthenware. Painted landscape decoration and linear designs were introduced later, and the figures, usually in white glazed earthenware with touches of colour, are characterised by garlands of flowers painted in bright blue, yellow, maroon, light green and yellow. The original workforce of 14 had risen to 30 by 1925, and the pottery continued in business until 1935.

The mark is usually a printed tree, with *Ashstead Potters*.

AULT POTTERY

William Ault (b. 1841) was an English potter who worked in Staffordshire before going into partnership with Henry Tooth in 1882 to open an art pottery at Church Gresley, Derbyshire. In 1887 he opened his own pottery near Burton-on-Trent, where he produced earthenware vases, pots, pedestals and grotesque jugs.

The painted decoration of flowers and butterflies was often executed by his daughter Clarissa. Between 1892-96 Christopher Dresser designed some vases for Ault, which he sometimes covered in his own aventurine glaze. Between 1923-37 the firm traded as Ault and Tunnicliffe and thereafter became Ault Potteries Ltd.

Marks include a tall fluted vase over *Ault* on a ribbon, or a monogrammed *APL*.

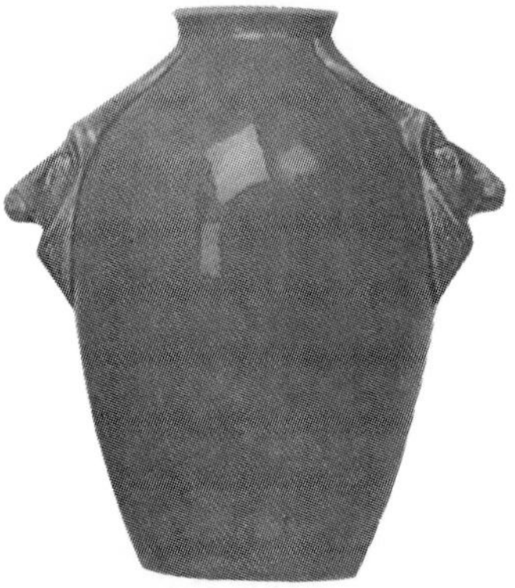

An Ashtead lamp base, of ovoid form moulded in relief on each shoulder with the head of gazelle, 11in. high. (Christie's S. Ken) £198

An Ashtead advertising plaque, for the Ideal Home magazine, moulded in relief with ballet dancer, 6in. high. (Christie's S. Ken) £121

Three of five Art Deco Ashtead pottery wall plates. (Phillips) £269

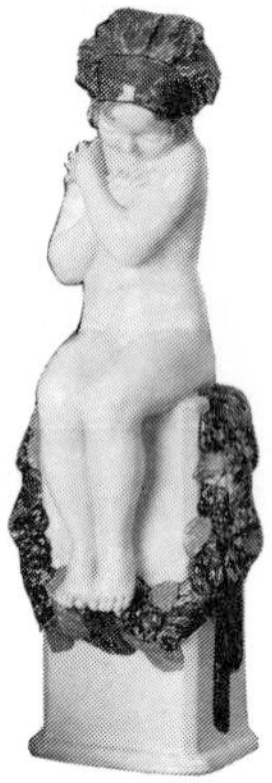

'Shy', an Ashtead pottery figure modelled as young girl seated on a pedestal draped with a garland of flowers, 15$\frac{1}{4}$in. high. (Christie's S. Ken) £715

An Ault vase, designed by Dr. Christopher Dresser, with curling lip continuing to form two handles, streaked turquoise glaze over dark brown, 18cm. high. (Christie's) £935

An unusual Ault Pottery pouring vessel, designed by Christopher Dresser, of compressed globular shape with two pouring spouts, 28cm. wide. (Phillips London) £2,200

BELLEEK

The Belleek porcelain factory was established in 1863 in Co. Fermanagh, Ireland, by David McBirney and Robert Armstrong, and continues in existence today. Its production is characterised by the use of parian covered with an iridescent glaze, and its wares consist principally of ornamental and table wares, such as centrepieces, comports, ice buckets etc. Belleek is especially noted for its frequent use of naturalistically moulded shell forms, perforated decoration and woven basketwork effect.

The early impressed or printed mark from 1863–80 consisted of a crown above a harp, while later versions had a wolfhound seated alongside a harp over *Belleek.* After 1891 *Ireland* or *Co. Fermanagh* was added to comply with the McKinley Tariff Act.

A white Belleek chamber pot, the inside base with black-printed image of Gladstone, 10cm., registration mark for 1877. (Phillips) £400

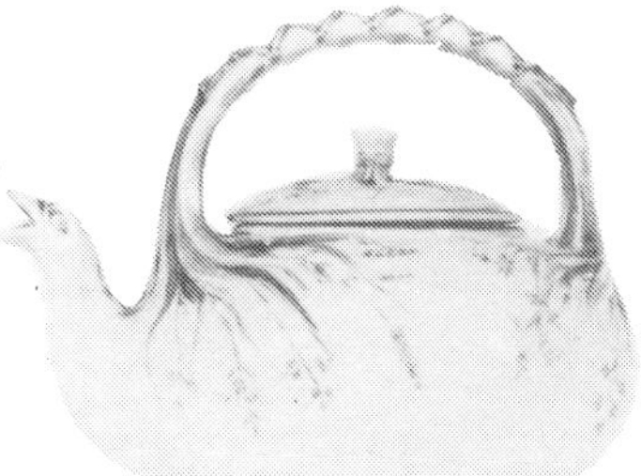

A Belleek tea kettle and cover, the overhandle bound with gilt tassles and with spreading leaf moulded terminals, 8¼in. across. (Christie's) £132

A fine Belleek circular basket, the looped rim applied with opalescent twig handles and sprays of lily-of-the-valley, 23.5cm. diameter. (Bearne's) £640

A mid 19th century Belleek porcelain honey pot and cover in the form of a beehive, 14.5cm. high. (Spencer's) £400

One of a pair of Belleek tapering jugs with fluted bodies applied in high relief with bouquets of flowers, 9in. high. (Christie's) Two £330

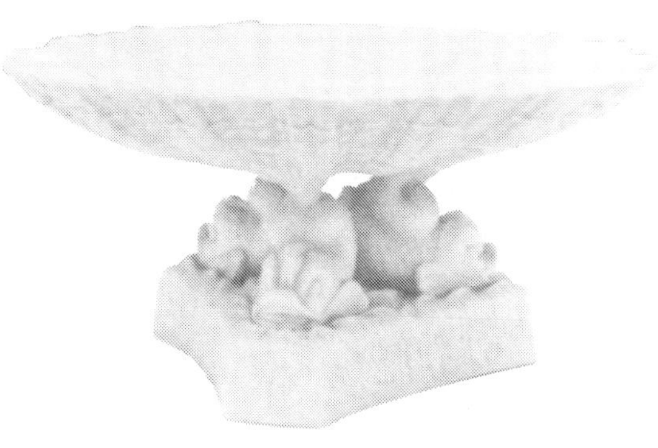

A Belleek centre piece, modelled as a fluted circular shell supported by three dolphins, 26.5cm. (Lawrence Fine Arts) £176

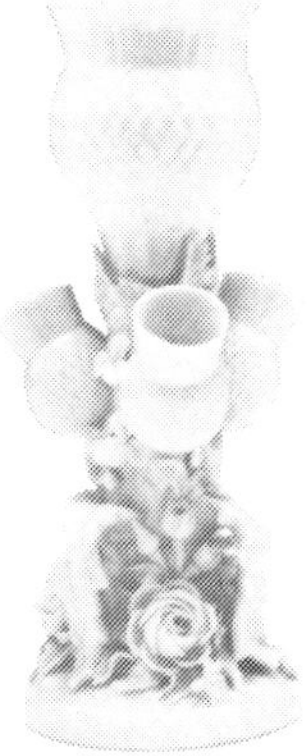

A Belleek vase, modelled as three thistles supporting a larger thistle, on circular base, 22.5cm. (Lawrence Fine Arts) £176

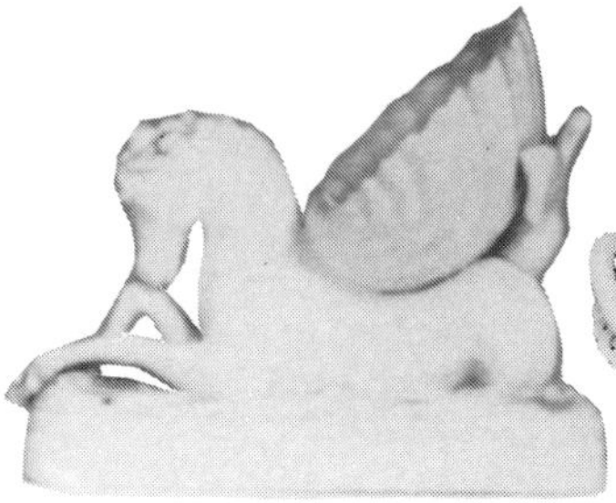

One of a pair of Belleek salts modelled as sea-horses with mermaid tails recumbent on rectangular bases, 5in. long, late nineteenth century.
(Christie's S. Ken.) £385

A Belleek 9in. oval basket and cover in good condition.
(Phillips) £760

A First Period Belleek parian ware box and cover, modelled as a young boy wearing a souwester and waders, 16cm. wide.
(Spencer's) £320

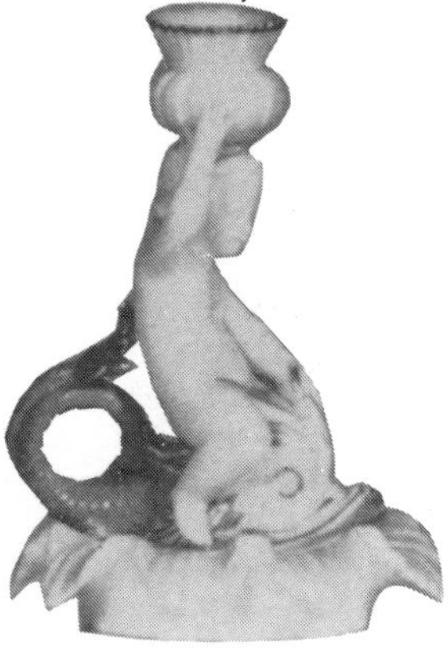

One of a pair of Belleek candleholders modelled each as a putto supporting a sea-urchin on their heads.
(Christie's S. Ken.) £990

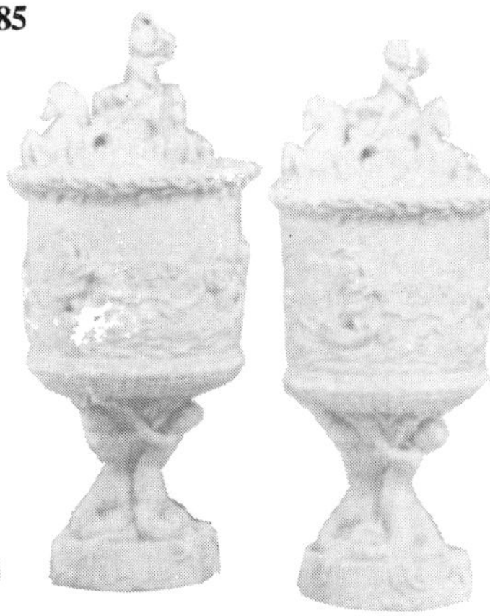

A pair of rare First Period Belleek ice pails and covers, from the service ordered by the Prince of Wales, mark for 1868, 46cm. high.
(Allen & Harris) £4400

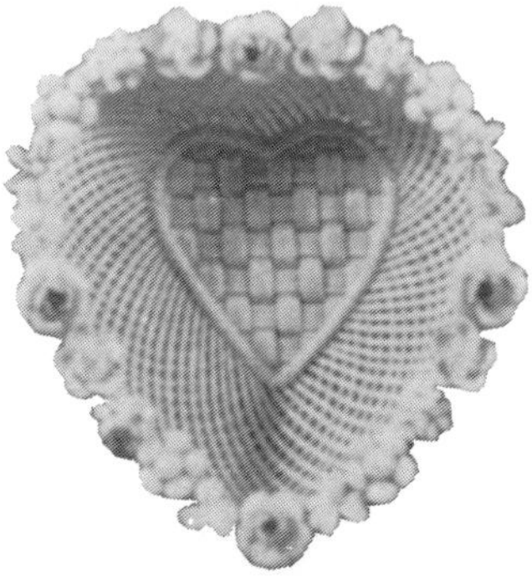

Belleek heart form basket, floral design rim, four straw weave, 6in. wide.
(Du Mouchelles) £200

One of a pair of Belleek vases modelled as conch shells supported on the backs of flying fish, 11.5cm. high. £600

A Belleek rectangular plaque painted by Horatio H. Calder, black printed Belleek mark, First Period, 17 x 11.3cm. £2,500

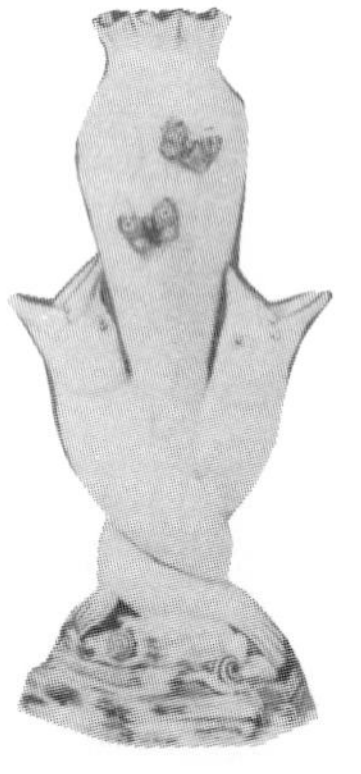

A Belleek double fish vase with two open-mouthed entwined scaly fish supporting a central vase, 1st period printed and impressed marks, 30cm.
(Phillips) £700

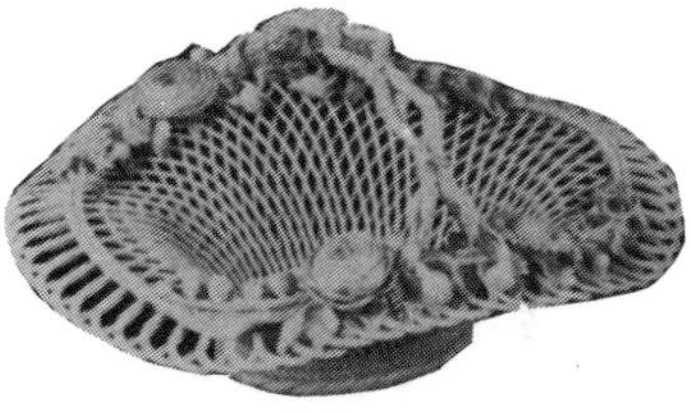

A Belleek oval basket with pierced trellis sides and everted looped rim, first period, 27cm. wide. £300

Late 19th century pair of Belleek spill vase figures, 18cm. high. £2,500

A Belleek porcelain trefoil basket, osier pattern, 5in. diam. £200

A Belleek cornucopia vase on shell moulded base, 9¼in. high. £350

A pair of Belleek candlestick figures of a boy and girl basket bearer, 22cm. high. £4,000

A Belleek parian figure entitled 'The Prisoner of Love', after the model by G. Fontana, 65cm. high. £5,000

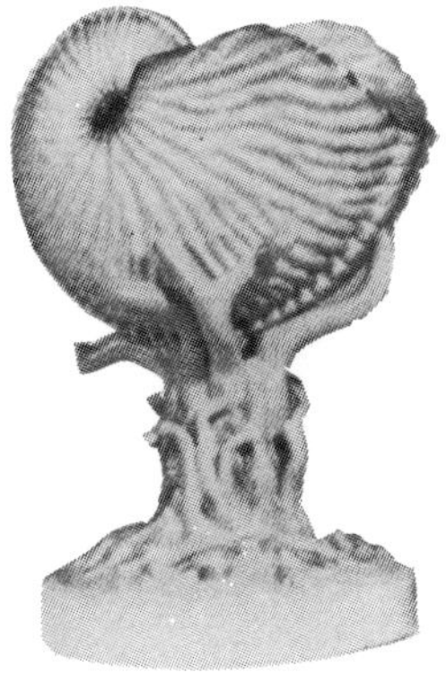

One of a pair of Belleek nautilus vases, naturally modelled and heightened in pink, 21cm. high. £1,500

A Belleek circular plaque painted by E Sheerin with a view of Ballynahimch Connemara, $11^1/_4$in. diam. (Christie's S. Ken.) £308

A Belleek standing figure of Hibernia, the whole unglazed with details picked out in iridescent glaze, 43.5cm. high. £2,500

BENNINGTON

Bennington is the name often, and erroneously, given to American Rockingham ware in general. The Vermont town had two potteries; the smaller was a stoneware factory belonging to the Norton family (operated 1793–1894) while the larger belonged to Christopher Fenton (called the US Pottery Co from 1853), who produced many different wares, from yellow and Flint Enamel, to parian ware and porcelain.

Flint enamel lion mantle ornament, Lyman Fenton and Co., Bennington, Vermont, circa 1849-1858, 9½in. high, 11in. long. (Skinner Inc.) £6,135

Cobalt decorated stoneware crock, J. & E. Norton, Bennington, Vermont, 10½in. high. (Robt. W. Skinner Inc.) £242

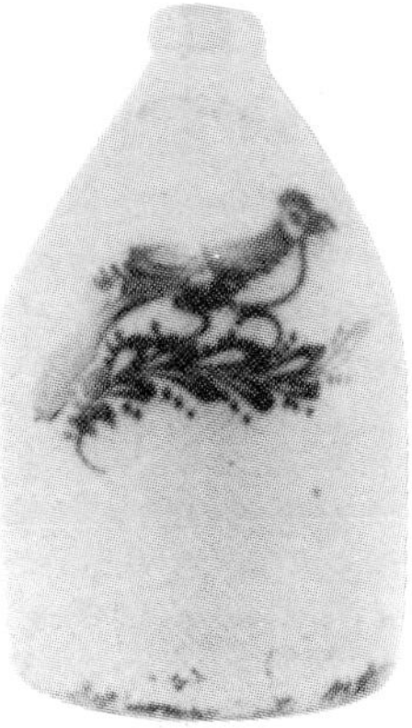

Four gallon Bennington jug with bird, Bennington, Vermont, 1859-1861, 18in. high. (Robt. W. Skinner Inc.) £400

'J. & E. Norton, Bennington, VT' two-gallon stoneware crock, 1850-59, 9¼in. high. (Robt. W. Skinner Inc.) £714

Large Toby pitcher, possibly Bennington, Vermont, 1849, seated gentleman with tricorn hat, 10¾in. high. (Robt. W. Skinner Inc.) £171

A four-gallon salt-glazed and decorated stoneware crock, 'J. Norton & Co., Bennington, VT,' 1859–1861, with everted neck above applied lug handles, 17in. high. (Christie's) £617

A flint glaze enamel poodle with basket of fruit, Bennington, Vermont, 1849-58, 8½in. high. (Robt. W. Skinner Inc.) £1,031

Two gallon Bennington stoneware jar, circa 1855, 13¾in. high. (Robt. W. Skinner Inc.) £842

BERLIN

Berlin ceramics date back to the late 17th century, when from 1678 faience and red earthenware was produced. In 1763 the factory came under royal patronage when Frederick the Great purchased it to become the Königliche Porzellan Manufaktur, and production turned to hard-paste porcelain. From the end of the First World War it became known as the Staatliche Porzellan Manufaktur in Berlin. Throughout its existence it has continued to produce fine table-ware with high quality painted decoration, though various designers have also pursued contemporary trends. During the late 19th century, for example, its wares were often characterised by elaborate glaze effects under oriental influence, as seen in the work of H Seeger. Notable figures were designed by Scheurich and in the early years of this century tableware was also produced to Bauhaus designs.

A Berlin blue and white cylindrical chocolate-pot and cover, circa 1775, 13cm. high. (Christie's) £385

A Berlin (Funcke Factory) blue and white faience octagonal baluster vase and cover painted with chinoiserie figures taking tea, circa 1760. 42cm. high. (Christie's) £2,090

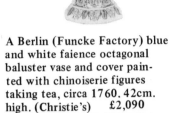

Two Berlin faience polychrome flared octagonal vases, painted with birds perched and in flight among flowering shrubs, circa 1730, 29.5cm. high. (Christie's) £1,650

A Berlin plaque painted after Peter Paul Rubens, 39 x 31cm., KPM and sceptre mark. (Phillips) £5,200

KPM Porcelain Plaque of a Young Woman, Berlin, late 19th century, hair bound at the top of her head, sceptre marks, 7¾in. high. (Skinner Inc) £1818

A pair of Berlin Russian Ballet figures from models by Hubatsch, the figures in theatrical poses, each polychrome enamelled and with gilt decoration, 21.5cm high. (Christie's) £1,100

A Berlin porcelain rectangular paperweight, finely painted with flowers, printed and impressed marks, 16 x 8.5cm. (Bearne's) £180

A Berlin oval plaque painted with a half length portrait of a girl in Greek national dress, impressed K.P.P., sceptre and F5 marks, circa 1880, 26.5cm. high.
(Christie's) £2,970

A KPM plaque, late 19th century, depicting Europa and the Bull at the water's edge with attendant maiden and two figures in the distance, 9 x 11in.
(Christie's East) £3,790

A Berlin cabinet plate, the centre painted with huntsmen in seventeenth century dress, with their game around a table within a gilt border, incised 16 for 1816, 24.5cm. diameter.
(Christie's) £935

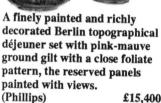

An extremely impressive topographical presentation Berlin vase and stand of Franzosische form, the ovoid body finely painted on one side with a panoramic view of the town of Hildesheim, 55.2cm.
(Phillips) £12,000

A finely painted and richly decorated Berlin topographical déjeuner set with pink-mauve ground gilt with a close foliate pattern, the reserved panels painted with views.
(Phillips) £15,400

A Berlin campana-shaped gilt-ground two-handled vase painted with a broad band of garden flowers including roses, carnations, poppies, hydrangeas, delphiniums and nasturtium, circa 1810, 56cm. high.
(Christie's) £7,700

A finely painted Berlin plaque of 'Die Neapolitaner', a head and shoulders portrait of a young girl in pensive mood,
24.5cm. x 18.5cm.
(Phillips) £4,200

A large and finely painted Berlin plaque of the Holy Family after Raphael painted by Otto Wustlich, signed,
48.5cm. x 39cm., impressed *KPM*
(Phillips) £9,000

A Berlin porcelain plaque painted with the head and shoulders of a Neapolitan peasant boy, after the original by Richter, 30.5cm. by 24cm.
(Bearne's) £3,600

A KPM plaque of Antigone, late 19th century, depicting a fair-haired maiden with an amphora, $9^{1}/_{2}$ x $6^{1}/_{2}$in.
(Christie's East) £3,498

A pair of Berlin rectangular plaques painted with head and shoulders portraits of young girls wearing early 17th century style dress, impressed KPM, circa 1880, 8¾ x 6in.
(Christie's) £7,700

A Berlin rectangular plaque painted with a gypsy girl wearing a red scarf, signed *C.S.*, impressed K.P.M., sceptre and H marks, circa 1880, 23.5 x 16.5cm.
(Christie's) £2,970

A Berlin rectangular plaque of Judith finely painted in half-profile, signed H. Sch., impressed sceptre and K.P.M. marks, incised numerals, circa 1880, 53 x 29cm.
(Christie's) £11,000

A pair of Berlin armorial oval gold-ground tureens, covers and plinths with linked scroll handles, painted in colours with two putti supporting bronzed swags of fruit hung from satyrs' heads, circa 1820, 45.5cm. wide.
(Christie's) £22,000

A Berlin reetangular plaque painted by Wm. Walther with a half length portrait of a young girl standing in an interior, holding a taper-stick, circa 1880, 9¼ x 6in.
(Christie's) £1,980

A Berlin rectangular plaque of the three Fates, Clotho scantily draped and carding the thread of life, flanked by Lachtsis and Atropos, impressed K.P.M., circa 1880, 40.5 x 26cm.
(Christie's) £6,050

A German plaque of 'The Interlude' late 19th century, depicting two gypsies, one playing the violin for his slumbering companion, signed J Schmidt, framed, 15 x 12in.
(Christie's) £9,328

A Berlin rectangular plaque painted by Schunzel with Psyche seated on a grassy bank, impressed KPM and sceptre mark, 9¼ x 6in.
(Christie's) £4,400

A Berlin figure of a putto emblematic of Plenty standing holding a gilt spirally moulded cornucopia of fruit, blue sceptre marks, 19th century, 7½in. high. (Christie's S. Ken) £187

A large ormolu Berlin punch bowl and cover surmounted by a kneeling Bacchic boy holding a glass and a bottle, decorated with amusing scenes after Hogarth, 47.5cm. (Phillips London) £1,300

A Berlin figure of a cooper standing at a barrel with his hammer raised, blue sceptre mark, circa 1780, 9.5cm. high. (Christie's Geneva) £172

A Berlin oval plaque, painted with the head and shoulders of a nude sleeping woman, impressed sceptre and KPM marks, late 19th century, 22cm. high. (Christie's London) £605

A Berlin ornithological large lobed circular dish painted in colours with two parrots, circa 1770, 39cm. diam. (Christie's) £2,420

A Berlin porcelain circular wall plate, painted in sepia with a bare breasted Egyptianesque maiden, 40.5cm. diam. (Phillips London) £580

A Berlin figure of Apollo, standing with an eagle at his side on a square base with canted corners, KPM mark, late 19th century, 9in. high. (damaged) (Christie's S. Ken) £154

A pair of Berlin blue and white octagonal vases and covers, painted in the Oriental style with chinoiserie figures in landscapes (repairs to one neck), circa 1725, 44cm. high. (Christie's) £3,280

A Berlin figural group of Ruhm and Zeit modelled as a classical maiden above an old man, blue sceptre and iron red KPM and globe mark, late 19th century, 16in. high. (Christie's S. Ken) £495

BOLOGNA

Bologna, together with Padua, is particularly associated with a rare and early type of earthenware known as sgraffito or sgraffiato. This terms refers to the technique used in their decoration. The body was of red clay covered with a white slip with the design scratched through to show the red base. The pieces were then covered with a yellow toned lead glaze and often dappled with patches of green or golden brown.

Many reproductions of the rare originals have been made by Carlo Giano Loretz of Milan. In Bologna too, in the 19th century Angelo Minghetti & Son produced fine reproductions of Renaissance maiolica.

BÖTTGER

It was J F Böttger's discovery of red stoneware and porcelain in 1708–9 which gave Augustus the Strong's Meissen factory a lead in porcelain production which it did not lose until after the Seven Years War some fifty years later. Böttger's success as an arcanist was not equalled by his success as a business man, however. He remained under Augustus's close eye almost until his death, and it was not until after that event that the factory reached the period of its true greatness and prosperity.

A Bologna sgraffito dish, the centre with a profile of a young man with curly brown hair, 16th century, 24.5cm. diam. (Christie's London) £990

A Bologna sgraffito trilobed jug, the bulbous body incised with scrolls of foliage, late 15th century, 20.5cm. high. (Christie's) £880

A Bottger red Steinzeug hexagonal tea caddy and cover moulded with alternating panels of birds in trees issuing from terraces, circa 1715, 12.5cm. high. (Christie's Geneva) £25,740

A Böttger Hausmalerei saucer painted in iron-red with an equestrian figure in full dress, holding a banner, his horse dressed with plumes, circa 1720, 12.5cm. diameter. (Christie's) £1,210

A Bottger gold Chinese milk jug and later domed cover gilt in the Seuter workshop, the porcelain circa 1725, 18cm. high. (Christie's) £748

A rare and attractive Bottger polished stoneware tea canister, the vertical panels moulded in relief and gilt with birds in flight and perched in trees, 12.5cm. (Phillips) £8,000

BOW

The Bow factory was one of the most prolific of the mid 18th century and concentrated mainly on producing 'useful' tablewares in blue and white.

Ve y few pieces dating from before 1750 survive, and these are mainly painted in vivid famille rose colours against a greyish paste. A selection of items were also produced unpainted but with relief decoration in imitation of Fukien blanc de Chine. The 'quail' pattern derived from Japanese Kakiemon ware is also especially characteristic of the factory as are other exotic bird patterns and botanical designs.

Blue and white production falls broadly into three periods. The first, 1749–54, saw the production of thickly potted, heavy wares painted in a vivid cobalt blue. Decoration was often in the Chinese style with a slightly blurred appearance.

During the middle, and most successful period, from 1755–63, a wide range of products were made, especially sauceboats, centre-pieces, mugs, bowls etc. These were less thickly potted, often in powder blue, and favourite designs are 'Image', 'Jumping Boy', dragon, and a harbour scene, all still showing a very strong oriental influence.

From 1764 quality declined both in terms of opacity and painting. Sauceboats and plates remained a speciality, but were now much less elaborate, and after 1770 production fell considerably.

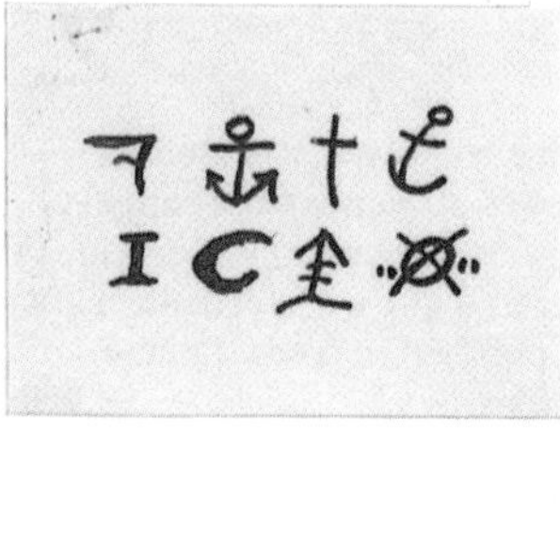

An attractive Bow polychrome cream boat, the fluted sides enamelled with floral sprays detailed in black, the interior with floral and leaf sprigs, 4¼in. long, circa 1765. (Tennants) £220

A most impressive Bow candlestick group modelled as a retriever chasing two grouse, standing before a colourful, flowering tree, 29cm. high. (Phillips) £2,500

Two Bow fable candlestick-groups representing the fable of The Fox and the Stork, the stork with its beak in the neck of a bottle-shaped vase painted in a famille rose palette with a loose bouquet, the fox crouching on the other side gazing up at the bird, circa 1758, 22cm. high. (Christie's) £4,000

A Bow model of a tawny owl, its plumage in shades of yellow and brown, circa 1758, 19.5cm. high. (Christie's) £6,000

A Bow documentary cylindrical ink pot with a central circular well surrounded by five holes to the shoulder, painted by James Welsh, circa 1758, 9cm. diam. (Christie's London) £13,200

A Bow group of new dancers standing before a tree stump applied with flowers and turned towards each other with their hands raised, wearing feathered hats, circa 1765, 18cm. high. (Christie's) £3,000

A Bow figure of a dancer, the boy holding the remains of a garland and standing in pastel clothing with typical opaque sky-blue detail, $5^{3}/_{4}$in. high, circa 1755–60.
(Tennants) £680

A Bow candlestick fountain-group modelled as a gallant and his companion flanking a grotto, 24cm.
(Phillips) £900

A Bow figure of a cook wearing a white turban, a pink-lined blue jacket with gilt seams and buttons, white blouse and pale-yellow striped breeches, circa 1756, 17cm. high.
(Christie's) £3,520

A Bow candlestick group of 'Birds in Branches', modelled with two yellow buntings perched in a flower-encrusted tree, 24cm.
(Phillips) £800

A Bow model of a squirrel with bushy tail, seated erect nibbling a nut held in its right paw, 1758–60, 20.5cm. high.
(Christie's) £1,980

A Bow figure of the Doctor wearing blue hat, pale-pink cloak, his flowered jacket edged in yellow and blue breeches, standing with his left hand raised, circa 1755, 16cm. high.
(Christie's) £3,080

A Bow figure of Columbine in a dancing pose with her right hand raised to her puce-lined pale-yellow hat and holding a slap-stick in her left hand, circa 1760, 15.5cm. high.
(Christie's) £1,540

A rare Bow fountain chamber-candlestick group with simulated water spouting from a mossy mask and overflowing the basin below, $7^{1}/_{4}$in. high, circa 1765.
(Tennants) £300

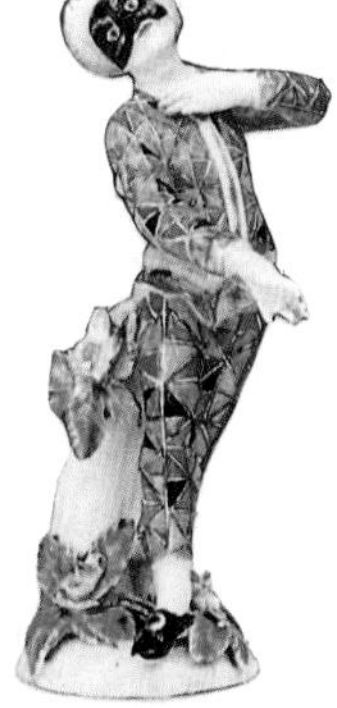

A Bow figure of Harlequin holding his slap-stick beneath his right arm, wearing a black mask and feathered hat, circa 1756, 16cm. high.
(Christie's) £1,980

A Bow porcelain figure of a nurse. (Hobbs Parker) £720

A Bow documentary blue and white octagonal plate, the centre with the entwined monogram RC surrounded by trailing flowers, 21cm. diam. (Christie's) £2,200

A Bow figure of Pierrot with outstretched arms, wearing pale-yellow clothes edged in puce, circa 1762, 14.5cm. high. (Christie's) £715

A Bow figure of a seated tabby cat, a brown rat in its right paw, another disappearing into a rathole, circa 1758, 8cm. high. (Christie's) £2,090

A pair of Bow white busts of Mongolians, she with her hair plaited, he with a moustache and pointed beard, circa 1750, 27.5cm. high. (Christie's) £49,500

A rare early Bow 'Muses' figure of Hope, the lady resting one arm on a puce column, her other on an anchor, 21.5cm. high. (Phillips) £800

A Bow figure of a shepherd playing the bagpipes, circa 1757, 26.5cm. high. (Christie's) £990

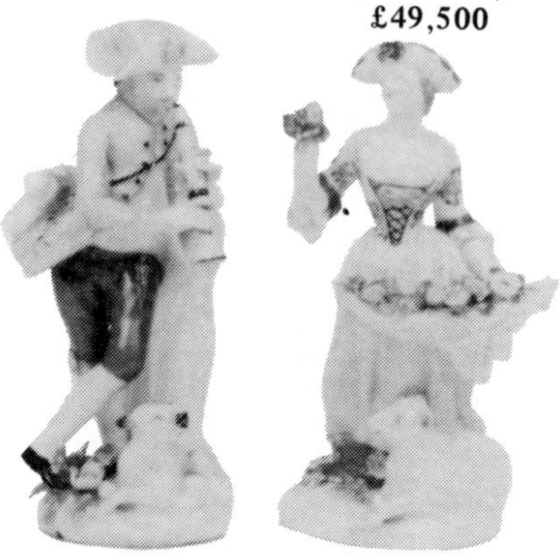

A pair of Bow figures of a shepherd and a shepherdess, on circular mound bases applied with coloured flowers, circa 1758, 14.5cm. high. (Christie's) £1,650

A Bow figure of Matrimony modelled as a young woman holding a turquoise square birdcage, circa 1765, 20cm. high. (Christie's) £1,045

A Bow figure candlestick, formed of a cupid kneeling on a rococo base (slight damage), anchor in red circa 1765. (Phillips) £605

A Bow partridge tureen and a cover, naturally modelled to the right on an oval basket-work nest, circa 1760, 12.5cm. wide. (Christie's London) £880

A Bow figure from a set of the Seasons, emblematic of Summer, modelled as a girl in black and white hat, 12cm. (Phillips London) £460

A Bow fountain group, modelled as a sportsman and companion in flowered clothes, circa 1770, 21.5cm. (Christie's) £495

A pair of Bow candlestick figures of a stag and doe with mottled brown coats, circa 1765, 23.5cm. high. (Christie's) £2,640

A Bow figure of a nun in pink lined black cowl and white habit, circa 1758, 14.5cm. high. (Christie's London) £550

An extremely rare Bow figure of the Marquis of Granby from the engraving by Richard Houston after a painting by Sir Joshua Reynolds, 34.5cm. (Phillips London) £3,900

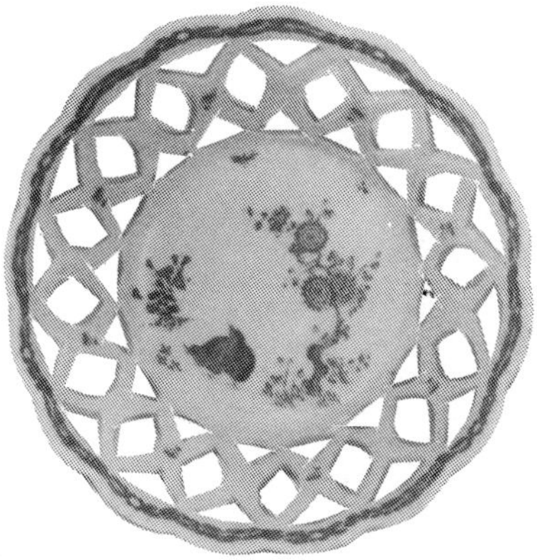

A Bow flared pierced circular basket, painted in the Kakiemon palette with The Quail Pattern, circa 1756, 16.5cm. diam. (Christie's) £1,810

A Bow white figure of Apollo by the Muses Modeller, the god scantily draped and with a laurel wreath in his hair, circa 1752, 17cm. high. (Christie's London) £2,200

BRANNAM

Charles H Brannam (1855–1937) worked as a potter in Barnstaple, Devon, at first making kitchenware and ovens. From 1879 he started making art pottery, known as Barnum ware, usually of brownish clay with simple designs in white slip, mostly in the form of small jugs and vases. His work is usually signed and dated.

BRETBY

The Bretby pottery was founded in 1883 at Woodville, Derbyshire, by Henry Tooth and William Ault. It produced figures, jardinières, bowls, jugs, vases etc., at first in earthenware decorated with coloured glazes (notably sang de boeuf), and applied with flowers, insects etc. in light coloured clay. Later they also produced earthenware decorated in imitation of hammered copper, steel, and bronze with applied ceramic jewels.

William Ault struck out on his own in 1887, but Bretby continued, making 'carved bamboo' ware, and, from 1912 onwards, Clantha ware, which was decorated with geometrical designs on a matt black glaze. Art pottery was made until 1920.

From 1891 the mark was an impressed sun rising behind *Bretby*.

A large Brannam pottery oviform vase, decorated in sgraffito on one side with stylised fish swimming amid aquatic foliage, 79cm. high. (Phillips) £400

A Brannam twin-handled vase by Frederick Braddon, the handles formed as open-mouthed and scaly dragons, 23.7cm. high. (Phillips) £130

A Charles Brannam barium blue glaze stoneware vase, incised with a mythical bird and beast below stylised foliage, dated 1881, 17in. high. (Spencer's) £700

A Brannam pottery cat, seated, his grinning face turned to one side, with the words *'Keep smiling'* modelled along the creature's tail, 24.3cm. high. (Phillips) £170

A Bretby tobacco jar and cover, inscribed 'Nicotiank', 16.5cm. high. £65

Very fine Bretby pottery floor vase, with peasant girl figure by J. Barker, approx. 36in. high. (G. A. Key) £250

BRISTOL

Hard paste porcelain production began in Bristol in 1770, when William Cookworthy removed his factory there from Plymouth, as a place with a stronger potting tradition. Mugs, sauceboats, bowls, creamboats, coffee cups and pickle leaf dishes were among the items produced, and it is in fact often quite difficult to tell Plymouth from early polychrome Bristol.

Cookworthy and Champion's Bristol factory came to concentrate mainly on tea and coffee services, and while some decoration still shows Chinese influence, Meissen and Sèvres styles predominate. Elsewhere, sparsely decorated floral and garland patterns are common but the colours are usually sharp and clear and the gilding is superb.

There was little blue and white material produced, and creamboats, pickle leaf dishes and coffee cups are about all that will be found. The blue is very bright and the glaze relatively unflawed, and the whole approaches more nearly the Chinese original than the output of any other contemporary factory. Most Bristol blue and white ware is marked with a cross in underglaze blue.

A Bristol dessert basket of oval shape with pierced lattice sides, 1770-72, 8½in. over handles. £400

A Bristol sauceboat with foliate scroll handle, circa 1775, 7¼in. over handle. £300

A Bristol christening mug of barrel form, circa 1775, painted X in blue, 10 in gilding, 3in. high. £250

A Champion's Bristol figure of a classical female, circa 1773, 10in. high. £600

A Bristol globular teapot and cover with ear-shaped handle, Richard Champion's Factory, circa 1775, 16cm. high. £1,405

A Bristol two-handled cup and trembleuse saucer of ogee outline, marked B6 in blue enamel. £660

A Bristol baluster milk jug from the Smyth Service, Richard Champion's factory, circa 1776, 10.5cm. high. £540

BRITISH

The British pottery tradition before the industrial period is rooted in the medieval use of tin glazed earthenware. This was often manufactured in monasteries, such as the Cistercian pottery of the 16th century, and was the direct forerunner of the Staffordshire slipwares of the succeeding centuries, which were to form the mainstream of English potting development.

The first inspiration towards refinement came, in England as elsewhere, when the Dutch brought back the first examples of Chinese porcelain. English delft, though never in the same class as its Dutch counterpart, was made at Liverpool, Bristol and elsewhere, painted in very high temperature colours, with little overglaze enamelling.

In Staffordshire, the call for a more delicate ware was answered by the development of a fine saltglazed white stoneware, and then Wedgwood's creamware, which, with its numerous imitators, soon achieved a worldwide market.

18th century English porcelain was distinguished by its variety of composition, ranging from the French style soft-paste type made at Derby, Chelsea and Longton Hall, to the soapstone pastes favoured at Worcester, Caughley and Liverpool and the hard paste varieties of Plymouth and Bristol, while it was the bone ash type pioneered at Bow which was to become the standard body.

No English factory enjoyed the royal patronage which so often fostered their European counterparts, and most were short lived. Inspiration, however, did not fail, and throughout the 19th century, English potters continued to make wares ranging from simple cottage and lustre ware to the fine porcelains of Worcester, Derby and Spode.

An interesting green glazed teapot and cover, moulded in relief with sprays of chrysanthemums and bell-like flowers, 14cm. (Phillips London) £4,000

A ceramic chamber pot with everted rim, decorated with a design by Christopher Dresser, printed in black, brown, beige and green, 23cm. diam. (Phillips) £260

An 'Old Hall' Aesthetic movement plate, designed by Christopher Dresser, with canted corners transfer-decorated with formalised foliage, 23cm. (Phillips) £160

An English porcelain foxhead stirrup cup with gilt collar inscribed *Tallyho*, with bright eyes and pricked ears, 13cm. (Phillips) £780

A Fowler's phrenology head, the cranium printed with the areas of the sentiments, the base with maker's label and title, 11¾in. high. (Christie's S. Ken) £605

A Yorkshire pottery model of a horse, wearing a moulded bridle, saddle cloth and surcingle, 15cm. high. (Henry Spencer) £1,900

An early 19th century English yellow ground tureen and cover, black printed with two children's scenes entitled *L'oiseau le* and *Le fit cheval,* 8in. diam. (Phillips Sevenoaks) £220

A Wiltshire inscribed and dated four-handled loving-cup, on a circular spreading foot with a lightly moulded geometric pattern, 1706, 23.5cm. diameter. (Christie's) £825

A 19th century English drab-ware honey pot and cover in the form of a beehive, with attached dished circular stand, 9.5cm. high. (Henry Spencer) £80

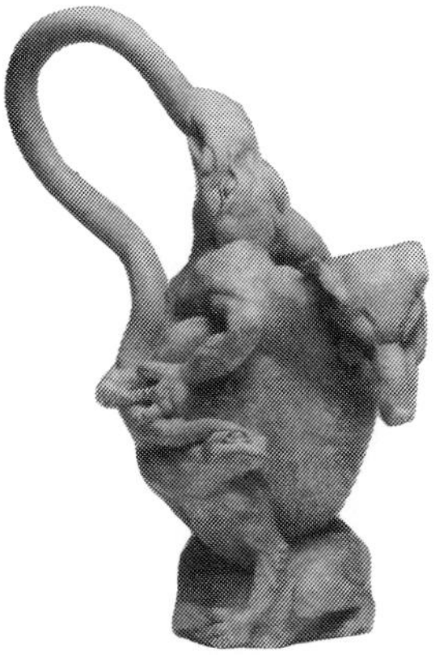

'Bestiary Form', a porcelain jug form by Ruth Barrett-Danes, 28.5cm. high. (Christie's) £825

A pair of figures of a rifleman and an archeress, each wearing hats, blue coats, he with yellow breeches and she with a flowered dress, circa 1830, 8in. high. (Christie's S. Ken) £825

A pottery stick stand, formed as a bear, the naturalistically modelled beast raised upon his hind legs clutching a gnarled branch, 87cm. high. (Lawrence Fine Art) £330

A Don Pottery Orange Jumper jug, the ovoid body printed and coloured with a figure of Mellish standing in profile, 18cm. (Phillips London) £560

Admiral Beatty dressed in naval uniform, supporting a shell entitled *Dread-nought* between his legs, 26.5cm. high. (Phillips) £120

One of a set of twelve Elkin & Co. blue and white pottery plates, each printed with an Irish river landscape, 25.5cm., early 19th century. (Bearne's) (Twelve) £400

A fine blue and white bowl, painted in bright violet tones with a stylised lotus spray at the centre, 19.5cm. diam., fitted box. (Christie's) £1,963

A 'Teepee' teapot and cover of conical form designed by M.B. Sylvester, modelled with totem pole handle and Indian brave spout, 7in. high. (Christie's S. Ken) £374

An interesting small mug or coffee can, painted in underglaze blue with a central rock and tree, probably Vauxhall, 6cm. (Phillips) £620

A rare pierced jar and cover by M. J. Deacon, pierced with a scale pattern heightened in turquoise enamel, 13.5cm. (Phillips London) £170

A pair of large treacle glazed models of spaniels both wearing collars and name tags around their necks, 43cm. (Phillips) £1,100

An 18th century blue and white pottery jug with loop handle, 7.75in. high. (Prudential Fine Art) £130

A large plate, brightly decorated with an urn of flowers, coloured by and signed *E. Barker,* 27cm., 1933. (Phillips London) £360

An unusual ceramic covered mug, modelled as a made-up clown, with a tumbling acrobat forming the handle, with a lithophane base showing two gentlemen greeting each other, 18cm. high. (Phillips) £140

A Portobello cow creamer and cover, 13cm. wide. (Phillips) £360

An 18th century decorated baluster two-handled 'leech' jar with cover, approx. 14in. tall. (J. M. Welch & Son) £1,700

A Wade Heath novelty teapot as Donald Duck in blue sailors outfit, printed marks, circa 1935, 8in. wide. (Christie's S. Ken) £968

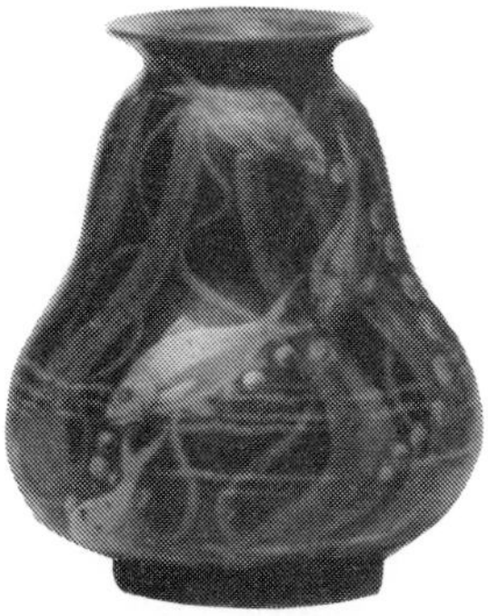

A rare Sabrina ware vase of pear shape, decorated with fish swimming among seaweed, 14cm., date code for 1931. (Phillips London) $195 £120

A rare Brameld type treacle glaze pottery figure of a cat, seated with free-standing forelegs, 28.5cm. high. (Henry Spencer) £260

An amusing Goebels ceramic decanter set comprising: a decanter modelled as a young man and a set of six liqueur goblets each painted in colours with the head of a girl. (Phillips London) £380

A very rare documentary toby jug of Fiddler type, inscribed *J. Marsh, Folley,* 27.5cm., the head a replacement made in bell metal. (Phillips London) £2,200

A Cistercian ware tyg, the conical cup with three loop handles, the black glaze stopping just above the foot, 6.8cm. high. (Phillips) £200

An English porcelain tapering bough pot and cover with five apertures and four feet, 8in. high. (Christie's S. Ken) £572

'Guardian Vessel', a porcelain form by Ruth Barrett-Danes, 22.2cm. high. (Christie's) £825

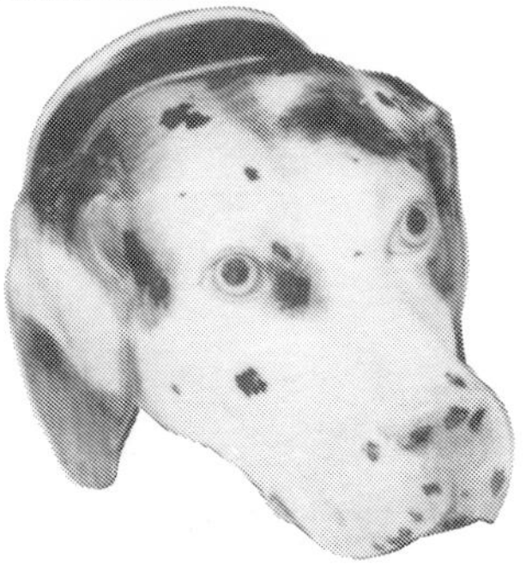

A large English porcelain stirrup cup modelled as the head of a hound, his coat spotted in brown, 15cm. (Phillips London) £340

A rich Cauldon dessert plate, the shaped centre painted by Joseph Birbeck Snr., 21.5cm. (Phillips London) £220

An English porcelain cream glazed basket modelled as a cat standing with its fore paws resting on the brim of a straw hat, possibly Brown Westhead Moore and Co Ltd. (Christie's S. Ken) £242

A Glasgow (Delftfield) polychrome slender baluster vase and cover painted in a Fazackerly palette in blue, manganese, yellow and green with flowering foliage issuing from rockwork, circa 1760, 44cm. high. (Christie's) £8,800

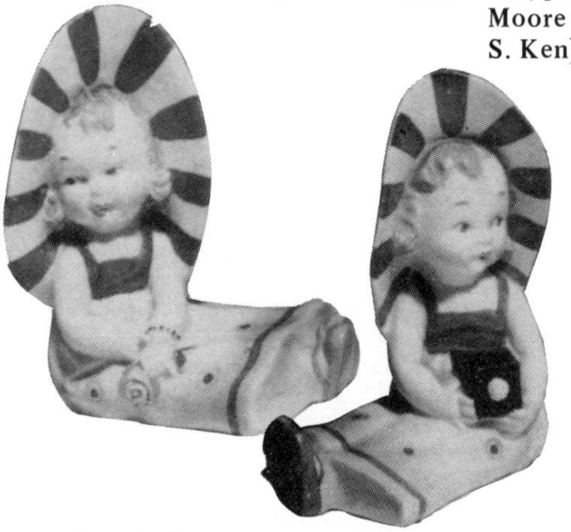

A pair of pottery book-ends in the form of little girls sitting under sunhats, holding a camera and a rose, 5¾in. high, with the William Goebel crown mark. (Christie's S. Ken) £242

A Charles Bourne beaded spill vase painted with floral sprays, on a scale blue ground, 11cm. (Phillips London) £200

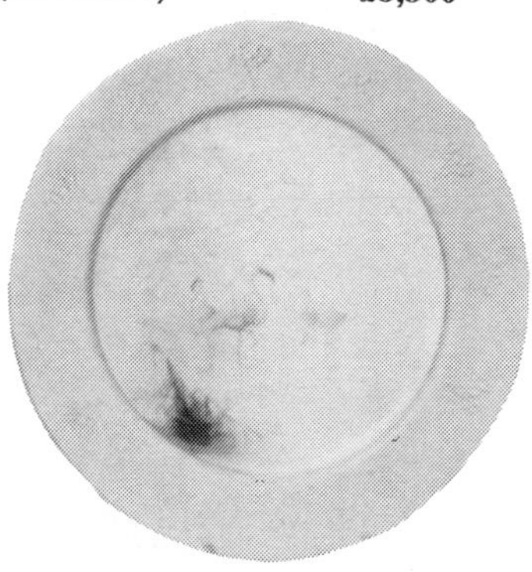

A plate, the centre painted with flamingos in a misty river landscape, signed *W. Powell,* 26cm., date code for 1912. (Phillips London) £550

A figure of a child in a plumed hat seated on the back of a deer with iron-red fur markings, 10in. high. (Christie's S. Ken) £242

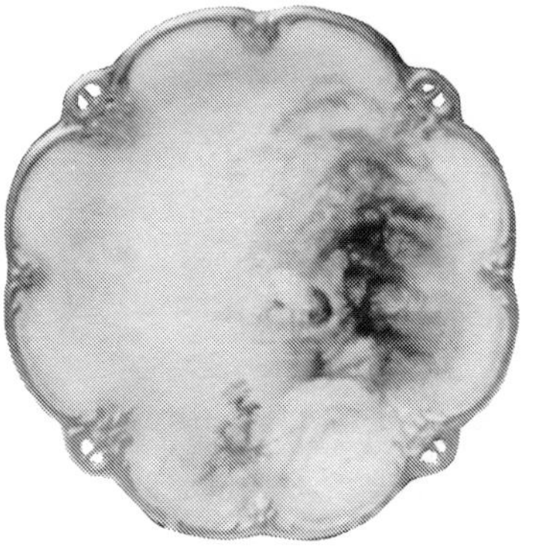

A wall plaque painted with two storks standing on the edge of a river, signed *W Powell,* 22.5cm., date code for 1910. (Phillips London) £850

An English porcelain pot pourri basket and cover, with reserving panels painted with coloured flowers, 6.5cm. diam. (Phillips London) £120

A large Rogers meat dish of canted rectangular shape, printed in blue with the 'Camel' pattern, 54cm. (Phillips) £300

A plate, painted with a view of Tynemouth Priory, signed *H. Davis,* 23cm., date code for 1903. (Phillips London) £320

A well coloured traditional toby jug, the man seated holding a foaming brown jug on one knee, 25cm. (Phillips London) £700

A pair of porcelain figures of 'My Grandmother and My Grandfather', painted in colours and enriched in gilding, 6½in. high, circa 1830. (Christie's S. Ken) £495

Frank Roberts, a tall slender vase and cover, the ovoid body painted with bell flowers and yellow daisies, signed *Roberts*, date code for 1902. (Phillips) £2,800

A porcelain pastille burner in the form of a house, the gold tiled roof edged with moss, 16.5cm. (Bearne's) £380

An English porcelain blue-ground plate, the centre painted with figures on a shore and in a boat in a lakescape, circa 1820–30, 9in. diameter. (Christie's S. Ken) £143

A Crimean group of an officer and his companion, seated either side of a fire place surmounted by a wall clock, circa 1855. (Christie's S. Ken) £440

Late 19th century chamber pot with floral decoration. (British Antique Exporters) £15

19th century pottery soup tureen and cover, by Turner, blue and white Willow pattern in the style of Nankin. (G. A. Key) £80

A Bodley rectangular tray, painted by Joseph Birbeck, with a cow, sheep and a goat in an extensive view in North Wales, 27.5cm. (Phillips London) £270

A Maw & Co. pottery vase of bulbous form with extended and flared neck painted with large stylised red floral buds, 33cm. high.
(Phillips) £460

An H. & R. Daniel blue-ground part tea service, comprising an 'Etruscan' shape teapot, cover and stand, a two-handled sugar bowl and cover, a milk jug, a slop-basin, eight teacups and saucers, pattern no. 3859, circa 1825.
(Christie's) £440

English Pottery Toby Jug, probably Yorkshire, early 19t century, Toby holding a cup i one hand and a pitcher in the other, 10¼in. high.
(Skinner Inc) £197

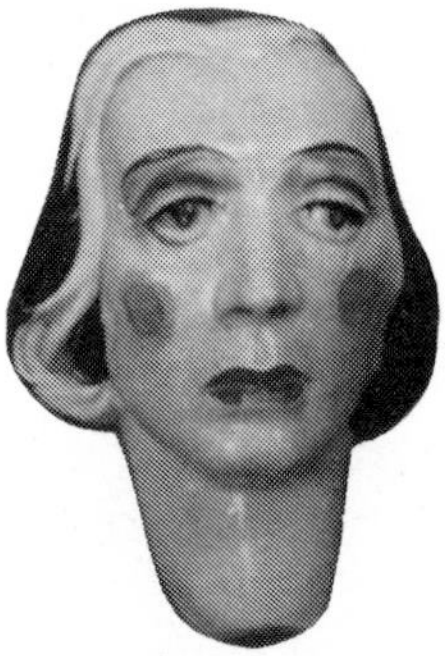

A Susie Cooper wall mask modelled as the head of a woman with grey streaked black hair, 10¾in. long.
(Christie's) £990

A rectangular plaque, painted with Highland cattle and sheep, signed E. Townsend, 23.5 x 36cm.
(Phillips) £1,050

A bisque figure of a cricketer with articulated head, modelled in the form of a cricket ball, inscribed *Hassall* on the base.
(Christie's S. Ken) £27

A Mayer & Newbold shaped oval dessert dish moulded with roses and other garden flowers, 23.8cm., circa 1820.
(Bearne's) £180

A Burleigh ware character jug of Sir Winston Churchill titled *'Bulldogs'*, 28cm.
(Phillips) £520

A very rare Limehouse dish of canted rectangular shape, painted in blue with two Oriental figures at a table, 17cm. x 22cm.
(Phillips) £3,100

A Sung flambe figure 'Boy on a Seahorse', signed Frederick Moore, 8.5in. high, probably a pilot. (Louis Taylor) £550

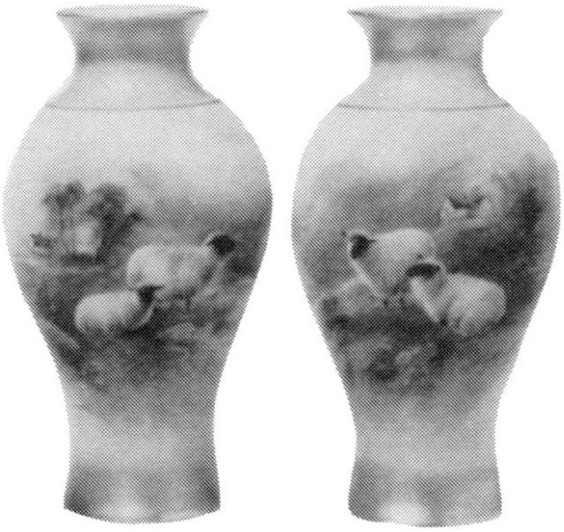

A pair of baluster vases painted with sheep in highland landscapes, signed *H. Davis,* 15cm., date codes for 1925. (Phillips London) £2,400

A large Castle Hedingham Essex jug, moulded in relief with Classical panels of chariot racing and the Muses, 30in. high. (Christie's S. Ken) £352

An ironstone occupational shaving mug, late 19th/early 20th century, on spreading gilt foot, 4½in. high.
(Christie's) £32

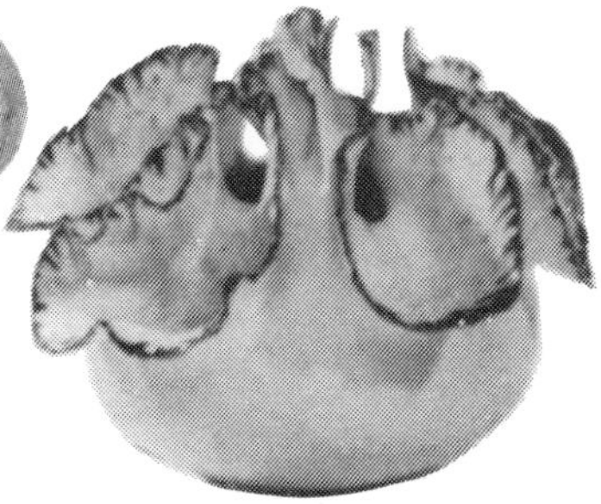

A porcelain pinched vase by Deirdre Burnett, covered in a white glaze with olive brown run and fluxed rim, impressed *DB,* 7.5cm. high. (Christie's London) £77

One of a rare pair of pate sur pate square plaques by Charles Noke, signed, decorated with portraits of a man and woman representing old age,
19 x 16.5cm. (Phillips London)
Two £380

BURMANTOFTS

Burmantofts is the name given to products from the pottery of Wilcock and Co, which was established in 1858 in Leeds. Initially terracotta earthenware was produced, but after 1880 they also made a hard buff coloured high fired earthenware with a feldspathic glaze, which became known as Burmantofts faience. This was used to make tiles and, from 1882, art pottery. Their output included vases, bowls, jardinières and figures, covered in coloured glazes and showing oriental or Middle Eastern influence. Other decorations in the range included underglaze designs trailed in slip, painted or incised and copper and silver lustre was also used on dark colours. From 1904 they reverted to specialising in terracotta.

Marks include the name in full or the monogram *BF*.

BURMANTOFTS
FAÏENCE

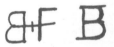

BURSLEM

Burslem was one of the major centres of the Staffordshire pottery industry in the 18th and 19th century, with scores of factories, large and small, (among the former, notably, Doulton) turning out stoneware and earthenware.

A Burmantofts jardiniere and stand, 31in. overall, stamped marks. (Christie's) £300

A rare Burmantofts pottery plaque in shallow relief, depicting a heron in naturalistic setting, about to gorge himself on a family of frogs, 25in. approximately. (Geering & Colyer) £460

A fine Burmantofts faience charger with domed centre, decorated in the Isnik manner in blue, turquoise, green and amethyst with dragons, 45.6cm. diam. (Christie's) £2,860

A Burmantofts faience vase, decorated in cobalt blue, turquoise, green and pink, on a white ground, 46.4cm. high. (Christie's London) £902

A Doulton, Burslem, ovoid vase, the panel painted by Fred Sutton, 17cm. high. (Phillips) £400

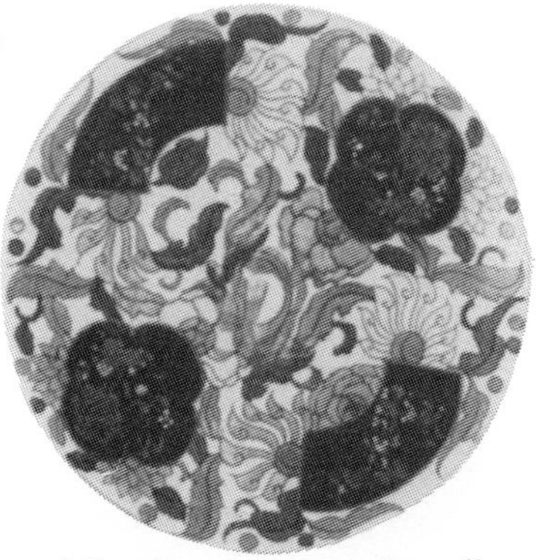

A Burslem ware ceramic wall plaque, the design attributed to Charlotte Rhead, decorated with stylised brown, and cream chrysanthemums with blue leaves and berries, 41cm. diam. (Phillips London) £220

CANTON

There is a reference which suggests that earthenware cooking vessels were made in Kuangtung (Canton) as early as the T'ang dynasty (618–906). The dating of what has come to be known as Canton stoneware is, however, very difficult. It is certain they go back at least to late Ming times, and they are still made and exported in large quantities.

Canton ware is usually dark brown at the base, varying to pale yellowish grey and buff with a thick smooth glaze which is distinctive for its mottling and dappling effect. The colour is often blue, flecked and streaked with grey green or white over a substratum of olive brown. Sometimes brown tints predominate, but it is the blue toned ware which is most highly prized.

Very large jars, vases etc. were made for outdoor use, sometimes with elaborate applied work, and incense burners, water pots etc. were also made in form of small animal figures.

Workshops at Canton decorated porcelain in the famille rose style for export, as well as the 'Canton enamels' painted on copper.

A Canton chamber candlestick with matching candle snuffer, each piece painted with figures.
(Bearne's) £300

Canton blue and white teapot and cover, China, mid 19th century, drum shape, coastal village scene with cloud border, $5\frac{1}{2}$in. high.
(Skinner Inc.) £82

A pair of Canton vases, applied at the neck and shoulders with dragons and Buddhist lions, 61.8cm. high.
(Bearne's) £2500

A Canton famile rose jug and cover, the ovoid body painted with figures in a pavilion, $11\frac{1}{4}$in. high, 19th century.
(Bonhams) £1,050

A Canton enamel fish tank decorated in famille rose enamels, 25.5in. £1,100

One of a pair of Canton hexagonal baluster jars and covers, 25in. high. £5,390

Late 18th century famille rose Canton enamel circular segmented supper set formed as eight fan-shaped dishes, 18in. diam. £715

Canton blue and white porcelain charger, 19th century, circular scene with patterned banded borders, 16in. diam.
(Skinner Inc.) £375

Antique Canton two-handled sugar bowl, 4½in. high.
(Eldred's) £44

A yellow-ground Canton enamel saucer dish, seal mark and period of Qianlong, 8.7/8in. £310

A pair of Canton vases of hexagonal section, applied at the neck and shoulders with Buddhist lions and dragons, 60.8cm.
(Bearne's) £820

A Canton coffee pot, the domed cover with gilt finial, 9¾in. high. £270

A highly important pair of Canton vases, profusely figure decorated with sealion handles and gold serpents to the neck, 37½in. high. (Coles Knapp Fine Arts) £3,800

Antique Canton rectangular deep platter decorated with a lake scene, length 12in.
(Eldred's) £440

Pair of Canton blue and white tea caddies, China, mid 19th century, hexagonal shape, with lids, 6in. high.
(Skinner Inc) £3,782

Antique Canton drum-shaped teapot, decorated with lake scene, 8in. high.
(Eldred's) £628

CAPODIMONTE

The Capodimonte factory near Naples was established by King Charles III in 1742 to make soft-paste porcelain of the French type.

It was not until 1744, however, after numerous failed attempts, that Gaetano Schepers managed to produce a paste which was suitably 'white and diaphanous' and which achieved a brilliance to rival Meissen.

The most famous modeller at the Capodimonte factory was Giovanni Caselli, a former gem engraver and miniature painter. Figurines were among the earliest output of the factory, but snuff boxes, tea services and scent bottles were also made. The small objects were often mounted on gold or silver gilt, and the fine floral decoration was usually painted in finely drawn hair lines.

In 1759 Charles acceded to the throne of Spain, and the factory closed. He set up again at Buen Retiro, but the quality of products produced there is generally inferior to their Capodimonte antecedents.

A Capodimonte oviform teapot with scroll handle and spout, blue fleur-de-lys mark, circa 1750, 14.5cm. wide. £825

A Capodimonte baluster coffee pot and low domed cover, painted by Giuseppe della Torre, circa 1744, 26.5cm. high. £13,500

An extremely rare and finely painted Capodimonte candlestick base of triangular shape, modelled by Gaetano Fumo and Giuseppe Gricci, 18.5cm. high. (Phillips) £1,500

A Capodimonte (Carlo III) group of fisherfolk, modelled by Giuseppe Gricci, circa 1750, 17.5cm. wide. £9,020

A Capodimonte group of a youth riding a mastiff modelled by Guiseppe Gricci, the youth in peaked pale-pink cap with gilt bow, 1755–1759, 17cm. high. (Christie's) £4,180

A Capodimonte (Carlo III) shaped gold mounted snuff box, the porcelain circa 1755, 8.5cm. wide. £900

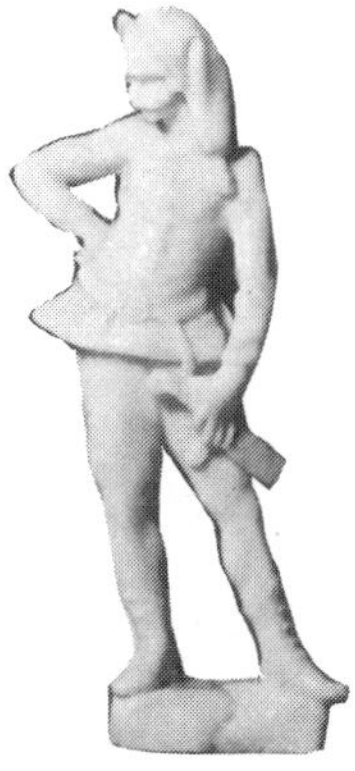

A Capodimonte (Carlo III) white figure of Capitano Spavento from the Commedia dell'Arte, circa 1750, 14cm. high. £4,320

MICHAEL CARDEW

Born in 1901 Michael Cardew was a pupil of Bernard Leach. His earliest products from his Winchcombe Pottery, dating from the 1920s, consist mainly of slip-decorated earthenware for domestic use, often with sgraffiato decoration. He later experimented with tin-glazed earthenware and in 1941 went out to teach at Achimota College in Ghana. Following the closure of the college in 1945 he open a pottery on the Volta river, producing stoneware often decorated with African inspired motifs. He returned to this country in 1948 and at Wenford Bridge began making light coloured stoneware, often with brushed decoration, before returning to Africa to work for the Nigerian government in 1950, establishing a training centre at Abuja. He died in 1983.

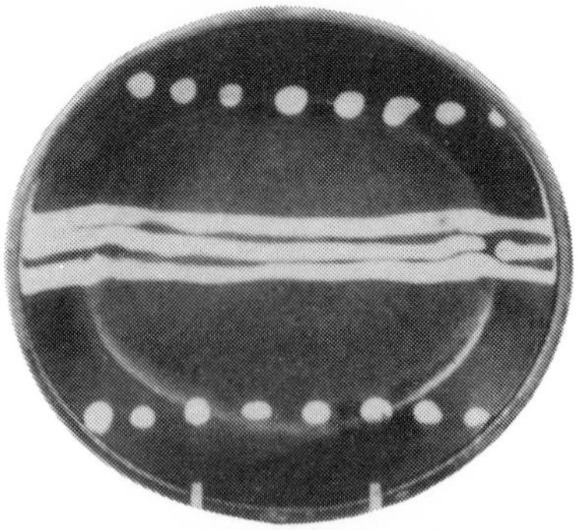

An oval earthenware slip decorated dish by Michael Cardew, the interior covered in a dark toffee-brown glaze with trailed mustard-yellow slip, circa 1930, 21cm. wide. (Christie's) £154

A mustard glazed stoneware two handled vase, cover and pierced liner by Michael Cardew, impressed seal mark, 11in. high. (Spencer's) £100

A small earthenware cider flagon by Michael Cardew, covered in an amber and olive green glaze over which a mustard-green, stopping short of the foot, impressed MC and Winchcombe Pottery seals, 21cm. high. (Christie's) £110

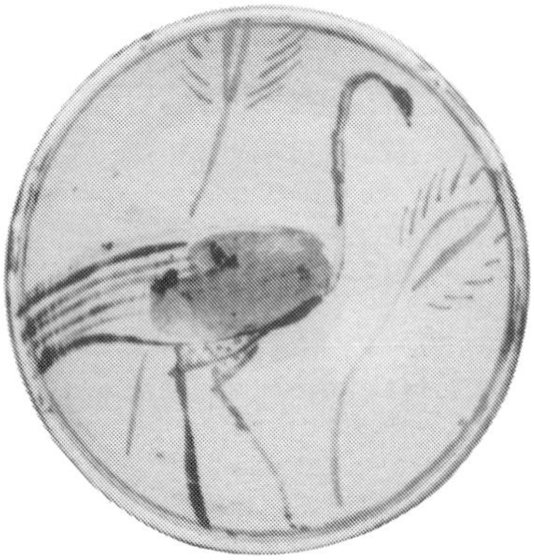

A stoneware bowl by Michael Cardew, the interior with incised decoration and blue and brown brushwork of a bird amongst grasses, MC and Wenford Bridge seals, 24.5cm. diam. (Christie's) £715

An earthenware coffee pot and cover by Michael Cardew, impressed MC and Winchcombe Pottery seals, circa 1933, 17cm. high. (Christie's) £286

A stoneware globular casserole by Michael Cardew with tall neck, two lug handles and a concave cover with knob finial, circa 1975, 20.7cm. high. (Christie's) £286

A small earthenware jug by Michael Cardew, impressed MC and Winchcombe Pottery seals, 12.4cm. high. (Christie's) £93

A large stoneware rose bowl by Michael Cardew on circular foot, the interior covered in an iron speckled greenish-mushroom coloured glaze, impressed MC and Wenford Bridge seals, 21.6cm. high. (Christie's) £418

A stoneware casserole and cover by Michael Cardew, Wenford Bridge seals, circa 1970, 32cm. diam. (Christie's) £440

An important and fine stoneware bowl by Michael Cardew, banded with vertical lines alternate with abstracted pattern, impressed MC and Wenford Bridge seals, 12¼in. diameter. (Bonhams) £1,500

An Abuja stoneware oil jar by Michael Cardew, with screw stopper, covered in a mottled olive-green glaze, impressed MC and Abuja seals, circa 1959, 33cm. high. (Christie's) £550

A stoneware charger by Michael Cardew, covered in an oatmeal glaze, the interior with olive green glaze and combed waved bands through to oatmeal glaze, 34.3cm. diam. (Christie's London) £440

An earthenware jug by Michael Cardew, covered in a translucent brown glaze over a mottled lime green and olive brown glaze, 25.6cm. high. (Christie's London) £154

An earthenware two-handled motto tankard by Michael Cardew, impressed MC and Winchcombe Pottery seals (circa 1930), 10.1cm. high. (Christie's) £198

An earthenware cider flagon, by Michael Cardew, Wenford Bridge seals, circa 1970, 39cm. high. (Christie's) £825

A stoneware footed bowl by Michael Cardew, covered in a speckled mushroom coloured glaze with chocolate brown decoration of cross hatching and spiralling brushwork, 13.5cm. high. (Christie's London) £605

CARLTON WARE

Carlton ware was the name given to the Staffordshire earthenware produced from 1890 at the Carlton Works, Stoke on Trent, by the firm which traded until 1957 as Wiltshaw & Robinson. From January 1958 it was retitled Carlton Ware Ltd.

The factory produced ornamental ware such as vases, characterised by bright enamelling and gilded floral and fanleaf decoration, black very often being used as the base colour. Early products normally bear a circular printed mark with *W & R Stoke on Trent* enclosing a swallow and surmounted by a crown.

A Carlton ware ginger jar and cover, with gilt coloured chinoiserie decoration depicting temples and pagodas, 31cm. high.
(Phillips) £300

A Carlton ware twin-handled boat shape bowl on splayed cylindrical column painted with an exotic bird of paradise, 23.5cm. high.
(Phillips) £180

Shaped vase, 'Persian' design, marked with a gold star underneath, 280mm. high. £400

A Carltonware service decorated in polychrome enamels, coffee pot 20.4cm. high. £810

Pale pink shaped vase with Art Deco design, 195mm. high. £125

'Handcraft' design vase following the Arts & Crafts movement, using a white background with blue, beige, pink and purple stencilling, 225mm. high. £200

Carlton Ware lustre jug with gilt loop handle, the body painted and gilded with stylised floral and fan decoration, 5in. high. (Prudential Fine Art) £115

A leaf green Art Deco vase with large and small lustrous trees of unusual colours, black inside, 265mm. high. £250

Vibrant lustrous red 'Rouge Royale' leaf, one of a series introduced after 1930, 220mm. long. **£25**

A light red shaped vase with multi-coloured duck in flight, 240mm. high. **£200**

A large Carlton ware two handled punch bowl, moulded and painted on one side with King Henry VIII and Cardinal Wolsey on the other. (Bearne's) **£360**

Oviform vase with dark grey ground simulating nightfall, signed by E. F. Paul, with Kate Greenaway style fairies design, 230mm. high. £550

Egyptianesque jardiniere with frieze decoration and hieroglyphics on a blue ground, 160mm. high. £950

Standard Carltonware vase of pale blue ground with tube lined floral decorations on primary colours, also blue inside the vase, 165mm. high. £85

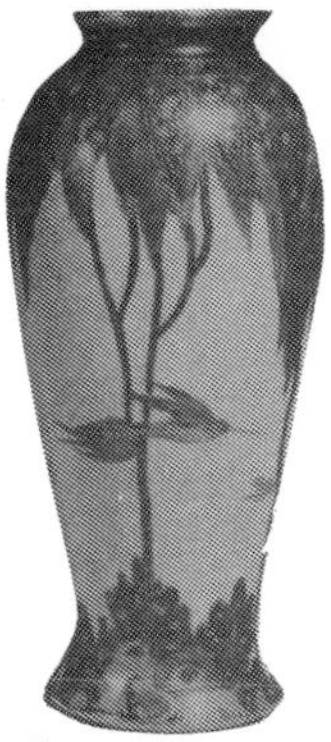

A Carltonware vase with polychrome decoration on a mottled purple and white ground, circa 1930, 26.7cm. high. £215

Deep red jug with gold handle and sea-green interior, one of the famous birds series, featuring fantastic and mythical birds, 295mm. high. £200

An hexagonal vase with chinoiserie decoration, still made today, 175mm. high. £95

CARTER STABLER & ADAMS

In 1921 John and Truda Adams went into partnership with Harold Stabler and Owen Carter of Carter & Co of Poole Dorset.

Together they made hand thrown and hand decorated pottery, mostly designed either by Stabler and his wife Phoebe, or the Adams. Their shapes, mostly tableware and stoneware, were noted for their simplicity and were usually decorated in bold colours under a creamy matt glaze. Around the 1930s candlesticks were also made in the Art Deco style. The company continues today as Poole Pottery Ltd and is currently enjoying a period of great popularity, with some sales being devoted exclusively to their output.

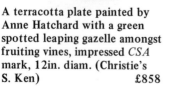

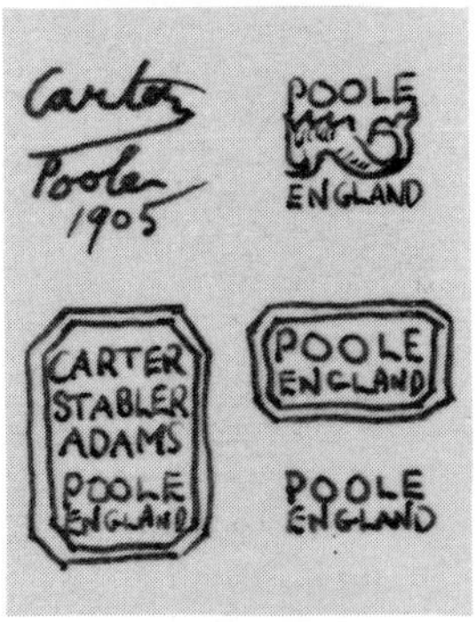

A Carter Stabler & Adams Ltd. vase, designed by James Radley Young, 25cm. high. (Lawrence Fine Arts) £198

A Carter Stabler & Adams Ltd. vase, designed by James Radley Young, with vertical panels of dots within striped borders, 15.5cm. high. (Lawrence Fine Arts) £209

A terracotta twin handled oviform vase painted by Ruth Pavely with bluebirds and foliage between contrasting borders, impressed *CSA Ltd.* mark, 6½in. high. (Christie's S. Ken) £660

A Carter, Stabler & Adams Ltd. biscuit fired stoneware vase, with stepped and ribbed decoration, decorated in shades of brown with geometric, linear and floral designs, 33.7cm. high. (Christie's London) £550

A terracotta plate painted by Anne Hatchard with a green spotted leaping gazelle amongst fruiting vines, impressed *CSA* mark, 12in. diam. (Christie's S. Ken) £858

A Carter Stabler Adams Poole pottery vase, attributed to Truda Carter, painted in blue, green, mauve, black and yellow, 22.1cm. high. (Phillips London) £100

A Carter Stabler Adams pottery dish, possibly a design by Erna Manners, painted in mauve, green and blue with stylised leaves and scrolling tendrils, 37.8cm. diam. (Phillips) £180

CASTEL DURANTE

Castel Durante, in the province of Urbino, is the birthplace of two of the outstanding figures concerned with Italian maiolica, Nicola Pellipario, the master of maiolica painting, and Cipriano Piccolpasso, who wrote the definitive work Litre libri dell'Arte del Vasaio.

The earliest Castel Durante wares can sometimes be attributed to the painter and potter Giovanni Maria, who specialised in grotesque and trophy borders around deep-welled plates containing beautifully drawn heads of girls or youths.

Even in Pellipario's earliest works the pictorial painting style is fully developed. In 1519, he painted the d'Este service for the wife of the marquis of Mantua, where every dish and plate, in addition to heraldic arms, bears a different subject from Classical mythology, often taken from slightly earlier woodcuts.

Pellipario left Castel Durante about 1527 to join his son in Urbino.

A Castel Durante squat drug jar painted with the naked Fortune arising from the waves on the back of a dolphin, circa 1580, 23.5cm. wide. (Christie's London) £17,600

A Castel Durante tondino with a central yellow and ochre foliage mask inscribed *PACIFICAB* on a ribbon above reserved on a blue ground, circa 1525, 22cm. diameter. (Christie's) £4,180

A Castel Durante dated dish painted in green and grey about a central medallion of an Emperor to the left crowned with laurels, circa 1555, 26.5cm. diameter. (Christie's) £2,200

A Castel Durante wet-drug jar with short yellow spout and wide strap handle, named for *S. ABSINTII* on a yellow rectangular cartouche, circa 1570, 21cm. high. (Christie's) £2,750

A Castel Durante portrait dish boldly painted with an almost full face portrait of 'Faustina Bella', her hair coiled and braided with a white bandeau, 23cm., circa 1540. (Phillips) £11,000

A 17th century Castel Durante baluster armorial pharmacy bottle, 22cm. high. (Christie's) £1,760

A Castel Durante Armorial saucer dish with a coat of arms above a hilly landscape, within a wide blue border, 22.5cm., circa 1570. (Phillips) £4,800

CASTELLI

Castelli, in the kingdom of Naples, owes its fame to the maiolica made there from the late 17th century onwards, principally by the Grue and Gentili families. They produced a style which is rich in architectural detail, with borders adorned by flowers and putti, the main colours being buff, yellow and a greenish brown.

The original stylistic inspiration is generally thought to have come from Carlo Antonio Grue (d. 1723), whose four sons, Francesco Antonio, Anastasio, Aurelio and Libero continued the tradition until the death of the last in 1776.

Few factory marks were used, but the artists frequently signed their work, enabling accurate attributions to be made.

A Castelli rectangular plaque painted in the Grue workshop with the Flight into Egypt, circa 1720, 20 x 25.5cm. (Christie's) £1,540

A Castelli armorial plate painted in the Grue workshop with a traveller and companion riding a horse and a donkey, circa 1720, 24cm. diameter. (Christie's) £2,420

A Castelli rectangular plaque painted with Abraham sacrificing a lamb, circa 1720, 27 x 20.5cm. £990

A Castelli rectangular plaque painted with Pan being comforted after the musical contest with Apollo seated, circa 1725, 28cm. square. £970

Late 17th century Castelli plate painted in colours with a mounted hunting party, 23cm. diam. (Christie's) £2,860

A Castelli armorial plate by Aurelio Grue, after a print from the Hunt Series by Antonio Tempesta, yellow and brown line rim, circa 1725, 29cm. diam. (Christie's London) £13,200

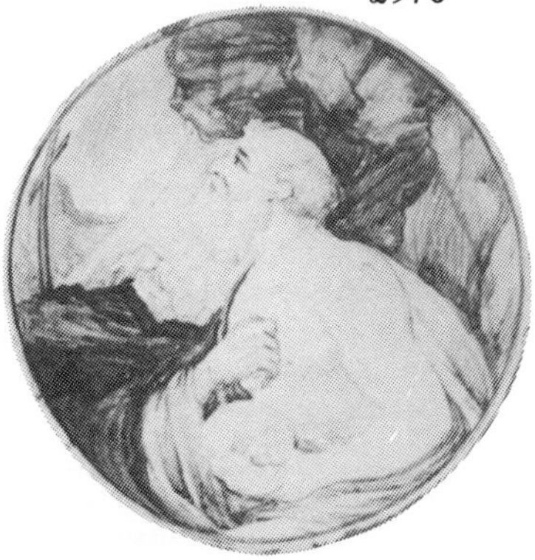

A Castelli scudella of circular form, painted in the Grue Workshop, with Saint Jerome holding a skull in one hand, 13.5cm. (Phillips London) £260

A Castelli armorial small dish painted in the Grue workshop and lightly enriched in gilding, the centre with Venus scantily draped and combing Cupid's hair, late 17th/early 18th century, 24.5cm. diameter. (Christie's) £4,620

A Castelli oval plaque painted by Saverio Grue with St. Francis, circa 1730, 38cm. high. (Christie's) £3,850

A Castelli circular tondo painted with the Dispute in the Temple, circa 1725, 43cm. diam. (Christie's) £660

A Castelli large vase of campana form painted in colours and gilt, circa 1720, 41cm. high. £1,500

A Castelli rectangular plaque painted with the Meeting between St. John and the Infant Christ, circa 1690, 30 x 40cm. (Christie's) £1,650

A Castelli campana vase, probably painted by Liborio Grue, circa 1740, 41.5cm. high. (Christie's) £1,430

A Castelli plate painted with two women washing clothes in the river, buildings and mountains in the background, 17th century, 18cm. diam. (Christie's London) £220

A Castelli rectangular plaque painted by Saverio Grue with Joseph sold by his brothers to the Midianites, circa 1770, 32.5 x 23.5cm. (Christie's) £6,600

A Castelli armorial circular dish, the centre painted with equestrian figures hawking, circa 1720, 40.5cm. diam. (Christie's) £5,280

CAUGHLEY

Around 1772 Thomas Turner established his factory at Caughley in Shropshire. Turner had been manager at Worcester, and had trained as an engraver under Robert Hancock. He persuaded Hancock to join him in his new venture, and set out to rival the Worcester production of blue printed porcelain. He was so successful that by the 1780s Caughley was completely dominating the market, making mass produced, affordable wares in simple shapes with very elaborate decoration.

Turner then dealt his rivals a further blow by persuading their chief decorators, the Chamberlains, to set up on their own, and having done so, they gilded blue and white Caughley wares, and also made enamel pieces to order for Turner.

Turner countered elaborate Chinese patterns with transfer printing, and it is often claimed that he was the first to introduce the celebrated Willow pattern. The factory made a wide range of attractive shapes, including sauceboats, mugs, creamboats, pickle leaf dishes and bowls, as well as a number of small items, such as spoontrays, asparagus servers and egg drainers. Miniature teawares were very common and were produced in two patterns, one printed and one painted. These are very sought after today.

Both Caughley and Worcester used a number of the same transfer prints, but some are unique to Caughley, notably that commemorating the erection of the Ironbridge at Coalbrookdale in 1779.

Painted Caughley wares tend to be earlier than the more common printed pieces.

Some later printed wares were enhanced with gilding, but this tends now to detract from their value.

An important Caughley loving cup, printed in blue with a view of the Iron Bridge, 11.7cm. (Phillips London) £3,500

A Caughley egg drainer, decorated in blue and white the Fisherman pattern, circa 1790, 3 1/5 in. across handle.
(Woolley & Wallis) **£180**

**A Caughley cream-jug painted with the Badge of George IV as Prince of Wales, enclosed by the crowned Royal Garter and motto within a blue dot and gilt cartouche, circa 1790, 14cm. wide.
(Christie's) £825**

A Caughley porcelain cabbage leaf moulded jug, with rotund body and slant eyes to the mask spout, 22.5cm. high. (Henry Spencer) £260

A Caughley coffee pot of baluster shape, printed with 'The Fisherman' pattern, 9½in. high. (G. A. Property Services) £180

A Caughley shanked sugar bowl and cover painted with landscapes within gilt circular cartouches, circa 1792, 12cm. diam. (Christie's) £286

CHANTILLY

The Chantilly porcelain factory was founded in 1725 by Louis Henri de Bourbon, Prince du Condé, under the direction of Cicaire Cirou. The Prince was an avid collector of Arita pottery and set his factory to manufacture this type of ware. The unique feature of Chantilly is its glaze, which in contrast to the usual transparent lead glaze of soft paste porcelains was an opaque white tin glaze such as that used in the production of faience. The use of this precluded underglaze decoration, but was ideal for painting in the delicate colours of the Kakiemon style typical of Arita ware.

These Japanese designs were exquisitely painted, sometimes from the original and sometimes from Meissen copies, which they excelled both in quality of shape and decoration. After the death of the Prince in 1740 Kakiemon styles were abandoned, and a year after the death of Cirou in 1751 disaster struck the factory in the form of a Royal edict forbidding the manufacture of porcelain for a period of 12 years at any factory other than Vincennes, which was the particular pet of Louis XV and Madame de Pompadour.

While the edict was not, in fact, strictly enforced, Chantilly now abandoned the use of tin glaze in favour of a transparent lead glaze which revealed an attractive cream coloured body. Over the next few years most decoration was done in camaieu (monochrome). Favourite styles were crimson cupids after Boucher and the use of a border of diapered quatrefoils in blue enamel.

Typical of the Cirou period is the red hunting horn mark, while later pieces carry a blue horn, often more crudely drawn and sometimes accompanied by *Chantilly*.

**A 1870s Chantilly dish with gros bleu ground and a central gilt cartouche depicting, in puce, a chateau by a lakeside, 24cm. across.
(Phillips) £235**

A Chantilly teabowl painted in Kakiemon style with a panel of **flowering prunus issuing from rockwork, 4.5cm., red horn mark.
(Phillips) £500**

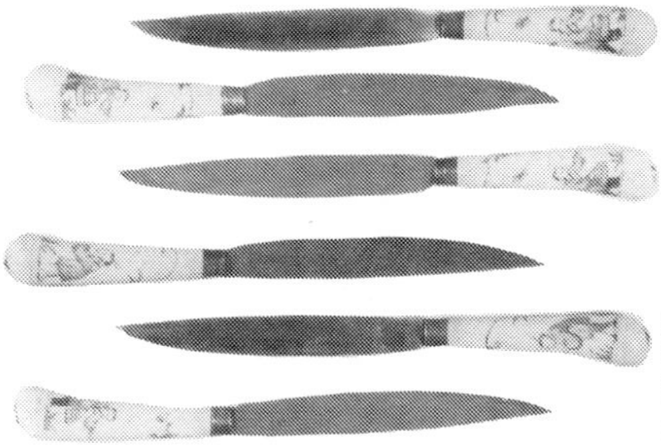

Six Chantilly Kakiemon pistol shaped knife handles, painted with a boy (four cracked), circa 1740, mounted with contemporary silver blades, impressed swan marks, the handles 8.5cm. long. (Christie's London) £1,210

A Chantilly Kakiemon square box and cover, iron-red hunting horn mark, circa 1740, 25cm. high. £16,500

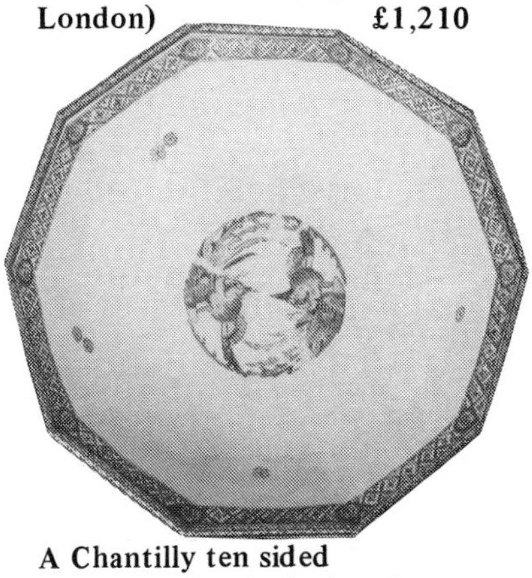

A Chantilly ten sided Kakiemon bowl, the interior with a roundel composed of two ho-ho birds, circa 1735, later French gilt metal mounts by A. Risler & Carre, Paris, 26cm. diam. (Christie's London) £1,430

A Chantilly green ground two handled pot pourri, the waisted campana body applied with swags of flowers, circa 1750, 19cm. high.
(Christie's London) £5,500

CHELSEA 'GIRL IN A SWING'

The relationship between the main Chelsea factory and the Girl in a Swing factory in the mid 18th century is not clear, but it seems certain that many workmen were employed there from Chelsea, and its guiding light was probably the jeweller Charles Gouyn.

The factory was noted between 1749–54 for its scent bottles, but also produced some rare figures, modelled in a unique and dainty style, as well as some dressing table ware. Often these have been attributed to Chelsea proper, but it seems likely that the two factories were entirely separate.

A 'Girl in a Swing' cream jug with brown twig handle, circa 1750, 8cm. high. £12,960

A rare Girl-in-a-Swing scent bottle as a lady seated on a rocky mound, wearing a low cut yellow bodice, the base inscribed in red *Pour Mon Amour*, 7.5cm. (Phillips) £1,400

A 'Girl in a Swing' seal modelled as Harlequin in black mask and multi-coloured chequered clothes, circa 1749-54, 3.2cm. high. (Christie's) £462

A scent bottle of 'Girl in a Swing' type modelled as Wm. Shakespeare, circa 1755, 8.5cm. high. £395

A 'Girl in a Swing' gold-mounted scent bottle and stopper, 1751-54, 8.5cm. high. £1,405

CHELSEA

The new Chelsea factory, founded in the 1740s, was largely inspired by Nicholas Sprimont, a Huguenot silversmith from Flanders, and it was probably the first of the six or so soft paste factories which sprang up in England by 1750.

Early Chelsea products were very attractive, highly translucent and based on glass ingredients. Pieces from this period often carry an incised triangle and have a strong affinity with Sprimont's silverwork, with particular emphasis on shellwork and scroll motifs. Many pieces were left in the

A Chelsea group of two children, naked except for a pink drapery, with large fish, 24cm. high. (Lawrence Fine Art) £900

A Chelsea blue-ground square tapering vase, gold anchor mark, circa 1765, 32cm. high. (Christie's) £1,100

white, although some were coloured in Kakiemon style. Figures, often also of oriental inspiration, were made at this time and were invariably left white.

The next, or Raised Anchor Period (1749–53) saw the porcelain becoming more opaque as less lead was used. Figures are now more usually coloured, this often being done in the London studio of William Duesbury. While oriental influence remained very strong, many decorations of this period are obviously of Meissen origin. Another interesting decorative development of the time was fable painting on cups, teapots etc., as was the 'Hans Sloane' plant decoration based on the drawings of Philip Miller, head gardener at Hans Sloane's botanical gardens in Chelsea. The range of shapes also widened.

By 1752 a painted Red Anchor Mark was becoming common, and this Red Anchor period, which lasted until about 1758, saw the apogee of Chelsea figure modelling. Table wares still showed oriental and Continental motifs while a new development was the manufacture of handsome vegetable and animal tureens and stands.

The final Gold Anchor period shows a departure towards the opulent and the elaborate, with coloured grounds in the Meissen and Sèvres style, and figures in ornate bocages and flowery backgrounds. There was much gilding, and rich colour often came to disguise inferior modelling.

By 1770 Chelsea had passed into the hands of William Duesbury of Derby, and by 1784 porcelain manufacture was concentrated there. The brilliant history of Chelsea was over.

A Chelsea fluted teabowl and saucer painted in colours with flower sprays and scattered sprigs, red anchor mark.
(Phillips) £420

A Chelsea fable-decorated octagonal teapot painted in the manner of Jefferyes Hammett O'Neale with a wolf barking at a boar, circa 1752, 10cm. high.
(Christie's) £2,640

A Chelsea candlestick group, with leaf moulded candle nozzle and drip guard, 16.8cm. high, red anchor mark. (Phillips) £500

A fine Red Anchor period Chelsea porcelain 'Hans Sloane' plate, of shaped circular form, painted with panache in green, yellow, blue, puce, brown and burnt orange, 23.5cm. diam.
(Henry Spencer) £6,800

A Chelsea octagonal dish, painted in the Kakiemon palette with pheasants, circa 1750, 20.5cm. wide.
(Christie's) £1,100

A Chelsea figure of a monk seated on a stool and reading an open prayer book inscribed *Respice Finem*, 14cm.
(Phillips) £1,200

A Chelsea acanthus leaf moulded teapot and cover with bamboo moulded handle, incised triangle mark, circa 1745-49, 12cm. high. (Christie's London) £24,200

A rare Chelsea Kakiemon style leaf dish, with an exotic bird in display and another perched on a prunus branch, raised anchor period, 8½in. long. (Tennants) £4,200

A Chelsea lozenge shaped spoon tray painted in the Kakiemon palette with the Quail Pattern, circa 1750, 14.5cm. wide. (Christie's London) £4,620

A Chelsea mottled claret ground bucket shaped sugar bowl and cover painted with Oriental musicians, gold anchor mark, circa 1765, 11.5cm. diam. (Christie's London) £4,950

Two Chelsea eel tureens and covers naturally modelled with their bodies curled, their tails forming the handles, circa 1755, 18.5cm. wide. (Christie's London) £22,000

A Chelsea cauliflower tureen and cover, red anchor mark to inside of base, circa 1755, 12cm. long. (Christie's) £2,420

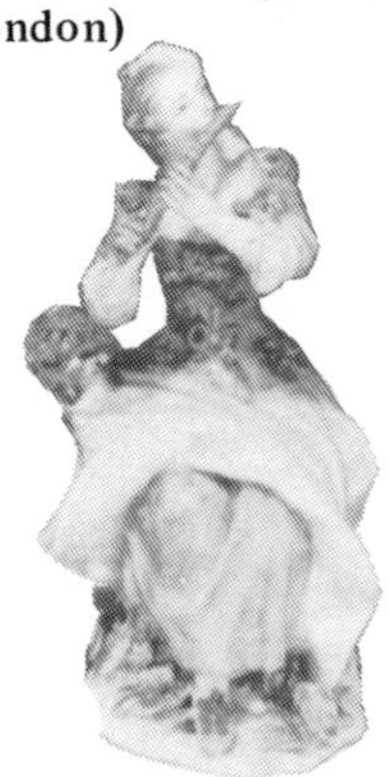

A Chelsea figure of a flautist, wearing a white beret, pink bodice and purple and yellow skirt, 15cm. (Phillips London) £900

A pair of Chelsea blue ground lobed tapering oviform vases and covers with pierced gilt scroll handles and finials, gold anchor marks, circa 1765, 32cm. high. (Christie's London) £6,050

A Chelsea mottled claret-ground oviform vase and cover with gilt loop handles, painted in the manner of Richard Askew with three putti, circa 1765, 30cm. high. (Christie's London) £880

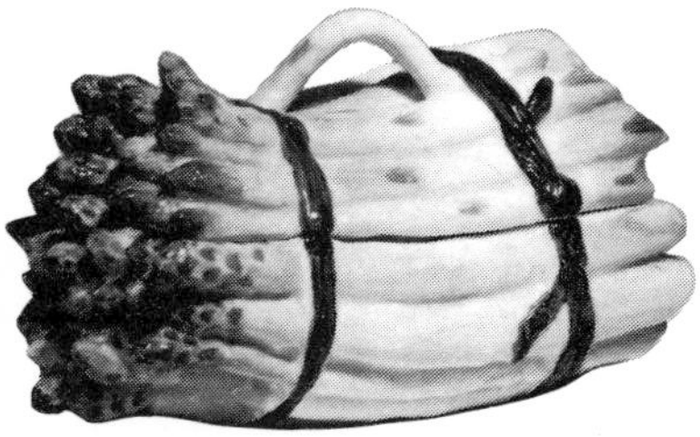

A Chelsea asparagus tureen and a cover, naturally modelled as a bunch of asparagus enriched in puce and green and tied with chocolate-brown ribbon, circa 1755, 18.5cm. wide.
(Christie's) £3,080

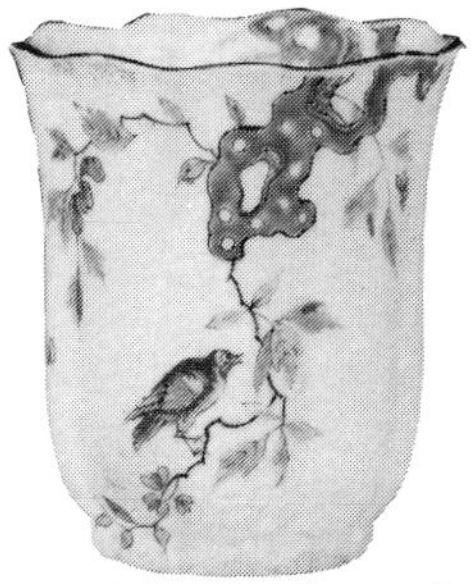

A Chelsea lobed beaker painted in a famille rose palette with a bird perched on a trailing branch pendant from blue rockwork, circa 1750, 7cm. high.
(Christie's) £9,680

A Chelsea peach-shaped cream-jug, finely painted in the Meissen style with a river landscape scene showing a figure rowing a boat watched by two travellers, 1749–52, 11.5cm. wide.
(Christie's) £9,350

A Chelsea white Chinaman teapot and cover modelled as a grinning figure of Budai, his loose robe open to reveal his protuberant stomach, 1745–49, 17.5cm. high.
(Christie's) £35,200

A pair of Chelsea figures of the imperial shepherd and shepherdess, he leaning on a staff held in his left hand, his companion holding a basket of flowers under her right arm, circa 1765, 34cm. high.
(Christie's) £4,180

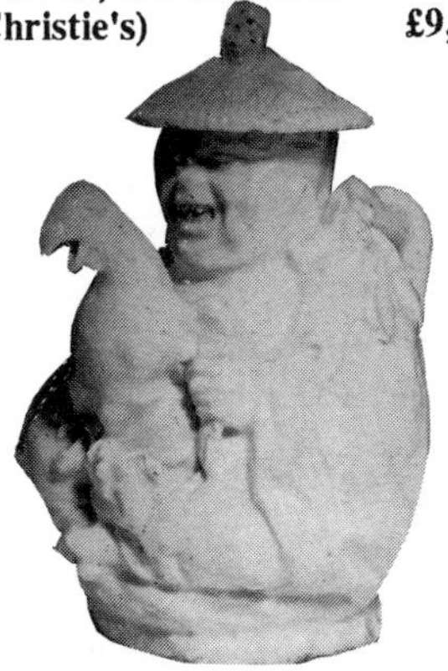

A Chelsea white chinaman and parrot teapot and cover modelled as a grinning figure of Budai, his loose robe open to reveal his protuberant stomach, 1745–49, 17.5cm. high.
(Christie's) £28,600

A Chelsea group of Harlequin and Columbine standing hand-in-hand in a dancing pose before a tree-stump applied with flowers, circa 1760. 17cm. high.
(Christie's) £2,860

A Chelsea fluted baluster cream jug of silver shape, the scroll handle with elaborate foliage-moulded scroll terminals, painted with a butterfly, an insect and scattered flowerheads, 1745–49, 12cm. high.
(Christie's) £8,800

A Chelsea model of a little hawk owl, its head turned and with pale-yellow, dark and light-brown and black feather markings, circa 1752, 18cm. high.
(Christie's) £10,450

A Chelsea figure of the Doctor after the Meissen original, on a circular base applied with flowers, circa 1756, 14.5cm. high. (Christie's) £418

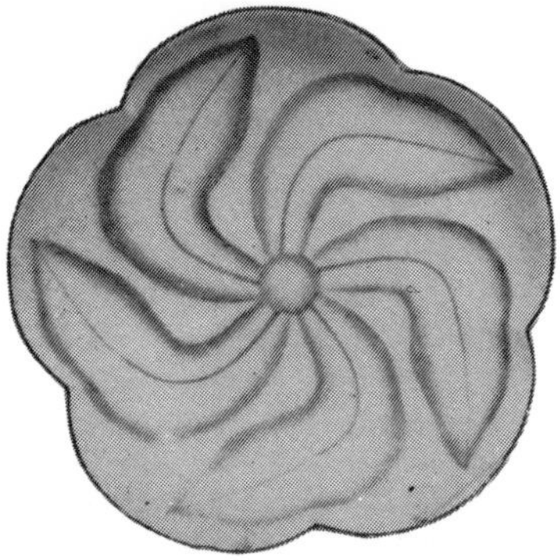

A Chelsea cinquefoil scolopendrium dish, circa 1755, 20.5cm. diam. (Christie's) £2,200

A Chelsea figure of a Chinaman in black conical hat and long-sleeved robe (restored through waist), circa 1755, 11.5cm. high. (Christie's) £880

A Chelsea figure of a shepherdess wearing pale-lilac hat, pink-lined yellow jacket and a striped green-spotted skirt reserved and gilt with flowerheads, circa 1765, 24cm. high. (Christie's) £1,430

A pair of Chelsea figures of fruit-sellers modelled by Joseph Willems, seated on tree-stumps beside baskets filled with fruit, circa 1756, 22cm. and 24cm. high. (Christie's) £1,760

A Chelsea figure of a shepherd playing the recorder, wearing pink hat, green jacket and his breeches painted in blue, iron-red and gilt, circa 1765, 21cm. high. (Christie's) £935

A Chelsea figure of a musician playing the pipe and tambourine, leaning against a flower-encrusted tree, circa 1760, 27cm. high. (Christie's) £1,045

An attractive Chelsea fluted teabowl and saucer painted in Vincennes style with vignettes of figures and buildings in rustic landscapes, red anchor period. (Phillips) £1,800

A rare Chelsea 'toy' figure of a gardener, pushing a roller over a grassy base strewn with applied flowers, 6.3cm. high. (Phillips) £650

CHELSEA DERBY

A Chelsea-Derby two-handled chocolate cup and saucer, painted with groups of flowers. (Lawrence Fine Arts) £220

A pair of Chelsea Derby figures of a youth and girl standing before a bocage supporting candle sconces, 29cm. high. £660

A Chelsea Derby teacup with entwined handle, and saucer, by James Bamford, circa 1775. £340

A Chelsea-Derby figure of Diana, standing on a rocky, flower encrusted base, a stag at her feet (slight damage), circa 1770-5. (Phillips) £600

Pair of Chelsea Derby candlestick figures of a gallant and his companion, 6½in. and 6in. high, no nozzles. £550

One of a pair of Chelsea-Derby groups of Renaldo, Armida, Cephalus and Procris, 20cm. high, incised numbers 75 and 76 with the initials J. W. (Phillips) £1,000

One of a pair of Chelsea Derby custard cups and covers, interlaced A and anchor in gold, circa 1775, 3.1/8in. high. £420

A pair of Chelsea Derby figures, Neptune and Venus and Cupid, on high rocky bases, 24cm. and 25cm. high. £550

A Chelsea-Derby jardiniere of 'U' shape, Chelsea style with fabulous birds on rockwork and in the branches of leafy trees, 17cm. high. (Phillips) £900

CHELSEA KERAMIC ART WORKS

Alexander Robertson founded the Chelsea Keramic Art Works near Boston Mass. in 1872, in partnership with his brother Hugh and later his father James. They produced reproductions of Greek vases, ornamental plaques and tiles, often with decorations in high relief.

Shortly after 1876, Hugh introduced an earthenware with underglaze decoration in coloured slip, which was marketed as 'Bourg la Reine' ware, and also turned to oriental glazes and designs. The firm failed in 1888, but a new company, the Chelsea Pottery, was reopened in 1891 and in 1896 moved to Dedham, where it became known as the Dedham Pottery.

Marks include an impressed *CKAW* or the name in full, with artist's marks also incised.

Late 19th century Chelsea Keramic Art Works square moulded vase, 7½in. high, 4in. diam. £315

A Chelsea Keramic Art pottery vase with blue-green glossy glaze, circa 1885, 11¼in. high. £385

Chelsea Keramic Art Works slipper, Massachusetts, circa 1885, mottled olive green and brown glaze, 6in. long. (Skinner Inc.) £156

Chelsea Keramic Art Works double handled vase, Massachusetts, circa 1885, blue-green and brown glaze, 6¼in. high. (Skinner Inc.) £104

Late 19th century Chelsea Keramic Art Works oxblood vase, 8¼in. high. (Robt. W. Skinner Inc.) £454

Late 19th century Chelsea Keramics Art Works pottery vase, Mass., 10½in. high. (Robt. W. Skinner Inc.) £1,428

Late 19th century Chelsea Keramic Art Works pottery 'oxblood' vase, 8in. high. (Robt. W. Skinner Inc.) £1,190

CHINESE

The antiquity of Chinese ceramics and their beauty and variety down the ages make their study and collection particularly attractive, and provide scope for every taste.

The earliest unglazed earthenware jars date from as early as 2,000 BC, but it was not really until the Han Dynasty (206BC–220AD) that finer techniques, especially the art of glazing had been definitively mastered.

The next truly great period was the T'ang Dynasty (618–906AD) when the pottery was characterised by a beautiful proportion and vitality. A lead glaze was revived, which was often splashed or mottled, and many decorative themes reflect Hellenistic influence.

It was during the Sung Dynasty (960–1279AD) that the first true porcelain seems to have been made, and this period too saw the production of some of the most beautiful shapes and glazes of all time. It also saw the beginning of underglaze blue painting, which was to be perfected during the Ming period.

During the Ming Dynasty (1368–1644AD) a more or less standardised fine white porcelain body was developed which acted as a perfect vehicle for brilliant colour decoration. Glazes tended to be thick or 'fat'. Coloured glazes too were introduced and used either together or singly.

The K'ang Hsi period (1662–1722) marked a further flowering of the potter's art, which continued under his sons Yung Cheng and Ch'ien Lung (Qianlong). The body by now consisted of a very refined white porcelain, thinly and evenly glazed, providing the best possible base for elaborately painted decoration sometimes in the famille rose, famille verte, or famille noire palettes

**Rose Mandarin footed oval fruit platter, China, circa 1830, central panel of Mandarin figures alternating between precious antique clusters, 15½in. wide.
(Skinner Inc.) £1,698**

An ormolu mounted Chinese crackle glazed celadon vase with twin lion mask and entwined drapery handles on spreading gadrooned base, 14in. wide. (Christie's London) £6,600

A magnificent Yuan blue and white jar, guan, painted around the globular body with an arching peony scroll comprising six blooms, circa 1340-50, 39cm. high. (Christie's) £495,000

**Rose Mandarin hot water bottle and cover, China, circa 1830, oval panels of figural courtyard scenes surrounded by floral and ornament designs, 14¾in. high.
(Skinner Inc.) £202**

**A large Chinese blue and white shallow dish, the centre painted with deer in a landscape, the rim with a band of insects, 44cm.
(Bearne's) £250**

A rare Robin's egg blue Yixing wine ewer and cover, 18th century, 7¾in. high. (Christie's) £3,927

A fine Dehua blanc-de-chine group of the Bodhisattva Manjusri, seated on her recumbent Buddhistic lion, 18th century, 26.8cm. high. (Christie's) £10,450

A rare Chinese teapot and cover, decorated in London, the reverse inscribed '57 Miles to London', a milestone inscribed 'XIV Miles from London', 16cm., 1750-1760. (Phillips) £460

A straw-glazed and painted figure of a richly caparisoned horse, Sui Dynasty, 32cm. high. £3,520

An Oriental export porcelain garden seat, China, late 19th century, barrel-shaped body moulded with two rows of bosses, 18¼in. high. (Robt. W. Skinner Inc.) £1,136

A large pair of Oriental vases, China, late 19th century, wide flared scalloped rims; on long tapered necks, 30in. high. (Robt. W. Skinner Inc.) £1,022

A 19th century Chinese porcelain ginger jar and cover, all-over decorated with dragons, fishing boats, mountains, pagodas, flowers and leaves, 35cm. high. (Henry Spencer) £220

A transitional mug, painted in underglaze blue with two children bringing gifts to a sage seated under a willow tree, 19cm. (Lawrence Fine Arts) £770

A Cizhou polychrome-enamelled baluster jar, Guan, painted in iron-red, green and black, Yuan Dynasty, 30cm. high. (Christie's) £11,000

Chinese porcelain vase with Mandarin decoration, late 19th century, raised lizards to the collar, 25in. high. (Skinner Inc.) £452

A blue and white flask, painted with full moons in mountainous river landscapes, the semi domed shoulders with similar scenes, $10^{1}/_{4}$in. high, 17th century.
(Bonhams) £1,200

A pair of turquoise glazed later ormolu mounted brush pots of cylindrical form with pierced sides simulating bamboo and leafy bands, $8^{1}/_{2}$in. high, 18th century.
(Bonhams) £4,900

A massive blue and white 'dragon' jardinière, Qianlong seal mark and of the period, vividly painted with four striding five-clawed dragons above turbulent waves and rockwork, divided by clouds in cruciform formation, 25in. diameter. (Christie's) £12,891

A Cizhou slip-decorated pillow, the concave headrest of ruyi shape, the design of a seated cat with ears erect wearing a floral scarf painted in a brown slip, Northern Song/Jin Dynasty, 32cm. wide.
(Christie's) £77,000

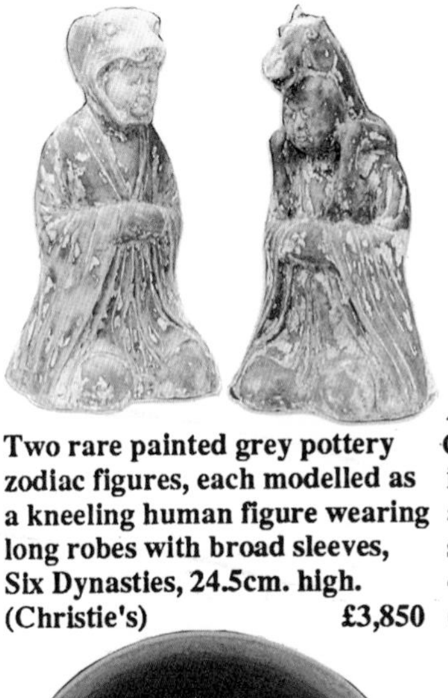

Two rare painted grey pottery zodiac figures, each modelled as a kneeling human figure wearing long robes with broad sleeves, Six Dynasties, 24.5cm. high.
(Christie's) £3,850

A rare Yuan blue and white jar, Guan, the globular body painted in vivid blue tones with an arching peony scroll comprising six flower-heads, 1350–1360, 46.5cm. high.
(Christie's) £110,000

A rare large Yuan blue and white bowl, circa 1350–60, the interior with a swimming carp between clumps of waterweeds, $11^{1}/_{2}$in. diameter.
(Christie's) £107,422

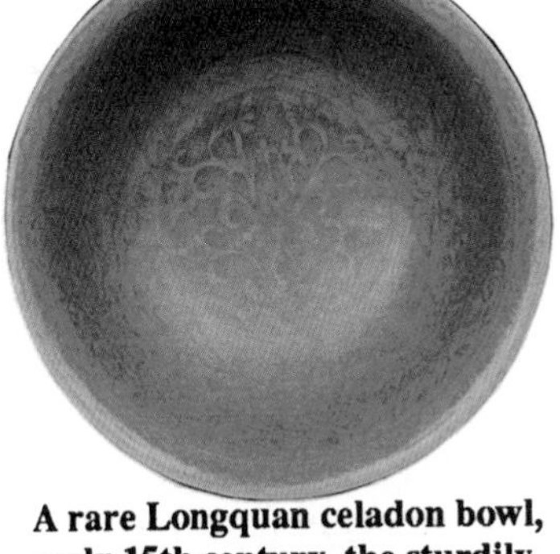

A rare Longquan celadon bowl, early 15th century, the sturdily potted rounded sides rising to a flaring rim, the centre of the interior carved with a feathery lotus spray below an arching lotus scroll, $7^{1}/_{4}$in. diameter.
(Christie's) £6,444

A rare Yuan blue and white bowl, circa 1350, painted to the exterior with a lingzhi scroll above a band of lotus panels, the interior with a lush lotus pond with flowering plants in the medallion, $7^{1}/_{4}$in. diameter.
(Christie's) £6,803

A fluted oval soup tureen and cover, enamelled with bouquets and sprays of flowers, 34cm., Ch'ien Lung. (Lawrence Fine Arts) £715

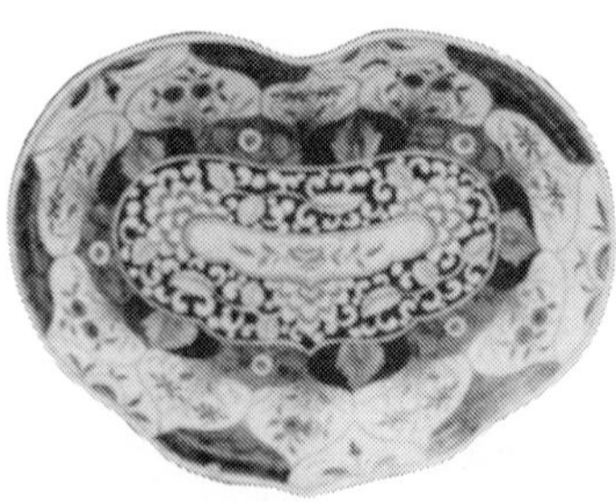

A good heart shaped dessert dish painted in blue with the Kang Hsi Lotus pattern, circa 1770, 26cm. (Phillips London) £400

Fitzhugh blue and white salad bowl, China, early 19th century, medallion surrounded by four floral panels, 9½in. wide. (Skinner Inc.) £431

A Chinese Chien Lung bulbous shaped vase, decorated in famille verte, iron-red and other colours with mythological beast reserves, 12in. high. (Geering & Colyer) £170

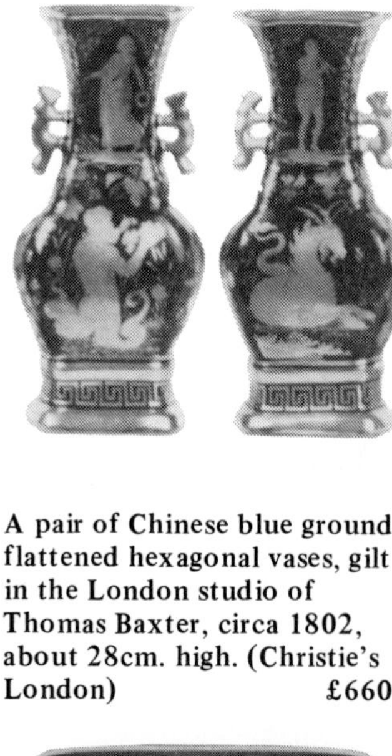

A pair of Chinese blue ground flattened hexagonal vases, gilt in the London studio of Thomas Baxter, circa 1802, about 28cm. high. (Christie's London) £660

A blue and white baluster vase and matched cover, painted with a continuous scene of court figures, six character mark of Ch'êng-hau, K'ang-hsi, 15½in. high. (Lawrence Fine Arts) £682

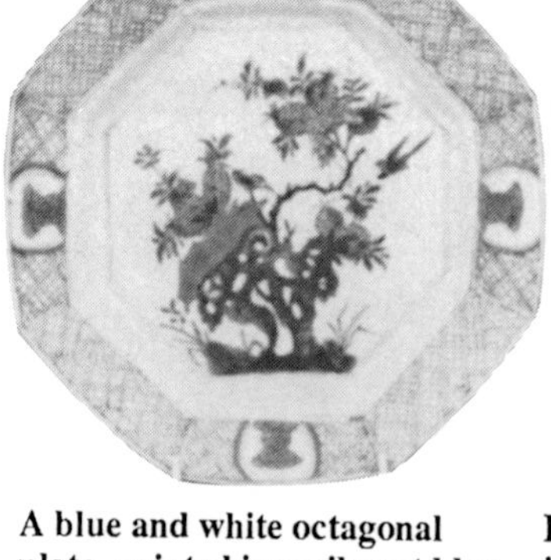

A blue and white octagonal plate, painted in a vibrant blue with fruiting pomegranates, six character mark of Ch'êng-hau, K'ang-hsi, 10¼in. diam. (Lawrence Fine Arts) £165

Important blue Fitzhugh "Pagoda" decorated footed tray, China, circa 1810, central pagoda design surrounded by four floral panels, 10in. wide. (Skinner Inc.) £810

A blue and white dish, the exterior with dragons chasing the flaming pearl, 7⅞in., Guangxu six character mark and period. (Bonhams) £100

CHINESE EXPORTWARE

The first Chinese Exportware was produced as a result of the presence of the Jesuit fathers, who established themselves there from 1600. About fifty years later pieces of porcelain began to appear decorated with crucifixes and the letters *IHS*. Later, religious scenes were painted, mostly on plates, but sometimes even on tea sets!

Heraldic ware was the first form called for from China in great quantities in the early 18th century. Great services were manufactured with decoration often in imitation of the silver they were to replace. Punchbowls and other utilitarian pieces followed, decorated with creditable reproductions of European paintings or illustrations of events. Figures in European dress were also attempted.

The factories which produced these were grouped at Ching te Chen and they were decorated mostly at Canton. Some pieces were also made in Fukien Province, which were characterised by their creamy white appearance. These were usually decorated in Europe and were known as blanc-de-Chine.

A Chinese 18th century Export model of a pony, 26cm. wide. £9,070

A large Chinese Export punch bowl, the exterior boldly painted with the coats of arms of four Livery Companies, 40cm. diameter, Qianlong.
(Bearne's) £1,200

Chinese Export "Blue Fitzhugh" platter, 19th century, 18½in. wide.
(Skinner Inc.) £397

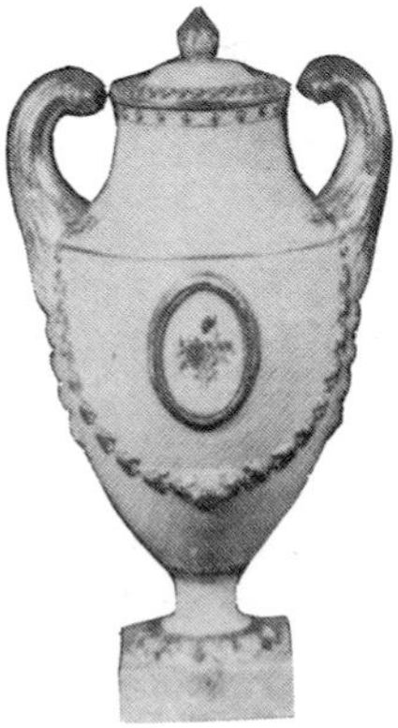

One of a pair of late 18th century Export porcelain covered urns, China, 17½in. high. £4,340

One of four late 18th century Chinese Export soup plates, 8.7/8in. diam. £1,220

An Export figure of a hound seated, Qianlong, 14.5cm. high. £1,405

A large Export armorial dish painted in shades of blue, yellow, iron-red, green and gilt, circa 1740, 17in. diam. £3,300

CLARICE CLIFF

The legendary Clarice Cliff was born in 1899 in, perhaps inevitably, Staffordshire, where she started work at 13 in one of the local potteries, painting freehand onto pottery.

Her formal training comprised a year, when she was 16, at the Burslem School of Art, and a later year at the Royal College of Art, where she studied sculpture . At 17, she had gone to work at the firm of A.J. Wilkinson, and she remained with them, and their subsidiary the Newport Pottery, for the next two decades, ending up as Art Director and marrying the boss, Colley Shorter, when she was forty.

During the 1920's she painted Tibetan ware, large jars painted with floral designs in bright colours and gold, and she also transferred on to pottery designs by such distinguished artists as Paul Nash and Laura Knight.

In 1928, however, she painted 60 dozen pieces of her own design to test the market at a trade fair. These proved so popular that by 1929 the whole factory was switched to producing her Bizarre ware.

Cliff's style is characterised by combinations of bright colours, such as orange, blue, purple and green, or black, yellow, orange and red. Her pieces are often angular in shape and strongly Art Deco in style. Major ranges, besides Bizarre, include Crocus, Fantasque, Biarritz and Farmhouse.

At the beginning of the Second World War, the factory was commandeered by the Ministry of Supply, and Wilkinson produced only a few white pieces. After the war, the market had changed and production was not resumed.

A 'Fantasque' pottery comport designed by Clarice Cliff of 'Melon' pattern, 7in diameter.
(Hobbs & Chambers) £90

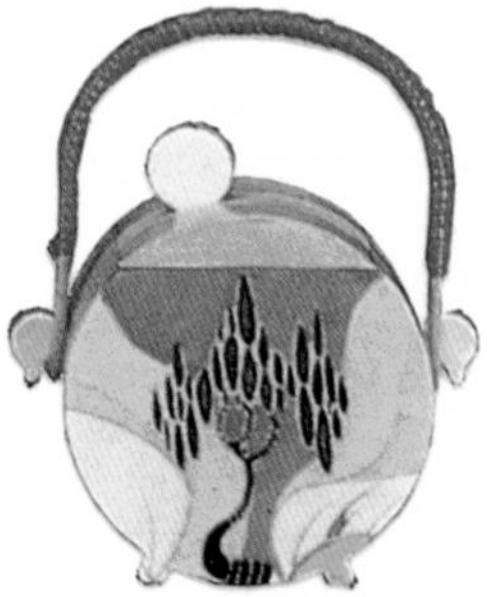

A 'Bizarre' Bonjour biscuit barrel and cover with wicker handle, decorated in the 'Windbells' pattern, 6in. high.
(Christie's) £220

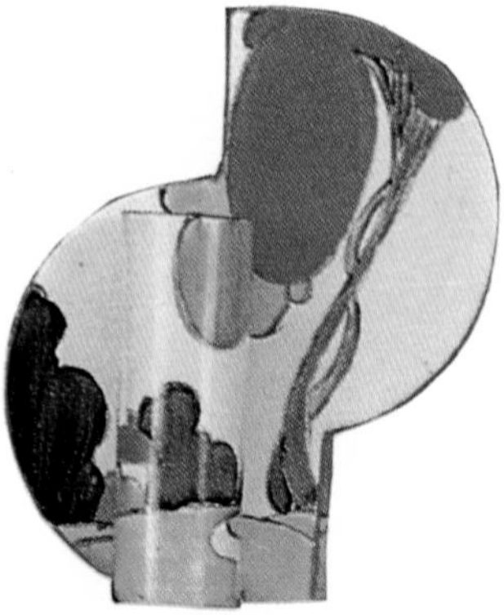

A 'Bizarre' double tube spill vase, decorated in the 'Orange Autumn' pattern, painted in colours, 7¾in. high.
(Christie's) £880

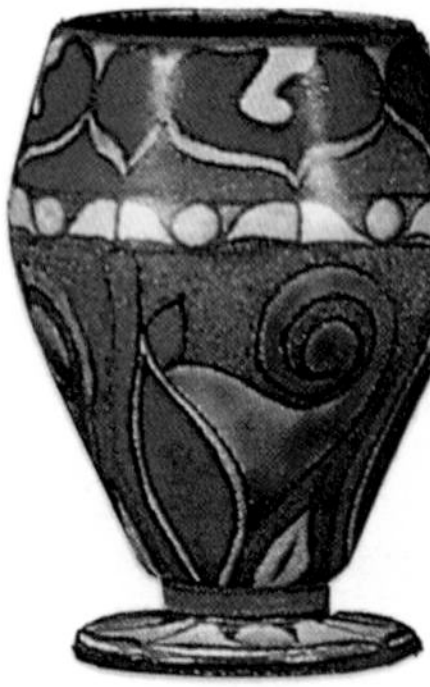

An 'Inspiration Bizarre' vase, shape No. 363, decorated in an Insnik-style pattern in shades of blue, yellow and green, 6½in. high.
(Christie's) £495

A 'Fantasque Bizarre' vase, shape No. 358, decorated in the seven colour 'Trees and House' pattern, 8in. high.
(Christie's) £605

A 'Latona Bizarre' spherical vase decorated in the 'Dahlia' pattern, painted in colours on a yellow ground, 6in. high.
(Christie's) £935

A 'Bizarre' vase, decorated in the 'Applique Lugano' pattern, painted in colours with blue roof and orange sky, 8in. high.
(Christie's) £1,100

A 'Fantasque Bizarre' squat oviform ribbed vase, shape No. 671, decorated in the 'Pastel Autumn' pattern, 4¼in. high.
(Christie's) £308

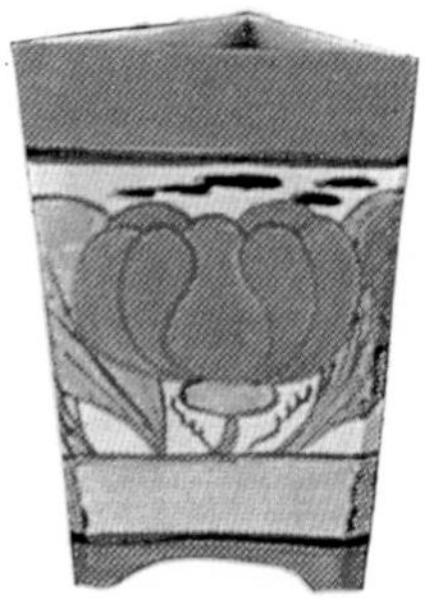

A 'Fantasque' triangular section vase, decorated in the 'Orange Lily' pattern, painted in colours, 7¼in. high.
(Christie's) £308

A 'Patina Bizarre' spherical vase painted with red tree bearing blue and green foliage, under blue spattered slip, 6in. high.
(Christie's) £825

A 'Fantasque' Archaic vase, painted with blue centred orange flowers on a black ground, between blue and orange banding, 7in. high.
(Christie's) £880

A 'Bizarre' Conical vase, decorated in the 'Honolulu' pattern, painted in colours, 6in. high.
(Christie's) £1,210

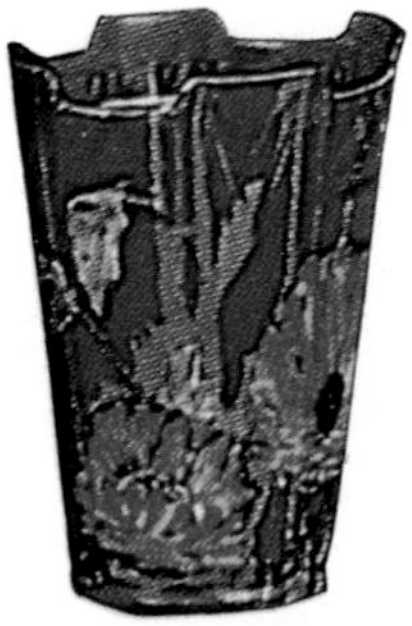

A 'Bizarre' vase, decorated in the 'Marigold' pattern, painted with orange flowers on a streaked blue ground, 7¾in. high.
(Christie's) £385

A 'Bizarre' biscuit barrel and cover, shape No. 336, decorated in the "Swirls" pattern, 6½in. high.
(Christie's) £440

A 'Fantasque' mushroom vase, decorated in the 'Sunrise' pattern, painted in orange, green and blue, above orange banding, 5¼in. high.
(Christie's) £308

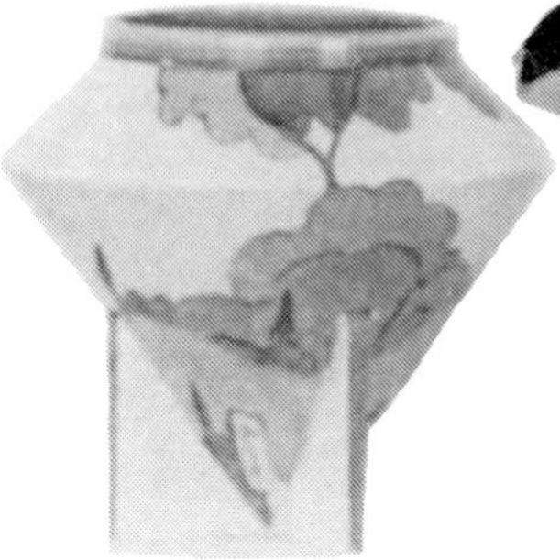

A Clarice Cliff Bizarre vase of cone shape with four triangular feet painted in pink, 6½in. high. (Christie's) £462

A Clarice Cliff 'Fantasque' bowl, painted on the rim with shaped oval stylised flowers and leaves, 30.5cm. diam. (Phillips) £340

A rare miniature Clarice Cliff wall plaque moulded as the head of a woman, 2¾in. high. (David Lay) £210

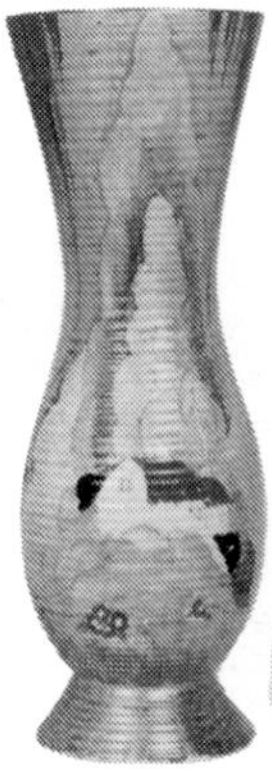

A Clarice Cliff vase, painted in yellow, brown, blue, green and orange with a cottage in a landscape, signed Hand-Painted, Bizarre by Clarice Cliff, Wilkinson Ltd., 46.5cm. high. (Christie's) £880

A set of three Clarice Cliff 'Age of Jazz' block ceramic figures, painted in bright colours of black, red, brown, lime-green and yellow. (Phillips) £3,100

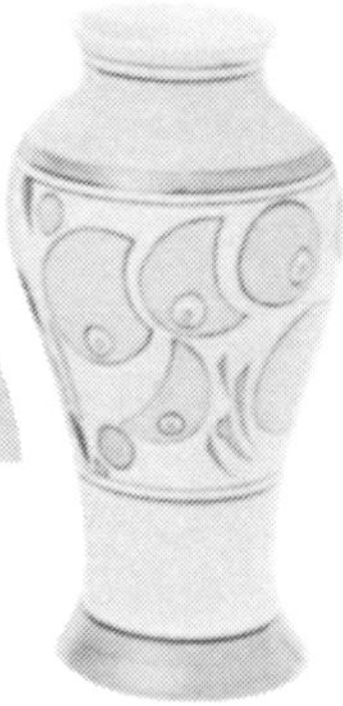

A Clarice Cliff vase, painted in black, orange, blue, yellow and green with tumbling fruit, leaves and rods, 22.2cm. high. (Phillips) £800

A Clarice Cliff pottery vase of globular form, boldly painted with dots and geometric designs in orange, green and black on a yellow ground, 20.5cm. high. (Bearne's) £820

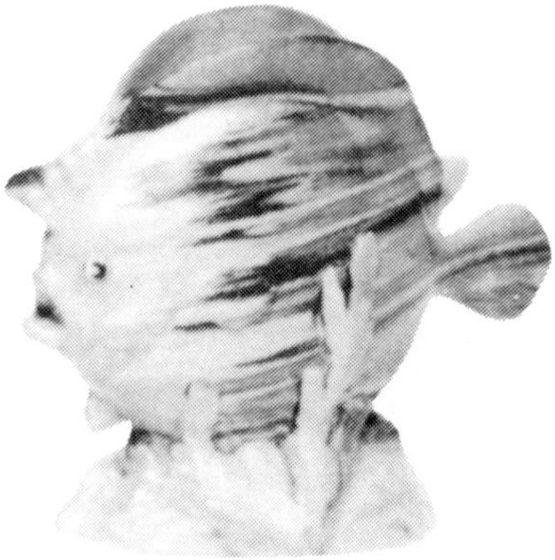

A rare Clarice Cliff vase shaped as a fish swimming amongst seaweed, 8¾in. high, 10½in. long. (David Lay) £300

A Clarice Cliff Sliced Circle pattern 'Lotus' jug, the vessel with twin handles and painted in bright colours, 29cm. high. (Phillips London) £2,700

A Clarice Cliff Bizarre single-handled horizontally ribbed jug painted in the 'Delecia' pattern, 7in. high. (Christie's) £105

A Clarice Cliff Newport pottery bough pot, of flared stepped square form with similar fitted pierced centre, printed Fantasque and Bizarre, 23cm. square. (Henry Spencer) £460

A Clarice Cliff jug of lotus form, boldly painted with the 'Alpine' design, 28.5cm. (Bearne's) £1,550

A large Clarice Cliff 'Fantasque' circular wall plate, 45.50cm. diam., printed marks and fac-simile signature. (Phillips) £980

A Wilkinson Ltd. toby jug of Winston Churchill modelled by Clarice Cliff, seated on a bulldog draped with a Union Jack, 30.5cm. (Phillips) £600

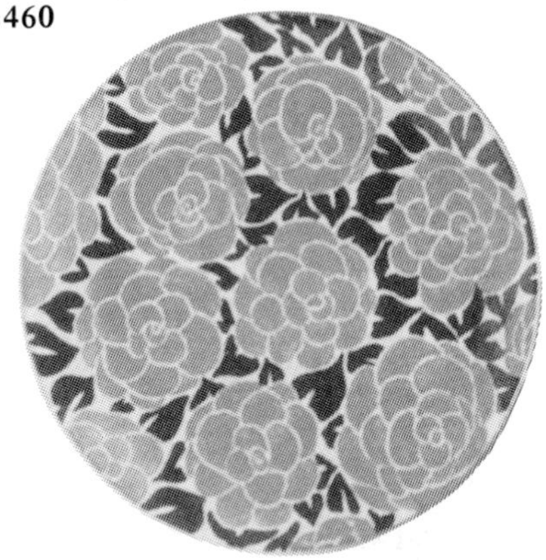

A Clarice Cliff plaque, the cavetto boldly painted with orange peonies and black leaves on a cream ground, 33cm. (Bearne's) £1,250

An 'Appliqué Bizarre' Conical jug decorated in the 'Lugano' pattern of farmhouse in alpine landscape, 9½in. high. (Christie's S. Ken) £3,850

A superb wall plaque by Clarice Cliff painted with a scene inspired by Diaghilev's costume design for The Ballet Russe. £8,000

A Clarice Cliff Applique-Lucerne lotus jug, painted with an orange roofed chateau perched on the side of yellow and green hills, 29.5cm. high. (Phillips London) £5,800

An 'Appliqué' octagonal plate decorated in the 'Caravan' pattern, painted in colours, 11in. diameter.
(Christie's S. Ken) £2,200

A 'Bizarre' grotesque mask designed by Ron Birks, covered in a dark blue Inspiration glaze, the features picked out in red.
(Christie's S. Ken) £1,320

A Clarice Cliff 'Fantasque' ginger jar and cover decorated in the 'Melon' pattern, painted in colours, 8in. high.
(Christie's S. Ken) £572

A Clarice Cliff 'Fantasque' vase, shape No. 358, decorated in the 'Trees and House' pattern, painted in colours, 8in. high.
(Christie's S. Ken) £495

A pair of Clarice Cliff teddy bear book ends decorated in the 'Red Flower' pattern, painted in colours, 6in. high.
(Christie's S. Ken) £4,180

A 'Bizarre' Yo-Yo vase decorated in the 'Orange Luxor' pattern, painted in colours, 9in. high.
(Christie's S. Ken) £2,200

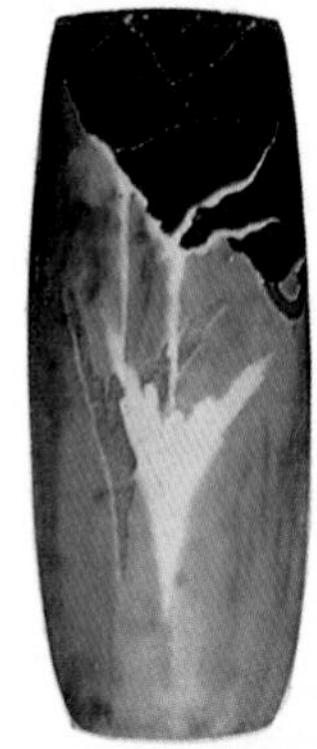

A Clarice Cliff 'Inspiration Bizarre' stick stand, decorated in the 'Caprice' pattern, in shades of pink, lavender and blue on a turquoise ground, 24in. high.
(Christie's S. Ken) £1,980

A pair of 'Bizarre' bookends, shape No. 406 decorated in the 'Honolulu' pattern, painted in colours, 6in. high.
(Christie's S. Ken) £495

A 'Bizarre' single-handled Lotus jug decorated in the 'Blue W' pattern, painted in colours between orange borders, $11^1/_2$in. high.
(Christie's S. Ken) £2,200

A 'Fantasque Bizarre' Dover jardinière decorated in the 'Trees and House' pattern, rubber stamp mark, 8in. high.
(Christie's S. Ken) £1,210

A 'Fantasque Bizarre' ginger jar and cover decorated in the 'Blue Autumn' pattern, painted in colours with contrasting banding, $7^3/_4$in. high.
(Christie's S. Ken) £935

A 'Fantasque' plate decorated in the 'Flora' pattern, painted in orange, yellow, green and black.
(Christie's S. Ken) £209

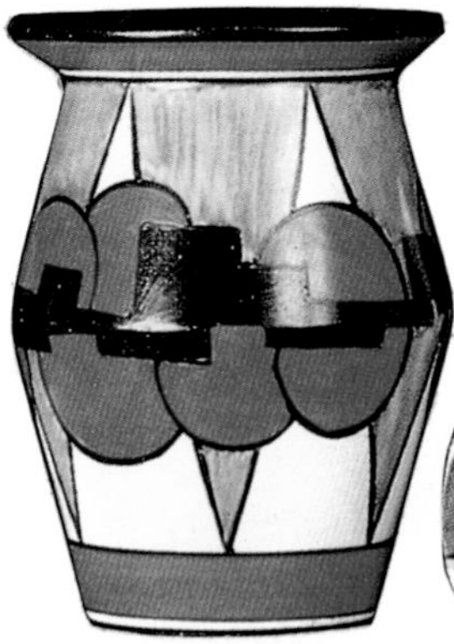

A Clarice Cliff 'Bizarre' vase, shape No. 342, decorated in the 'Sliced Circles' pattern, painted in orange, green and black, $7^3/_4$in. high.
(Christie's S. Ken) £605

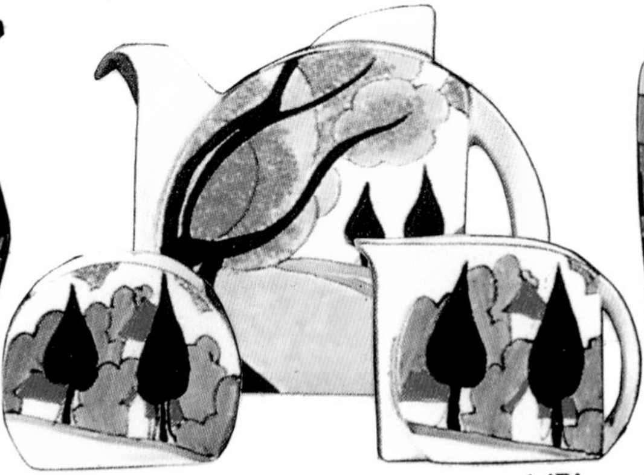

A Clarice Cliff 'Fantasque Bizarre' Stamford trio decorated in the 'May Avenue' pattern, painted in colours, height of teapot $4^1/_2$in.
(Christie's S. Ken) £2,420

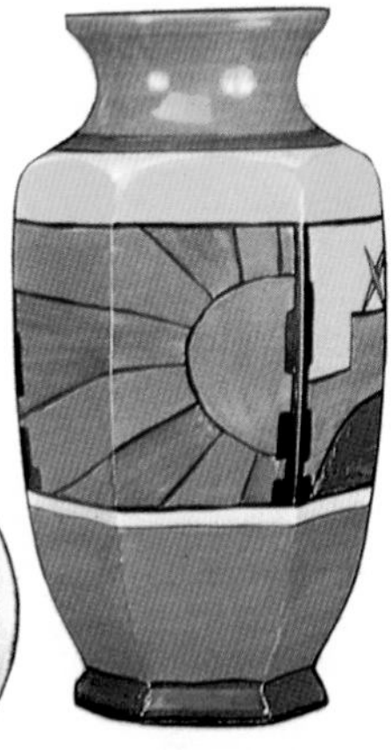

A 'Bizarre' hexagonal baluster vase decorated in the 'Sunray' pattern, painted in colours between multibanded borders, 15in. high.
(Christie's S. Ken) £2,200

A 'Bizarre' single-handled Lotus jug decorated in the 'Lightning' pattern, painted in colours between orange borders, $11^1/_2$in. high.
(Christie's S. Ken) £2,640

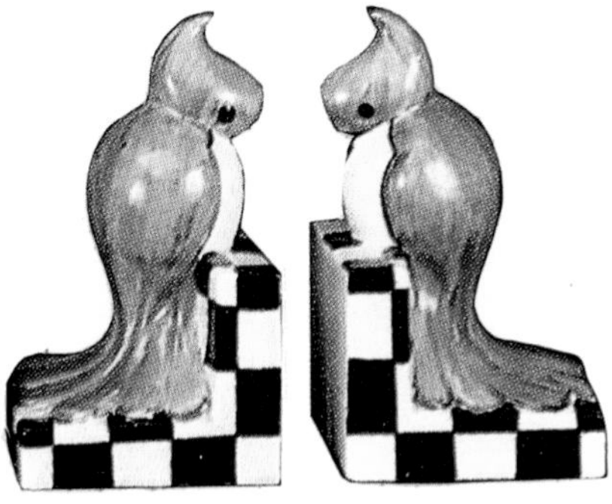

A pair of 'Bizarre' bookends, modelled as a pair of parakeets with green plumage on chequered base, 7in. high.
(Christie's S. Ken) £880

A 'Fantasque Bizarre' cylindrical biscuit barrel and cover decorated in the 'Blue Autumn' pattern, $6^1/_4$in. high.
(Christie's S. Ken) £308

CLEMENT MASSIER

Clement Massier was a French artist potter who worked around the turn of the century at Golfe-Juan in the Alpes Maritimes. He produced a lustre decorated earthenware, often embellished with plant motifs.

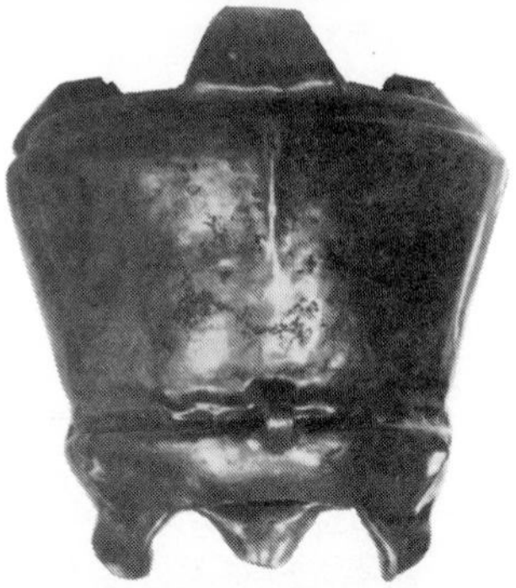

A massive Clément Massier jardinière, of irregular tapering form, decorated in an overall lustre glaze of green, yellow, amethyst and amber, 56cm. high. (Christie's) £770

A Clément Massier earthenware jardinière with a pedestal, decorated in relief with irises, the pedestal naturalistically moulded with a heron among bulrushes, 38cm. diameter of jardinière. (Christie's) £270

COALBROOKDALE

The Coalport or Coalbrookdale factory was established in Shropshire around 1796 by John Rose. Soft paste porcelain, sometimes in imitation of Chelsea, Swansea, or even Sèvres, continued to be made by his descendants until 1862. Around this time the factory passed into the hands of the Bruff family and in 1924 it was sold to Cauldon Potteries, moving to Staffordshire in 1926.

Pieces are often clearly marked *J Rose Coalbrookdale*, though some Chelsea pieces have an imitation blue anchor mark. Crossed tridents and *Swansea* are printed on red on imitation Swansea, and *RP* in crossed *Ls* on imitation Sèvres.

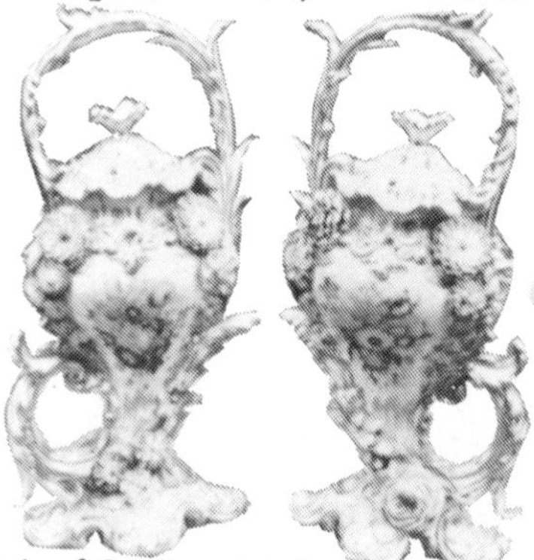

Pair of Coalbrookdale porcelain vases, mid-19th century, with handpainted floral bouquet, accented in gilt, (both handles showing breaks and repair) 15½in. high. (Skinner Inc.) £478

An English porcelain basket, probably Coalbrookdale, applied and painted with flowers, 27.5cm. (Bearne's) £1,980

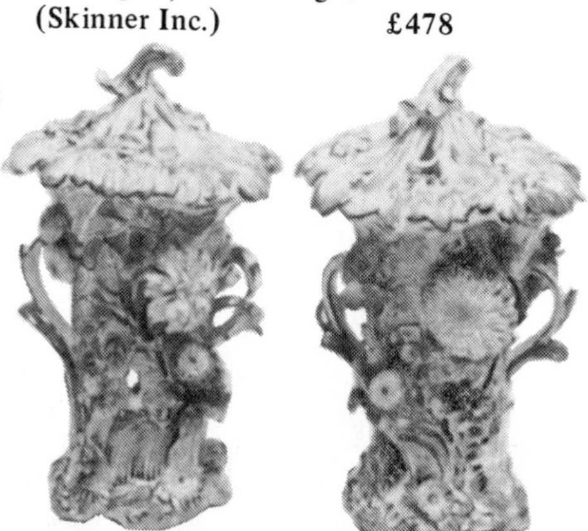

Pair of Coalbrookdale porcelain covered potpourri, mid-19th century, with scrolled leaf handles, pierced body and lid, 8in. high. (Skinner Inc.) £955

Coalbrookdale porcelain handled ewer, mid 19th century, white ground with applied flowers, leaves and vines (minor flower and petal damage), 8in. high. (Skinner Inc.) £191

COALPORT

The Rose family established the Coalport Porcelain Works in Coalport Shropshire in 1796, and it remained in the family until the last member retired in 1862. In general, their output copied 18th century French and German porcelain, with decoration often in the Sèvres style. They employed some notable decorators, such as Jabez Ashton, who painted naturalistic flowers and fruit on large plaques, and James Rouse.

The business was declared bankrupt (1875-80) and then was acquired by Peter Bruff, who was later succeeded by his son Charles. They now turned out tableware decorated with landscapes of flower panels, or lightly decorated on pink and green grounds.

Parian and porcelain were used together for comports and centrepieces etc. and enamelled jewelled decoration was used on tall vases, which were also painted with views or landscapes.

In 1924 the firm was purchased by Cauldon Potteries and in 1926 it the operation was moved to Staffordshire. It is still in existence today at Stoke on Trent.

There are numerous different marks from the various periods, usually in underglaze blue, either *C*, *S*, or *N*, in loops of monogram *CS*, or *Coalport AD 1750*. Later *England* or *Made in England* (from circa 1920) were added.

A rare Coalport 'D'-shaped bough pot and cover, painted with a band of geometric panels in red and black within a gold diaper frame, 20cm. (Phillips) £500

A pair of rare Coalport mantelpiece vases in neo-Classical style, painted almost certainly by Thomas Baxter, 29cm. high. (Phillips) £700

A pair of Coalport vases and covers in Sevres style, painted by William Cook, with ripe fruit and flowers, 37cm. (Phillips London) £950

A Coalport flared flower pot and stand with gilt dolphin mask handles, decorated in the London studio of Thomas Baxter, circa 1805, 16.5cm. wide. (Christie's London) £605

A Coalport pierced plate painted by Joshua Rushton, signed with a portrait of Lady Sarah Bunbury after Sir Joshua Reynolds, 23.5cm. (Phillips London) £500

An impressive pair of Coalport vases and covers, decorated with alternating panels of flowers in a vase, 40cm. (Phillips London) £1,300

A Coalport oval dish from the celebrated Animal service, painted with a proud lion, after Bewick, 28cm. (Phillips London) £300

A Coalport jewelled ramshead vase and cover, the ovoid body with graduated turquoise beading, 19cm., 1909. (Phillips London) £350

One of a pair of Coalport porcelain lozenge-shaped dessert dishes, painted in the manner of Thos. Baxter, circa 1810, 10¾in. by 8in. (Dacre, Son & Hartley) £1,050

A Coalport miniature jewelled vase of shield shape, decorated with graduated turquoise and gilt jewelling, 9.5cm. (Phillips London) £85

A Coalport rectangular plaque with Cupid holding a dove, signed J. Rouse, 1856, 36.5 x 30.5cm. (Christie's) £1,210

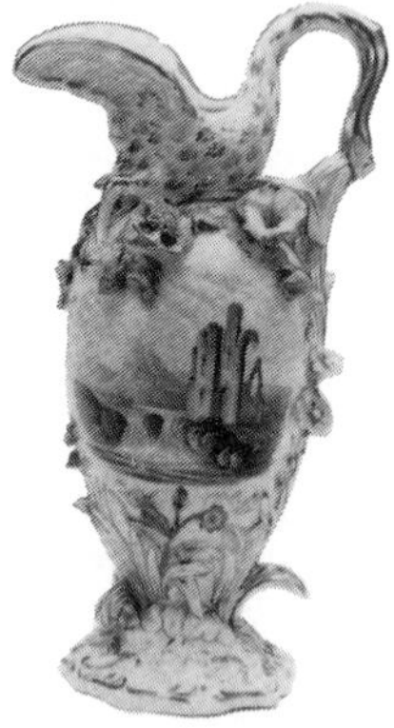

An English porcelain ewer, probably Coalport, the ovoid body applied with a handle, neck and spout in the form of a swan, 28cm. (Bearne's) £250

An important Coalport plate, the deep blue border reserved with the arms of the City of London, 1844, 26cm. (Phillips London) £800

One of a pair of Coalport jewelled ewers with gilt scrolling handles, the ovoid bodies painted by Edward Ball, 24cm. (Phillips London) Two £700

A Coalport miniature cabinet cup and saucer, painted by Edward Ball, signed, with scenes of San Stefano and Culloden Moor. (Phillips London) £240

COALPORT

A Coalport bough pot and cover, after a Derby original, possibly by James Rouse, 18.5cm. (Phillips London) £320

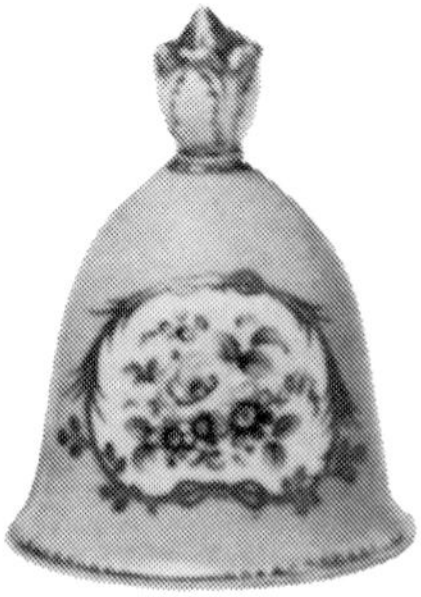

A rare Coalport table bell with gilt leaf finial, the flower panels framed in raised gold, 9cm. (Phillips London) £100

Coalport style porcelain cream jug, early 19th century, blue ground, gilt leaf pattern with cartouches of flowers. (G. A. Key) £120

An impressive Coalport two handled vase and cover, painted by John Plant, signed, with a view of Conway Castle, 36cm. (Phillips London) £850

A pair of Coalport Imari-pattern tapering hexagonal vases and covers with seated gilt dog-of-fo finials and two gilt grotesque animal handles, circa 1805, 20½in. high. (Christie's) £4,400

A Coalport sponged pale blue ground urn shaped vase and cover, painted in the studio of Thomas Baxter, circa 1805, 27cm. high. (Christie's London) £495

A Coalport plate, painted probably in London, with two Arabs standing by their donkeys, 21cm. (Phillips London) £65

A Coalport vase and cover, painted with lovers seated in a landscape, he playing a pipe, she holding a staff, 32cm. (Lawrence Fine Art) £726

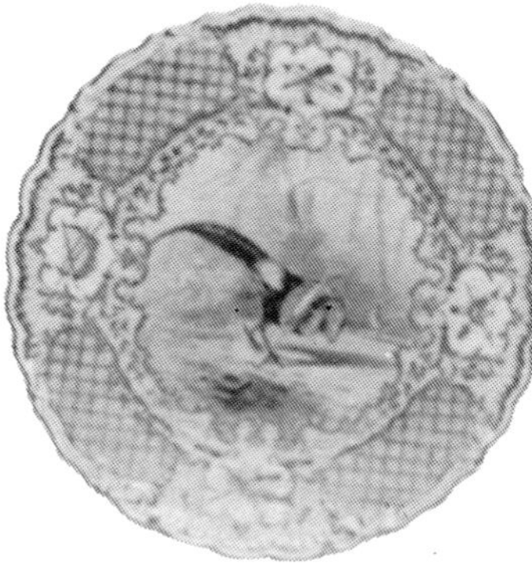

A Coalport plate painted by J. N. Bradley, signed, with a golden pheasant, 24cm. (Phillips London) £150

Commemorative is the word used to describe the myriad objects made and decorated to mark some person or event of special significance, coronations, jubilees, battles etc.

The first china to be made in any quantities with such intention appeared in Stuart times, and delft of the period often bears royal names and portraits.

The arrival of Queen Victoria on the throne opened the floodgates for the manufacture of commemorative china. Her predecessors as rulers were more often lampooned than venerated, but Victoria changed the popular attitude towards royalty. China commemorating events in the reigns of William and Mary, George III, George IV and William IV are rare but pieces with pictures of Victoria and Albert were made in their thousands and enjoyed pride of place on the walls and mantlepieces of rich and poor up and down the land. Plates, tobacco jars, mugs, vases, pipes, teapots, doorstops and spill jars marked every event in the royal life. The china cost little to buy and proved so popular that the range spread to include political happenings, military displays, exhibitions and even famous crimes and criminals.

Obviously age and rarity play a large part in determining the value of any piece of commemorative china, but the whole field is an attractive one. It is possible to start a collection with very little outlay, and each piece, whether modern or older, has its own intrinsic interest, which can only increase as time goes by.

An octagonal nursery plate with embossed daisy border, printed in brown and coloured with a scene entitled 'The Royal Christening', 16.5cm. (Phillips) £30

A crisply moulded jug of hexagonal shape, embossed with half length profile portraits of Victoria and Albert flanked by scrolling flowers, 15.5cm. (Phillips) £100

A large brown-glazed pottery vase, gilded with a silhouette portrait of George III and inscribed in gold '*Mercy and Truth Preserve the King*', 26.5cm, replacement foot. (Phillips) £250

A Dillwyn & Co. pottery plate, painted in bright enamel colours, the centre printed in black with the seated figure of the young Queen Victoria, 20.5cm. (Bearne's) £290

A Scottish moulded plate, with panels of crowns and Royal emblems, the centre with a profile portrait, coloured and titled 'King George IIII', 21.5cm. (Phillips) £350

A very rare small mug commemorating the birth of the Princess Royal, printed in black with ladies in waiting leading a horse drawn baby carriage, 6.3cm. (Phillips London) £860

A William Kent bust of John Wesley in clerical attire, on a mottled yellow and green base, 31cm.
(Phillips) £120

A china plate commemorating the start of the digging of the Channel Tunnel 1987/88, 27cm.
(Phillips) £40

A rare Crown Staffordshire double caricature of the Kaiser entitled *'Which'll He be'*, 15cm.
(Phillips) £320

A black printed jug bearing portraits of William IV and Queen Adelaide, probably commemorating the Coronation in 1830, 14cm.
(Phillips) £130

A pair of Whitman and Roth caricature figures of Gladstone and Disraeli, both standing on mottled turquoise and brown bases, 40cm.
(Phillips) £3,200

A cylindrical pottery mug printed in colours with flags and inscribed *'G.R. Peace of Europe signed at Paris May 30th, 1814'*, 11 cm.
(Phillips) £220

A bulbous jug with animal-headed handle, printed in puce with an unusual portrait of the young Queen Victoria, 18cm.
(Phillips) £140

A pottery jug with three medallions containing profile heads of Victoria and Albert flanking their son Albert Edward dated 1860, 26cm.
(Phillips) £150

A G.F. Bowers rope handled jug printed in colours with scenes of the Light Cavalry Charge at Balaclava, and the Sebastopol Attack, 20cm.
(Phillips) £550

A rare Davenport pottery mug, blue printed with a central medallion enclosing a bust portrait of Queen Victoria wearing a crown, 3in. high, circa 1838.
(Bonhams) £1,250

A Royal Doulton bone china limited edition figure of her Majesty Queen Elizabeth the Queen Mother, modelled by Derek Griffiths and issued in celebration of her 90th birthday, numbered 6, 8¼in. high.
(Bonhams) £250

A brown and buff stoneware mug, with central applied Royal coat of arms decoration, flanked by titled bust portraits of Queen Victoria and the Duchess of Kent, 4in. high, circa 1838.
(Bonhams) £230

An English pottery jug, moulded and enamelled with titled equestrian portraits of The Duke of York and Prince Cobourg, both in military attire, 6in. high, circa 1793.
(Bonhams) £500

A rare pair of miniature Herculaneum coronation plaques, one puce printed with a floral cartouche enclosing the caption *God Save The King*, 3in. diameter, circa 1821.
(Bonhams) £2,600

A rare first period Worcester bell-shaped mug, printed in puce with a profile portrait of George III taken from plates engraved by Robert Hancock, 6in. high, circa 1760.
(Bonhams) £3,000

A blue and white pearlware tea caddy, moulded in relief at each side, with a profile portrait of King George III, 6in. high, circa 1793.
(Bonhams) £650

A Brislington delft royal portrait charger, painted predominantly in blue with a half portrait of Queen Mary, diameter 9½in., circa 1690. (Bonhams) £11,000

A Prattware cylindrical mug, with a central moulded half portrait of George III on an orange-peel ground within an oval acanthus medallion, 6in. high, circa 1790.
(Bonhams) £900

A Continental porcelain bust, modelled as Queen Victoria, wearing a crown, veil and sash, height 9in., circa 1880.
(Bonhams) £160

A Staffordshire accession pottery teapot and cover, printed in black on each side with a portrait of the young Queen together with the dates of her birth and proclamation, height 7in., circa 1837.
(Bonhams) £350

An English porcelain flared cylindrical vase, with central rectangular panel painted with a colourful portrait of King George IV wearing ceremonial robes, height 6in., circa 1820.
(Bonhams) £1,300

A Swansea pottery mug, commemorating the coronation of Queen Victoria, the waisted form printed in mauve, height 3¼in., circa 1838.
(Bonhams) £1,200

A Staffordshire equestrian portrait of Queen Victoria wearing full riding habit, and a plumed hat, height 9in., circa 1845.
(Bonhams) £110

A Read and Clementson pottery coronation mug, entitled *Victoria Regina* in bold capitals, together with the inscription *Proclaimed 20 of June 1837 Crowned June 28th 1838*, height 3½in.
(Bonhams) £1,100

A rare Scottish pottery oval plaque, moulded in relief with a head and shoulder portrait of King George III, height 9in.
(Bonhams) £1,900

A well coloured Staffordshire portrait figure, modelled as King Edward VII, standing bare-headed, in military uniform, height 12¾in., circa 1901.
(Bonhams) £45

A Chinese Export porcelain tankard, enamelled with a medallion enclosing a half portrait of the Duke of Cumberland, height 6¼in., Qianlong period.
(Bonhams) £1,700

An Alnwick election pink lustre jug printed in sepia with a portrait, inscribed *Bell For Ever, True Blue*, 12cm.
(Phillips) £320

A Coalport plate printed in blue in commemoration of Captain Matthew Webb being the first person to swim the English Channel in 1875, 27cm.
(Phillips) £130

A caricature composition bust of Lloyd George with an extended tongue, inscribed *'Make George Lick the Stamps'*, 8cm.
(Phillips) £380

A large white Luck and Flaw two-handled caricature loving cup formed as the head of Prince Charles, 20cm.
(Phillips) £60

A fine quality English biscuit figure of King William IV seated crossed legged on an elegant sofa, 11cm.
(Phillips) £280

A pearlware spill vase printed in black with a bust after William Beechey of *His Sacred Majesty, King George III*, 12cm.
(Phillips) £400

An unusual yellow glazed jug, commemorating the death of Lord Nelson in 1805, the reverse with portrait of the Duke of Wellington, 11.5cm.
(Phillips) £220

A T & R Boote tapering jug commemorating the death of Sir Robert Peel, showing a full-length relief portrait of Peel, on a green ground, 23cm.
(Phillips) £380

A bulbous porcelain jug, with coloured relief-moulded portrait busts of Queen Caroline within beaded medallions, inscribed *'Success to Queen Caroline'*, 18.5cm.
(Phillips) £120

COPELAND

In 1833 William Copeland bought the Staffordshire firm of Josiah Spode, and it was in 1842 that Copeland and Garrett of Stoke on Trent first produced statuary in what came to be known as Parian ware. Its success was due to the large quantity of feldspar contained in the soft paste, and a firing process which allowed an unusually large quantity of air into the kiln. The result was a porcelain notable for its lustrous transparency and delicacy of moulding. A second quality parian statuary, slightly different in composition, was produced in 1850, and became known as standard parian. It lacked the silky surface of the first, but could withstand repeated firings and could be decorated in colours and gold. Copeland's were also noted for a variety of tableware produced in porcelain and earthenware and often lavishly ornamented, together with handpainted tiles.

A variety of marks were used, bearing variations of Copeland and Spode. From 1970 the firm has traded as Spode Ltd.

A pair of Copeland Crystal Palace Art Union parian ware busts, 'The Prince of Wales' and 'Princess Alexandra' by Marshall Wood and F. M. Miller. (Greenslades) £260

A fine Copeland Spode vase and pierced cover, richly decorated with a jewelled and gilded green ground, 17.5cm. (Phillips London) £400

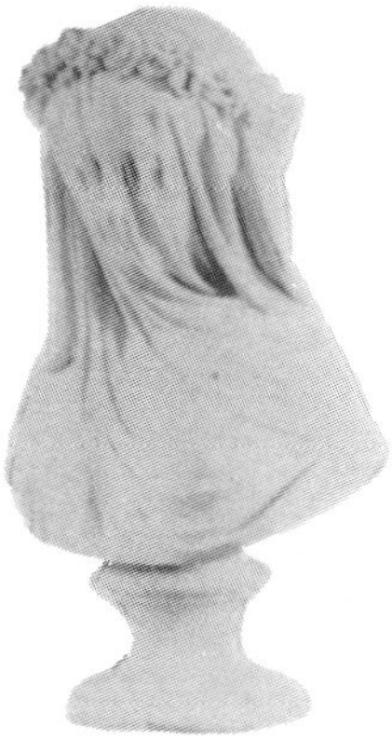

Copeland, Parian porcelain bust 'The veiled bride', 14in. high. (Riddetts) £1550

A rare part set of five Copeland Frog tiles, painted in shades of blue with amusing scenes of frogs variously engaged. (Phillips London) £640

A Copeland vase and cover, the ovoid body painted by L. Besche, signed, circa 1880, 15in. high. £1,250

A large pair of Copeland vases, each painted by C. F. Hurten, signed, circa 1870, 19¾in. high. £2,500

A Copeland bust of Juno, possibly after W Theed, in a coronet and with short ringlets, impressed mark, 20½in. high. (Christie's S. Ken) £1078

HANS COPER

Hans Coper (1920–1981) trained as an engineer in his native Germany, but fled to England in the late '30's. During the war, he met another refugee, Lucie Rie, and went to work in her studio. They started making ceramic buttons, then graduated to domestic ware and in the evenings Coper could experiment with his own designs.

His biggest 'break' came when Basil Spence commissioned two candlesticks from him for Coventry Cathedral. His work is now established among the foremost modern pottery with prices to match.

A stoneware 'sack' form by Hans Coper, with spherical belly, the interior with cylindrical holder, the belly with incised linear decoration, the exterior covered in a buff slip, 21cm. high.
(Christie's) £3,960

An early stoneware goblet pot by Hans Coper, dark brown over a shiny 'toffee' glaze, the foot unglazed, circa 1952, 6in. high.
(Bonhams) £2,400

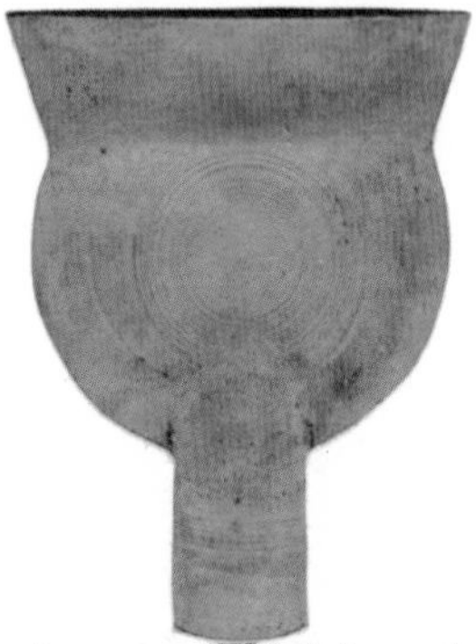

A stoneware 'Thistle' vase by Hans Coper, the body incised with concentric rings, the foot with incised turning, lightly burnished to reveal areas of matt manganese, 25.3cm. high.
(Christie's) £3,300

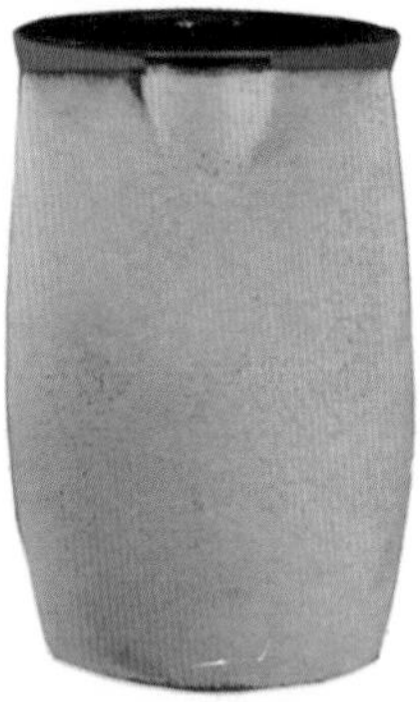

A fine stoneware 'sack' form by Hans Coper, white with bronze disc top, impressed HC seal, circa 1970, 7½in. high.
(Bonhams) £7,500

A fine black stoneware cup form by Hans Coper, made in three pieces, impressed *HC* seal, circa 1965, 6in. high.
(Bonhams) £6,000

An early stoneware cylindrical pot by Hans Coper, buff with manganese neck and rim, distinctive decoration of incised vertical lines comprised of dots, circa 1954, 8in. high.
(Bonhams) £2,000

A rare stoneware bell form pot by Hans Coper, the top third manganese merging into beige, circa 1963, 5in. high.
(Bonhams) £4,200

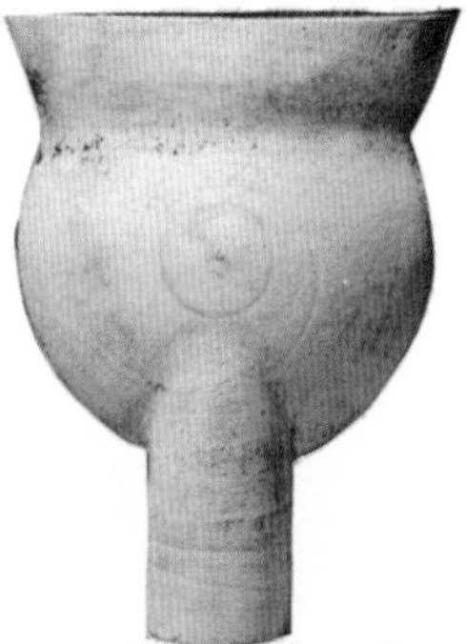

A stoneware 'thistle' form by Hans Coper, the disc-shaped body with flared rim, incised decoration of concentric rings, the exterior covered in a buff slip lightly burnished, 25.5cm. high.
(Christie's) £6,050

An outstanding stoneware spade pot by Hans Coper, white with a deep manganese band at the rim merging into a textured surface, impressed HC seal, circa 1966, 7¼in. high.
(Bonhams) £8,000

A stoneware shallow bowl by Hans Coper, the interior covered in a matt manganese glaze, the centre carved with circular band, impressed *HC* seal, 17.5cm. diameter.
(Christie's) £1,870

A superb stoneware 'egg-in-cup' form by Hans Coper, white with distinctive brown and bluish shading, impressed HC seal, circa 1975, 7⅜in. high.
(Bonhams) £7,000

A stoneware buff cup form by Hans Coper, on a conical base surmounted by a manganese disc, impressed HC seal, circa 1970, 6¾in. high.
(Bonhams) £1,300

An early stoneware goblet form by Hans Coper, manganese over a 'toffee' glaze, unglazed foot, impressed HC seal, circa 1952, 4¾in. high.
(Bonhams) £2,400

A rare cup form stoneware pot by Hans Coper, distinguished by two dark textured panels and two vertical incised lines, impressed HC seal, circa 1970, 6¼in. high.
(Bonhams) £6,000

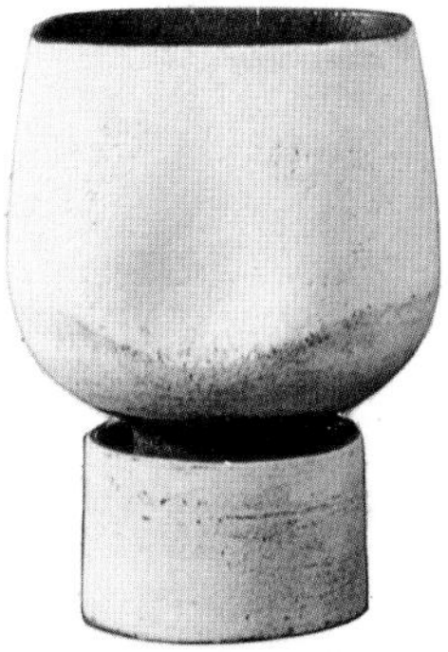

A fine stoneware white pot by Hans Coper, the squared form on a drum base, hollowed impressions on both sides, impressed HC seal, circa 1975, 5in. high.
(Bonhams) £5,000

A beautiful stoneware 'hour-glass' vase by Hans Coper, white and brown with distinctive white inlaid lines round the base, impressed HC seal, circa 1963, 12in. high.
(Bonhams) £9,500

An important early stoneware 'thistle' form pot by Hans Coper, with diagonal texturing, impressed HC seal, circa 1958, 12¼in. high.
(Bonhams) £6,500

A stoneware Beaker by Hans Coper, bronze with white interior, impressed HC and LR seals, circa 1955, 4½in. high. (Bonhams) £150

A stoneware cup and saucer by Hans Coper, white with brown edge to rim, circa 1956. (Bonhams) £380

A tall 'hour-glass' vase by Hans Coper, impressed HC seal, 45.5cm. high. (Christie's) £18,700

A tall stoneware flattened tapering cylinder with spherical belly-form by Hans Coper on drum base, incised with spiral decoration, covered in a bluish-buff slip, circa 1968, 21.2cm. high. (Christie's) £7,700

An early stoneware shallow dish by Hans Coper, covered in a matt manganese glaze, the interior with carved abstract spiralling decoration through to a pitted translucent white glaze, circa 1950, 35.3cm. diam. (Christie's London) £5,500

A rare large black-glazed stoneware waisted cup form by Hans Coper, with incised spiral decoration, covered in a brownish-black burnish and textured glaze, impressed HC seal, circa 1965, 19.4cm. high. (Christie's) £8,250

A Hans Coper stoneware vase of broad oviform on a tapering base, incised with panels of angled vertical lines, 29.1cm. high. (Phillips) £2,500

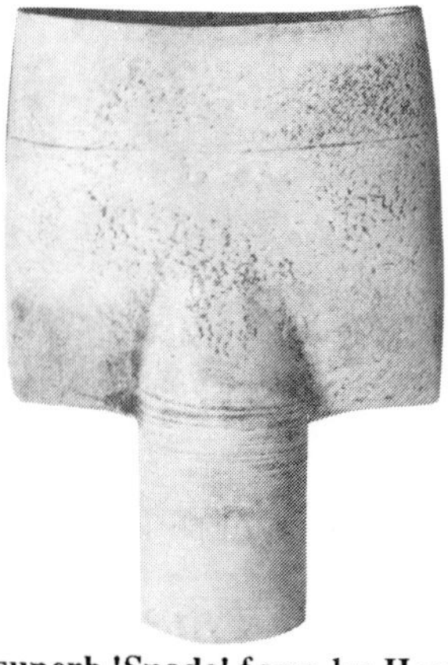

A superb 'Spade' form by Hans Coper, buff with textured surface and incised rings, circa 1965, 7¾in. high. (Bonhams) £7,000

A 'cup and disc' stoneware form by Hans Coper, buff with dark brown disc, impressed HC seal, circa 1965. 4½in. high. (Bonhams) £2,600

CREAMWARE

Creamware was developed by Josiah Wedgwood in response to the huge middle class demand for tableware which would be both durable and attractive. It was first introduced in 1761, at which time the glaze was not very resilient, and could be easily scratched. Nor could it withstand boiling water, which made it unsuitable for tea and coffee pots. By 1764, however, Wedgwood had solved all these problems. The final result was pleasing and modestly priced, and moreover was well suited to mechanical decoration.

It enjoyed immediate and lasting popularity. In 1765 Queen Charlotte commissioned a 60 piece tea service, which was so admired that Wedgwood was granted permission to call his new material Queensware, which name it has borne ever since. On the strength of such success, Wedgwood began using creamware for neo-Classical decorative items as well. Much creamware was sold without decoration or, in other cases, this was restricted to a simple border or pierced rims and lattice work. It was adaptable to all tastes, however, and lent itself to transfer printed scenes or painted decoration.

An attractive Derbyshire creamware teapot and cover, painted on both sides with a spray of green flowers in shell shaped panels, 11cm. (Phillips) £1,700

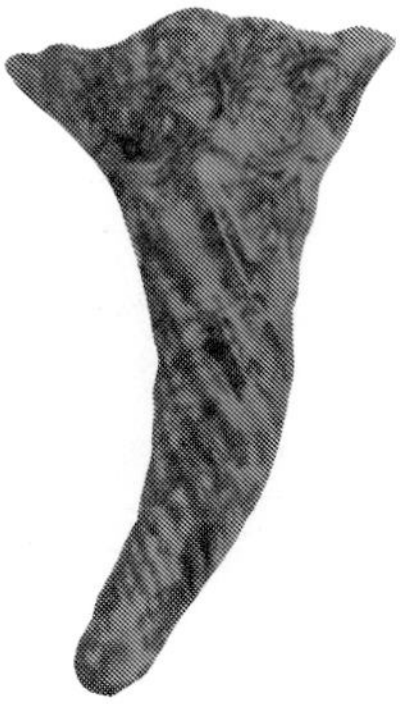

A Staffordshire creamware spirally moulded wall-pocket of Whieldon type, circa 1760, 21cm. high. (Christie's) £528

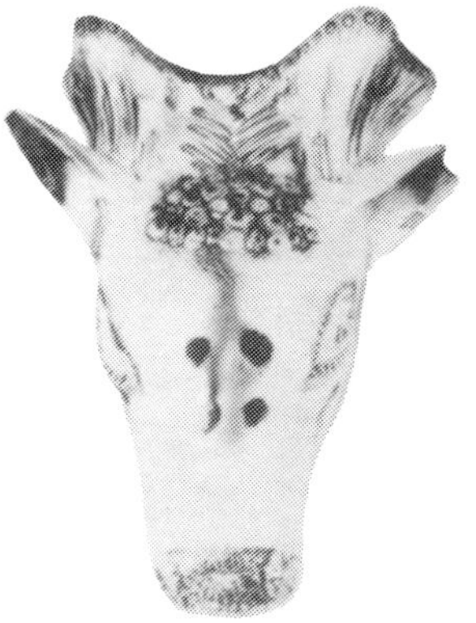

A rare late 18th century creamware deer-head stirrup cup, decorated in brown and green streaky glazes, 12cm. long. (Henry Spencer) £1,050

A creamware baluster jug with grooved loop handle, the tortoiseshell ground applied with green swags of foliage, circa 1780, 16.5cm. high. (Christie's London) £385

A Staffordshire creamware cow-creamer milking group, of Whieldon type, spotted in brown and the milkmaid in a brown coat, circa 1765, 18cm. long. (Christie's) £825

A Staffordshire creamware baluster cream jug and cover of Whieldon type, applied with trailing fruiting branches, circa 1760, 12cm. high. (Christie's) £1,210

An attractive creamware teapot and cover, the body painted with an all over scale pattern in red and black, 14cm. probably Leeds. (Phillips London) £500

A hollow base creamware model of a reclining deer with ochre and brown markings, on a green grassy mound, 11.2cm. high.
(Bearne's) £520

A rare pair of creamware cornucopiae vases, modelled as two goats standing before cornucopiae, 20cm.
(Phillips) £5,500

A Staffordshire creamware miniature model of a squirrel of Ralph Wood type, the mottled brown animal seated erect eating from his forepaws, with bushy tail and wearing a collar suspending a chain, circa 1785, 5cm. high. (Christie's) £1,045

A creamware model of a finch with dark-brown beak, brown crest and yellow wing and tail feathers, perhaps Yorkshire, circa 1785, 12cm. high.
(Christie's) £660

A Pratt creamware sauce boat in the form of a duck, painted in ochre, yellow, brown and green, 18.5cm. long.
(Bearne's) £620

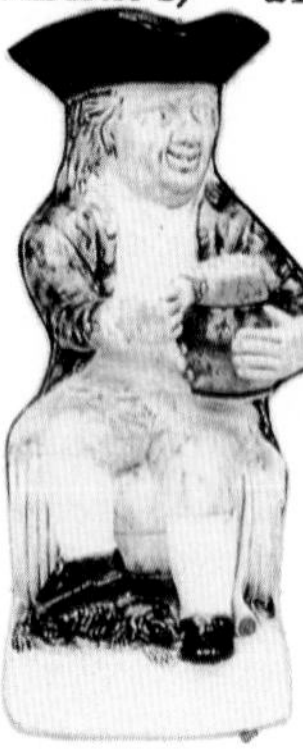

A Staffordshire creamware man-on-a-barrel toby-jug of Ralph Wood type holding a jug of frothing ale, wearing black tricorn hat, circa 1780, 25cm. high. (Christie's) £4,620

A creamware footed jug, inscribed ***The Fountain of Honour*** and above the verse ***Britons rejoice Cheer up and Sing, And Drink His Health, Long Live the King***, dated March 17, 1789, 6½in. high.
(Bonhams) £650

A Wedgwood creamware dated shipping plate printed and coloured with a three-masted ship, the Maria & Adriana, 1779, 10in. diameter.
(Christie's) £418

A creamware coffee pot and domed cover of baluster form with reeded lower section and interlaced handle, painted in puce with scattered foliate sprays, 26.5cm.
(Phillips) £750

A hollow creamware model of a reclining deer with black ears and hooves and brown decorated body, on a pale green grassy mound, 11.8cm.
(Bearne's) £250

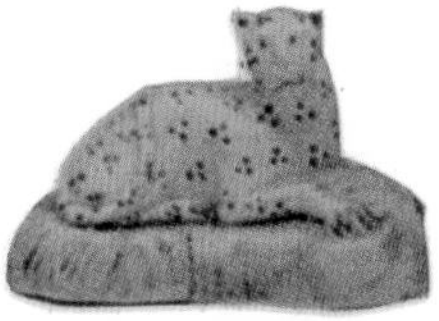

A creamware hollow base model of a leopard with groups of black spots, reclining on a green grassy mound base, 9.3cm. long.
(Bearne's) £500

A creamware model of a recumbent lion, its head turned to the front, with pale-green mane and its coat splashed in brown, perhaps Yorkshire, circa 1790, 8.5cm. wide.
(Christie's) £264

A rare creamware jug, black printed with a ribbon cartouche containing the affectionate sentiments *My dear little angel, charmer of my soul* and underneath the bold inscription *Mrs Clarke the late favourite lady of His Royal Highness The Duke of York*, dated 1809, 5½in. high.
(Bonhams) £700

A large creamware teapot and cover, probably Leeds, of oviform with reeded, double interlaced handles, 15.5cm. high.
(Phillips) £1,000

An English creamware oviform jug with a loop handle, printed in black and coloured with a satirical cartoon entitled *British Slavery* after James Gillray, circa 1800, 6½in. high.
(Christie's S. Ken) £528

A Wedgwood creamware cylindrical mug, black printed with a design by Thomas Billinge of Liverpool showing a profile portrait of the young King George III, 6¼in. high, circa 1793. (Bonhams) £1,700

A Staffordshire creamware model of a lion of Ralph Wood type, its mane splashed in manganese, on a pale-green mound base, circa 1785, 7cm. high. (Christie's) £462

An English pottery jug, printed in brown and enamelled in Pratt colours, with King George III and Queen Charlotte, 5in. high, circa 1793.
(Bonhams) £480

Rare Mayer Creamware oval chestnut basket with cover and underdish, England, c. 1800, moulded basketweave decoration, 10¾in. handle to handle.
(Skinner Inc) £3,026

A creamware mug painted with a portrait of Lord Rodney wearing a green shirt and an inscription *Success to brave Rodney,* 12.5cm. (Phillips London) £190

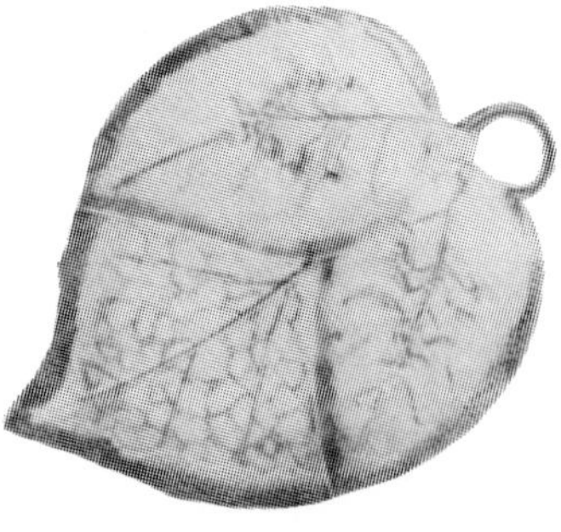

A Staffordshire creamware leaf-shaped dish of Whieldon type, crisply moulded with two racemes of pea flower resting on three veined leaves, circa 1760, 18cm. wide. (Christie's) £770

A Staffordshire creamware figure of a Turk, of Whieldon type, wearing a turban and in flowing cloak, circa 1760, 14cm. high. (Christie's) £6,600

A Staffordshire creamware melon-shaped teapot and cover of Wedgwood-Whieldon type with leaf-moulded spout, circa 1760, 12.5cm. high.
(Christie's) £4,180

Late 19th/early 20th century creamware mug, 4¾in. high, together with a jar and a castor. (Christie's) £297

A Staffordshire creamware plate of Whieldon type with a moulded diaper-pattern ground, circa 1760, 23.5cm. diam.
(Christie's) £605

A creamware swelling jug painted in iron-red and black, circa 1770, 20.5cm. high.
(Christie's) £770

A Staffordshire creamware pierced oval stand of Whieldon type, circa 1770, 24cm. wide. (Christie's)
£1,100

An early creamware cow creamer and cover, 18cm. wide. (Phillips) £1,350

A very rare creamware tea canister and cover of hexagonal section, embossed and coloured with half-length portraits of George III and Queen Charlotte, 17.5cm. (Phillips) £750

A Cockpit Hill creamware globular teapot and cover, painted predominantly in iron-red and enriched in green and yellow, circa 1770, 14cm. high. (Christie's) £990

A Staffordshire creamware pineapple-moulded milk jug of Wedgwood-Whieldon type, the naturistically moulded body with serrated green leaves, circa 1760, 13cm. high. (Christie's) £495

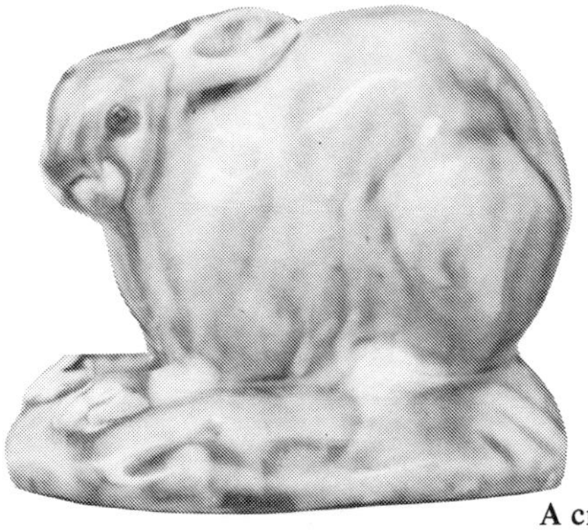

A Staffordshire creamware figure of a leveret, of Whieldon type, with brown slip eyes, circa 1760, 8.5cm. long. (Christie's) £6,050

A creamware cylindrical mug, painted in black and enriched in green and yellow with an Oriental standing beneath a shelter, Staffordshire or Yorkshire, circa 1780, 13.5cm. high. (Christie's) £625

One of a pair of octagonal creamware plates and a similar soup plate, 1810-30, 8¾in. diam. (Christie's) £124

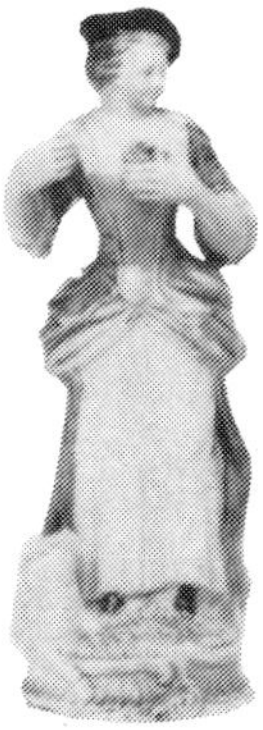

A Staffordshire creamware figure of a shepherdess of Ralph Wood type, holding a flower to her bosom, a sheep at her feet, circa 1780, 22.5cm. high. (Christie's) £660

A creamware dated plate transfer printed by John Sadler with The Sailor's Return (minute rim chip at 1 o'clock), circa 1769, 24cm. diam. (Christie's London) £1,760

CRESTED CHINA

The greatest name in crested china was Goss but there were some 200 other makers who copied the lead set by William Henry Goss and his enterprising son Adolphus. The names of their British rivals include Arcadian, Carlton, Foley, Fords China, Grafton China, Macintyre, Melba, Nautilus, Podmore, Savoy, Shelley, Tuscan and Victoria. There were also foreign competitors who often made mistakes with British coats of arms.

Crested china boomed as a result of the enthusiasm for day trips and holidays that overtook the British public at the end of the 19th century. Trippers wanted a souvenir of their trip away from home and the perfect solution was a cheap little piece of china with the holiday town's coat of arms on it. Several subjects dominate the china manufacturers' output – the Great War – one of the more unusual items was a figure of Old Bill produced by Shelley; animals and birds; transport; memorials including the Cenotaph; statues; cartoon and comedy characters; sport and musical instruments. A cup and saucer was one of the most common items sold and, as a result today the price for such an item would be considerably less than for an Old Bill or a model of the Cenotaph. The rivals to Goss never took such fastidious care about their products as the trail blazers and their china is never as fine. However when buying crested china it is important to remember that imperfections of manufacture do not affect the price so much as subsequent damage.

Arcadian 'Jester on a spade shaped tray', 65mm. wide. £65

Arcadian 'Drunkard leaning against a statue', 100mm. high. £125

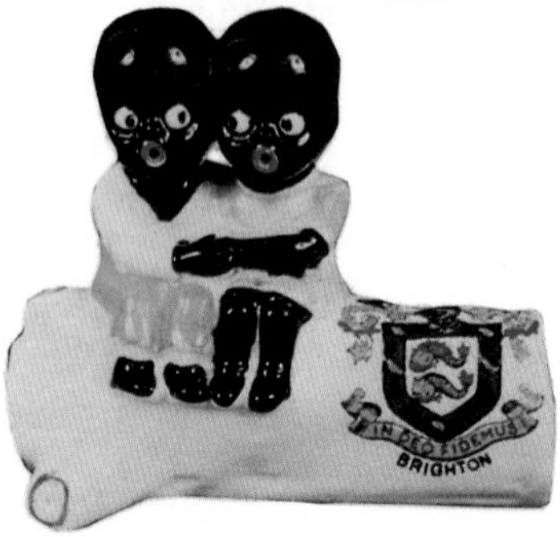

Arcadian 'Black boy and girl on log', 80mm. wide. £82

Carlton 'Goose standing on a green base', 85mm. wide. £33

Arcadian 'Black cat in a boot', 61mm. high. £55

Carlton 'Trefoil Dish with five flags of the Allies'. £30

Willow art 'Old Curiosity Shop', 80mm. wide. £150

Arcadian 'Black cat climbing pillar box to post letter', 56mm. high. £65

(Goss & Crested China Ltd)

Carlton 'Jackie Coogan', 1920's cartoon character inkwell with lid, 73mm. wide. £48

Carlton 'Black cat on settee', 80mm. wide. £30

Carlton Donkey inscribed 'Gee up Neddy', 110mm. wide. £40

Arcadian 'Black boy holding pumpkin mustard pot with lid. £115

Savoy china, 'Snail', 84mm. long. £30

Arcadian 'Policeman holding truncheon', 106mm. high. £65

Carlton fireplace with cauldron in the fireplace, 80mm. wide. £20

Grafton, 'Child kneeling on beach with bucket and spade, 75mm. wide. £125

Savoy china fireplace 'Keep the home fires burning', 94mm. wide. £20

Carlton 'Laxey Wheel', 92mm. wide. £55

Carlton 'Irishman in black hat with yellow pig', 90mm. wide. £150

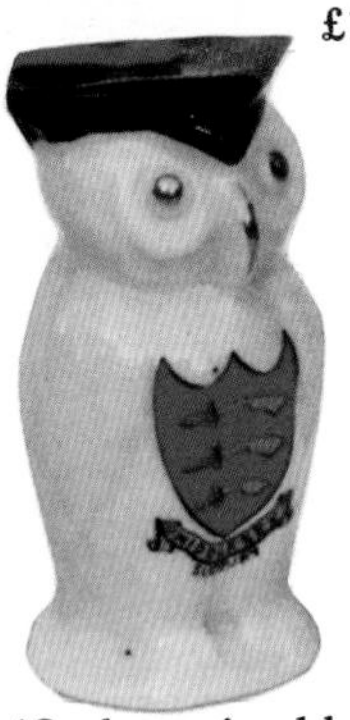

Carlton, 'Owl wearing black mortar board', 75mm. wide. £20

(Goss & Crested China Ltd)

Gemma fat kitten with painted black cat on cushion on side and *Good luck from Brighton*. (The Crested China Co.) £20

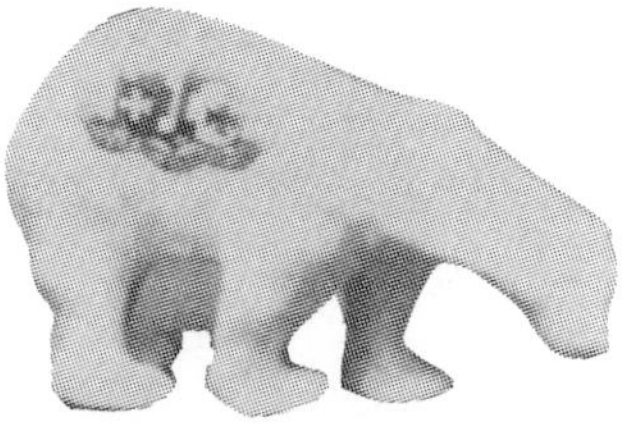

Polar bear walking, neck stretched forward, by Savoy, See of Lichfield crest. (The Crested China Co.) £95

'Cheshire cat' by Willow Art, 95mm. high, inscribed *Still smiling*. (Goss & Crested China Ltd) £10

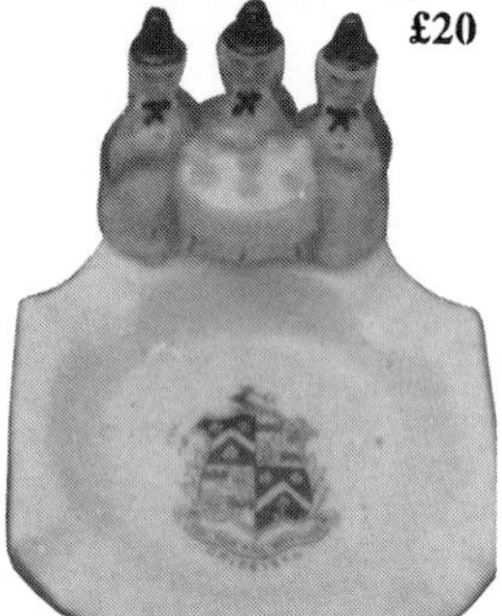

Arcadian Welsh tea party ashtray, with three ladies in coloured hats and cloaks taking tea, with arms of Criccieth. (The Crested China Co.) £55

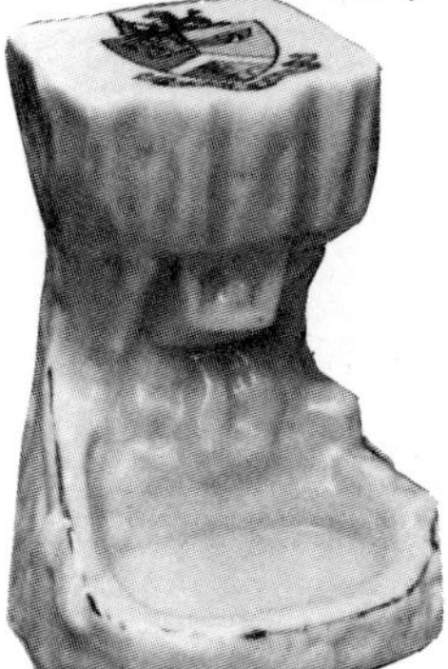

'Dropping Well, Knaresborough' by Carlton, 75mm. high. (Goss & Crested China Ltd) £30

A Willow Art 'Truck of Coal' 90mm. long. (Goss & Crested China Ltd) £25

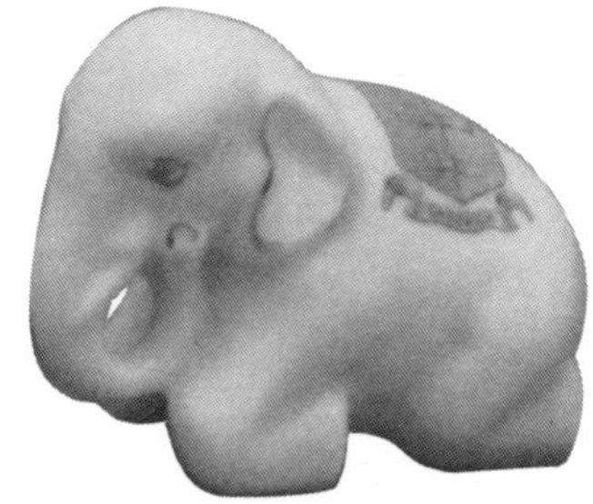

British manufacture lying elephant with arms of Sandwich.
(The Crested China Co.)
£32

Arcadian black boy in bath of ink, towel hanging at side, inscribed *How ink is made*, with arms of Torquay.
(The Crested China Co.) £95

'Dutch boy holding cheese' by Grafton.
(Goss & Crested China Ltd)
£15

Willow John Knox's house.
(The Crested China Co.)
£150

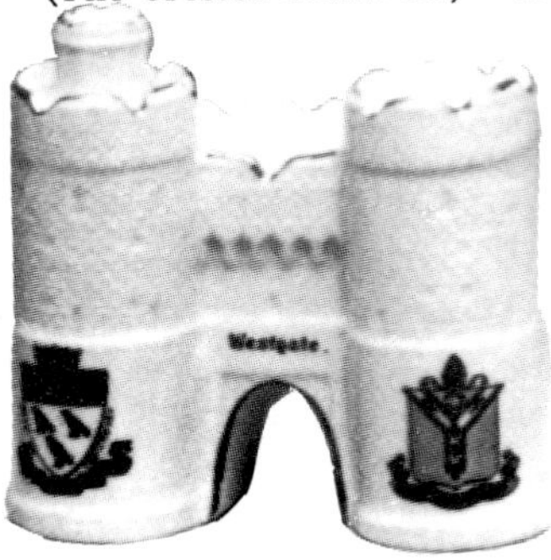

'Canterbury Westgate' by Arcadian, 95mm. long.
(Goss & Crested China Ltd)
£25

Willow Upleatham Church, with arms of Redcar.
(The Crested China Co.) £65

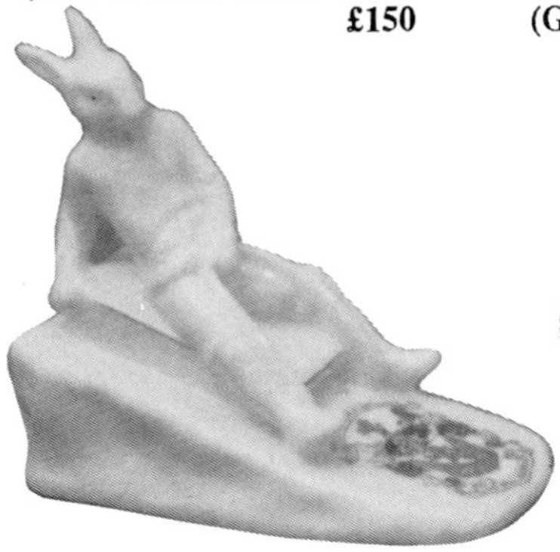

Gemma rabbit on a sledge.
(The Crested China Co.)
£65

A Shelley 235 motor coupe, Blackpool crest. (The Crested China Co.) £295

Arcadian cat on yacht, Great Yarmouth Crest. (The Crested China Co.) £95

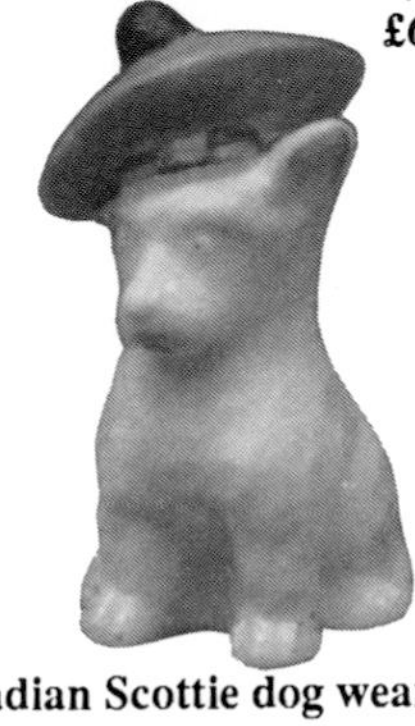

Arcadian Scottie dog wearing a Tam o'Shanter.
(The Crested China Co.) £15

Savoy brown St Paul's Cathedral.
(The Crested China Co.) £110

Arcadian boy eating melon, Matlock Bath crest. (The Crested China Co.) £120

CROWN DUCAL

Crown Ducal was a range manufactured in the 1930s by the A G Richardson factory in Staffordshire. It was decorated in the Art Deco style, notably by Charlotte Rhead who used the 'tube lining' technique. The result looks as if the decoration has been applied with an icing bag, as indeed it has!

A pair of Charlotte Rhead Crown Ducal pottery wall plaques, tubelined in brown and decorated with orange flowers and scattered blue and red flower heads, 14in. diameter.
(Spencer's) £200

A Crown Ducal shaped and ribbed two handled cylindrical vase decorated with a pattern by Charlotte Rhead, printed factory mark, 5½in. high.
(Christie's S. Ken) £61

DAVENPORT

Davenport's Staffordshire Pottery was established in 1773 at Longport, and produced earthenware, ironstone china, and porcelain. In the 1880s, under John Davenport, many tea services were produced, with Japanese patterns. The firm was noted for its strong and durable wares, many of which were used aboard ships of the period. Porcelain plaques, decorated both in-house and by independent artists, were also made. Marks include *Davenport* painted in blue over an anchor, or, from 1850, a crown over *Davenport* and the address. The firm finally closed in 1887.

A Davenport caneware wine cooler, moulded in relief with a bust of Nelson, the reverse with naval trophies, 25.5cm., impressed mark.
(Phillips) £700

A Davenport shaped oval two-handled foot bath, printed with the 'Mosque and Fisherman' pattern.
(Christie's S. Ken) £1650

A pair of Davenport green-ground plates from the Royal Dessert Service made for William IV, the centres painted with a bouquet of rose, thistle, shamrock and leek, circa 1830, 25.5cm. diameter.
(Christie's) £3,850

A Davenport stone china ice pail, liner and cover, with floral and bird decoration. £750

DE MORGAN

William Frend de Morgan (1839–1917) was an English ceramic designer, perhaps now particularly remembered for his tiles. His designs were much influenced by his friend William Morris and include, birds, fish, flowers and mythical beasts. He established his own pottery in Chelsea in 1872, producing his own tiles, and experimented with lustre decoration in an attempt to reproduce the red lustre of maiolica painted in Gubbio. He also designed dishes in cream earthenware decorated in red lustre, and the Sunset and Moonlight suites decorated in gold, silver and copper. With Morris at Merton Abbey he continued to make tiles and dishes, and also established a factory at Fulham with Halsey Ricardo producing tiles and murals. He retired in 1905 and the factory closed in 1907

A De Morgan lustre vase, decorated in ruby lustre with fish swimming against pale amber waves, 15.6cm. high, 1888-97. £375

A Craven Dunhill & Co. metal mounted four tile jardiniere, each tile decorated with a design by William de Morgan, 21.2cm. high. (Christie's London) £682

A William De Morgan eight inch tile forming part of the Fan pattern, painted with two stylised flowers. (Phillips London) £500

A De Morgan lustre vase, decorated by Fred Passenger, 1890's, 32.6cm. high. £880

A De Morgan plate, decorated by F. Farini, 1890, 22.8cm. diam. £500

A De Morgan vase decorated in shades of mauve, green, blue and turquoise with panels of flowers, 1890's, 15.6cm. high. £300

A De Morgan charger, decorated by Chas. Passenger, 1890's, 41.5cm. diam. £7,150

A William de Morgan red lustre charger, the white ground with ruby lustre decoration of a startled antelope with band of elaborate geometric patterns to rim, 29.6cm. diam. (Christie's London) £385

A William de Morgan Persian style pottery vase, early Fulham period, possibly painted by Halsey Ricardo, 25cm. high. (Phillips London) £4,000

A William De Morgan ruby lustre wall plate, painted in the recessed centre with an eagle spreading its wings, 30.5cm. diam. (Phillips London) £720

A William de Morgan two handled earthenware vase, decorated in the Isnik style in blue, turquoise and shades of green, 21.3cm. high. (Christie's London) £1,540

A William de Morgan two handled baluster vase, decorated in green and purple with fruiting vines, the foot, handles and neck interior in turquoise, 27.3cm. high. (Christie's London) £1,320

A William de Morgan ruby lustre vase, with cup neck and twin handles painted with a pelican and a crane against a background of scales, 19cm. high. (Phillips) £1200

A good William de Morgan 'Persian-style' circular wall plate, painted by Charles Passenger, depicting in the sunken centre, a pair of dolphins, encircled with stylised floral and scale borders, 43.5cm. diam. (Phillips) £5200

A William de Morgan Persian style pottery vase, Fulham period, painted by Jo Juster, 28.5cm. high. (Phillips London) £1,350

A William de Morgan red lustre charger, the white ground decorated in shades of red with stylised birds and beasts amid floral patterns, 36.3cm. diam. (Christie's London) £2,420

One of a pair of William de Morgan 'Persian-style' pottery bowls painted by Charles Passenger, signed 'W. de Morgan & Co', 17cm. diam.
(Phillips) £400

Two of a set of six William de Morgan 'Persian-style' pottery bowls painted either by Joe Juster or John Hersey, 11.5cm. diam.
(Phillips) £720

A William De Morgan lustre dish painted by Charles Passenger, with a crane with blue silver, mauve and pale ruby amid silver and ruby lustre bulrushes, 28cm. diam.
(Phillips London) £3,200

A William de Morgan ruby lustre circular dish, painted with a pair of griffin-like creatures prowling in alternate directions, 36cm. diam.
(Phillips) £2500

A William de Morgan vase, painted with white birds in flight against a deep blue ground, 19.5cm. high.
(Phillips) £1800

A William de Morgan ruby lustre circular dish, painted by Fred Passenger with two birds of prey with their wings overlapping, 37cm. diam.
(Phillips) £1700

A William de Morgan ruby lustre twin-handled oviform vase, painted with scaley carp swimming in alternate directions, 37cm. high.
(Phillips) £2100

A William de Morgan circular plate, painted with a central griffin-like creature and bordered by a frieze of birds, 22cm. diam.
(Phillips) £780

A William de Morgan 'Persian-style' vase and cover, painted with foliate fronds in turquoise, blue and pale-green against a white ground, 36cm. high.
(Phillips) £4600

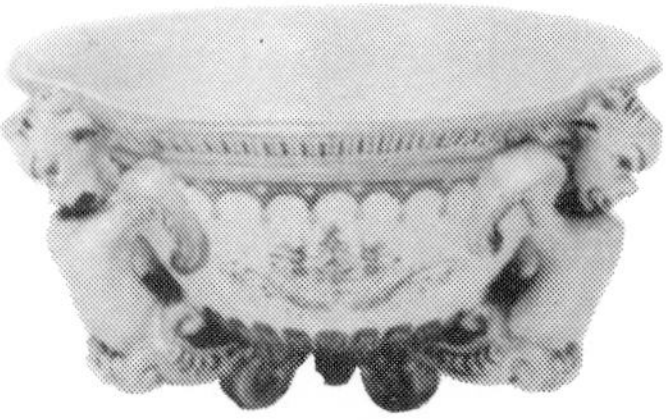

A William de Morgan lustre 'Italian style' bowl, decorated by Farini, supported on the backs of three stylised winged creatures, 25.5cm. diam. (Phillips) £300

A ruby and yellow lustre bowl on short flared foot painted by Fred Passenger for De Morgan, 25.6cm. diam. £810

A William de Morgan bowl, decorated by Charles Passenger, painted in red lustre with a stylised floral pattern, with artist's monogram C.P., 22.7cm. diam. (Christie's) £660

One of a set of three William De Morgan eight inch Chicago pattern tiles, painted in Persian colours. (Phillips London) Three £650

A De Morgan lustre vase, decorated by James Hersey, impressed Sand's End mark, painted initials and numbered 2227, 21.1cm. high, 1888-97. £330

A William De Morgan eight inch tile, hand painted with a large stylised rose in one corner. (Phillips London) £400

A De Morgan lustre vase, the bulbous body with slender cylindrical neck, 1890's, 37.3cm. high. £1,320

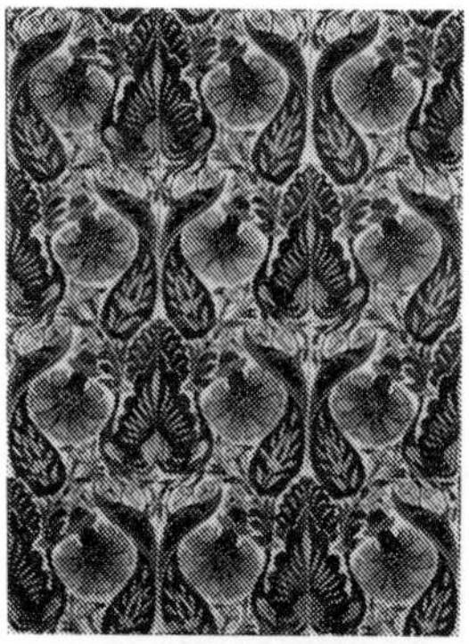

Part of a set of twelve William De Morgan Peacock pattern six inch tiles, with stylised birds, flowers and leaves. (Phillips London) Twelve £2,800

A William de Morgan red lustre vase and cover, the white ground decorated in red, with three bands of stylised birds and beasts, with scolloped borders at rim and base, 33.6cm. high. (Christie's) £2,420

DEDHAM

The Dedham Pottery was established in 1895, following the move of the Chelsea Keramic Art Works to Dedham Mass. under Hugh Robertson, who had succeeded his father as master potter at Chelsea. At Dedham, Robertson produced a crackle glaze on a heavy stoneware decorated with borders of bird and animal designs. Dedham Ware was made in forty eight patterns and proved very popular. Its mark is *Dedham Pottery* over a crouching rabbit.

A Dedham pottery round serving tray with rabbit pattern, signed by Maude Davenport, circa 1910, 13½in. diam. £1,030

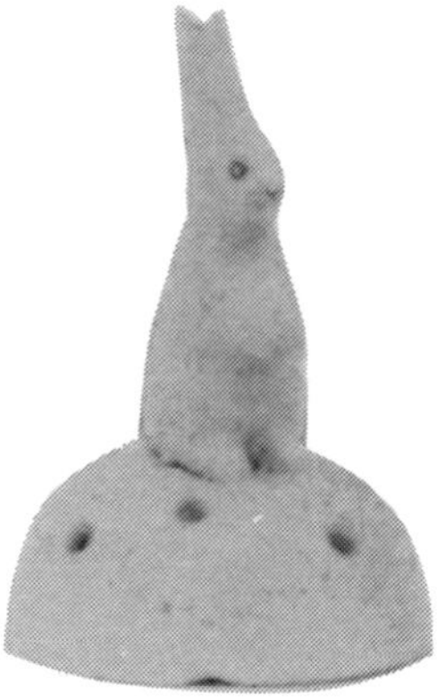

Early 20th century Dedham pottery rabbit figural flower frog, 6¼in. high. £490

Dedham pottery crackleware vase, Dedham, Massachusetts, late 19th century, initialled *HCR,* for Hugh Robertson, (repair to neck) 9in. high. (Skinner Inc.) £1,049

Eight Dedham pottery Birds in Potted Orange Tree plates, Massachusetts, early 20th century, 8in. diam. (Skinner Inc.) £1,049

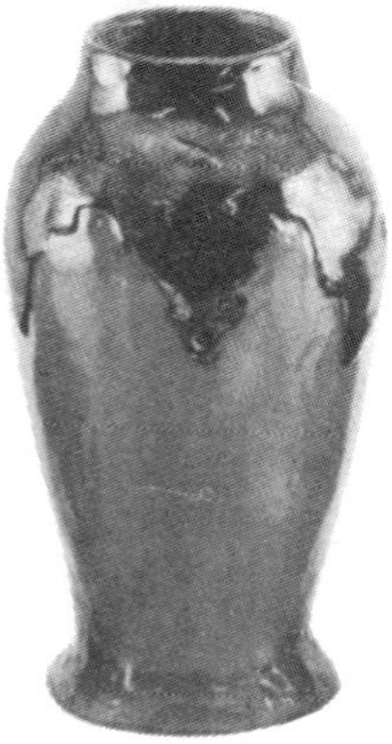

Late 19th century Dedham pottery experimental drip vase, 6¼in. high. £400

Dedham Pottery Stein, Massachusetts, early 20th century, rabbit pattern, impressed and ink stamped marks, 5¼in. high. (Skinner Inc.) £117

Early 20th century Dedham pottery plate, stamped and dated 1931, 8¾in. diam. £1,330

Early 20th century Dedham pottery cylindrical pitcher in grape pattern, 4½in. high. £580

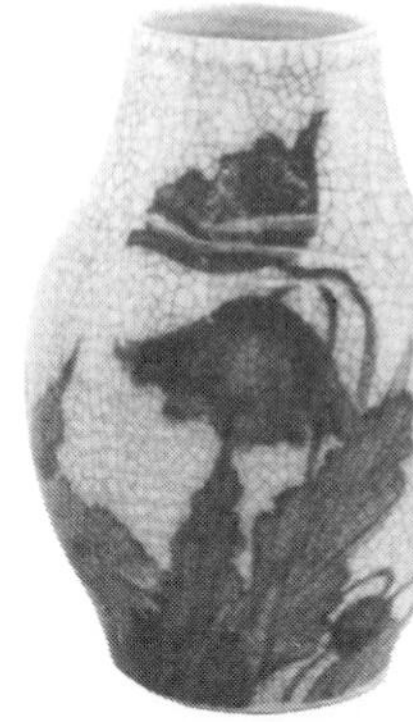

A Dedham pottery crackle-ware vase, 8in. high, circa 1900. £1,460

Dedham pottery plate with turtle alternating with scenic border, Mass., circa 1920, 10in. diam. £320

Early 20th century Dedham pottery large milk pitcher, Rabbit pattern, 8½in. high. (Robt. W. Skinner Inc.) £227

Late 19th century Dedham pottery vase with oxblood and black glaze, 7¼in. high. £1,000

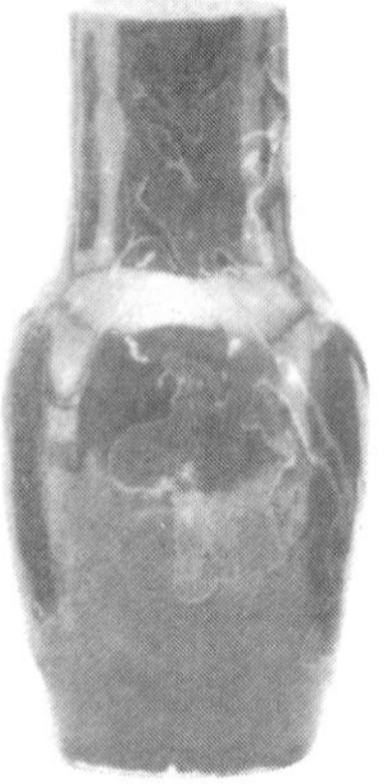

Late 19th century Dedham pottery experimental vase, pink star drip design on green, 10¼in. high. £3,845

Dedham Pottery experimental vase, Massachusetts, late 19th/early 20th century, executed by Hugh C. Robertson, 6in. high. (Skinner Inc.) £181

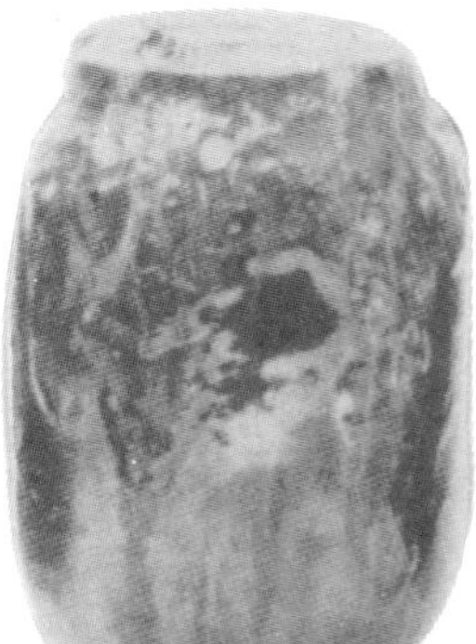

Late 19th century Dedham pottery volcanic oxblood vase, 7.1/8in. high. £4,615

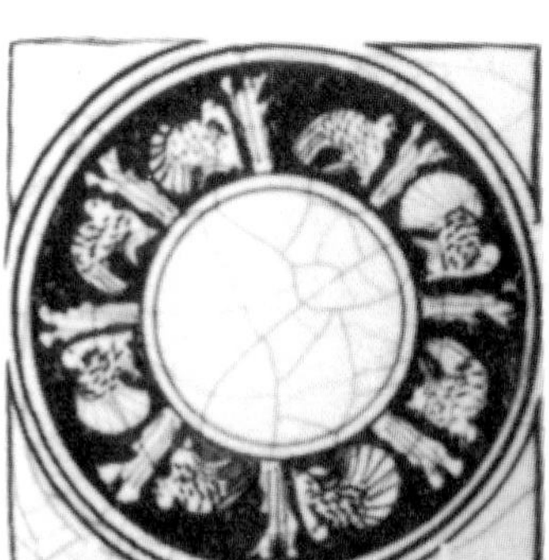

Early 20th century Dedham pottery turkey trivet, 6in. square. £330

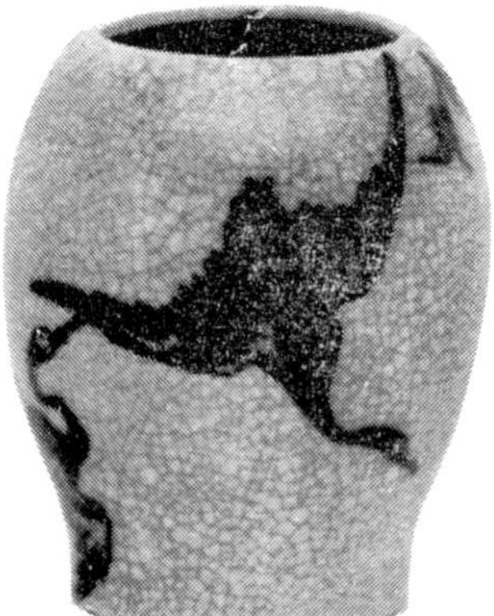

Early 20th century Dedham pottery decorated crackle-ware vase, 7½in. high. (Robt. W. Skinner Inc.) £1,190

DELFT

When Chinese porcelain arrived in the West, Europe was literally dazzled. Nothing of such beauty and brilliance had ever been manufactured there, and the indigenous pottery industries now had to compete with the flood of imports. Majolica had been made in small workshops throughout Holland by potters who were experienced yet open to new techniques. A result of this was delft, a decorated, tin-glazed earthenware, known elsewhere as faience. It first appeared in the early 17th century and the next 120 years were to see the steady development of both technique and quality. Majolica had been mainly multicoloured, but delft was nearly all blue and white, imitating Chinese porcelain. Decoration too at first followed Chinese traditions, but later pieces saw innovative themes, such as the peacock jar, with a motif of two peacocks facing a central basket.

The finest period lasted until about 1730, when the seduction of enamel colours and the prettiness of porcelain began to sap the vitality of the medium.

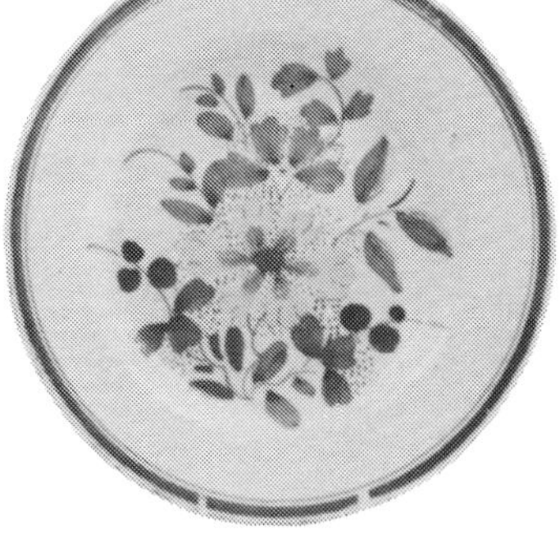

A delftware polychrome plate, painted in a bright Fazackerly palette, perhaps Delftfield factory, Glasgow, circa 1765, 23cm. diam. (Christie's) £462

A Brislington royal portrait charger with a full face, half length portrait of James II, 33.5cm. (Phillips London) £3,400

A Delft mantel garniture, comprising two covered jars and a vase, vase 13in. high. (Christie's) £434

A large mounted panel of delft tiles, the centres alternately plain or painted in polychrome with birds in branches, each 14.5cm. (Phillips London) £180

A German delft dish of silver shape, the centre painted with an animal running to the left within a border of tulips, early 18th century, $13^{1}/_{2}$in. diam. (Christie's S. Ken) £330

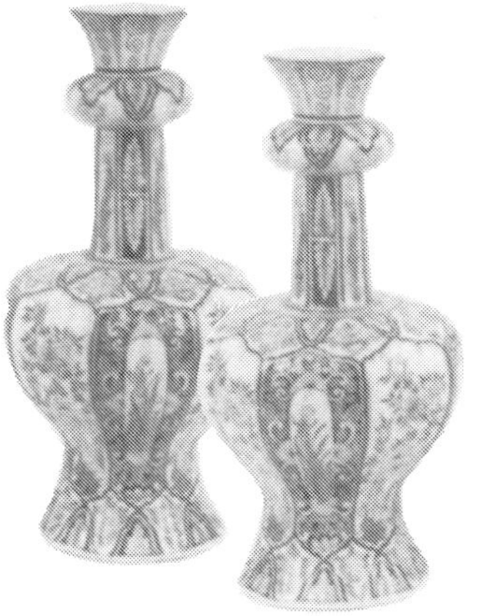

Pair of delft faience vases, painter's mark *MG*, 45cm. high. (Auktionshaus Arnold) £358

English polychrome delft bowl, early 18th century, V-outer border and scrolled inner border in blue, 9in. diameter. (Skinner Inc.) £521

A Bristol delft polychrome small rectangular flower-brick, painted with yellow-centred iron-red flowers, circa 1750, 12cm. long. (Christie's) £825

A Bristol delft plate, painted in blue with a Chinese river scene, 22.5cm. (Lawrence Fine Arts) £110

A Bristol delft powdered manganese-ground bowl, the exterior with four blue fish swimming in a clockwise direction, circa 1740, 26cm. diam. (Christie's) £3,300

A Bristol delft Adam and Eve charger, boldly painted with the ill-fated couple holding iron-striped yellow leaves, circa 1740, 34cm. diam. (Christie's) £2,860

A Bristol delft blue and white dated miniature shoe, the date 1721 beneath the sole (crack to front, slight chips), 10cm. long. (Christie's) £1,210

A Bristol delft blue-dash Queen Anne portrait charger, boldly painted in bright blue, yellow and ochre, 1702, 35cm. diam. (Christie's) £3,300

A Bristol delft polychrome tea-bowl, painted in iron-red with a man and a stag, circa 1730, 7.5cm. diam. (Christie's) £880

A Bristol delft blue and white stand, painted in the manner of Bowen with a milkmaid and four cows, circa 1760, 23cm. diam. (Christie's) £825

A Bristol delft dated blue and white bleeding-bowl, the shaped flat handle pierced with two hearts and a circle, 1730, 19.5cm. wide. (Christie's) £1,045

A Bristol delft powdered-manganese-ground bowl, reserved with four fish, the interior with flowers and foliage, circa 1750, $10^{1}/_{2}$in. diameter.
(Christie's S. Ken) £1,870

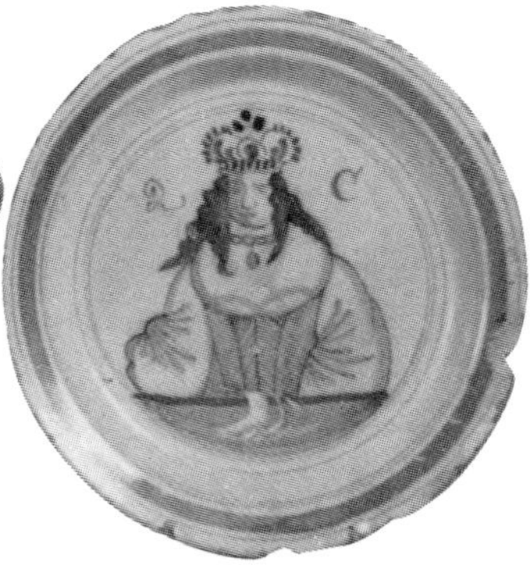

A Bristol delft Royal portrait plate, printed in blue with a half length portrait of Queen Caroline, $8^{1}/_{2}$in. diameter, circa 1727.
(Bonhams) £3,600

A Bristol delft blue and white footed bowl, circa 1730, 26.5cm. diam.
(Christie's) £1,320

A Bristol delft blue dash royal portrait charger, painted predominantly in blue with Queen Anne seated in her coronation robes, diameter $13^{1}/_{4}$in., circa 1702.
(Bonhams) £5,500

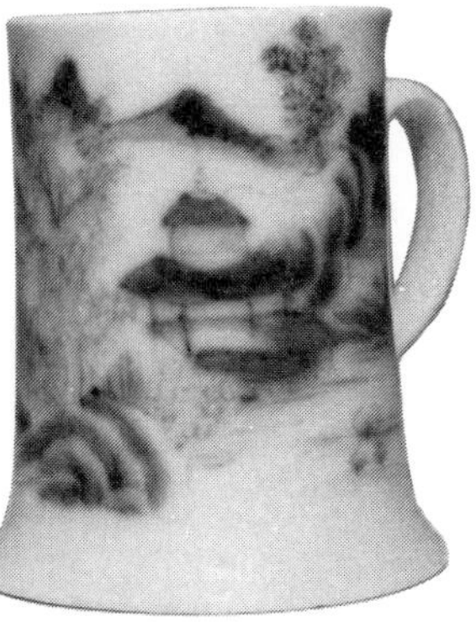

A Bristol blue and white mug with loop handle, painted with pagodas among trees on a rocky island, Benjamin Lund's factory, circa 1750, 12cm. high.
(Christie's) £7,700

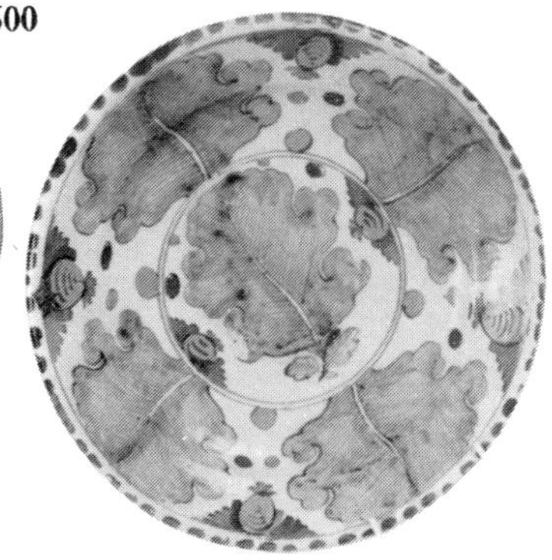

An early 18th century Bristol delft 'oak leaf' charger, the central circular panel painted in blue, green, yellow and brown, 13in. diameter.
(Spencer's) £1,700

A Bristol delft plate painted in a bright palette with a peacock, circa 1740, 21cm. diam. (Christie's) £880

A fine pair of Bristol delft blue and white small rectangular flower-bricks painted with huts, circa 1760, 11.5cm. wide.
(Christie's) £462

A Bristol delft polychrome plate painted with a bird in flight, flanked by manganese and iron red trees, circa 1740, 22.5cm. diam. (Christie's London) £660

A Bristol delft blue-dash Adam and Eve charger, circa 1720, 34cm. diam. £755

A Bristol delft blue and white documentary deep bowl, circa 1735, 35cm. diam. £8,640

A Bristol polychrome delft circular dish, 34cm. £285

A Bristol campana shaped vase with double rope twist handles and frilled rim, circa 1750, 6¾in. high. £2,300

A Bristol delft blue and white barber's bowl, circa 1740, 25.5cm. diam. £970

A Bristol polychrome posset pot and cover decorated in the Chinese style with flowers in red, blue and green, circa 1710-30, 9in. high. £3,200

A Bristol delft circular dish, the centre painted with an Oriental lady, blue 7 mark, circa 1740, 33cm. diam. £990

A Bristol delft blue and white cylindrical mug with broad strap handle, circa 1730, 12cm. high. £880

A large Bristol delft dish, decorated in blue with two figures in a punt, circa 1760, 13in. diam. £260

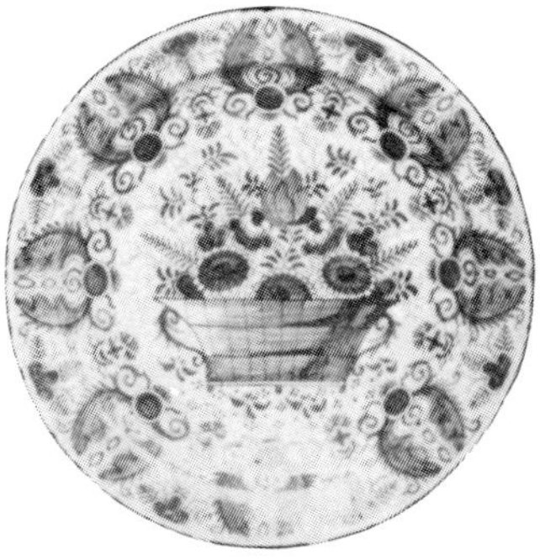

Blue and white Dutch delft charger, Holland, 18th century, with floral bouquet surrounded by a stylised floral border, 15½in. diameter.
(Skinner Inc.) £459

Dutch delft tile picture of a cat, late 18th century, mounted in a wood frame, 12½ x 17½in. (Skinner Inc.)
£1,419

A Dutch delft model of a cow, the animal painted in colours with garlands of flowers, yellow horns and blue features, circa 1750, 22cm. wide.
(Christie's London) £825

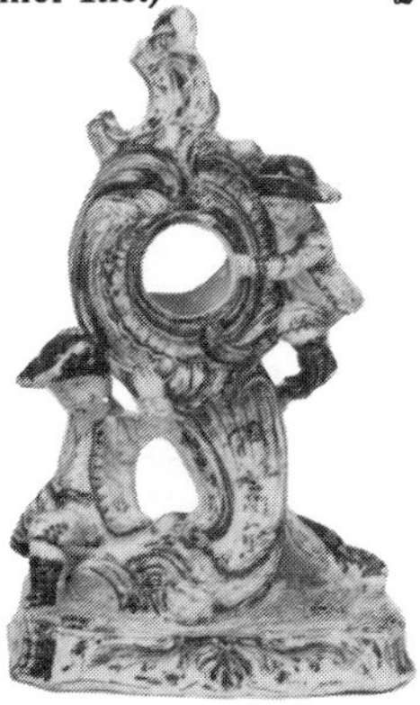

A Dutch delft blue and white rococo watch-stand modelled as a scroll-moulded watch-case supported by two youths, their clothes enriched in blue, circa 1750, 32.5cm. high.
(Christie's) £880

A Dutch delft lobed dish painted in yellow, blue and green, the centre with a man on horseback flanked by trees, circa 1700, 34.5cm. diameter.
(Christie's) £396

A Dutch delft blue and white baluster table-fountain, painted in a bright blue, the lower part moulded with a lion's mask to hold a tap, blue AK mark, circa 1690, 41.5cm. high.
(Christie's) £990

A Dutch delft dore plate painted in colours with a Chinese lady on horseback with three attendants, circa 1700, 23cm. diam. (Christie's) £3,520

A Dutch delft figure of Harlequin standing holding a blue hat, wearing a suit enriched with blue, yellow green and iron-red lozenges and dots, circa 1720, 23cm. high.
(Christie's London) £2750

A Dutch delft royal portrait plate, painted in blue with a bust of King William III wearing a crown, flanked by the initials *K.W.*, diameter 8½in., circa 1689. (Bonhams) £750

One of a pair of 18th century Dutch Delft polychrome chicken tureens and covers, 14cm. long. £8,100

One of a pair of Dutch Delft leaf dishes, blue VH/3 marks probably for Hendrick van Hoorn at the Three Golden Ash Barrels, circa 1765, 21cm. wide. £2,810

A Dutch Delft spittoon, the compressed globular body with spreading neck painted in blue, 18th century, 5in. diam. (Christie's S. Ken) £110

A Dutch delft candlestick, painted in dark blue with bands of flowers and stylised leaf scrolls, 16cm. (Phillips London) £460

A pair of rare Dutch polychrome delft vases and covers, painted in blue with stags and does within yellow bordered panels, 32.5cm. (Phillips London) £1,900

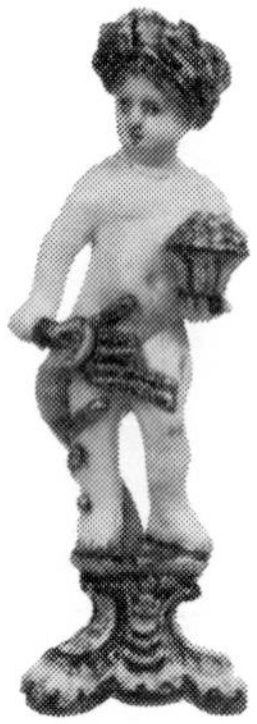

A Dutch delft figure of a putto emblematic of Summer painted in blue, yellow and iron red, circa 1750, 40cm. high. (Christie's London) £825

A Dutch delft blue and white chamber-pot, the exterior painted with foliate lappets between medallions with flowers, animals and cockerels above monkeys and horses among rockwork, circa 1720, 33cm. wide. (Christie's London) £880

One of a pair of Dutch delft pictures both made up of four tiles, painted in blue with extensive Arctic whaling scenes, 25cm. square. (Phillips London) Two £340

One of a pair of Dutch delft tobacco jars, painted in blue with a negro with feathered head-dress and skirt, smoking a pipe, 26cm., 15th century. (Lawrence Fine Art) (Two) £3,520

An important English delft plate, with a mounted figure on a rearing horse, and inscribed *Duke William for Ever 1746*, 21.5cm. (Phillips) £4,000

A rare and attractive English delft model of a shoe, with squared-off toe and medium sized heel, painted with sprays of flowers in Oriental style, 16cm. (Phillips) £750

An English delft powdered manganese-ground plate, painted in underglaze blue with two Orientals, Bristol or Wincanton, circa 1745. (Christie's) £1,045

An English delft oviform dry drug jar, named in manganese for *Ther: Androm,* within a rectangular cartouche, 20cm. (Phillips London) £400

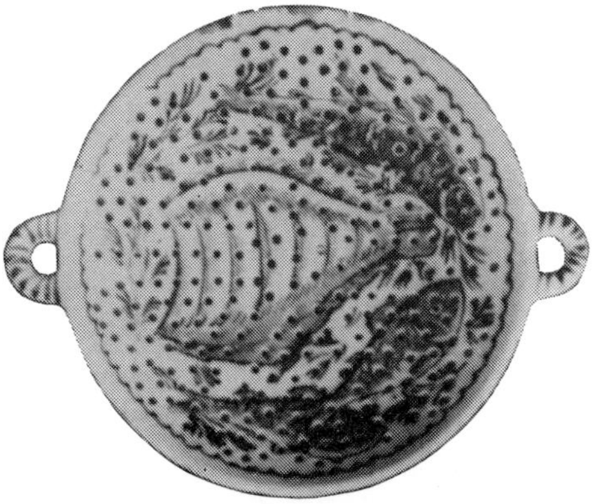

An English delft fish strainer, the shallow pierced bowl decorated with fish in cobalt blue, mid 18th century, 17in. (Hy. Duke & Son) £490

A very impressive and dated English delft wassail bowl and two covers, the latter surmounted by a spice cup, 36cm. diam., overall height 53cm. (Phillips London) £24,000

An English delft plate, painted with the inscription *God Save King George 1716* enclosed by a green garland, diameter 9in., dated 1716. (Bonhams) £1,200

An interesting early English delft mustard pot, possibly Brislington, painted with a Chinese figure amidst trees, shrubs and rocks, 7.5cm. high. (Phillips) £1,200

A English delft plate, painted in blue with a half portrait of George I wearing coronation robes and crown, diameter 8¾in., circa 1714. (Bonhams) £11,000

An English delft blue and white deep bowl painted with flowers and grasses, Bristol or London, circa 1725, 35cm. diam. (Christie's London) £1,540

Mid 17th century Southwark delft polychrome armorial salt of rectangular form, 13cm. wide. £4,535

A large English delft bowl, painted in light blue with panels of parrots alternating with flower sprays, 34.5cm. diam. (Phillips) £800

A large English delft blue dash Adam and Eve charger of flanged form, circa 1700, 35.9cm. diam. (Tennants) £700

A fine English delft political plate, the centre painted in blue with an allegory of Justice triumphing over Evil, 22.5cm., marked B in blue. (Phillips London) £1,500

An English delft polychrome dish painted with a bird flanked by shrubs within a leaf garland border, circa 1750's, 7¾in. diam. (Christie's S. Ken) £264

A rare English delft plate, painted in blue with the dispossessed King Charles II hiding in the Boscobel Oak, 9¼in., circa 1745. (Bonhams) £9,000

An English delftware puzzle jug, 6½in. high. £1,100

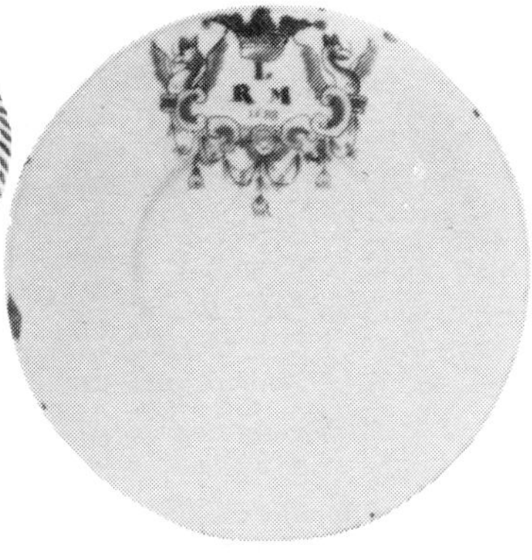

An English delft plate, monogrammed L.R.M. in blue, within heraldic surround, dated 1688, 10in. diam. (Hy. Duke & Son) £420

A Lambeth delft 'Union' tankard of cylindrical form, 5¾in. high. £1,500

A Lambeth delft charger, painted in green, orange, red and blue with a head and shoulder portrait of King George I, diameter 13in., circa 1714. (Bonhams) £17,000

A Lambeth delft blue and white drug jar for U:Sambuc, circa 1740, 17.5cm. high. £215

A Lambeth delft blue and white octagonal pill slab, circa 1780, 26cm. high. (Christie's) £1,870

A Lambeth delftware white glazed posset pot and cover, 7in. £3,600

A Lambeth delft plate, painted in blue with a central crown above the initials *A.R.*, diameter 9in., circa 1702 (chips to rim). (Bonhams) £1,300

A late 17th century Lambeth blue and white delftware dish, 14in. wide. (Dacre, Son & Hartley) £400

A Lambeth delft blue and white wet drug jar with scrolling strap handle, circa 1680, 18cm. high. £540

A Lambeth delft plate, commemorating the Union of England and Scotland in 1707, with painted polychrome decoration, diameter 8¾in. (Bonhams) £2,500

An English delft blue and white dish, perhaps Liverpool, circa 1740, 30.5cm. diam. (Christie's) £1,650

A Liverpool delft rectangular flower brick painted in a Fazackerly palette with flowering shrubs and blue foliage, circa 1765, 13cm. long. (Christie's London) £2,090

A Liverpool delft plate, boldly painted in the Fazackerly palette with a spray of flowers by a fence, mid 18th century, 33.5cm. diam. (Bearne's) £290

A rare English delft coffee cup, possibly Liverpool, with an everted rim and a blue-dash loop handle, 5.5cm. (Phillips) £900

Liverpool delft wall-pocket of spiral form, lightly moulded and painted in a Fazackerly palette with a bird perched on a flowering branch, circa 1760, 20.5cm. long. (Christie's) £880

A Liverpool delft blue and white armorial bowl, the centre to the interior painted with two figures in a rowing-boat before buildings on an island, circa 1770, 26cm. diameter. (Christie's) £990

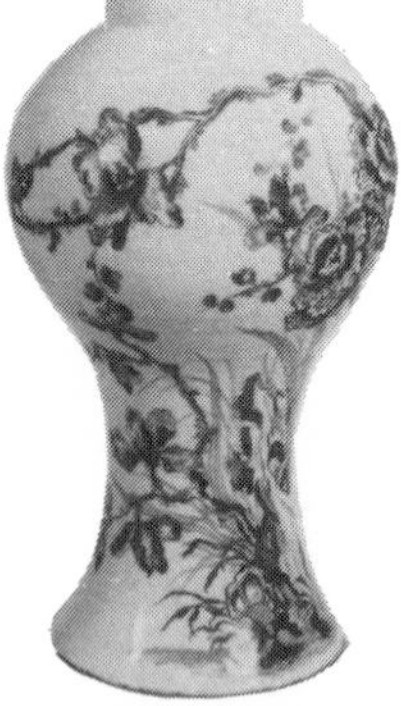

A Liverpool delft blue and white slender baluster vase, circa 1750, 14½in. high. £1,530

A Liverpool delft polychrome dish sketchily painted with a swan on a lake flanked by a willow tree, circa 1760, 33cm. diam. (Christie's London) £935

An inscribed Liverpool delft puzzle jug, the rim with three spouts and hollow handle, circa 1750, 8in. high. £2,200

DELFT, LONDON

A London delft dated blue and white armorial plate, painted in a dark blue with the arms of The Clothworkers Company, 1701, 23cm. diam. (Christie's) £10,450

A London delft white salt, the shallow circular bowl with flat rim and three scroll lugs, circa 1675, 12cm. diam. (Christie's) £6,600

A London delft dated blue and white oval royal portrait plaque of Queen Anne, the reverse with the date 1704, pierced for hanging (minute chips to beads), 23.5cm. high. (Christie's) £15,400

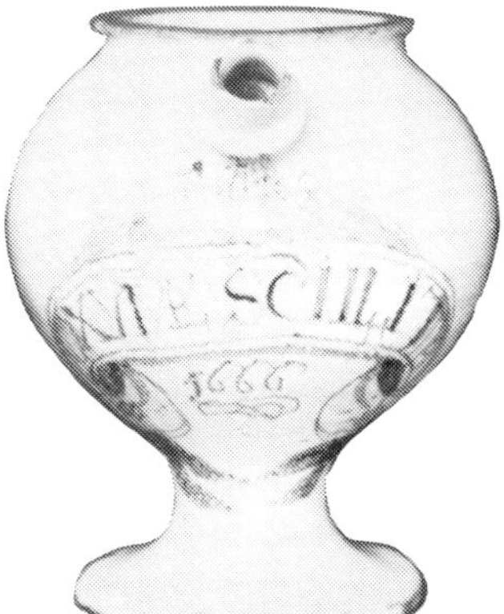

A London delft dated blue and white wet-drug jar, on a circular spreading foot (cracks to rim), 1666, 17.5cm. high. (Christie's) £3,080

A London delft blue and white two-handled beaker of flared form, painted with stylised flowers, circa 1720, 7cm. high. (Christie's) £308

A London delft blue and white drug-jar (rim chips and slight glaze flaking), circa 1680, 9.5cm. high. (Christie's) £605

A London delft blue-dash royal portrait charger painted with a full-length portrait of Charles II in his coronation robes, circa 1685, 32.5cm. diam. (Christie's) £16,500

A London delft blue and white octagonal pill-tile, boldly painted with the arms of The Worshipful Society of Apothecaries, late 17th century, 27.5cm. high. (Christie's) £3,300

A London delft blue and white dated barber's bowl, the centre painted with a comb, scissors, shaving brush and other implements of the trade, 1716, 26cm. diam. (Christie's) £24,200

A London polychrome delft Royal portrait footed dish, printed in blue and yellow with half length portraits of King William III and Queen Mary, 8¼in. diameter. circa 1690. (Bonhams) £1,200

An English delft polychrome miniature mug, painted in iron-red, blue and green with stylised shrubs and rockwork, London or Bristol, circa 1730, 5cm. high. (Christie's) £1,650

A London Royal portrait delft footed dish, printed in blue with half length portraits of King William III and Queen Mary, 8½in. diameter, circa 1690. (Bonhams) £750

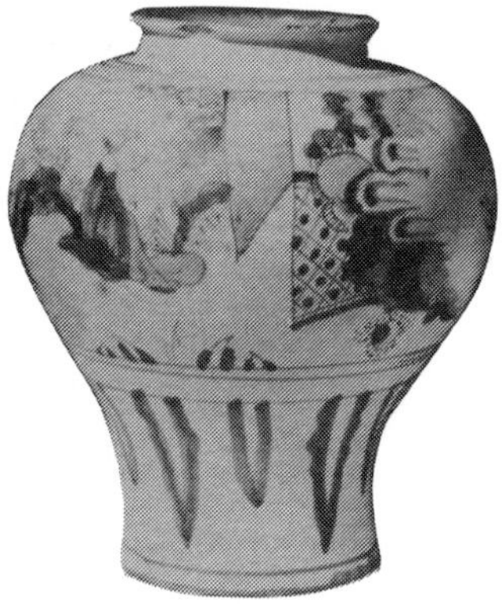

A London delft vase painted in blue 24cm. high. (Phillips) £500

A good London delft 'Blue Dash' charger, painted with The Fall, Eve with long manganese hair handing an apple to Adam, 35cm. (Phillips) £2,300

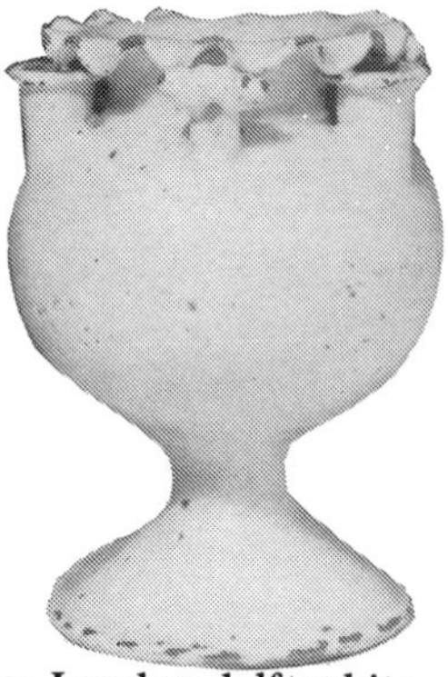

A rare London delft white flower vase, raised on a spreading circular foot, the wavy rim encircled by three cylindrical flower nozzles, 16.5cm., mid-17th century. (Phillips London) £3,100

A very rare and interesting London delft pierced basket, attributed to Vauxhall, of circular shape supported on three bun feet, 26cm. (Phillips London) £4,600

A massive London delft dated polychrome armorial drug jar of swelling form, circa 1656, 36cm. high. £19,440

A London delft plate, painted in manganese and blue, with a half portrait of King George III, diameter 9in. (chips to rim). (Bonhams) £15,000

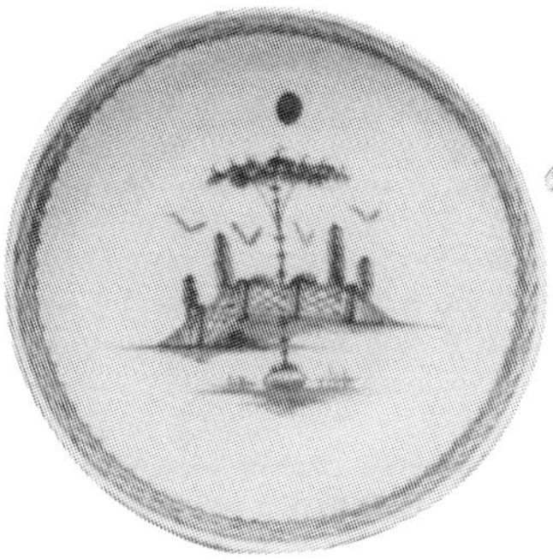

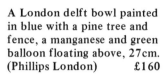

A London delft bowl painted in blue with a pine tree and fence, a manganese and green balloon floating above, 27cm.
(Phillips London) £160

A very rare London delft teapot and cover, painted in blue, iron-red and green with whorl and lozenge-shaped motifs, 9cm.
(Phillips) £21,000

A London delft dated blue and white two handled globular jar painted with winged putti and birds among shrubs, circa 1700, 19cm. wide.
(Christie's London) £880

An English delft polychrome baluster posset-pot and cover, painted in iron-red, blue and green with flowers and insects flanking the spout, London or Bristol, circa 1710, 19cm. high.
(Christie's) £4,950

A delft blue and white oval Royal portrait plaque of Queen Anne, blue E mark to the reverse, probably London, circa 1705, 23cm. high.
(Christie's London) £11,000

A rare early London delft baluster vase with slightly spreading foot, painted in blue with bold plant motifs and a butterfly, 29cm.
(Phillips) £480

A London delft blue dash royal equestrian charger, painted with a monarch wearing a crown, and holding a baton, diameter $13^{1}/_{2}$in., circa 1690.
(Bonhams) £17,000

An 18th century century English delft puzzle jug with blue printed flower decoration and inscribed *J.J. 1730*, possibly London, $7^{1}/_{4}$in. high.
(Andrew Hartley) £3,800

A mid 18th century London delft charger, decorated in blue, red, manganese, green and yellow, 13in. diameter.
(Spencer's) £320

DELLA ROBBIA

The Della Robbia pottery was established in 1894 at Birkenhead by H. Rathbone and the sculptor, Conrad Dressler. It produced vases, bottles, jars, plates and dishes with sgraffito decoration and sometimes elaborate modelled relief with a strong Italian maiolica influence. The factory closed in 1901, but reopened and continued until 1906. Their mark consists of *Della Robbia* with a ship device and the decorator's initials.

'The Third Day of Creation', a Della Robbia tile panel after a design by Edward Burne-Jones, 55.5 x 21.5cm.
(Christie's) £2,860

'Water Avens Tile', a Della Robbia tile panel designed by Conrad Dressler and decorated by E. M. Wood, 51.5 x 34.2cm.
(Christie's) £605

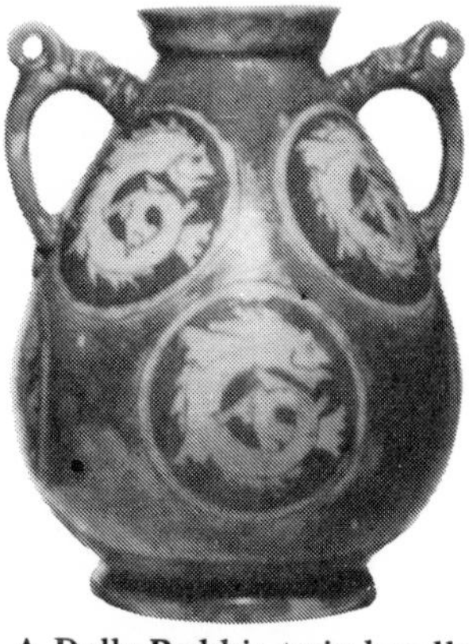

A Della Robbia twin-handled vase, decorated by Charles Collis, with eight circular medallions, each with a sea-creature whose long tail curls round on itself, 35.8cm. high.
(Christie's) £660

A Della Robbia bottle vase, designed by Charles Collis, with piped slip decoration of peaches and leaves covered in pink and turquoise glazes, 33.5cm. high.
(Christie's) £330

A Della Robbia pottery vase by Roseville Pottery, signed with Rozane Ware seal, circa 1906, 8¼in. high.
(Robt. W. Skinner Inc.) £590

A Della Robbia twin-handled vase decorated by Charles Collis, with a broad decorative frieze of stylised Tudor Roses, 31.6cm. high. (Christie's) £660

A Della Robbia wall charger, the base incised DR with a sailing ship and artist's monogram, 47.5cm. diam.
(Christie's) £378

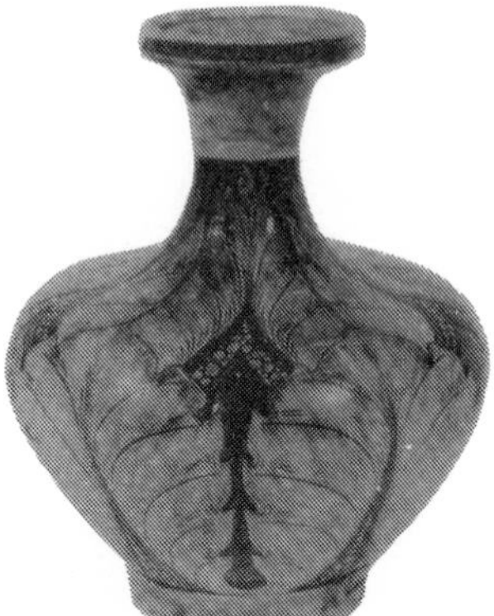

A Della Robbia pottery vase, with marks of Chas. Collis, potter and sgraffito artist and G. Russell, Paintress, circa 1903/06, 11in. high.
£180

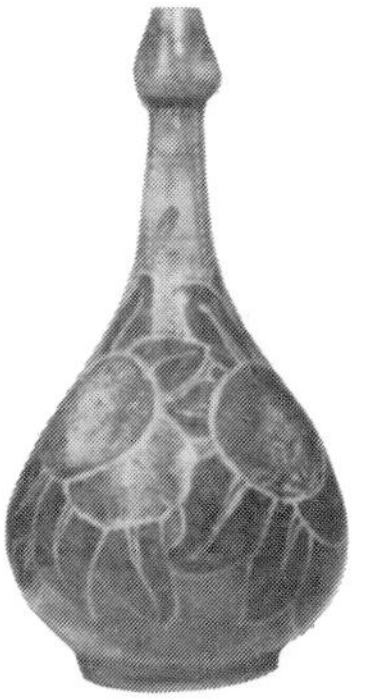

A Della Robbia vase and cover, with incised decoration of yellow tulips against a blue sky, 19.5cm. high.
(Christie's) £440

A Della Robbia jardiniere, bulbous shape with incised and slip decoration of a scrolling foliate band between foliate rim and foot borders, 25.6cm. high. (Christie's) £600

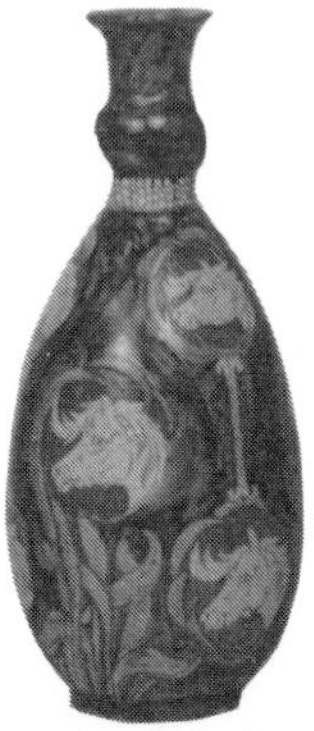

A Della Robbia vase, decorated by Liza Wilkins, the incised decoration of horses' heads within cartouches, 35.6cm. high.
(Christie's) £330

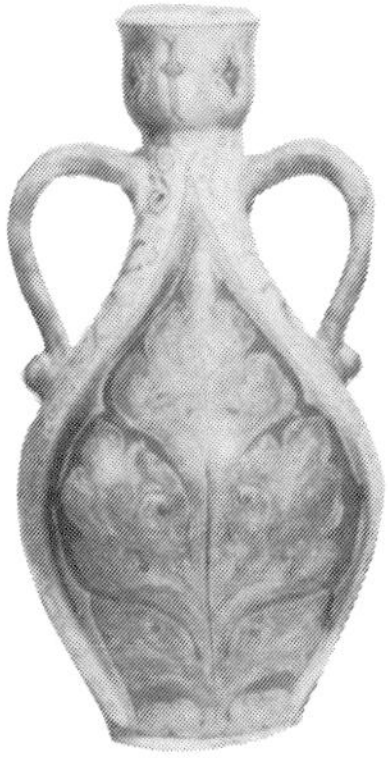

A Della Robbia two-handled vase, with incised and slip decoration of foliate designs within large cartouches and borders, 35.2cm. high.
(Christie's) £264

A Della Robbia two-handled vase, of bulbous cylindrical form with knopped neck, with incised Della Robbia mark and decorator's signature Enid, 34.8cm. high.
(Christie's) £715

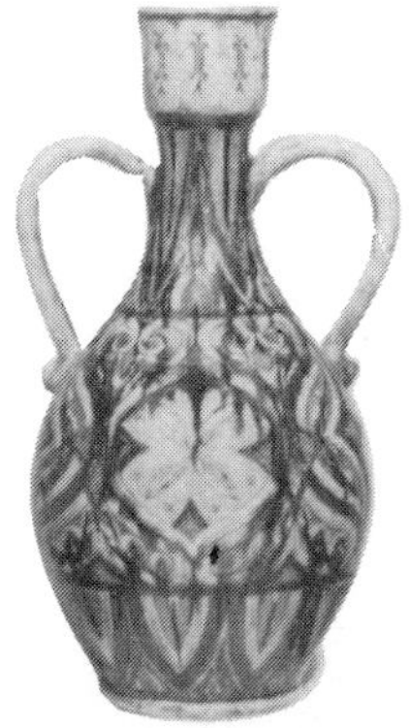

A Della Robbia two-handled vase, decorated by Annie Smith, of bulbous cylindrical form with knopped neck, dated 1895, 37.6cm. high.
(Christie's) £220

A Della Robbia vase, with incised and slip decoration of two friezes of equestrian and Ancient Greek figures, 18.4cm. high.
(Christie's) £165

A Della Robbia dish, with incised and slip decoration of a sea sprite riding a fish, covered with polychrome glaze, dated 1895, 26.2cm. diam.
(Christie's) £374

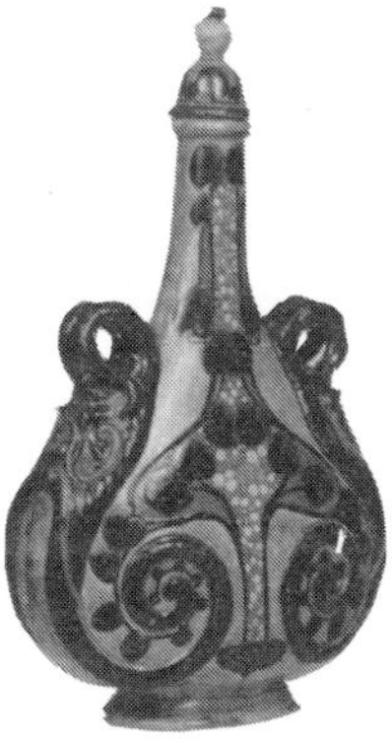

A large Della Robbia two-handled bottle-vase and cover, decoration by Ruth Bare, date 1924, 53cm. high.
(Christie's) £385

DERBY

Porcelain making in Derby commenced around the mid 18th century and has continued there ever since. During the early period, from 1750 onwards, production concentrated mainly on figures, with the result that, in contrast to most other factories of the period, comparatively few 'useful' wares were made. Emphasis from the beginning was on decoration, which was always very fine, even if some pieces of the pre–1760 period appear rather primitive and thickly potted. When more functional pieces were produced these still had decorative themes, with openwork baskets, pot pourris and frill vases featuring largely in the output. Fine tea and coffee wares were often painted with Chinese figure subjects.

William Duesbury, the London porcelain painter, became a key figure from 1756. He bought the Chelsea factory in 1770 and finally moved to Derby in 1784, where he was succeeded by his son, William II, in 1786. By the 1770s a really perfect porcelain body was being produced at Derby, and the employment of superb landscape and flower painters as decorators ensured that the finished product was of a quality second to none. In 1811 the factory was purchased by Robert Bloor, and production continued until 1848. While the quality of the body declined somewhat during this period, that of decoration remained high, and the factory continued to specialise in Imari and Japanese styles. From 1848 a new factory was opened in King Street, Derby, which continued till 1935 and specialised in copies of earlier Derby pieces. A further factory opened in 1876, called Derby

A Derby tea pot of quatrefoil outline, painted and gilt with birds and flowering plants in Chinese style, c. 1756, 17cm. high.
(Lawrence Fine Arts) £231

A Derby figure of a youth emblematic of Winter, in ermine trimmed red jacket and lemon breeches, 22.5cm.
(Phillips) £450

A pair of Derby dishes of kidney shape, painted with panels of birds in landscapes, by Richard Dodson, 25.5cm.
(Phillips) £800

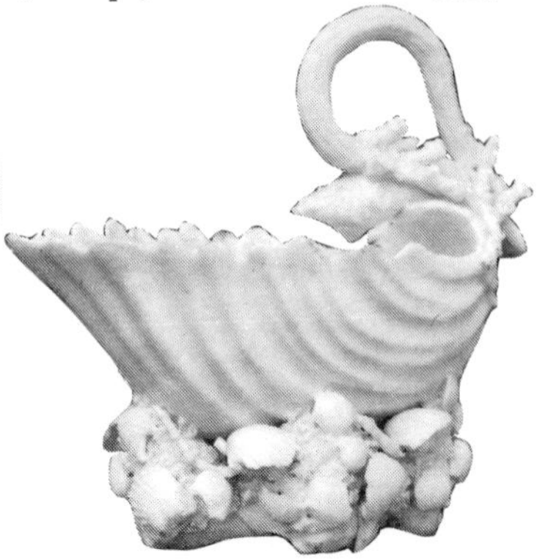

A Derby white crayfish sauceboat modelled as a fluted shell, the handle formed as a looped coral branch resting on the back of a crayfish, Andrew Planché's period, circa 1750, 15.5cm. wide.
(Christie's) £6,600

An attractive early Derby bell-shaped mug, painted with a bouquet of coloured flowers and scattered sprigs, the rim edged in brown, 11cm.
(Phillips) £850

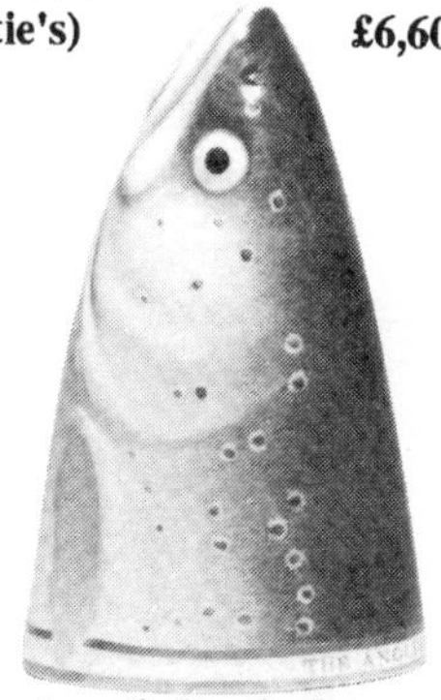

A Derby trout's head stirrup-cup naturally modelled and painted in shades of green, puce and pale-pink, the rim inscribed in gilt *THE ANGLERS DELIGHT*, circa 1825, 13.5cm. high.
(Christie's) £1,320

DERBY

Crown Porcelain Co, and was continued after 1890 by the Royal Crown Derby Co, which specialised in the use of raised gold and strong ground colours.

Many early period Derby flatware pieces have 'moons' or patches in the paste which look especially bright when held up to the light. Such 'moons' can also be found on some Chelsea and Longton Hall pieces.

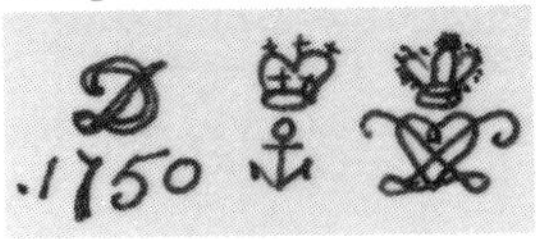

A Derby model of a stag at lodge in front of flower encrusted bocage, the white body dappled in brown, 17cm. (Phillips London) £800

A Derby vase in the form of a basket with a diaper moulded globular body applied with florettes, pierced everted rim and rope handles, 13.5cm. (Phillips) £1,200

A rare Derby chocolate pot and cover, painted in a deep blue with the Walk in the Garden pattern after Worcester, 23.5cm. (Phillips London) £2,000

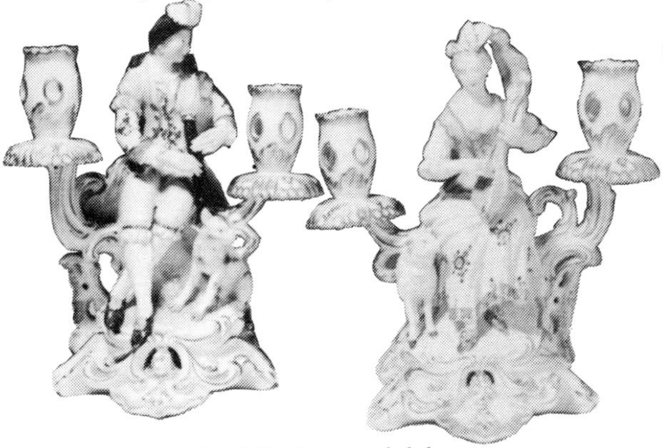

A pair of Derby candelabra figures of a shepherd seated playing the bagpipes, and a shepherdess playing the mandoline, 23cm. (Phillips London) £1,300

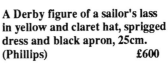

A Derby figure of a sailor's lass in yellow and claret hat, sprigged dress and black apron, 25cm. (Phillips) £600

A Derby figure group of a gallant and his companion walking with their arms entwined, he in a pink jacket, she with a lacy mob cap, 16.5cm. (Phillips) £1,300

A Derby porcelain plate, the centre painted with a castle by a lake within a blue border, inscribed *View in Wales*, 23cm. (Bearne's) £170

A Derby bocage group in the form of a seated young woman with a sheaf of corn and a sickle, late 18th century, 12.5cm. high. (Bearne's) £360

A Derby plate, painted by Harry Hancock, signed, with a profusion of summer flowers in a basket, 22cm. (Phillips London) £400

A fine set of three 18th century Derby flower vases with named views. (Worsfolds) £2,800

A Derby porcelain wine taster, circular with scalloped rim, leaf-shaped handle, circa 1770, 3.1/8in. long. (Christie's) £419

A Derby group of dancers in 18th century costume, she in floral dress and he in turquoise coat, crossed swords mark, 6½in. high. (Christie's S. Ken) £880

Two Derby figures emblematic of Europe and America, one in crown and flowing robes, the other dressed in coloured feathers and carrying a quiver of arrows, 24cm. £1,500 (Phillips)

A Derby porcelain figure representing Justice, her eyes closed, a sword in one hand and scales in the other, late 18th century, 32.2cm. high. (Bearne's) £380

One of a pair of Derby plates, the centres painted with roses, thistles, bluebells, ferns and other flowers, 22.5cm. diam. (Phillips) £550

A Derby group of a youth and girl, symbolic of Autumn, he carrying a bottle, she carrying a bunch of grapes, 20cm. (Lawrence Fine Arts) £2,530

A pair of Derby dishes after the Arita originals, of fluted shell shape decorated in blue, red, green and gold, 22cm. (Phillips) £360

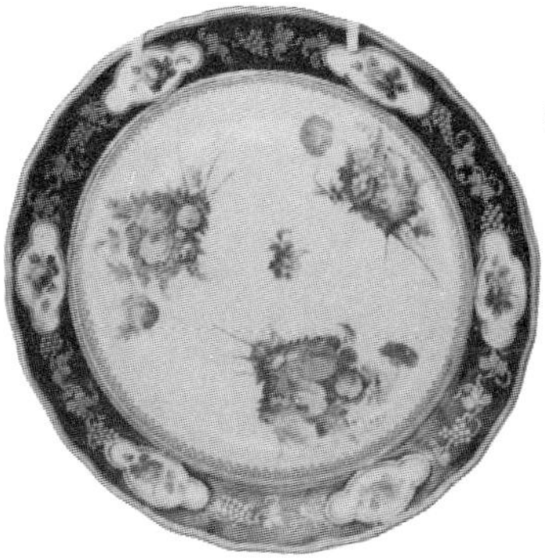

A Derby plate, probably painted by William Billingsley, with three naturalistic floral sprays and a single rose in the centre, circa 1790.
(Phillips) £1,750

Late 18th century puce marked Derby porcelain bough/crocus pot with twin ram's head handles, $5\frac{1}{4}$in. high.
(Bigwood) £4,100

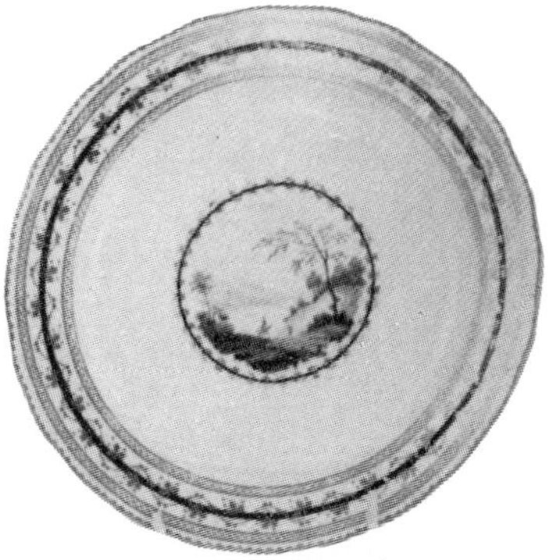

A Derby plate, painted in the centre, probably by Zachariah Boreman, with a river landscape panel within a blue circle, 1785-90.
(Phillips) £600

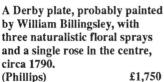

A Derby coffee can and saucer, the can painted, possibly by George Complin, with two finches perched on a still life of fruit, 7.5cm. high, 1789-95.
(Phillips) £13,000

A pair of Derby candlestick figures of seated putto in loosely draped robes and crowned with flowers, circa 1760, 7in. high.
(Christie's S. Ken) £350

A Derby figure of Apollo crowned with laurels in a green and pink cloak, circa 1765, $7\frac{1}{2}$in. high.
(Christie's S. Ken) £400

A Derby plate, painted in the centre, probably by Thomas Steel, with a still life of a vase and fruit, including peaches, grapes, cherries and blackberries, 20,7cm. diameter.
(Phillips) £500

A Derby figure of a reaper in a black hat, turquoise jacket and yellow apron with a scythe on his shoulder, circa 1760, $11\frac{1}{4}$in. high.
(Christie's S. Ken) £450

A Derby botanical plate, painted in the centre, possibly by John Brewer, with a deep border of roses, probably by William Billingsley, 22.5cm. diameter, circa 1795.
(Phillips) £2,100

A Sampson Hancock, Derby, group of Dr. Syntax chased up a tree by a bull, 17.5cm. high, red painted mark. (Phillips) £300

Pair of Derby porcelain wine coolers decorated in the Imari manner with heavy gilt handles and gilt designs, 19th century, 8in. (G. A. Key) £210

A Derby figure of a seated pug-dog, wearing a gilt collar with red rosette, 6.5cm. (Lawrence Fine Arts) £286

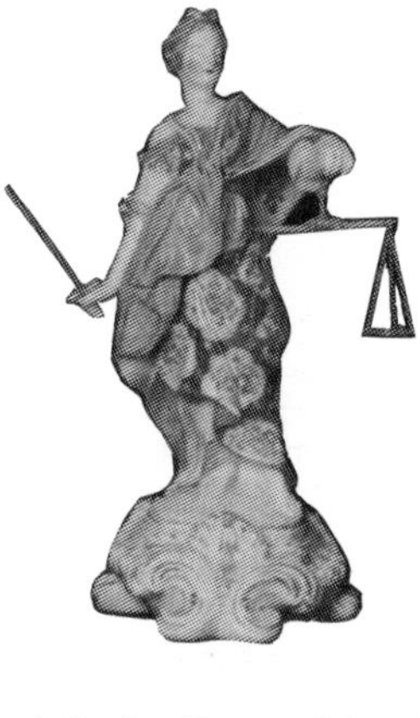

A Derby figure of Justice represented by a blind lady in richly decorated Classical robes, 32cm. (Phillips) £600

A pair of Derby Mansion House dwarfs, wearing brightly coloured striped and flowered clothes, Robt. Bloor & Co., circa 1830, 17.5 and 17cm. high. (Christie's London) £1,980

A Derby figure of Neptune standing beside a dolphin, on a high rocky base, 25cm. high. (Lawrence Fine Arts) £374

A Derby biscuit group of the two Graces adorning Pan with garlands of flowers, 31.5cm. (Phillips London) £740

A pair of Derby vases of encrusted flowers, on white and gilt square-shaped bases, 16.5cm. (Lawrence Fine Arts) £352

A Derby porcelain group 'The Dancers' after a Meissen original, late 18th century, slight restoration, 16.8cm. high (Bearne's) £800

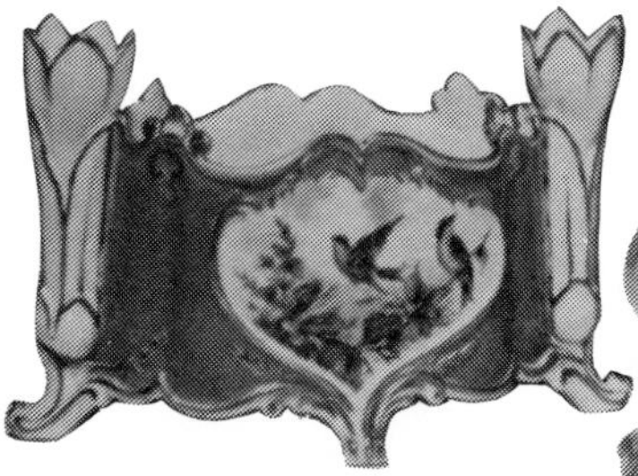

A Derby Crown porcelain small lobed jardiniere, 19cm. wide, black printed mark. (Phillips) £460

A pair of Derby groups, both of a cow with calf in front of a flowering bocage background, 16cm. high. (Phillips) £440

A Derby sauceboat modelled as a swimming duck with an orange beak and feet, and a gilt dentil rim, 10.5cm.
(Phillips) £650

A Derby figure of a young lady in elaborate brightly painted 18th century costume, crossed swords marks, circa 1825, 10in. high. (Christie's S. Ken) £143

A Bloor Derby jar with foliate handles, applied with a panel of flowers, together with a pair of similar flower encrusted vases. (Bearne's) £940

A Derby figure of a flower seller in lemon coat, turquoise sprigged breeches and pink shoes, holding a posy of flowers in one hand, 24.5cm.
(Phillips) £650

A Stevenson Hancock Derby figure of a Greenwich pensioner, the seated man in blue coat and yellow breeches, 5in. high. (Christie's S. Ken) £165

A pair of Royal Crown Derby candlesticks, each baluster stem and candle sconce set on a shaped rectangular base moulded with dolphins, 1979, 26.5cm. high. (Bearne's) £400

An early Derby figure of a flautist, on a circular base with moulded puce scrolls, 14cm. (Phillips) £620

A Derby figure of a gallant seated on a tree stump, Wm. Duesbury & Co., circa 1760, 13cm. high.
(Christie's) £715

A pair of Derby arbour musicians, he playing the bagpipes and his companion the mandolin, Wm. Duesbury & Co., circa 1775, 35.5cm. high.
(Christie's) £6,380

A Derby shepherdess in yellow-lined pink jacket, Wm. Duesbury & Co., circa 1765, 24.5cm. high. £410

A Derby figure of Shakespeare in yellow-lined purple cloak, Wm. Duesbury & Co., circa 1765, 27.5cm. high. £395

A pair of Derby pear shaped vases and covers of tapering form, Wm. Duesbury & Co., circa 1760, 18cm. high. £825

A Derby turquoise-ground fountain vase of urn shape, the handles formed as putti riding on dolphins alternating with seated putti holding garlands, Wm. Duesbury & Co., circa 1775, 42cm. high.
(Christie's) £6,050

A Derby crested tapering oviform mask jug with loop handle, Wm. Duesbury & Co., circa 1780, 23.5cm. high.
(Christie's London) £715

A pair of Derby figures of a shepherd and shepherdess, on scroll-moulded bases enriched in puce and green, Wm. Duesbury and Co., circa 1760, 26cm. and 27.5cm. high.
(Christie's) £1,430

A Derby figure of John Milton leaning on a pile of books, Wm. Duesbury & Co., circa 1765, 29cm. high.
£395

A Derby 'dry-edge' group of a goat and kid, decorated in the workshop of Wm. Duesbury, Andrew Planche's period, circa 1752, 12cm. wide. £4,620

A pair of Derby figures emblematic of Summer painted in the London studio of Wm. Duesbury, Andrew Planche's period, circa 1753, 16.5cm. high. £2,810

A Derby figure of a bagpiper, Wm. Duesbury & Co., circa 1768, 21cm. high. £380

A Derby botanical plate painted with a spirally moulded border gilt with foliage, Wm. Duesbury & Co., circa 1790, 21.5cm. diam. (Christie's London) £528

A pair of Derby turquoise-ground two-handled vases, covers and plinths, the oviform bodies painted in the manner of Richard Askew with putti at play with a dolphin, Wm. Duesbury & Co., circa 1775, 34cm. high. (Christie's) £3,300

A Derby group of two lovers and a jester after the model by J.J. Kändler, the lovers seated before white flowering bocage, Wm. Duesbury & Co., circa 1765, 29cm. high. (Christie's) £3,300

A Derby baluster coffee pot and cover, painted with scattered cornflowers between gilt line rims, Wm. Duesbury & Co., circa 1785, 24.5cm. high. (Christie's) £550

Two Derby figures of John Wilkes and General Conway, Wm. Duesbury & Co., circa 1765. (Christie's) £1,320

A Derby baluster pot pourri vase and pierced domed cover, Wm. Duesbury & Co., circa 1760, 19cm. high. £440

DERUTA

The pottery industry in Deruta, Umbria, dates from the late 15th century. At that time wares in the usual high temperature colours were produced, together with some with metallic lustre decoration. Some, too, were very distinctive in that, in order to achieve a 'near-flesh' tint, the enamel was scraped away to reveal the pinkish clay body, to which a clear lead glaze was then added.

Early 16th century Deruta lustre is brassy yellow outlined in soft blue, often showing a nacreous iridescence. Later wares have a deeper tone, sometimes approaching olive green.

Large plates predominate as a form, with tin glaze on the front only and a colourless lead glaze on the underside. Some dishes and bowls with raised decoration were made using moulds. Many of these feature a raised central boss, perhaps to fit the base of a matching ewer.

Reproductions of Deruta wares were made in the 19th century, notably by Ulysse Cantagalli in Florence. Most of these are marked with a blue cockerel.

A Deruta istoriato dish with Salome holding the head of John the Baptist before Herod, circa 1580, 34cm. diam. (Christie's London) £16,500

A Deruta bottle for A. Graminis painted with the figure of Santa Barbara, circa 1530, 40cm. high. (Christie's) £5,500

A Catalan coloured albarello painted in the workshop of Francisco Niculoso in the Deruta style, 17th century, 31cm. high. (Christie's London) £2,200

Early 17th century Central Italian circular plaque with a raised rim dated 1606, probably Deruta, 27cm. diam. (Christie's) £550

A Deruta figural salt, the bowl supported by four three footed winged caryatids on a square pedestal with four claw feet, early 17th century, 15cm. high. (Christie's London) £1,980

A Deruta Armorial dish painted in the centre with a shield with a wide band in ochre on a dark blue ground, 38cm. (Phillips) £3,100

A Deruta documentary oviform drug jar with two serpentine handles, dated 1707, 32cm. wide. (Christie's) £770

DOCCIA

The Doccia porcelain factory, which flourishes today, was established in 1735 by Carlo Ginori. He produced a hard grey porcelain which was at first inferior to the output from Germany factories of the time, the wares being heavily potted, with spouts in the form of snakes and high domed lids. Many pieces were painted in underglaze blue, their greyish tone suggesting that they were fired at somewhat excessive temperatures.

From 1757 to 1791 Lorenzo Ginori was running the factory and introduced many improved materials and shapes, and a fine white hard-paste product was now being manufactured. In the early 19th century, the body included kaolin, and some fine egg-shell pieces, often decorated in blue and gold chinoiserie, were produced.

As well as tablewares, plaques and vases were produced from the beginning, which were finely modelled, the vases often decorated with full relief figures overpainted in the full enamel palette with gilding.

Figures were made in a hard grey paste with an unevenly applied glaze which often shows fine cracks. Early examples were mostly based on the figures of the Commedia dell'Arte, and are usually set on a simple square base, painted to suggest marble.

After about 1780, many were left white and these are usually arranged round a tree on a hollow rock-like base. These show the true spirit of the Baroque.

The factory mark, from the late 18th century, comprised a six pointed star in red, blue or gold. It is sometimes in Star of David form, and *Ginori*, *Gin* or *GI* is often found impressed on wares dating from the mid 19th century onwards.

A Doccia slop bowl moulded con basso relievo istoriato with mythological figures and monuments in landscapes (foot-rim chip repaired), circa 1770, 15cm. diam. (Christie's London) £990

A Doccia teacup and saucer, circa 1765. £330

A Doccia white group of the Virgin and Child, modelled after Giovanni Battista Foggini, the mother suckling her infant, last quarter of the 18th century, 42cm. high. (Christie's London) £10,450

A Doccia armorial beaker painted in colours with quartered arms on baroque mantling with rampant lion supporters, painted in the manner associated with Klinger, 1740-45, 7.5cm. high. (Christie's London) £825

A Doccia figure of a bearded Turk wearing a long puce and yellow striped coat over a blue and gilt flowered robe, circa 1765, 14cm. high. (Christie's London) £2,420

A Doccia baluster coffee-pot and cover painted with scattered sprays of flowers, the reeded dragon's head spout and scroll handle enriched in yellow, blue and puce, circa 1760, 20cm. high. (Christie's) £770

DOUCAI

Doucai, or Tou t'sai, means literally 'contrasting colour' and refers to a decorative technique consisting of a pattern outlined in a thin, pencilled, underglaze blue, infilled with translucent, enamelled overglaze colours, principally red, yellow and green.

Examples exist from the early Ming Dynasty, and the technique seems to have been perfected in the Cheng-hua period.

Imitations and new-style wares were made under Yung Cheng and Ch'ien Lung and the 18th century saw the period of greatest output in this style.

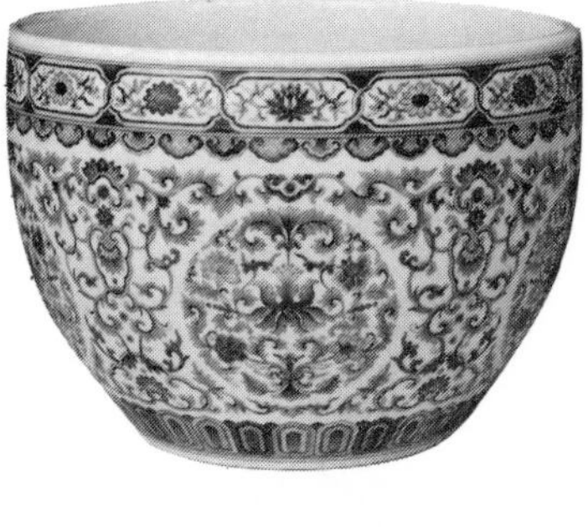

A fine large Doucai jardiniere, Qianlong seal mark, finely painted to the side with five medallions filled with lotus flowers and feathery foliate, 13in. diameter.
(Christie's) £143,229

A very fine Doucai 'dragon' saucer-dish, encircled Yongzheng six-character mark, the centre of the interior enamelled with a ferocious five-clawed dragon chasing a flaming pearl amidst clouds, $6\frac{3}{4}$in. diameter. (Christie's) £32,227

A fine Doucai and famille rose moonflask, Qianlong seal mark, elaborately painted to each circular face with the 'three abundances', pomegranate, peach and finger citrus, $12\frac{1}{4}$in. high. (Christie's) £272,135

A pair of Doucai 'Dragon' saucer-dishes, the interior with a five-clawed dragon chasing a flaming pearl amidst cloud scrolls below four stylised clouds, $5\frac{3}{4}$in. diameter.
(Christie's) £3,887

A Doucai Zhadou, the globular body painted with a lotus scroll, the flower-heads alternating with peaches, Qianlong seal mark, 7.9cm. diameter.
(Christie's) £7,150

A Doucai bowl, finely painted to the exterior with six iron-red lotus blossoms framed within elaborate scrollwork, all between a double line below the rim, $5\frac{3}{4}$in. diameter.
(Christie's) £3,265

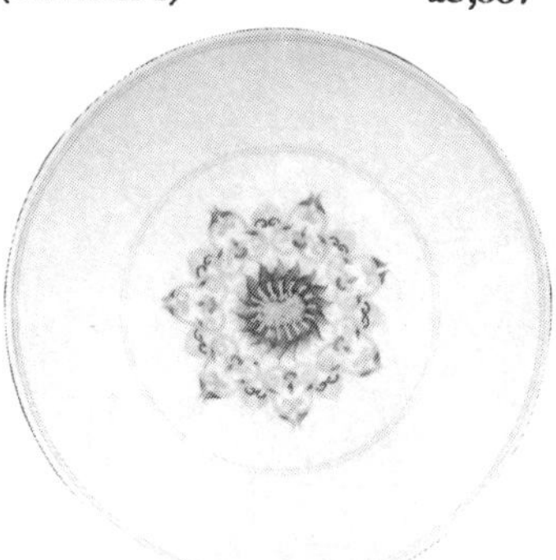

A fine Doucai dish, the interior painted with a double-centred lotus flower-head encircled by stylised ruyi-head scrolls and leaves below double blue lines, $8\frac{1}{4}$in. diameter.
(Christie's) £13,216

A pair of Doucai saucer-dishes, encircled Kangxi six-character marks, the central medallion painted with a crane in flight reserved on a shou character, $8\frac{5}{8}$in. diameter.
(Christie's) £8,952

DOULTON

The Doulton story began in 1815, when Henry's father John, known as the 'best thrower of pint pots in London' set up a pottery business in partnership with a widow called Jones and a journeyman called Watts. The Watts Doulton part of the association continued until the former's retiral in 1853, by which time the premises had moved to Lambeth High Street, where earthenware bottles, chimney pots, garden ornaments and tiles were produced.

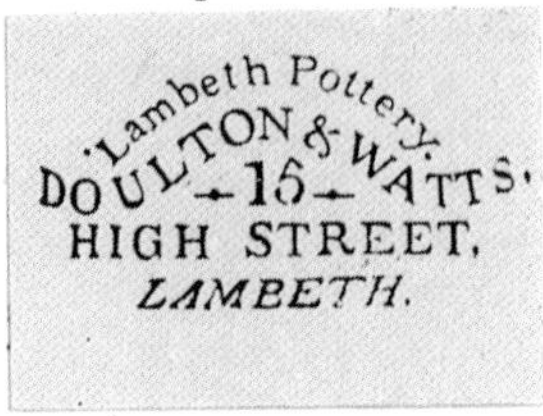

In 1835 John's second son Henry joined the company. He responded to the calls to improve urban sanitation by commencing the manufacture of sewage and water pipes, and at one time the Doulton works were producing these at the rate of 10 miles a week and exporting them all over the world.

With a solid financial base established, Henry decided he could afford to branch out and indulge some of his other interests. In the late 1850's his father had already been approached by John Sparkes, head of the newly established Lambeth School of Arts, who had requested that some of his students should try potting. It was Henry who finally responded to this request. He set up a pottery studio in a corner of the works, and it is worth noting that George Tinworth and the Barlows, Arthur, Florence and Hannah, were among the first intake.

Henry had the wisdom to show the results at the various international exhibitions which were taking place in that period,

A Royal Doulton face mask 'Jester' HN1630, 28.5cm. high, 1937. £160

Bone china teapot with raised paste gilding and exotic birds painted by J. Birbeck, 5½in. high, circa 1910. £250

A pair of Doulton Lambeth tiles painted by Margaret Armstrong, in the pre-Raphaelite style, painted in colours, each in original frame, 7 x 18½in. (Christie's S. Ken) £528

Bone china vase featuring Pan playing his pipes, in Sung glazes by Charles Noke, 7in. high, circa 1925. £650

A Doulton Lambeth circular pottery plaque, painted in colours with a portrait of young man in antique dress, 13½in. diameter. (Christie's S. Ken) £198

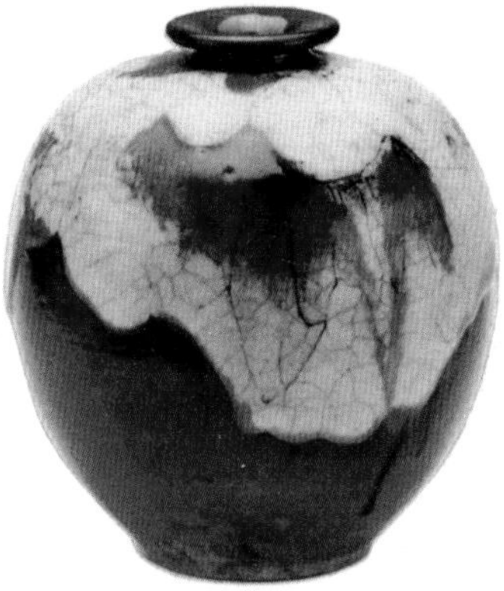

A fine Royal Doulton 'Chang' vase by Harry Nixon, Charles Noke and Fred Allen, 22.5cm., painted mark in black. (Bearne's) £2,050

and they were so enthusiastically received that by 1880 the number employed by the studio had risen to 200. Within the next twenty years it was to double again.

By this time Henry had also acquired an earthenware factory in Burslem, which he renamed Doulton and Co. Here, he began to make bone china in 1885, again creating a studio for artists and potters on the premises.

Experimentation and constant development were the keynotes for both establishments and they attracted terrific resources of talent. Charles J Noke, for example, joined the company in 1889 and finally became Artistic Director at Burslem. He experimented with Copenhagen and Sèvres type wares and in recreating oriental techniques. The results of the latter were the renowned Flambé, Sung, Chinese jade and Chang pottery. Under Noke, too, the company embarked on one of its most successful lines of all, figure models, the first of which were exhibited at Chicago in 1893.

A continuing supply of such talent ensured the survival of the Lambeth studio until 1956, while at Burslem activity continues unabated to this day.

A Royal Doulton Chang bowl by Noke, decorated with green, red, yellow, white and blue glazes on a blue ground, 7in. diameter. (Spencer's) £560

Doulton Burslem Royles Patent self pouring teapot, with pewter lid, circa 1900. **£130**

A large Royal Doulton Sung vase by Arthur Eaton, decorated with dragons amongst clouds, 13in. high, circa 1930. £800

Royal Doulton faience vase by John H. McLennan, decorated with panels representing Earth and Water, 13½in. high. £230

A Doulton cabinet plate painted by Leslie Johnson, signed, with a naked maiden seated beside a woodland pool, 22.5cm., date code for 1901. (Phillips London) £460

Doulton Burslem Morrisian Ware tobacco jar and cover decorated with a band of dancing girls, 5½in. high. £90

DOULTON CHARACTER JUGS

Charles Noke was the inspiration behind the immensely popular Doulton range of character jugs, the first of which, John Barleycorn Old Lad, was produced in the 1930s. A huge variety were made, featuring figures from folk lore and personalities past and present. Some continued in production for years. Others were quickly withdrawn, perhaps, as in the case of Churchill, because the subject didn't like them or, as in the case of Clark Gable, because it was claimed they infringed copyright. In consequence, these are now exceedingly rare, and are correspondingly valuable. Slight variations on a standard type also make an enormous difference to the value of a piece. A hatted version of Sir Francis Drake will fetch less than £100, whereas the hatless version is worth over ten times more.

Harry Fenton was one of the foremost designers of character jugs, and variations on his 'Arry and 'Arriet costermongers (when he has a blue collar and white buttons and she has a blue collar and maroon hat) will now command thousands of pounds. One useful factor for collectors is that each jug bears the back stamp of the company and is numbered according to Doulton's own system.

'Churchill' (White), D6170, designed by C. Noke, issued 1940, withdrawn 1941. £5,000

'Mad Hatter', D6598, designed by M. Henk, issued 1965, withdrawn 1983. £45

'Gladiator', D6550, designed by M. Henk, issued 1961, withdrawn 1967. £270

'Drake' (hatless), a Royal Doulton character jug, large, D6115, designed by H. Fenton, introduced 1940, withdrawn 1941. (Louis Taylor) £1,800

'Mephistopheles', D5757, designed by H. Fenton, issued 1937, withdrawn 1948. £900

'Clown' (Red Haired), D5610, designed by H. Fenton, issued 1937, withdrawn 1942. £1,250

Mae West D6688, designed by C Davidson, issued 1983, withdrawn 1985. £45

Vicar of Bray D5615, designed by C Noke and H Fenton, issued 1936, withdrawn 1960. £100

Pearly Boy (Blue), designed by H Fenton, issued 1947. £2,250

Churchill (Natural) D6170, Two handled Loving Cup, very rare, designed by C Noke, issued 1940, withdrawn 1941. £16,500

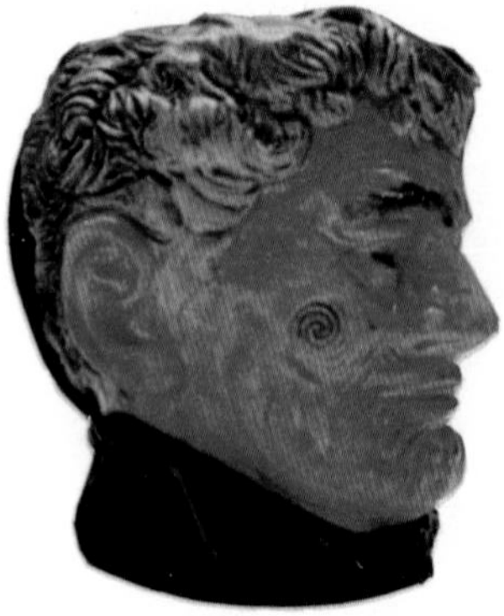

Maori, designer unknown, issued c.1939. £7,500

Clark Gable D6709, designed by S Taylor, issued 1984. £2,200

Touchstone D5613, designed by C Noke, issued 1936, withdrawn 1960. £90

'The McCallum', a large Kingsware character jug made for D & J McCallum Whisky Distillers, circa 1930. £1,450

Captain Hook D6597, designed by M Henk & D Biggs, issued 1965, withdrawn 1971. £260

William Grant character jug, specially commissioned by William Grant & Sons Ltd, limited edition of 500, 1986. £400

Old King Cole (Yellow Crown) D6036, designed by H Fenton, issued 1939, withdrawn 1940. £800

'Smuts', D6198, designed by H Fenton, issued 1946, withdrawn 1948. £680

Ugly Duchess D6599, designed by M Henk, issued 1965, withdrawn 1973. £230

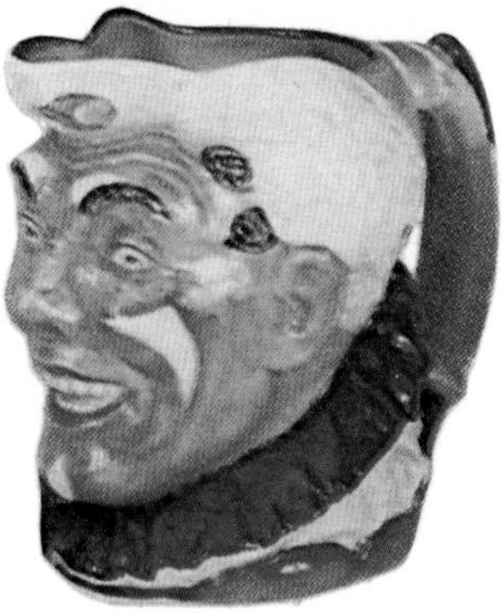

Clown D6322, (White Haired), designed by H Fenton, issued 1951, withdrawn 1955. £550

Jarge D6288, designed by H Fenton, issued 1950, withdrawn 1960. £145

Simple Simon D6374, designed by G Blower, issued 1953, withdrawn 1960. £260

John Barleycorn D5327, designed by C Noke, issued 1934, withdrawn 1960. £70

Pearly Girl (Blue), a very rare version of 'Arriet, designed by H Fenton, issued 1947. £4,000

Dick Whittington D6375, designed by G Blower, issued 1953, withdrawn 1960. £160

Uncle Tom Cobbleigh D6337, designed by M Henk, issued 1952, withdrawn 1960. £170

Granny (Toothless version) D5521, designed by H Fenton & M Henk, issued 1935. £450

'Ard of 'Earing D6588, designed by D Biggs, issued 1964, withdrawn 1967. £450

Mikado D6501, designed by M Henk, issued 1959, withdrawn 1969. £210

Samuel Johnson D6289, designed by H Fenton, issued 1950, withdrawn 1960. £160

Lord Nelson D6336, designed by G Blower, issued 1952, withdrawn 1969. £160

Punch and Judy Man D6590, designed by D Biggs, issued 1964, withdrawn 1969. £260

Jockey D6625, designed by D Biggs, issued 1971, withdrawn 1975. £200

DOULTON FIGURES

The first Doulton figures were made by George Tinworth, one of the original group of art potters who came to the company via the Lambeth School of Art. His output was small, however, and it was not until Charles Noke joined the firm in 1889 that figure making really became big business. Noke was inspired by the figures produced by Derby, Bow, Meissen and also, nearer home, by the Staffordshire figure making industry. Initially, the colours used tended to be rather dull, and the figures did not sell well, so their production was suspended until 1912, when a new range, including the famous 'Bedtime/Darling' by Charles Vyse, was introduced. (This was originally entitled Bedtime, but was rechristened after Queen Mary, seeing it while on a visit to the factory, exclaimed 'What a darling!')

The new figures benefited from brighter colours, and a talented team of modellers now set to work. These included Leslie Harradine, Harry Tittensor and later Peggy Harper.

More than 200 Doulton figures are still in production today, and even they can fetch surprisingly high prices.

'Lady of the Georgian Period', HN41, designed by E. W. Light, introduced 1914, withdrawn 1938, 10.25in. high. (Louis Taylor) £650

A Royal Doulton group entitled 'The Perfect Pair', H.N.581, withdrawn 1938. (Bearne's) £250

'The Farmer's Boy', HN2520G, 9.25in. high. (Louis Taylor) £460

A Royal Doulton porcelain figure, entitled 'Suzette', H.N. 1696, withdrawn 1949 (Bearne's) £135

A Royal Doulton porcelain figure entitled 'Carpet Vendor', H.N. 76. (Bearne's) £800

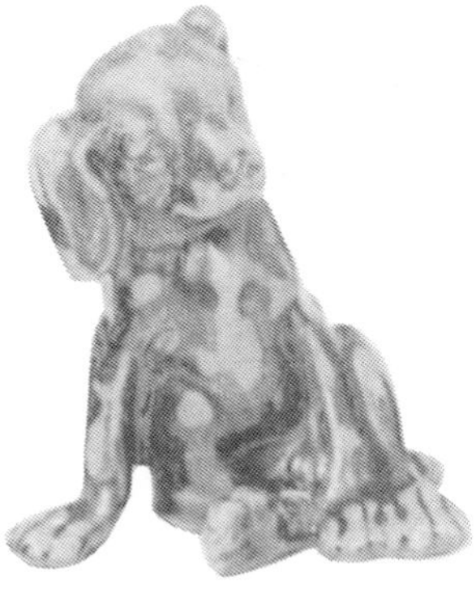

'Puppy Sitting', a Royal Doulton model of a puppy with one ear cocked, 10.4cm. high. (Phillips) £360

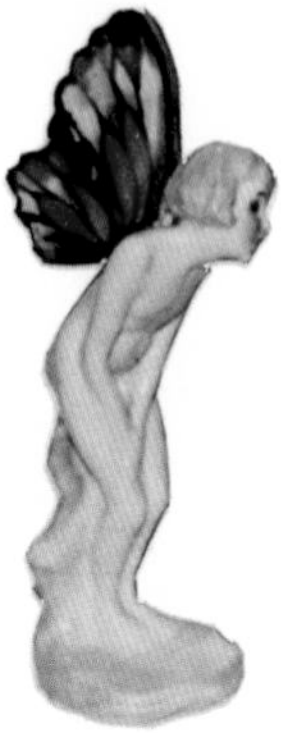

Fairy, (Style One) HN1324, designed by L Harradine, issued 1929, withdrawn 1938, 6½in. high. £250

Abdullah HN1410, designed by L Harradine, issued 1930, withdrawn 1938, 5¾in. high. £420

Myfanwy Jones HN39, designed by E W Light, issued 1914, withdrawn 1938, 12in. high. £1,000

Leda and the Swan HN2826, designed by R Jefferson, issued 1983-in a limited edition of 300, 9¾in. high. £950

Parson's Daughter HN564, designed by H Tittensor, issued 1923, withdrawn 1949, colour variation, 9½in high. £130

Rhythm HN1903, designed by L Harradine, issued 1939, withdrawn 1949, 6¾in. high. £300

Ermine Muff HN54, designed by C J Noke, issued 1916, withdrawn 1938, 8½in. high. £450

Sweet Anne HN1453, designed by L Harradine, issued 1931, withdrawn 1949, colour variation, 7in. high. £100

Hinged Parasol HN1578, designed by L Harradine, issued 1933, withdrawn 1949, 6½in. high. £250

One of the Forty (Style thirteen) HN665, designed by H Tittensor, issued 1924, withdrawn 1938, colour variation, 7¾in. high. £480

Sunshine Girl HN1344, designed by L Harradine, issued 1929, withdrawn 1938, 5in. high. £850

Phyllis HN1420, designed by L Harradine, issued 1930, withdrawn 1949, 9in. high. £200

Colonel Fairfax HN2903, designed by W K Harper, issued 1982, withdrawn 1986, 11½in. high. £145

Love Letter HN2149, designed by M Davies, issued 1958, withdrawn 1976, 5½in. high. £165

Bather (Style two) HN1227, designed by L Harradine, issued 1927, withdrawn 1938, colour variation, 7½in. high. £300

Young Miss Nightingale HN2010, designed by M Davies, issued 1948, withdrawn 1953, 9¼in. high. £350

Sweet and Twenty (Style one) HN1298, designed by L Harradine, issued 1928, withdrawn 1969, 5¾in. high. £120

Pied Piper HN1215, designed by L Harradine, issued 1926, withdrawn 1938, 8¼in. high. £400

'The Lady Jester', style two, HN1284, designed by L. Harradine, introduced 1928, withdrawn 1938, 4.25in. high. (Louis Taylor) £660

'Gladys', HN1740, designed by L. Harradine, introduced 1935, withdrawn 1949, 5in. high. (Louis Taylor) £320

A Royal Doulton figure entitled 'Kate Hardcastle', H.N.1719, withdrawn 1949. (Bearne's) £230

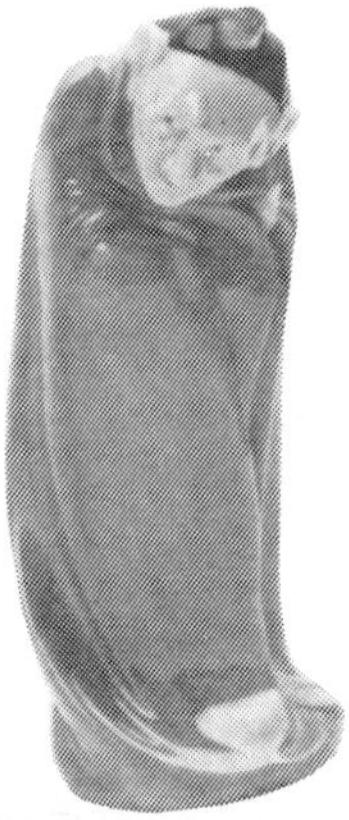

'Spook', a Royal Doulton porcelain figure designed by H. Tittensor H.N.50 No.12, 7in. high. (Christie's) £682

'A Yeoman of the Guard' HN688, a Royal Doulton porcelain figure, printed and painted marks, 6in. high. (Christie's S. Ken) £400

'The Bather', a Royal Doulton figure from a model by John Broad, of a nude maiden with flowers in her hair, 33.5cm. high. (Christie's) £1,320

A Royal Doulton porcelain figure of 'Mr W. S. Penley as Charlie's Aunt', 17.5cm. high. (Henry Spencer) £280

A Royal Doulton group entitled 'St George', H.N.2051. (Bearne's) £130

A Royal Doulton figure entitled 'Fortune Teller', H.N.2159, withdrawn 1967. (Bearne's) £130

'Boy with Turban', HN1210, designed by L. Harradine, introduced 1926, withdrawn 1938, 3.75in. high. (Louis Taylor) £300

A Royal Doulton figure of an English Setter carrying a pheasant in its mouth, HN2529, 30cm. wide. (Spencer's) £130

A Royal Doulton figure entitled 'Prudence', H.N.1883, withdrawn 1949. (Bearne's) £270

'Coquette', no number, designed by Wm. White, introduced 1913, withdrawn 1938, 9.25in. high. (Louis Taylor) £950

A Royal Doulton porcelain bust of H.M. Queen Elizabeth II designed by Peggy Davies, 4in. high. (Christie's) £275

A Royal Doulton figure entitled 'Carpet Seller', H.N.1464. (Bearne's) £85

A Royal Doulton figure entitled 'The Balloon Seller', H.N.583, withdrawn 1949. (Bearne's) £90

A Royal Doulton brown and white model of a standing bulldog, H.N.1045. (Bearne's) £310

A large Royal Doulton figure entitled 'Mantilla', H.N.2712, withdrawn 1977. (Bearne's) £150

DOULTON FLAMBÉ

The name describes the streaky, flame like effect of the deep blood red glaze which was produced by mixing copper oxide and other minerals and allowing certain amounts of oxygen to be admitted to the kiln during firing. The technique was first discovered by Bernard Moore, a chemist and innovator who worked in conjunction with Doulton at the turn of the century. After two years' experimentation the first examples of Flambé were shown at the St Louis Exhibition of 1904 and it had a huge appeal. Although it is expensive to make, Flambé is still being produced.

The Sung glaze was developed by Charles Noke, and it is remarkable for the mottled and veined effect produced by high temperature firing. The first examples were exhibited at the British Industry Fair at the Crystal Palace in 1920 and were animal and figure models. All Sung pieces are signed by Charles Noke.

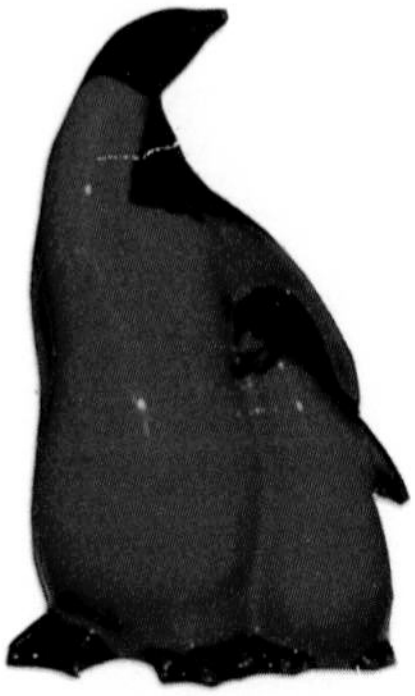

Pair of Royal Doulton flambe penguins designed by C.J. Noke, circa 1929, 6in. high. £160

'Mallard', a Royal Doulton flambe animal figure designed by C.J. Noke, introduced 1920, withdrawn 1961, 4in. high. £190

Royal Doulton flambe elephant with trunk down, circa 1930, 12in. high. £550

Royal Doulton tobacco jar with elephant finial decorated in Sung glazes, circa 1936, 6in. high. £325

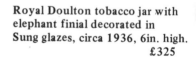

Doulton earthenware vase with view of Kendal beneath flambe glazes, signed Fred Moore, circa 1940, 11in. high. £450

Royal Doulton flambe figure of monkeys embracing, model 486, 5½in. high. £140

DOULTON JUGS

Apart from the Toby jugs produced at Doulton, Charles Noke also introduced in 1930 a range of limited edition jugs and loving cups, all extravagantly embossed and decorated in a certain theme.

These were based on the slip cast relief jugs of the Victorian era, and the first to be produced was the Master of Foxhounds Presentation Jug . This was followed by others in maximum editions of 1,000 and each was accompanied by a certificate of authenticity.

Some were subsequently produced for special occasions, such as the Coronation of Queen Elizabeth II and her Silver Jubilee in 1977.

'Master of Foxhounds' presentation jug designed by C.J. Noke, issued 1930 in a limited edition of 500, 13in. high. £350

Sir Francis Drake jug designed by C.J. Noke and H. Fenton, issued in 1933 in a limited edition of 500, 10½in. high. £350

'The Wandering Minstrel', a limited edition loving cup by Royal Doulton, designed by C.J. Noke and H. Fenton, issued 1934 in a limited edition of 600. £260

Royal Doulton George Washington Bicentenary jug designed by C. J. Noke and H. Fenton in a limited edition of 1,000, issued 1932, 10¾in. high, with colour variation on handle. £4,500

'Charles Dickens' jug designed by C.J. Noke and H. Fenton, issued in 1936 in a limited edition of 1,000, 10½in. high. £350

Queen Elizabeth II Coronation loving cup designed by C.J. Noke and H. Fenton, issued in 1953 in a limited edition of 1,000, 10½in. high. £350

DOULTON KINGSWARE

The ware known as Kingsware was introduced at Burslem in 1899 and was used to make pottery flasks for whisky, usually in editions of 1,000, for spirit producers such as Dewars and the Hudson Bay Company. Some upmarket versions even had silver fittings. The process involved applying colour slips in shades of muted greens, yellows and reddish browns to the interior of plaster moulds in which a design was impressed. When another brown slip was poured in the colours blended to give a deep, soft effect to the embossed design.

The glaze was usually treacly brown in colour, but another paler yellow was sometimes also used, and this much rarer effect is known as Kingsware Yellow glaze.

The principal designer of the embossed patterns was Arthur Bailey, who worked at Burslem between 1912 and 1932. They mostly consisted of drinking related motifs, and featured such popular characters as Falstaff and the Sporting Squire.

The Leather Bottle, a Royal Doulton Kingsware flask, circa 1918, 6¼in. high, 6in. long. £300

Micawber, a Royal Doulton Kingsware whisky flask made for Dewar's Scotch Whisky, 7in. high, issued 1909. £130

A Royal Doulton Kingsware jardiniere decorated with seagulls, circa 1910, 5½in. high, 9in. wide. £140

The Alchemist, a Royal Doulton Kingsware clock, 7½in. high, circa 1913. £400

Royal Doulton Kingsware single-handled jug depicting a golfer and his caddie. £280

Huntsman, a Royal Doulton Kingsware Toby jug, 7½in. high. £250

Peace flagon, a Kingsware flask with brown border, made for Dewar's, No.181, 7½in. high, circa 1919. £250

DOULTON SERIESWARE

It was Charles Noke who was responsible for the simple yet ingenious idea behind Seriesware. He realised that: standard pottery shapes could be embellished with popular images and sold as novelty art wares to people who could not afford the artist's individual creations.

The designs were transfer printed on to pieces made of earthenware and bone china and then hand coloured. The first series was called the Isthmian Games and appeared in 1889, with a new series following almost every year for the next half century. The design could be found on everything from toothbrush holders to plates, and obviously formed a rich scope for collectables.

In the 1970s Seriesware was revived, when special plates were issued for special events and anniversaries.

Oliver Twist jug designed by C.J. Noke, depicting 'Fagin and Bumble', D5617. £65

A Royal Doulton Cecil Aldin Series ware jardiniere, the decoration from the 'Old English Scenes', 18cm. high. £170

The Gleaners, Series ware sandwich tray. £38

Willow Pattern Series jar and cover, 6½in. high, circa 1912. £75

A large Royal Doulton pottery vase, decorated with an extensive fox hunting scene between bands of flowers, 57.5cm. (Bearne's) £170

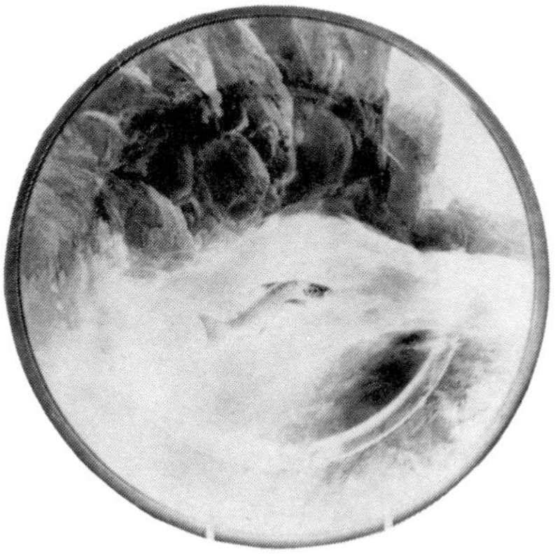

'Short Headed Salmon', a Royal Doulton rack plate, signed by J. Birbeck, 9½in. diameter, circa 1913. £120

A Jacobean jug 'Ye Old Belle' depicting a serving wench and two cavaliers, 6½in. high. £65

DOULTON STONEWARE

Stoneware was the first material produced by John Doulton in 1815, and the company concentrated at first on mass produced items such as bottles and jugs.

When Henry Doulton joined the firm he diversified into architectural stoneware and set his protegés from the Lambeth School of Art to work. They included such famous names as the Barlows, George Tinworth and Eliza Simmance. At first their designs were fairly simple, but they subsequently embarked on pâte-sur-pâte work, whereby a raised outline was built up by delicate brush work. This led to more sophisticated designs and particularly the stylised carved foliage which presaged the Art Nouveau style.

After 1914 production was limited, and it ceased entirely when the factory closed in 1956.

Salt glazed stoneware Chine ware vase decorated by L. Mear, 9½in. high, circa 1902. £120

'Hunting', a frog and mouse group with the frogs riding mice over a water jump, circa 1884, 4½in. high. £1,000

Doulton Lambeth stoneware jardinière, ovoid and embossed with classical profile heads and flowers within geometric borders, 8in. high.
(Hobbs & Chambers) £110

A Doulton Lambeth stoneware jug commemorating Victoria's Diamond Jubilee, inscribed *'She brought her people lasting good'*, 24cm.
(Phillips) £190

A Coronation mug commemorating the accession of Edward VII and Queen Alexandra, circa 1902, 7½in. high. £100

'Play Goers' by George Tinworth, the group glazed pale brown with a blue and brown shaped base, 1886, 5¼in. high. £1,250

A Doulton Lambeth stoneware 'Harvest Jug' applied with slip cast toping scenes, 6¼in. high. £30

Salt glazed stoneware jug depicting Lord Nelson by Doulton and Watts, Lambeth, circa 1830. £280

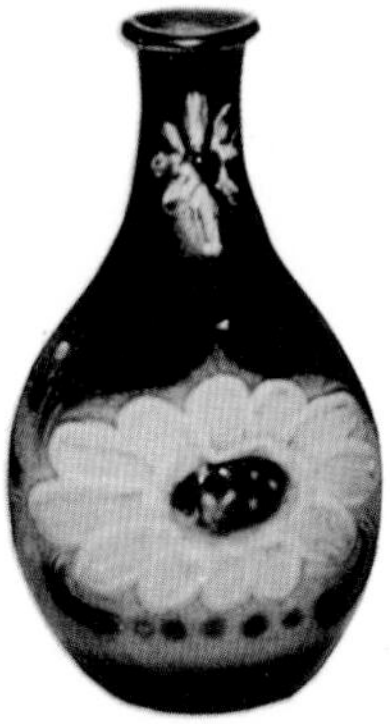

Doulton Lambeth stoneware vase decorated with applied slip flower and leaf designs, circa 1891, 4½in. high. £25

Salt glazed stoneware vase decorated with bird and stylized foliage and flowers by Harry Simeon and Winnie Bowstead, 15½in. high, circa 1922. £350

Pair of Doulton ewers decorated with applied slip flower leaf and bead designs, circa 1891, 7¼in. high. £75

Stoneware Dragon vase by Mark Marshall, circa 1885, 10¾in. high. £850

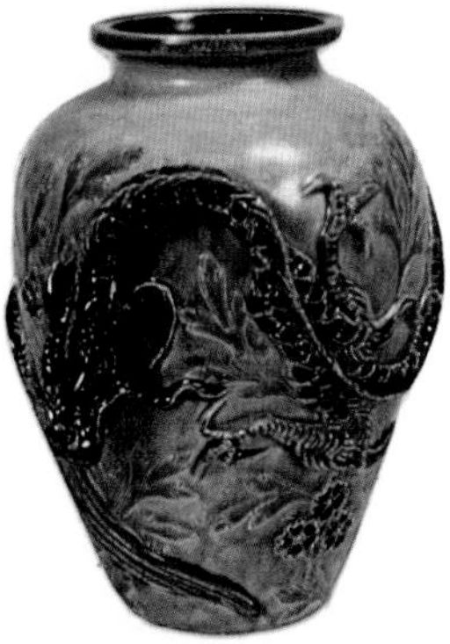

Salt glazed stoneware vase designed by Mary Ann Thompson and Jessie Bowditch, circa 1880, 9in. high. £650

A small tile panel in law relief by George Tinworth, 4in. by 5¾in. £130

Art Nouveau style umbrella stand decorated with stylized foliage, circa 1895, 24¾in. high. £450

A Doulton Lambeth biscuit barrel, by Hannah Barlow, with plated cover incised with lions, 15.6cm. high, dated 1881. (Phillips) £520

A Doulton Lambeth stoneware silver-rimmed lemonade set comprising a jug and a pair of beakers. (GA Property Services) £350

A Royal Doulton inkpot modelled as a baby in brown dress, inscribed *'Bill • Votes For Women'*, 9cm. (Phillips) £300

A good Hannah Barlow large Doulton Lambeth stoneware vase, decorated with a wide band incised with cattle, 18¼in. high. (David Lay) £400

A pair of Doulton stoneware bottle vases decorated by Eliza Simmance with foliage and a scrolling beaded design, 23cm. (Bearne's) £320

A Doulton Lambeth stoneware jug, impressed factory mark and incised monograms for Florence Barlow and Mary Aitken, 8in. high. (Peter Wilson) £300

A Royal Doulton stoneware jar and cover, decorated by Eliza Simmance with pate-sur-pate geranium-like flowers on a textured ground, 29.5cm. high. (Bearne's) £460

Large Royal Doulton pottery jardiniere by Hannah B. Barlow, with a middle band of Shetland ponies and cattle, approx. 12in. (G. A. Key) £400

A Royal Doulton stoneware jug moulded with portrait of Field Marshal Haig and swags, inscribed *'Peace with Victory'*, 18.5cm. (Phillips) £190

A Doulton Lambeth stoneware jug, the central medallion with a crown above the entwined letters G and M, and below the date 1893, 17cm. (Phillips) £160

A Doulton Lambeth Slaters china stoneware teapot and cover slip trailed in white and incised with blossoming apple boughs. (Spencer's) £75

A rare Doulton Lambeth stoneware jug, the bulbous body with three reserve panels depicting golfing scenes, 22cm. tall. (Phillips) £550

A large Doulton Lambeth stoneware vase by Hannah Barlow and Frank Butler, 21in. high. (Christie's) £880

A pair of Doulton Lambeth stoneware vases by Hannah Barlow, each incised with a broad band depicting stags and deer in landscapes, 19in. high. (Spencer's) £750

A Doulton stoneware jug, decorated by Hannah Barlow with cattle in an open landscape, impressed and incised marks, dated 1881, 24.4cm. high. (Bearne's) £480

A Doulton Lambeth stoneware figure attributed to George Tinworth modelled as a mouse playing a tuba, 3¼in. high. (Christie's) £440

A Doulton Lambeth stoneware three-handled loving cup by Mary Aitken, with an inscription commemorating the success of six Liberal candidates in West Riding, 16cm., 1881. (Phillips) £360

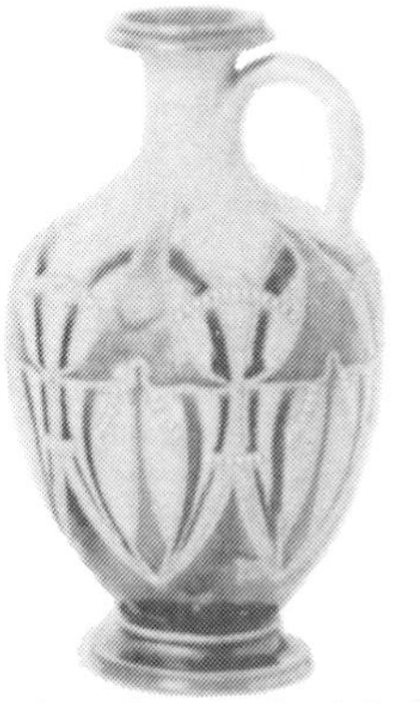

A Doulton Lambeth globular jug, by Eliza Simmance, incised with spear shaped motifs, 25.5cm. high, date shield for 1910. (Phillips) £200

DOULTON TOBY JUGS

Toby jugs have a long and distinguished history, and they were made by Doulton from the time the firm was established in 1815. Early examples were in the brown saltglazed style which had characterised them for centuries, but in 1925 coloured jugs were added to the range by Harry Simeon. Charles Noke at once recognised their potential, improved the colours, and they came to be one of the firm's most popular lines.

'George Robey', Toby jug by Royal Doulton, issued circa 1925, 10½in. high. £3,500

Doultonville Toby jug of 'Miss Studious', D6722, issued 1985, withdrawn 1988. £18

'Charlie Chaplin', Toby jug by Royal Doulton, issued circa 1918, 11in. high. £4,000

Cliff Cornell, blue suit, issued in 1956 in a limited edition of 500, 9¼in. high. £350

Small seated Toby jug of 'Sam Weller', D6265, designed by H. Fenton, issued 1948, withdrawn 1960, 4½in. high. £85

Royal Doulton Toby jug 'Squire', D6319, designed by H. Fenton, issued 1950, withdrawn 1969, 6in. high. £90

Royal Doulton Toby jug, 'Honest Measure', D6108, designed by H. Fenton, issued 1939, 4½in. high. £30

Royal Doulton Toby jug, 'Sherlock Holmes', D6661, designed by R. Tabbenor, issued 1981, 8¾in. high. £45

DRESDEN

There can be few people today who are not familiar with the term 'Dresden china', often used as a comparison when trying to convey an idea of delicacy and fragility. Try looking up 'Dresden' in any textbook, however, and it is mysteriously absent, for Dresden, in fact is simply an alternative for the more correct term of Meissen.

The misnomer dates from the 18th century itself, when 'Dresden' was enough to describe this first hard paste European factory, and when Derby was established in 1756, it became known as 'The New Dresden'.

Matters were further complicated by the fact that in the 19th century small workshops and decorators set up in the city of Dresden itself, making and decorating inferior copies of early Meissen. Often the marks were also copied.

Principal decorators in the mid-late 19th century working in Dresden were Donath, Hamann, Klemm, A Lamm and F Hirsch, all of whom decorated in the Meissen style. Many of their pieces are marked *Dresden*, with a crown or star.

A pair of Dresden salts, each shaped oval, held by a reclining male and female figure respectively, 19th century, 6½in. (Lawrence Fine Arts) £572

A Dresden group of a huntsman in 18th century costume restraining two leaping hounds, 15in. high. (Christie's S. Ken) £605

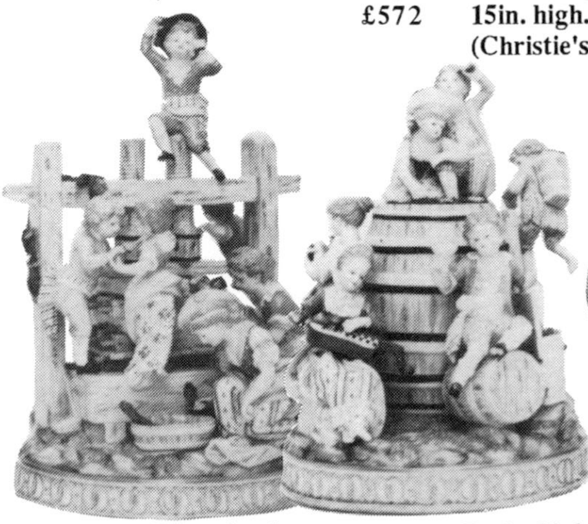

A pair of Dresden large groups of children playing round a wine press and a barrel, 30cm. and 34cm. (Lawrence Fine Arts) £5,060

Early 20th century Dresden porcelain vase and cover, white ground decorated with romantic figures and sprigs of flowers, 14in. high. (G. A. Key) £210

A massive pair of Dresden yellow ground oviform vases and covers, reserved and painted with exotic birds, blue AR marks, circa 1900, 64cm. high. (Christie's London) £3,300

A Dresden seated figure of Cupid pressing hearts in a press, on marbled circular base with gilt borders, 18.5cm. (Lawrence Fine Arts) £528

A pair of Dresden China table lamps, 19th century in the form of rose encrusted urns supported by three putti. (Lots Road Galleries) £740

Just about every European country had its indigenous pottery and later porcelain industries, even if it consisted mainly of minor factories aping the production of the greats such as Meissen and Sèvres. Even where no confident attribution can be made 'Continental' pieces often have a vitality and quality which make them worthy of inclusion in thoroughly respectable ceramic collections.

A mid 18th century Brussels faience boar's head tureen, cover and stand, the stand 40cm. long. £5,400

A Continental figure of a protesting suffragette holding a flag inscribed *'I want a vote'*, the base also inscribed *'Give me a vote and see what I'll do'*, 12.5cm.
(Phillips) £580

A Wiener Kunstkeramische two handled vase of irregular form painted in pastel shades with a loosely defined fairy-tale scene, 19½in. high.
(Christie's S. Ken) £165

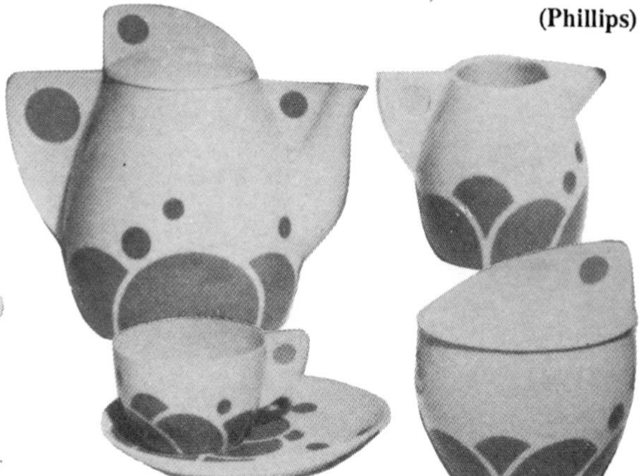

A School of Koloman Moser seven-piece porcelain tea service, designed by Jutta Sika, teapot 16.7cm. high. £1,945

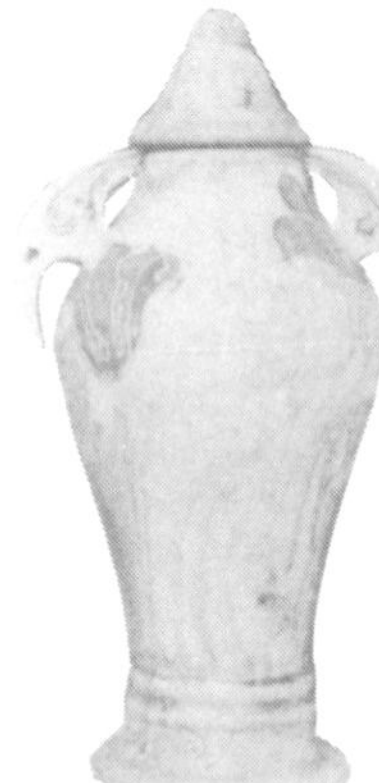

A Dutch 'Distel' pottery vase and cover, decorated with slip-trailed tulips in colours, 33cm. high.
(Phillips) £460

An Austrian plate, the centre finely painted with Venus, a musician and Cupid in attendance, 23cm.
(Bearne's) £840

Pair of 19th century Continental glazed and decorated stoneware figures, 'Policeman' and 'Woman', 12in. and 11in. tall. (J. M. Welch & Son) £90

An Austrian porcelain circular plaque, painted with a woman and child reluctantly leaving house and family, 28.7cm. diam.
(Bearne's) £400

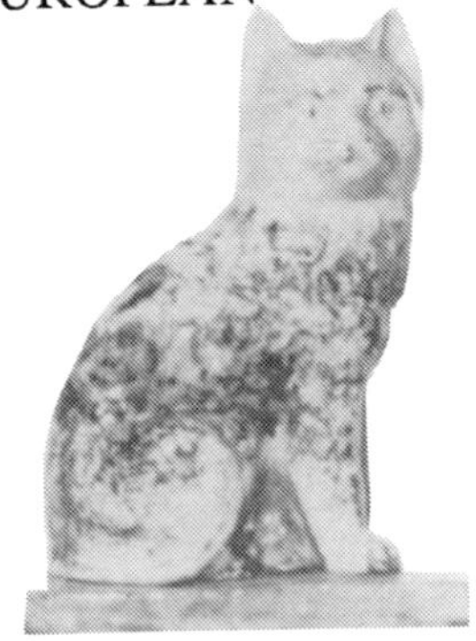

A Continental creamware figure of a cat on a rectangular green base, its fur sponged in black and yellow, 5½in. high. (Christie's S. Ken) £154

One of a pair of Nyon coffee cans and saucers painted in colours with sprays and garlands of flowers, fish marks. (Phillips) £600

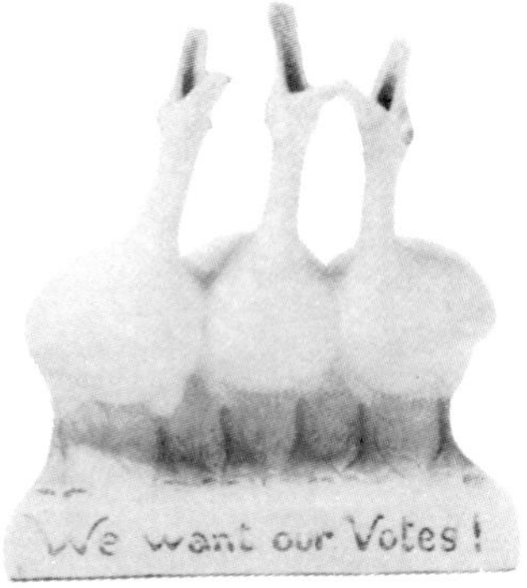

A Continental matchholder modelled as three geese squawking *'We want our votes'*, 12cm. (Phillips) £200

One of an attractive pair of Austrian ewers, both painted on each side with panels of maidens in garden landscapes, 34.5cm. (Phillips London) Two £1,600

A pair of Spanish blue and white oviform drug-jars named for *Flo. Ros. alec.* and *Fol. U inca.* on diagonal ribbons flanked by a double-headed eagle, a bust portrait, a winged angel's head and with stylised shrubs, early 18th century, 27cm. high. (Christie's) £1,540

A large Dutch Art Nouveau jardiniere and stand, decorated in batik-style in colours with stylised flowers, 99cm. high, signed 'Corona Holland'. (Phillips) £520

A Copenhagen oblong octagonal tray painted with two garlands of flowers tied with a purple bow flanked by two oval medallions painted in sepia, circa 1780, 42.5cm. diameter. (Christie's) £1,650

A fine pair of Pirkenhammer porcelain vases and covers, each decorated in gold with birds on boughs of blossom, 43.5cm. (Bearne's) £740

A pair of Helena Wolfsohn porcelain vases, each baluster body painted in the Meissen manner with harbour scenes, 36.8cm., 19th century. (Bearne's) $2,310

One of two Böttger two-handled moulded chinoiserie beakers and trembleuse saucers, one beaker and saucer moulded with rose branches, the other with fruiting vine, incised dots, circa 1720.
(Christie's) (Two) £8,250

An Elton pottery twin-spouted teapot and cover, of globular shape, one spout having human mask end, 18.5cm. high.
(Phillips) £300

A Böttger miniature pagoda figure seated with his left knee raised, holding a teabowl and saucer, his head, hands and pantaloons gilded and his robe enriched with gilt flowerheads, circa 1715, 5.5cm. high.
(Christie's) £4,180

A Fornasetti earthenware tea caddy, printed in colours with an array of kitchen implements, $8\frac{1}{2}$in. high.
(Christie's S. Ken) £82

Four Pesaro graduated albarelli boldly painted with yellow, orange, blue and manganese flowers and scrolling foliage, between concentric blue line rims, late 18th century, 12cm. to 17cm. high. (Christie's) £2,420

An Austrian terracotta twin-handled vase in Egyptianesque style, flanked by dragon handles, gilded and cold-painted in colours, impressed *Wsss*, $10\frac{1}{2}$in. high. (Christie's S. Ken) £22

A Katshutte Thuringia ceramic figure of a dancing girl, standing in profile with arms held aloft, printed factory mark (restored), $12\frac{1}{4}$in. high.
(Christie's S. Ken) £308

A Gustavsberg ceramic footed cylindrical vase, covered in a mottled green glaze and embossed in white metal with fish amongst bubbles, $5\frac{3}{4}$in. high.
(Christie's S. Ken) £165

A pair of Czechoslovakian polychrome painted wall masks, each modelled as a young girl wearing a jester's cap, with an owl perched on the left shoulder, $6\frac{3}{4}$in. high.
(Christie's) £352

**A Boch Frères pottery vase decorated by Catteau, moulded in low relief with a band of deer between bands of stylised foliage, $12^{1}/_{4}$in. high.
(Christie's) £198**

**A Baltic faience rectangular tray painted in puce monochrome with ships at sail by a harbour with a town in the distance, circa 1790, the tray 89cm. by 61cm.
(Christie's) £19,800**

**An Elton pottery jug, with compressed base and tall cylindrical neck, sparrow beak spout and sinuous handle, 28.5cm. high.
(Phillips) £300**

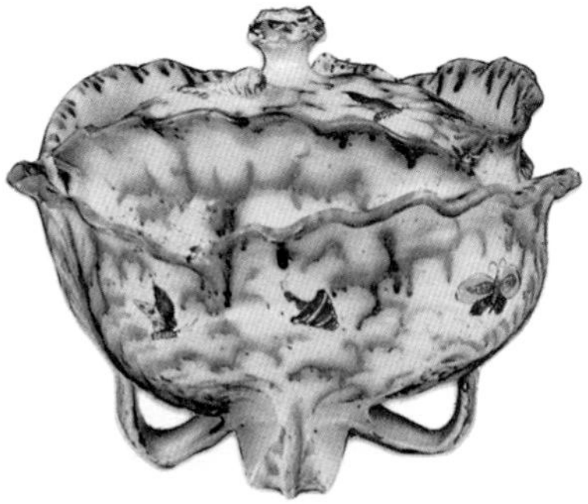

A Brussels cabbage-tureen and cover, the naturally modelled overlapping leaves with waved everted edges and raised midribs, circa 1770, 30.5cm. wide. (Christie's) £2,750

**A Portuguese faience blue and white tile-picture in the form of a gallant painted in bright-blue wearing a peruke, and long frock-coat with wide buttoned cuffs, late 17th/early 18th century, 173.5cm. high.
(Christie's) £9,350**

**A Faenza blue and white crespina, the centre with a circular medallion painted with a man shooting at duck on a pond within a border of buildings in mountainous wooded landscape vignettes, circa 1650, 30.5cm. diameter.
(Christie's) £990**

**A Boch Frères pottery vase, moulded in low relief with a band of stylised pelicans in flight, between borders of clouds, enamelled in yellow, blue and turquoise, $13^{1}/_{2}$in. high.
(Christie's) £242**

**A Buen Retiro two-handled seau crenelé painted with two continuous garlands of flowers hung from blue bows, the shell-shaped handles enriched with blue and gilt lines, circa 1765.
(Christie's) £3,630**

**'Allegro Pasto', a Manna polychrome painted ceramic group modelled as a young girl in gingham dress, $11^{1}/_{4}$in. high.
(Christie's S. Ken) £308**

Teplitz pottery vase, Czechoslovakia, early 20th century, swollen form widening towards base, signed *Stillmacher Teplitz* and stamped, 8¼in. high. (Robt. W. Skinner Inc.) £245

An unusual Continental porcelain wall plate, the image based on a design by Alphonse Mucha for Sarah Bernhardt as La Samaritaine, 50cm. diam. (Phillips London) £520

Continental porcelain figure of a Bolognese Hunde, late 19th century, moulded in a shaggy manner, unmarked, 8¾in. high. (Skinner Inc) £460

Pair of large good quality 19th century Continental porcelain figures of a lady and gallant, on circular naturalistic bases each bearing a pseudo Meissen mark, 18in. high.
(Lawrences) £640

A Continental tile picture painted in manganese and yellow with a two-handled urn on a pedestal, circa 1780, 37 x 25cm. (Christie's) £308

A large pair of Turn porcelain figures of young women, each wearing a long dress, gathered at the waist, slight chipping, 62cm. high. (Bearne's) £1,350

A Spanish lustre spirit barrel moulded with two circular ribs, 18th/19th century, 23cm. high. (Christie's) £550

A large Suprematist dish, after a design by K. Malevich, circa 1926, with underglaze mark of the Imperial Porcelain Factory, 11¼in. diam. (Christie's) £11,000

A Reval rococo baluster vase with rib and feathered moulding, encrusted with three branches, insects and flowers, circa 1780, 25.5cm. high. (Christie's) £4,400

FAENZA

It was the Italian city of Faenza, situated between Bologna and Rimini, that was to give its name to the tin glazed earthenware which came to be known as faience. From the late 14th century it had been associated with maiolica manufacture and from the mid 15th century developed a very distinctive style. Apart from the usual drug pots, fine baluster vases decorated with heraldic devices, contemporary figures or gothic foliage, were produced.

Later some large pieces in full relief were attempted. By the 16th century several Faenza painters were engaged in painting in the style now associated with Urbino, and referred to as istoriato. Far Eastern influence was also beginning to filter through and about this time a style called bianchi di Faenza, with a minimum of decoration and a white tin glaze was developed.

In 1693 Count Annibale Ferniani bought a Faenza pottery where tiles and tablewares were made, which continued almost to this day.

Full signatures of painters or potters appear only rarely on 15th century Faenza ware, but in the 16th century these become more common.

A Faenza or Tuscan vase, circa 1500-20, 32.5cm. high. (Phillips) £1,040

A Faenza crespina with fluted rim, and on a low foot, painted in the centre with a standing figure of a warrior, 30cm., late 16th century. (Phillips) £1,600

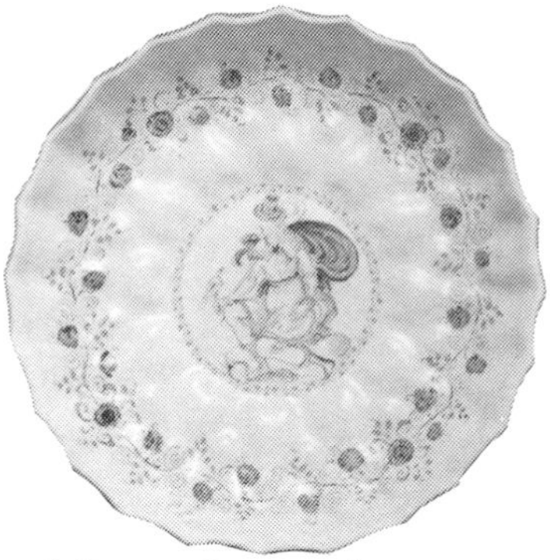

A Faenza documentary compendiaro crespina painted in the workshop of Maestro Virgiliotto Calamelli, with a falconer, circa 1565, 30cm. diam. (Christie's) £4,400

A Faenza wet drug jar of ovoid shape with an angled strap handle and straight spout, 22.5cm. high. £380

A Faenza circular tondino of Cardinal's hat form, circa 1525, 25cm. diam. £14,850

A Faenza drug vase of compressed baluster form, the contents a. api, circa 1550, 21.5cm. high. £430

A Faenza shaped dish, Cn mark to base, Ferniani's factory, circa 1770, 32cm. diam. (Christie's) £385

FAMILLE ROSE

Famille rose is a style of decoration based on Chinese porcelain painting introduced during the Yongzheng period around 1730. A deep rose pink enamel derived from gold features strongly in the palette and by mixing this with white a variety of pinks and deep rose colours were now obtainable. It was much in demand for tableware produced for the nouveau riche of the Industrial Revolution.

A pair of famille rose bowls, Qianlong seal marks and of the period, enamelled on the exterior with butterflies, ripe citrus and bamboo, $4^{1}/_{4}$in. diameter.
(Christie's) **£21,484**

A famille rose yellow-ground Tibetan-style vase, iron red Jiaqing seal mark, painted to the bulbous body with stylised lotus and scrolling foliage dividing the eight Buddhist emblems, $10^{7}/_{8}$in. high. (Christie's) **£10,742**

A pair of famille rose flattened double-gourd vases, blue enamel Le Xian Tang Zhi hall marks, 19th century, similarly painted to both faces with the wufu (five bats), in flight amidst clouds, 7in. high.
(Christie's) **£3,581**

A famille rose yellow-ground rose bowl, four-character Qianlong mark, painted around the exterior with four circular pink panels and ruby scrollwork each enclosing a character forming a phrase furi changming (the eternal light of Buddhism), $4^{1}/_{2}$in. diameter.
(Christie's) **£1,719**

A pair of famille rose oviform vases, Hongxian Yuzhi marks, painted in mirror image with an elegant gentleman leaning against a green bamboo fence, 11in. high.
(Christie's) **£3,151**

A fine and rare pair of famille rose square pear-shaped vases, iron-red Qianlong seal marks, painted on the exterior in various shades of pastel enamels, $11^{1}/_{2}$in. high.
(Christie's) **£68,034**

A fine famille rose bowl, iron-red Shen de Tang Zhi mark, enamelled with a continuous scene of Immortals and scholars variously engaged in dispute or relaxation, $6^{3}/_{4}$in. diameter.
(Christie's) **£10,026**

A pair of 19th century famille rose candlestick figures, standing in richly decorated robes and with peacock-feather mantelet, holding a lotus-petal vase, $11^{1}/_{2}$in. high.
(Tennants) **£2,800**

An unusual relief-decorated famille rose teapot and cover of pear shape, brightly enamelled on either side with a butterfly, $4\frac{1}{2}$in. high, Yongzheng/early Qianlong. (Tennants) £550

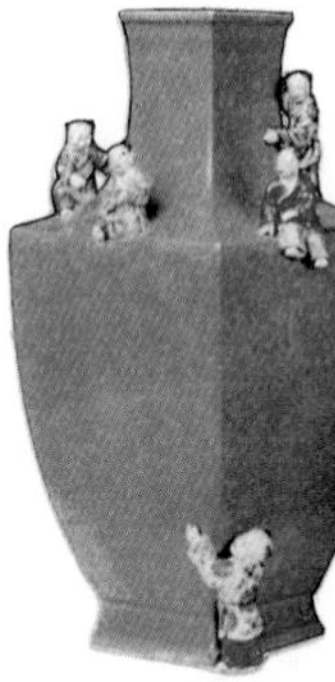

A famille rose baluster vase, iron-red Qianlong seal mark, the turquoise body enamelled in white with scrolling lotus, applied round the shoulders and base with six Chinese boys, $12\frac{1}{4}$in. high. (Christie's) £2,721

One of a rare pair of 19th century Canton famille rose lotus-petal jardinières and stands, each piece moulded on the exterior with overlapping petals detailed in bright enamels, $6\frac{3}{4}$in. high. (Tennants) (Two) £2,400

A very fine famille rose charger, Yongzheng, brilliantly enamelled in all the colours of the early Qing palette at the centre with two black and white birds perched on a long curling branch of leafy blossoming tree peony, $20\frac{3}{4}$in. diameter. (Christie's) £10,742

A rare famille rose watch stand and cover, the body with a circular aperture surrounded by insects and butterflies amongst moulded scrolling floral sprays, $8\frac{1}{4}$in. high, Qianlong. (Bonhams) £900

A fine famille rose rubyback eggshell deep plate, Yongzheng, the centre with a multi-robed elegant seated lady with two playing children flanking her, $8\frac{1}{4}$in. diameter. (Christie's) £10,742

A famille rose seated Buddha, Qianlong/Jiaqing, seated on a detachable double-lotus base, wearing a polychrome tiara above a serene expression, $11\frac{1}{4}$in. high. (Christie's) £5,013

One of a pair of brilliant famille rose lotus-flower teapots and covers, each moulded with petals and applied with flowering stems, $4\frac{3}{4}$in. high, Qianlong. (Tennants) (Two) £1,500

A large famille rose bottle vase, enamelled with nine peaches issuing from gnarled, flowering branches, Qianlong seal mark, 19th century, 47cm. high. (Christie's) £6,600

One of a pair of famille rose bowls, Yung Cheng marks and of the period, 7in. diam. (Phillips) £7,200

A pair of famille rose 18th century octagonal plates with the 'pseudo' 'tobacco pattern', 22in. diam. (Phillips) £200

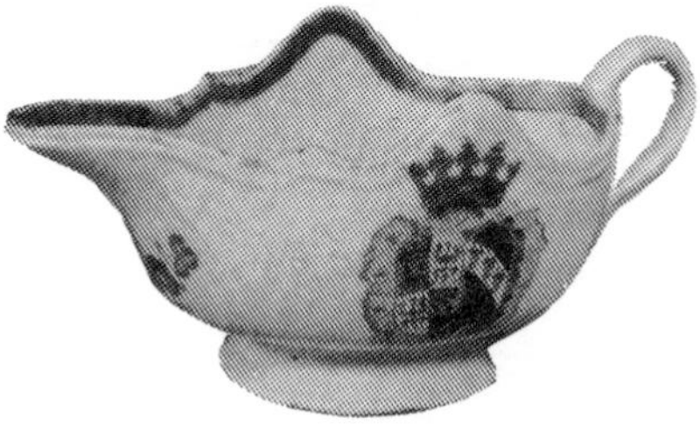

A Chinese famille rose sauce-boat, Qianlong, circa 1760, 8¼in. across handle. (Woolley & Wallis) £400

A famille rose eggshell dish, delicately enamelled at the centre with a seated lady painting a leaf at a table, 7¾in. diam. (Christie's) £3,028

A rare famille rose gilt decorated blue-ground vase, with canted corners and a knotted sash painted in pink enamel, 12in. high. (Christie's) £14,347

A Chinese famille rose plate, the centre painted with birds and flowers within a border of scrolling foliage, 23cm., Qianlong. (Bearne's) £230

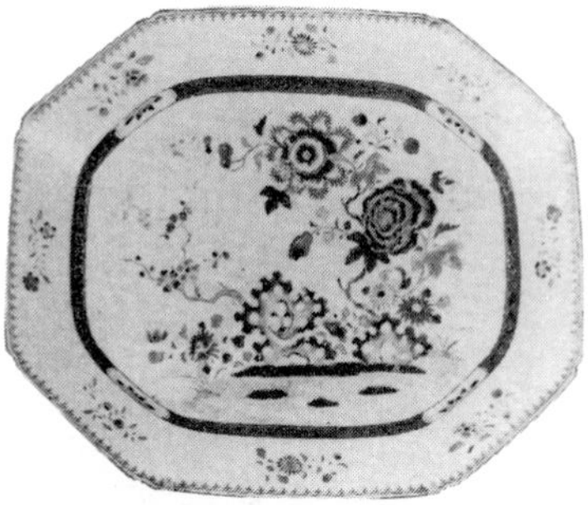

A large famille rose dish, painted with flowering peony, and other flowers amongst rockwork on a grassy bank, 18in., Qianlong. (Bonhams) £900

A famille rose bottle vase with globular body, ribbed shoulder and long waisted neck, the rim with a band of ruyi-heads, 15in. high. (Christie's) £3,826

A Bayreuth faience Hausmalerei famille rose baluster teapot and cover, painted in the manner of Adam Friedrich von Loewenfinck, in the delft dore style with indianische Blumen issuing from rocks, circa 1740, 18.5cm. wide. (Christie's London) £7,150

One of a pair of famille rose octagonal jardinieres, 10½in. wide. (Reeds Rains) £2,550

A famille rose yellow-ground teapot and cover, decorated at either side with an elaborate lotus scroll, the curling tendrils terminating in peony, 5½in. wide. (Christie's) £3,985

A famille rose punch bowl, enamelled with panels of courtiers within key and floral pattern borders, 15½in. diam. (Greenslade & Co.) £1,000

A famille rose oviform vase with a scene of the eight Daoist Immortals below pine trees. 28cm. high. (Christie's) £5,673

A pair of famille rose bough pots, of waisted octagonal form, decorated with groups of figures in panels, 19th century, 23cm. high.(Lawrence Fine Arts) £2,200

A Chinese famille rose jug, the neck with cartouches of landscapes in puce, having gilt dragon handle, Qianlong, 18th century, 9¾in. wide. (Woolley & Wallis) £540

A famille rose plate centrally painted with a lady in a chair breast feeding her child, Qianlong, 8¾in. diam. (Christie's S. Ken) £550

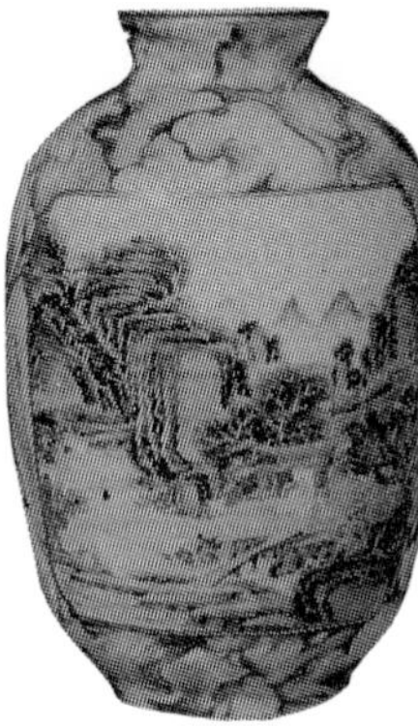

A rare famille rose marbled-ground oviform vase, 15.5cm. high. (Christie's) £7,419

An 18th century Chinese famille rose plate, 43cm. diam. (David Lay) £250

FAMILLE VERTE

Famille verte is a style of Chinese painting with prominent use of bright green and shades of yellow and aubergine purple together with line drawings in black. It was introduced during the Kangxi period at the end of the 17th century.

A famille verte 'month' cup finely painted to one side with a flowering peach tree, inscribed to the reverse with a couplet, 2$\frac{5}{8}$in. diameter.
(Christie's) £16,325

A famille verte 'month' cup, painted to one side with two clumps of flowering narcissus before rockwork and a single long stemmed red rose, representing the eleventh month, 2$\frac{5}{8}$in. diameter.
(Christie's) £13,993

A finely painted famille verte rouleau vase, painted in bright enamels with a group of armoured warriors holding their weapons in a garden landscape with pine trees issuing from rockwork, 18in. high.
(Christie's) £15,548

A pair of black-ground famille verte dishes, each painted to the rounded exterior with a composite floral scroll including lotus, clematis and peony blooms, 5$\frac{7}{8}$in. diameter.
(Christie's) £13,993

A rare black-ground famille verte baluster vase, enamelled around the body with a composite floral scroll with small foliate elements, all on a dense black ground, 8in. high.
(Christie's) £13,993

A famille verte 'month' cup, encircled Kangxi six-character mark and of the period, decorated to the exterior with blossoming tree peony issuing from a grassy patch among pierced rockwork, 2$\frac{1}{2}$in. diameter.
(Christie's) £10,742

A pair of famille verte and gilt 'duck' plates, the centre of each with a pair of swimming mandarin ducks on a lotus pond below another pair in flight, 8$\frac{5}{8}$in. diameter.
(Christie's) £2,332

A famille verte 'month' cup, encircled Kangxi six-character mark and of the period, painted to one side with two clumps of flowering narcissus before rockwork and a single long stem with a red rose, 2$\frac{5}{8}$in. diameter.
(Christie's) £4,297

A famille verte oviform jar, Kangxi, 19.5cm. high. £900

Chinese famille verte porcelain figure of Wenshu, 19th century, riding a lion, 15in. high. (Skinner Inc) £870

A famille verte oval incense basket and cover with high strap handle, Kangxi, 12.5cm. wide. £2,000

A famille verte pear-shaped vase, reverse painted with a long-tailed bird on rockwork, Kangxi, 19.5cm. high. £1,100

A famille verte fish bowl, the exterior painted with a scene of warriors proceeding to battle, 25in. diam. £3,800

Chinese famille verte porcelain rouleau vase, 19th century, large rectangular reserves of a battle scene, 24in. high. (Skinner Inc.) £594

A famille verte saucer dish painted with rockwork issuing flowering peony and camellia, Kangxi, 27cm. diam. £750

A pair of late 19th century famille verte baluster vases and covers, each painted with a horseman and attendants, 19½in. high. (Tennants) £850

One of a pair of famille verte saucer dishes, Chenghua six-character marks within a double circle, early 18th century, 39cm. diam. £8,800

FOLEY

The Foley pottery was established in Fenton, Staffordshire in the mid 19th century and was operated from 1903 by E Brain & Co. Its porcelain is noted for the simplicity of its design. That said, in the 1930's work was commissioned from leading contemporary artists such as Graham Sutherland and Laura Knight and is marked with the maker's name and the signature of the artist and decorator. The Foley marks include the brand name *Peacock Pottery*, with a peacock in a rectangle and Staffordshire knot.

A Foley Pastello twin handled vase of double gourd form printed and painted with rustic scene of house nestling in wooded landscape, 7in. high. (Christie's S. Ken) £440

A Foley Intarsio small oviform jardinière printed and painted in colours with a band of carp amongst waves, 4½in. high. (Christie's S. Ken) £220

A Foley Intarsio single handled jug, painted and enamelled in colours with two heralds blowing trumpets, printed factory mark, 11in. high. (Christie's S. Ken) £385

A Foley Intarsio circular wall plate, designed by Frederick Rhead, the centre decorated in colours with two classical maidens, 36.8cm. diam. (Phillips) £460

A Foley jardiniere and stand, each decorated in alternate green and yellow ground spiralling panels patterned with flowers and foliage, 42in. high. (Christie's) £1,760

A Foley Urbato ware vase, of globular form, decorated in white slip trailing with pink flowers and green leaves, 22.3cm. high. (Phillips) £170

A Foley Intarsio ceramic clock, painted in blue, turquoise, green, brown and yellow enamels, with Art Nouveau maidens representing day and night, 29cm. high. (Christie's) £825

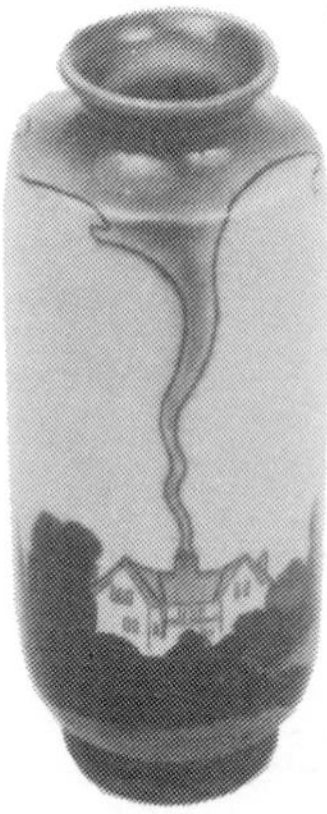

A Foley pastello solifleur, decorated with a cottage in a landscape in shades of blue, purple and yellow, 5in. high. (Christie's S. Ken) £132

A Foley Intarsio baluster vase printed and painted in colours with kingfishers perched on branches above a band of carp, 9in. high.
(Christie's S. Ken) £280

A Foley Intarsio teapot and cover modelled as Kruger wearing green jacket, blue waistcoat and brown trousers, $4^1/_2$in. high.
(Christie's S. Ken) £450

A Foley Intarsio cylindrical biscuit barrel with electroplate mount and cover, printed and painted in colours with panels of drinking scenes and flowers, $7^1/_4$in. high.
(Christie's S. Ken) £750

A Foley Intarsio three-handled vase and cover, printed and painted in typical colours with panels depicting the Queen of Hearts, 8in. high.
(Christie's S. Ken) £500

A Foley Intarsio single-handled spherical vase, printed and painted in colours with a band of buttercups and flowerheads on the shoulders, 6in. high.
(Christie's S. Ken) £190

A Foley Intarsio miniature grandfather clock printed and painted in colours with Father Time and bearing the inscription *Time and Tide wait for no man*, 10in. high.
(Christie's S. Ken) £500

A Foley Intarsio vase, printed and painted in colours with panels of seagulls in fiords, above a band of entrelac foliate motifs, $8^1/_2$in. high.
(Christie's S. Ken) £120

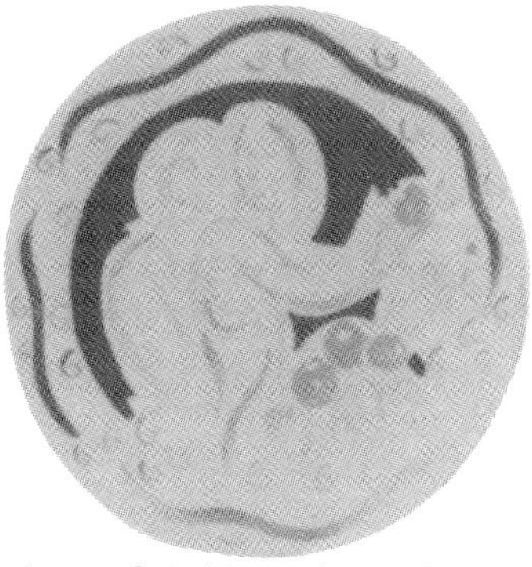

A set of six Foley bone china plates designed by Laura Knight, A.R.A., painted with two golden-haired young women picking fruit in colours and copper lustre, 21.5cm. diam.,
(Phillips) £900

A Foley Intarsio twin-handled baluster vase, printed and painted in colours with band of lavender and yellow flowers, $9^1/_4$in high.
(Christie's S. Ken) £90

FRANKENTHAL

When Louis XV, ever jealous for his Sèvres protegé, refused Paul Hannong a licence to continue making porcelain at Strasbourg in 1755, Hannong took his know-how across the Rhine to Frankenthal, where the Elector Carl Theodor allowed him to set up in some disused barrack buildings.

Hannong quickly set to work, and within a few months was producing pieces of a standard high enough to be used as court gifts. He subsequently returned to Strasbourg, leaving his elder son, Charles-François-Paul as director at Frankenthal. Charles died in 1757, however, whereupon his younger brother Joseph Adam took over, and in 1759 bought the factory from his father. In 1762, the Elector himself bought it out, and it continued in production until 1800. On its closure, many moulds went to Grünstadt, Nymphenburg and elsewhere, where they were later used to make reproductions of early Frankenthal pieces.

As they had at Strasbourg, the Hannongs made pieces which were strongly rococo in style. Their tableware owes more to Sèvres than any other German factory. Leading painters were Winterstein, who painted scenes after Teniers, Osterspey (mythology) and Magnus, who specialised in battle scenes.

Figure-making featured largely in the Frankenthal output. Early examples were designed by J W Lanz, whose subjects are characterised by their small heads and theatrical poses. J L Lück continued in a similar style, but his figures have a more robust appearance and are usually sited on extravagant scrollwork, with frequent use of arbours. The court sculptor Linck also made models for a

A Frankenthal silver shape rococo sauceboat, painted in colours with scattered sprays of roses, chrysanthemums and deutsche Blumen, incised *PH,* for Paul Hannong, circa 1755, 24.5cm. wide. (Christie's Geneva) £1,072

A Frankenthal group of four children, 23cm. wide, Carl Theodor mark in underglaze blue and dated 1783. (Phillips) £4,400

A Frankenthal group of card players modelled by J. F. Luck, crowned CT mark and letter B for Adam Bergdoll to base, circa 1765, 17cm. high. (Christie's) £5,500

A Frankenthal baluster ewer and cover probably painted by Jakob Osterspey with Bacchus and Venus reclining beside him scantily clad in brown and pink drapes, circa 1758, 23.5cm. high. (Christie's) £8,800

A Frankenthal figure of a lady emblematic of Spring modelled by J.W. Lanz, stepping forward and holding her flower-laden apron before her, circa 1760, 14cm. high. (Christie's) £1,210

A Frankenthal group of a seated young man and two young women, modelled by K. G. Luck, dating from 1778, 23cm. wide. £2,750

number of years on a very dramatic scale, sometimes running to entire opera scenes. Karl Lück, brother of J L, succeeded Linck as model master in 1765. He had studied under Kaendler, but his pieces, though exquisitely crafted, are notable for their fussiness and flamboyant colours.

During the later period Adam Bauer produced figures more in the neo-Classical style (though his Venuses were often rather voluptuous for a strictly Antique taste). Finally J P Melchior took over to produce groups similar to those he had been making at Höchst.

The usual mark is *CT* for Carl Theodor, under an Electoral crown, though *PH* and *PHF* are to be found impressed on a few early pieces. More rare is *JAH* with a crowned lion rampant.

A Frankenthal figure of a Chinaman modelled by K. G. Lueck, seated on a fence wearing a broad brimmed hat, date code 77, 11.5cm. high. (Christie's London) £715

A Frankenthal figure of Pantolone from the Commedia dell'Arte, blue lion and monogram of Joseph Adam Hannong to base, circa 1760, 11.5cm. high. (Christie's) £3,740

A pair of Frankenthal figures of Oceanus and Thetis modelled by Konrad Linck, the sea god standing extending his arm towards his companion, circa 1765, 28.5cm. and 24cm. high. (Christie's London) £60,500

A Frankenthal coffee cup and saucer, with panels painted in puce camaieu, circa 1765. £700

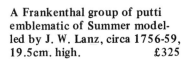

A Frankenthal group of putti emblematic of Summer modelled by J. W. Lanz, circa 1756-59, 19.5cm. high. £325

An early Frankenthal figure of Pulchinella, impressed PH3 (for Paul Hannong) on base, circa 1755, 12cm. high. (Christie's) £5,500

A Frankenthal group of a young woman embracing an elderly man, modelled by K. G. Luck, circa 1778, 15.5cm. high. £2,200

FRENCH

Early lead-glazed pottery was made in France from the 14th century onwards, The 16th century saw considerable refinements and the genre directly presages the peasant pottery made particularly in the north of France to this day.

French pottery production was always susceptible to outside influences. The 16th century maiolica production from Rouen, Nîmes, Lyons and Nevers is hard to distinguish from its Italian prototypes, although Nevers did develop a distinctive style in the 17th century with the use not only of maiolica colours but also of a deep blue polychrome.

A seminal blue-decorated faience was developed at Rouen in 1680, which influenced many other factories, such as Paris and St. Cloud, over a long period. In the 18th century Rouen again set a trend with Chinese and rococo style polychrome wares.

In the late 17th century Moustiers was influential in creating a fashion for finely painted pictorial panels, first in blue and later in yellow, green and manganese. In the mid 18th century Paul Hannong's Strasbourg factory copied the porcelain style of enamel painting for faience, and this practice was in turn copied by, among others, Niderviller, Rouen and

The first French porcelain was of the soft-paste type and was made at Rouen in 1673. Similar wares were Moustiers. subsequently produced also at Chantilly, Mennecy, St Cloud and finally Vincennes-Sèvres.

Vincennes Sèvres held the monopoly for porcelain production from about 1750-1770, after which other factories again tried to make hard-paste porcelain, and in the 19th century production became largely concentrated in the kaolin district of Limoges.

Late 18th/early 19th century French biscuit group emblematic of America, 29cm. high.
(Christie's) £495

French Pottery Group of a Young Man and Woman, 19th century, both holding a moulded floral decorated trunk with a hat and umbrella placed on the cover, 12¼in. wide.
(Skinner Inc) £131

Two French soft-paste figures of a man playing a guitar and his companion dressed as a huntress holding a rifle, he with incised *R*, circa 1750, 19cm. and 20cm. high.
(Christie's) £1,650

A large French ceramic jardinière and stand, the stand decorated in mottled browns and pinks flanked by bulrushes and foliage and a large naturalistic heron, total height 1.28m., signed *Jerome Massier fils, Vallauris A.M.* (Phillips) £2,700

A French oval porcelain plaque painted with a young girl wearing 18th century-style dress, late 19th century, plaque 6in. long.
(Christie's S. Ken) £308

An 18th century French biscuit figure emblematic of Africa, 31.5cm. high.
(Christie's) £715

A Le Croisic fluted dish painted with a portrait bust of a Neo Classical figure, relief epsilon mark, circa 1730, 31.5cm. diam. (Christie's London) £352

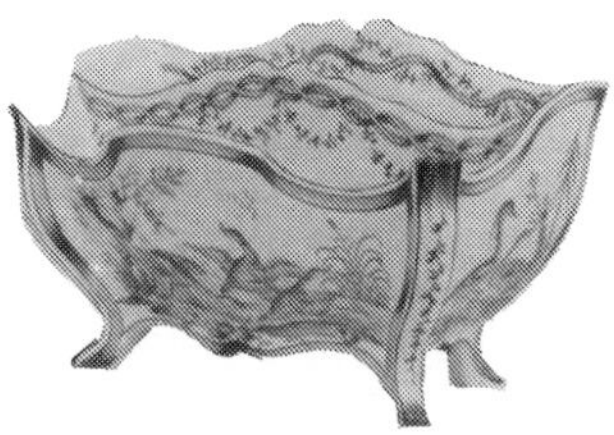

A St Clement bough pot, the bombe sides painted en camaieu with birds in landscape vignettes, circa 1785, 25.5cm. wide. (Christie's London) £770

A Rouen a la corne shaped circular plate painted in high fired colours, red OD mark, circa 1750, 25cm. diam. (Christie's London) £550

A French soft paste figure allegorical of Sight, the scantily clad youth seated on a rockwork base, circa 1750, possibly Orleans or Crepy en Valois, 15cm. high. (Christie's London) £440

Two figures of jazz musicians, one with trumpet and the other with saxophone, painted in silver lustre, painted factory mark, 11½in. maximum. (Christie's S. Ken) £495

An 18th century French biscuit group emblematic of Plenty, 34cm. high. (Christie's) £495

A French 'Empire' cabinet cup decorated at the Feuillet workshop in Paris, painted with a colonnaded country house, 12cm. (Phillips) £300

A pair of French biscuit porcelain figures in the form of a man and woman, late 19th century, 42.5cm. high. (Bearne's) £340

A French faience jug of fluted helmet shape on spreading foot painted in blue, (spout riveted) 8½in. high. (Christie's S. Ken) £99

A French coloured biscuit figure of a scantily draped young lady recumbent on a couch, 13in. wide (Christie's S. Ken) £99

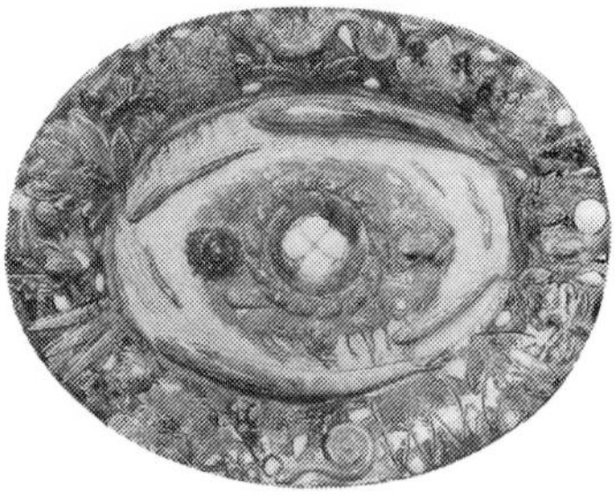

A Pallisy oval dish moulded in relief with fishes swimming on a pale blue wavy ground, 16th century, 49.5cm. wide. (Christie's) £2,640

A Strasbourg bullet shape teapot and cover with crabstock spout and handle, Paul Hannong period, 1748-1754, 17cm. wide. (Christie 's London) £1,980

A blue and white charger, the centre with a roundel painted with Jacob meeting Rachel at the well, circa 1700, probably St Jean du Desert, 51cm. diam. (Christie's London) £4,400

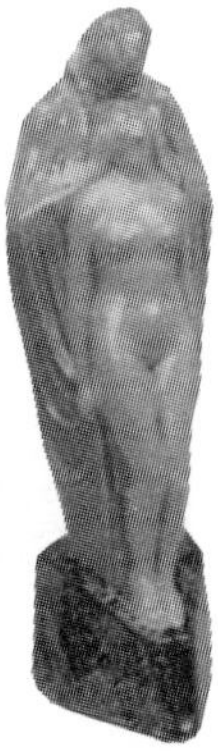

A French Art Deco pottery group modelled as a nude woman leaning back into the embrace of a man in cape, 12½in. high. (Christie's S. Ken) £198

One of a pair of Luneville shaped circular dishes painted in polychrome with chinoiserie figures with umbrellas, circa 1770, 33cm. diam. (Christie's) £3,520

A French oviform vase and cover, painted with roses on a blue ground, 38cm. (Lawrence Fine Arts) £297

A pair of French coloured biscuit figures of a gallant and companion, he holding a feathered hat, perhaps Gille Jeune, circa 1865, about 62cm. high. (Christie's London) £990

One of a pair of early 19th century ormolu mounted cobalt blue glazed porcelain urns, France, 16in. high. £1,825

A St Clement faience figure of a beggar holding his hat before him, his cane in the crook of his arm, circa 1775, 17cm. high. (Christie's Geneva) £1,201

Pair of French sweetmeat dishes formed as seated figures of a Girl and Boy, 5in. high. (G. A. Key) £300

An 18th century French biscuit group modelled as a bearded god attended by two cupids, 40cm. high. (Christie's) £660

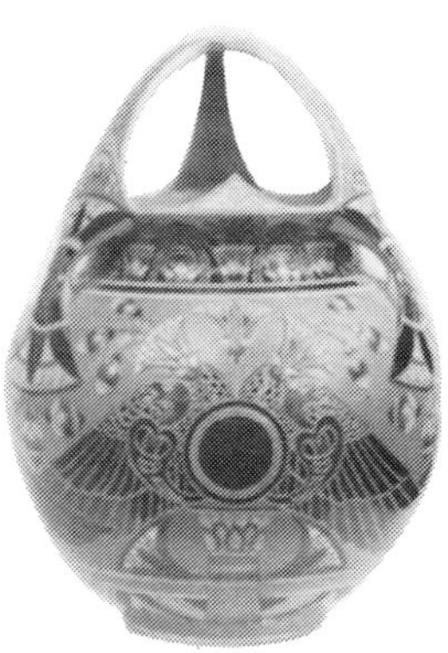

A Sarreguemines 'Egyptianesque' oviform vase, incised and decorated in colours with 'Egyptianesque' winged bird motifs, 39cm. high. (Phillips) £450

Pair of faience pottery lions, France, 18th century, fanciful Oriental style, seated with open mouths, 11in. high. (Skinner Inc.) £1,019

A Lallemant polychrome painted earthenware vase, painted with scenes of Chopin playing the piano to a couple standing behind, 11in. high. (Christie's S. Ken) £275

An earthenware plate decorated to a design by Marcel Goupy, painted in red, black and blue, $12^{1}/_{2}$in. diameter. (Christie's S. Ken) £110

'Reverie', a bisque and gilt-bronze bust of a lady cast from a model by Théophile François Somme, French, late 19th century, $10^{1}/_{4}$in. high. (Christie's East) £496

An Eastern French faience two handled ecuelle, cover and stand painted with sprays of fleurs chatironees with green branch handles, circa 1765, the stand 23cm. diam. (Christie's London) £770

FULPER

The Fulper pottery was originally established in 1805 in Flemington New Jersey, to produce drain tiles from local clay. From 1860 onwards it also turned out a range of domestic wares but it was not until 1910 that it turned to art pottery. Early pieces showed much Chinese influence and used colours from the famille rose palette. Lamps with pierced pottery shades were also produced and vases which were characterised by their angular shape. The pottery used a number of glazes including a brownish black intended to resemble dark oak. In 1926 Fulper bought out a pottery in Trenton, NJ, and the operation moved there in 1929, though a showroom was retained in Flemington.

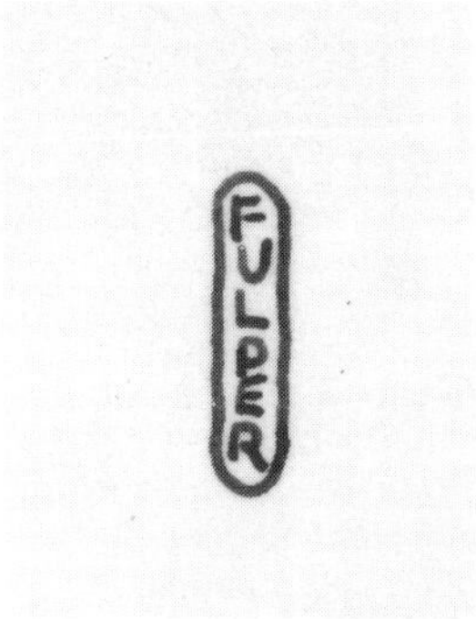

Fulper pottery copper dust vase with two handles, Flemington, New Jersey, circa 1915, 6in. diam. (Robt. W. Skinner Inc.) £107

A Fulper pottery 'Vase-Kraft' table lamp, circa 1915, 18in. high, 16½in. diam. (Robt. W. Skinner Inc.) £3,888

A Fulper pottery centrepiece on pedestal base, hammered olive-green on paler green glaze, circa 1915, 10½in. high. (Robt. W. Skinner Inc.) £864

Fulper pottery double handled vase, Flemington, New Jersey, circa 1915–25, no. 575, glossy green and eggplant glaze, impressed vertical mark, 6¾in. high.
(Skinner Inc.) £121

Fulper Pottery urn, Flemington, New Jersey, circa 1915, cucumber green crystalline glaze, vertical ink mark, 13in. high.
(Skinner Inc.) £883

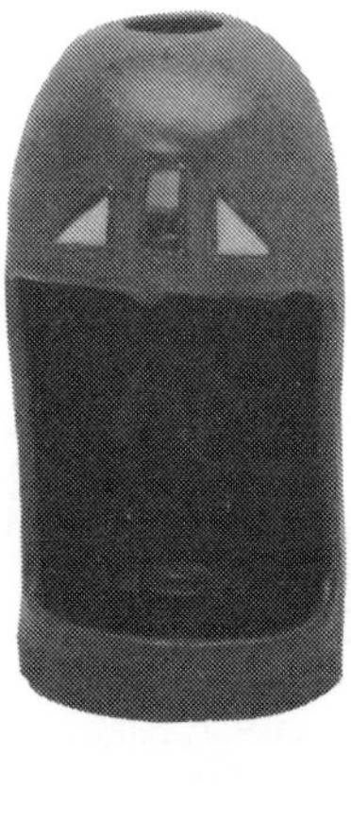

Early 20th century Fulper pottery candle lantern, 10½in. high. (Robt. W. Skinner Inc.) £357

A Fulper pottery and leaded glass table lamp, New Jersey, signed Vasekraft, stamped "Patents pending in United States and Canada, England, France and Germany", 20½in. high. (Robt. W. Skinner Inc.) £6,285

FÜRSTENBERG

For an operation which is still going strong today, the Fürstenberg porcelain factory got off to a distinctly unpromising start. In 1747, one Johann Christoph Glaser approached Duke Carl I of Bavaria, claiming to know all there was to know about making fine porcelain, and offering his services. The Duke was delighted, put a castle at Glaser's disposal, and the Duchess was so excited that she threw out all her porcelain, believing it could be ground down and formed afresh!

Glaser was a charlatan, but he managed to get a small operation going to make faience until 1753 when Johann Benckgraff was persuaded to come to Fürstenberg from Höchst. Though he brought with him the modeller Simon Feilner and the painter Johann Zeschinger, Benckgraff promptly died before he could reveal much about porcelain manufacture!

It has been claimed that the high relief and extravagant ornamentation on early Fürstenberg was used to conceal the many imperfections in the clay. However, by 1760 quality had improved sufficiently to allow the safe manufacture of simple forms which relied on enamel and gilt chinoiserie decoration, and in the 1770s some very fine figures were made by a number of modellers.

In 1795 L V Gerverot was in charge of the factory. He had worked previously at Sèvres and Wedgwood and followed neo-Classical fashions to produce black basalts and biscuit porcelain busts. In 1859 the factory was in private hands and still manufactures today.

Fürstenberg is marked with various forms of a cursive *F* in underglaze blue. Biscuit busts bear the impressed mark of a running horse.

A Furstenberg globular teapot and cover, blue script F and figure 3 to base, circa 1765, 19cm. wide. (Christie's) £1,870

A Furstenberg figure of Andromeda after a model by Desoches, seated on a rock to which she is chained by her wrist and ankle, circa 1774, 28.5cm. high. (Christie's London) £1,320

A pair of Furstenberg white portrait busts modelled by J. C. Rombrich, probably of Schrader von Schiestedt and his wife, circa 1758/9, 15cm. high. (Christie's) £6,050

A Furstenberg figure of Bagolin modelled by A. S. Laplau, circa 1775, 12cm. high. £2,400

A Furstenberg group of Perseus, modelled by Desoches, blue script F mark, circa 1780, 26.5cm. high. £385

A Furstenberg arched rectangular tea caddy, impressed no. 2, circa 1770, 10.5cm. high, silver cover. £770

GALLÉ

While Emile Gallé (1846–1904) is best known as an artist in glass, he also worked in other media as diverse as furniture and ceramics. He established a small workshop in 1874 at Nancy (Meurthe et Moselle) and there produced earthenware, which was first exhibited in 1890. Later, he also experimented with stoneware and porcelain.

His forms were for the most part simple, sometimes even a little clumsy, though some of his shapes were borrowed by the Rookwood pottery in the USA, who acknowledged their debt to him.

His decorative motifs included heraldic themes and scenes which were reminiscent of delft. Perhaps inevitably, too, he used standard Art Nouveau motifs such as plant designs of orchids, chrysanthemums, orchids etc, and his glazes were flowing and opaque, sometimes mingling two or more colours.

Apart from his own distinctive style, he was much influenced by Japanese styles, as reflected in some of the 'Origami' pieces he produced, the angular shapes of which presage Art Deco themes . Amongst the most charming of his pieces are his cats, which sit, regarding the onlooker with their glass eyes and an expression on their faces which is variously described as 'sweet faced' or a 'silly smile'.

All his pieces were marked, either with the impressed initials *EG*, *Em Galle Faiencerie de Nancy*, or with various versions of his signature.

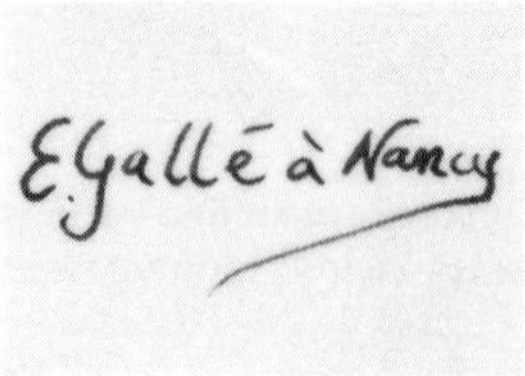

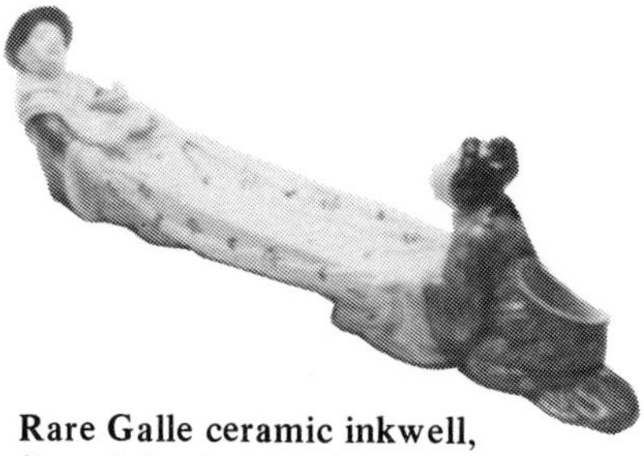

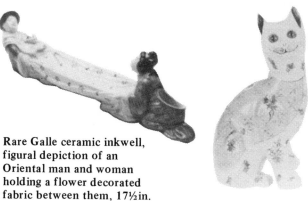

Rare Galle ceramic inkwell, figural depiction of an Oriental man and woman holding a flower decorated fabric between them, 17½in. long. (Robt. W. Skinner Inc.) £1,242

A Galle style pottery cat, seated with free-standing forelegs, wearing a pale blue coat scattered with gilt flowers, 34.5cm. high. (Henry Spencer) £460

A pair of Gallé faience 'Origami' models each as an abstract folded creature painted with yellow and blue bands, 8cm. high. (Phillips) £360

A Galle faience bowl of squat dimpled bulbous shape, 1890's, 14cm. £130

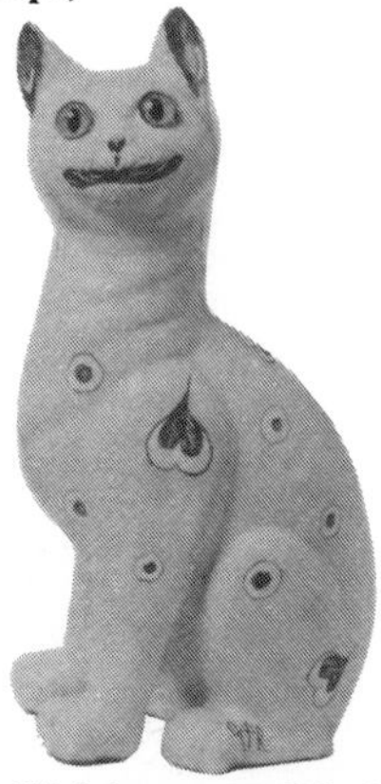

A Gallé faience model of a cat, the creature sitting back on its haunches and gazing with glass eyes and whiskered grin, 34cm. high. (Phillips) £900

A Galle faience Origami model as an abstract folded creature painted with stylised cornflower sprays, 8cm. high. (Phillips London) £100

GARDNER

The success of the Imperial Porcelain factory in the mid 18th century and the demand for its products led private individuals to set up their own porcelain making enterprises in Russia. Among them was Francis Yakovlevich Gardner, an Aberdonian by birth, who arrived in Russia in 1746 and made his fortune in a Moscow banking office. He received an Imperial permit in 1766 and started work the following year. While early Gardner pieces cannot rival the porcelain of Meissen, he was successful in making products of a lovely off-white hue, which soon attracted royal patronage. Many commissions followed for grand services for use on ceremonial occasions in the Winter Palace, adorned with badges and ribbons of chivalric orders. Gardner also turned out a series of delightful little biscuit 'dolls', producing 800 of these in 1770 alone.

While Gardner's products showed some neo-classical influence as the century wore on, they remained resolutely Russian in spirit. The factory was made a company in 1857, and was taken over by the firm of Kuznetsov in 1892.

The marks include a *G*, either in Cyrillic or Roman, while crossed swords or a star are found towards the end of the 18th century. After the early 19th century *Gardner* appears in Cyrillic with the Arms of Moscow. From 1855–1881 the Russian two headed eagle appears above the arms encircled with a band on which is inscribed *Fabrik Gardner v Moskve.*

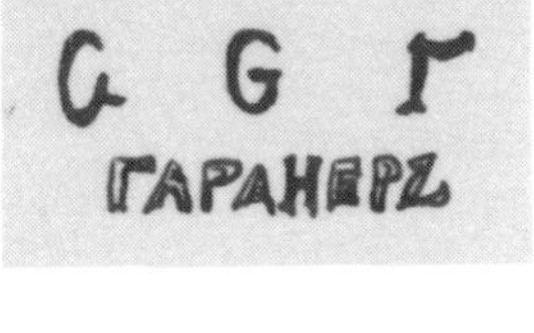

A porcelain figure of a naked young woman by Gardner, Moscow, circa 1840, 7½in. high. £440

A pair of Gardner figures representing a peasant couple, Moscow, circa 1850, 14.5cm. high. £260

A biscuit group of three tipsy men standing on an oval base, by Gardner, printed and impressed marks, 23.5cm. high. £700

A Gardener figure of a Finn in traditional costume, standing before a tree stump, in brown hat, grey jacket and breeches, 26cm., red printed mark. (Phillips) £320

A porcelain figure of a street vendor, with Gardner factory mark, Moscow, circa 1850, 15.3cm. high. £430

A biscuit group of two bearded men, by Gardner, printed and impressed marks, 22cm. high. £440

GERMAN

Medieval German pottery consists mainly of jugs and cups, most of which are undecorated. Cologne and the Rhineland were particularly prominent pottery areas at this time.

From the 16th century very fine salt glazed stoneware was made in the four centres of Cologne, Siegburg, Raeren and Westerwald, the last with incised decoration, while in the 15-17th centuries the Hafner, or local stove makers, were responsible for the production of earthenware with fine green and coloured glazes.

The German faience industry dates from the 17th century and aimed mainly at reproducing Chinese style blue and white. It centred round Hanau and Frankfurt, and Hanau is also notable for having pioneered the work of the Hausmaler, or outside decorators, whose work was to have such importance both for faience and later for porcelain. Faience was also produced at Nuremberg (where most of the Hausmaler worked) and Bayreuth; this was notably baroque in style and used high temperature colours. A clutch of factories in Thuringia also made blue and white and high temperature polychrome faience.

Germany took the lead in true porcelain manufacture, when Böttger discovered its secret for Augustus the Strong in 1708-9. No other German factory succeeded in copying it for almost fifty years, but from the middle of the century numerous other princes endeavoured to set up their own manufactories. Interest was at its height between 1750-75, and this was when much of the finest work was done.

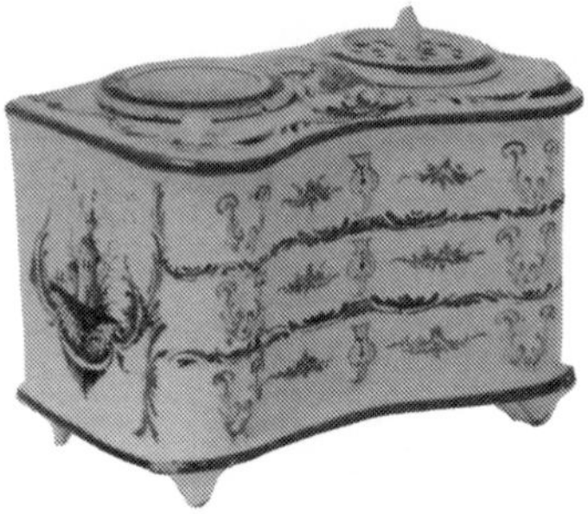

A Florsheim faience inkstand, modelled as a chest of three serpentine-fronted drawers, 15cm. high. (Phillips) £1,350

Late 17th century Habaner Ware inscribed and dated beer jug, 30cm. high. (Christie's) £3,850

A pair of German porcelain figures of Cupid-like figures, each with a bow and quiver, standing on a foliate base, 37.5cm. (Bearne's) £240

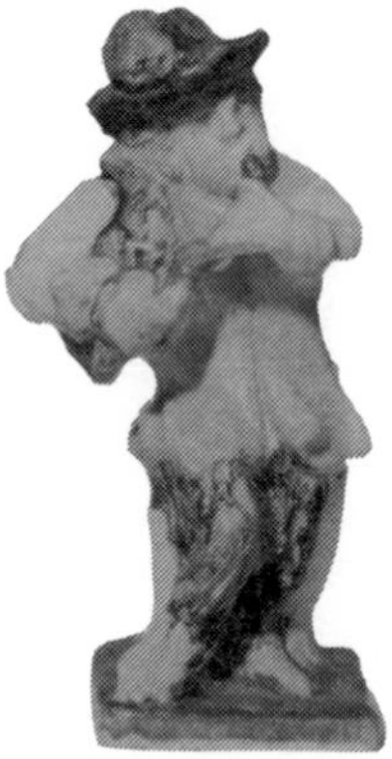

A Brunswick faience figure of a standing bagpiper, circa 1730, 18cm. high. (Christie's) £5,280

A German porcelain small rectangular plaque painted in colours with a mermaid and a youth seated on rocks, circa 1880, 2¾ x 2¼in. (Christie's S. Ken) £198

A German porcelain pierced tazza, with a military equestrian figure attended by a Moor, impressed numeral, 16¼in. high. (Christie's S. Ken) £385

An Erfurt cylindrical tankard painted with Harlequin holding his hat and slapstick, dancing on a blue mound before a fenced terrace, circa 1765, 26cm. high. (Christie's London) £1,540

A sugar box and cover, of flattened oval form, painted in sepia with a mounted sportsman surrounded by hounds, 12cm., German, circa 1740. (Lawrence Fine Arts) £2,200

A Wurzburg Commedia dell' Arte figure of Bagolin, possibly modelled by Ferdinand Tietz, broken through at knees and repaired, circa 1770, 13cm. high. (Christie's London) £2,420

A rare pair of bisque busts of children, the boy cradling a dog, the girl with a cat, 11in. high, probably early Heubach. (Christie's S. Ken) £1,980

A German porcelain oval plaque painted with a portrait of a young girl, 14cm. high. (Christie's) £528

A pair of German porcelain figures of a youth and companion, wearing floral rustic costume, 17½in. high. (Christie's S. Ken) £352

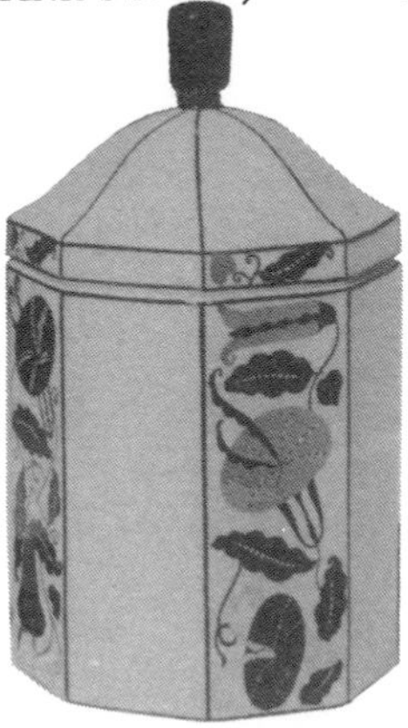

A Gmundner Keramik covered box, designed by Dagobert Peche for the Wiener Werkstaette in 1912, of octagonal section with domed lid, 16cm. high. (Phillips) £300

A Fraureuth porcelain group, by M. Hermann Fritz, modelled with a spirited goat frolicking amid vines with a young boy-child and a faun, 30cm. high. (Phillips) £110

An Erfurt cylindrical tankard (Walzenkrug) painted in colours with St George killing the dragon, circa 1770, 26cm. high. (Christie's) £1,430

A mid 18th century Fulda faience frog, 8cm. long. £3,025

A rare Florsheim figure of a parrot. £16,000

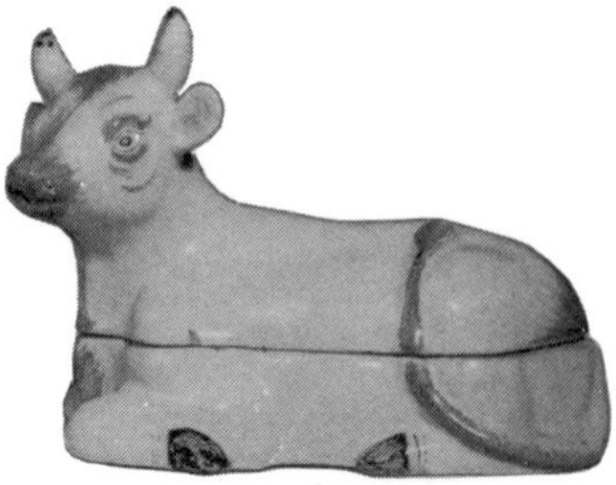

A mid 18th century Erfurt faience cow tureen and cover, 20.5cm. long. £810

A Nuernberg manganese ground writhen Birnkrug painted in underglaze blue with an oval rococo cartouche enclosing a flowering bush on a terrace, circa 1730, 25.5cm. high. (Christie's London) £1,760

A German porcelain massive garniture, the central pierced flared bowl supported by three bound slaves of three continents, 28in. high. (Christie's S. Ken) £9,900

A North German dated blue and white rectangular tea caddy, the base inscribed *Fuls Spu Huls 1740* pewter mount and cover, 18cm. high. (Christie's London) £462

A Merkelbach stoneware flagon, designed by Paul Wynand, applied with black graduated beaded bosses and two floral roundels, 24.5cm. high. (Phillips) £420

A German porcelain rectangular plaque depicting Gretel and her companion reading a letter, late 19th century, 19.5cm x 14cm. (Bearne's) £250

A Merkelbach stoneware bowl and cover, designed by Paul Wynand, of globular form on three feet, decorated with an all over design of scale like stippling, 28cm. high. (Phillips London) £160

GERMAN

A Wallendorf figure of a fruit vendor in a black hat, grey jacket, iron-red patterned waistcoat, puce breeches and black shoes, circa 1770, 13cm. high. (Christie's) £825

One of a pair of German heart shaped vases on domed circular bases chased with scrolls and rocaille decoration, 6¾in. (Christie's S. Ken)
Two £330

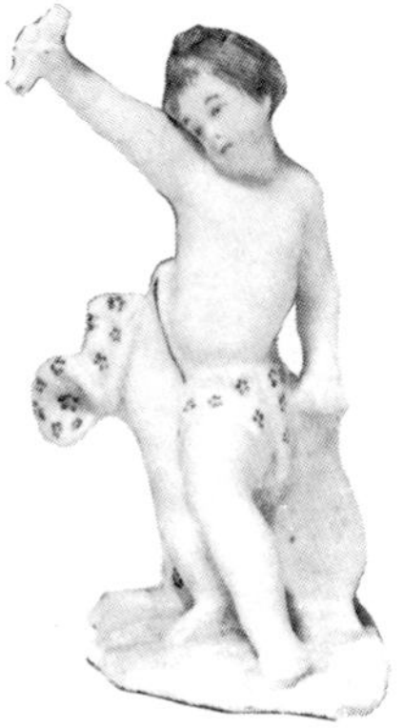

A coloured Wurzberg figure of a putto, after the Nymphenburg models by Bustelli, standing and leaning against a yellow lyre, 10cm. (Phillips) £550

A Crailsheim faience tankard (Walzenkrug) painted in colours with an exotic bird and pine trees, mid 18th century, 28.5cm. high. (Christie's)
£880

A pair of German seated pug dogs, with blue ribbon-tied collars hung with yellow bells, possibly Braunschweig, circa 1750, 14.5cm. and 15.5cm. high. (Christie's)
£3,300

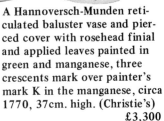

A Hannoversch-Munden reticulated baluster vase and pierced cover with rosehead finial and applied leaves painted in green and manganese, three crescents mark over painter's mark K in the manganese, circa 1770, 37cm. high. (Christie's)
£3,300

A Stralsund baluster vase with reticulated sides, circa 1770, 36.5cm. high.
£865

A German porcelain rectangular plaque painted with a three-quarter length portrait of a young girl, 7½in. high. (Christie's) £528

A German shaped circular trompe l'oeil plate moulded with leaves and applied with wild strawberries naturalistically coloured, circa 1765, 23cm. diam. (Christie's London) £1,980

A German faience hen tureen, naturalistically modelled as a roosting hen painted in manganese, yellow and blue, circa 1740, 22cm. wide.
(Christie's London) £880

A German faience **lobed dish painted in blue with birds in an extensive stylised landscape, 35cm.**
(Phillips) £160

Early 18th century German white faience figure of a Callot dwarf modelled as a smoker, 46cm. high.
(Christie's) £3,850

A massive German faience **armorial dish, the central Arms in yellow and underglaze blue surrounded by meandering flowers flanked by martial trophies, early 18th century, 50cm. diameter.**
(Christie's) £3,520

A German Faience tankard with pewter footrim mount, and cover with ball thumbpiece and engraved 'H. J. 1751', 25cm. high overall, the tankard circa 1730.
(Christie's) £880

A German faience dish, painted with a standing shepherd holding a lamb, 19th century, 12in. diam.
(Christie's S. Ken) £308

A German faience **cylindrical tankard with pewter hinged cover, painted in colours with a cathedral, dated 1848, 10¾in. high.**
(Christie's S. Ken) £220

A German faience Hausmalerei circular dish painted en camaieu rose, early 18th century, 25cm. diam.
£1,510

A German faience tankard painted in colours by a Nuremberg Hausmaler, with hinged pewter cover, the faience 1740, 25.5cm. high.
(Christie's) £10,450

GOLDSCHEIDER

It was in 1886 that Friedrich Goldscheider founded his factory in Vienna. After his death in 1897, production continued there under the direction of his widow and brother Alois, until, in 1920, the business was taken over by his two .sons Marcel and Walter. In 1927, however, Marcel broke away to form the Vereinigte Ateliers für Kunst und Keramik.

While such things as vases were produced, the factory is best known for the figures and wall masks which epitomised the Art Nouveau and perhaps even more, the Art Deco styles.

A Goldscheider terracotta wall mask modelled as the head of young girl holding a fan across her neck, 11in. high. (Christie's) £300

A Goldscheider terracotta figure of a blackamoor, 23½in. high. £1,600

A Goldscheider earthenware wall mask, 1920's, 17cm. high. £220

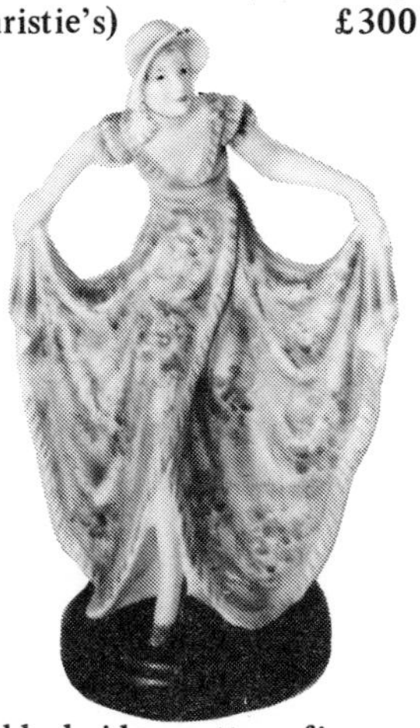

A Goldscheider pottery figure of a dancer, in a floral lilac dress with bonnet, 12in. high, circa 1930. (Morphets) £280

Goldscheider pottery mask of an Art Deco lady, approx. 12in. (G. A. Key) £360

A Goldscheider pottery figure of a young black boy, wearing a shabby brown jacket, greyish-brown trousers and a red and white striped shirt, 56cm. high, impressed maker's mark. (Phillips) £1,100

A Goldscheider earthenware head of a young woman, 1920's, 26.5cm. high. £300

'Suzanne', a Goldscheider figure, the design by J. Lorenzl, the nude figure loosely draped with a patterned grey enamelled robe, 33.6cm. high. (Christie's) £550

A Goldscheider pottery figure, modelled as a sailor holding a girl, 30cm. high. £330

A small Goldscheider terracotta wall mask of the head, neck and hand of a young girl, 8in. high. (Christie's) £200

A Goldscheider pottery group after a model by Lorenzl, of a flamenco dancer and a guitar player, 17in. high. £580

A Goldscheider pottery figure of a dancing girl, designed by Lorenzl, 16in. high. £680

A Goldscheider pottery double face wall plaque, the two females in profile, 12in. high. £385

A large Goldscheider 'Butterfly Girl', after a model by Lorenzl, circa 1930, 48.5cm. high. £1,650

A Goldscheider pottery mask of a girl looking down, Made in Austria, circa 1925, 23cm. high. £325

A Goldscheider pottery figure of a woman wearing a beaded costume, on a black oval base, 18in. high. £1,700

A Goldscheider pottery 'Negro' wall mask, 26.5cm. high. £150

A Goldscheider terracotta wallmask modelled as the head of a young woman with turquoise ringlets and a yellow tulip at the neck, 10in. long.
(Christie's S. Ken) **£462**

An unusual Goldscheider pottery wallmask modelled as Shirley Temple, painted in colours, 10in. long.
(Christie's S. Ken) **£462**

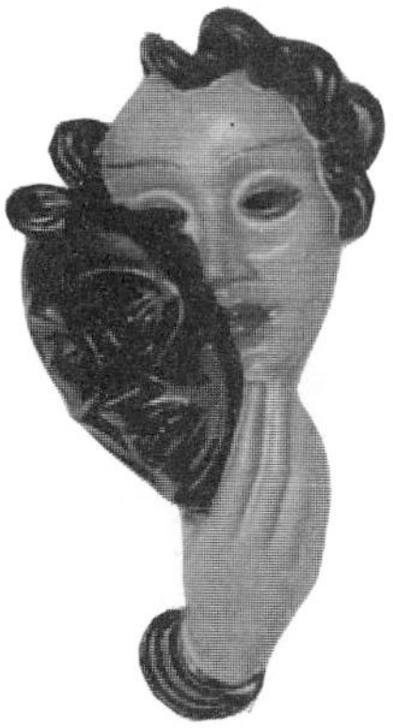

A Goldscheider terracotta wallmask modelled as an exotic woman partially concealed behind a mask, 14in. long.
(Christie's S. Ken) **£263**

A Goldscheider polychrome-painted pottery figure of a dancer, modelled by Dakon, wearing blue spotted bodice and floral divided skirt, $10^{1}/_{2}$in. high.
(Christie's S. Ken) **£528**

A Goldscheider terracotta wall mask of a female profile painted with turquoise ringlets, orange-banded black hat and yellow scarf, 10in. long.
(Christie's S. Ken) **£275**

A Goldscheider Art Nouveau pottery figure of a naked maiden supporting a circular mirror on her thigh, 30in. high.
(Christie's S. Ken) **£1,100**

A Goldscheider terracotta wallmask modelled as the profile of a young woman with orange hair and lips, and green eyes, 11in. long.
(Christie's S. Ken) **£330**

A Goldscheider terracotta wall hanging, modelled as a female bather standing amongst rushes, with towel draped over right forearm, 15in. long.
(Christie's S. Ken) **£660**

A Goldscheider terracotta wallmask, modelled as the stylised head of a woman with pierced eyes, orange hair and lips, 12in. long.
(Christie's S. Ken) **£440**

A Goldscheider figure of a woman in a long dress and hat, enamelled in shades of mauve, blue and black, 31.3cm. high. (Christie's London) £638

A pair of Goldscheider pottery figures of negro children, each in a long dress carrying a broad brimmed hat, late 19th century, 25cm. high. (Bearne's) £350

A Goldscheider figure of a woman with one hand on her hip, one on her hat, with artist's monogram, 33.5cm.high. (Christie's) £880

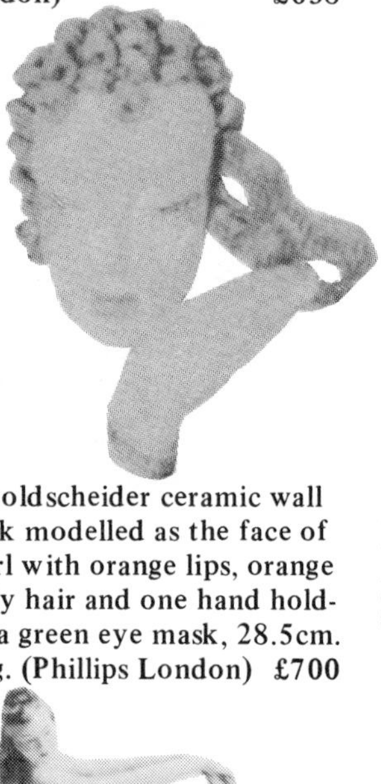

A Goldscheider ceramic wall mask modelled as the face of a girl with orange lips, orange curly hair and one hand holding a green eye mask, 28.5cm. long. (Phillips London) £700

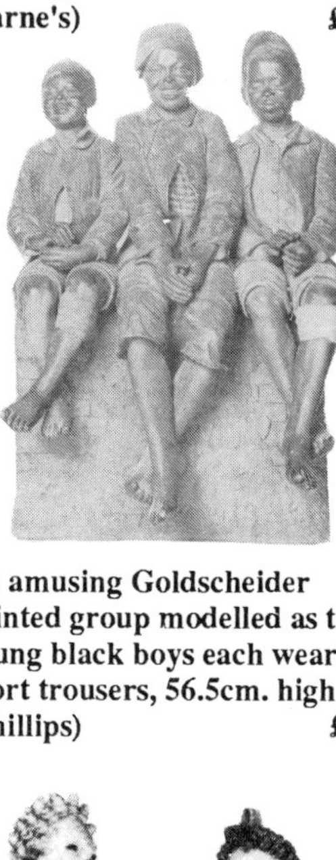

An amusing Goldscheider painted group modelled as three young black boys each wearing short trousers, 56.5cm. high. (Phillips) £1500

A Goldscheider terracotta wall mask of a young girl with orange curls and green beret holding a Scottie dog to her cheek, 10in. high. (Christie's S. Ken) £330

Parisienne, a Goldscheider polychrome ceramic figure modelled by H. Liedhoff, printed factory marks, 13¾in. high. (Christie's S. Ken) £418

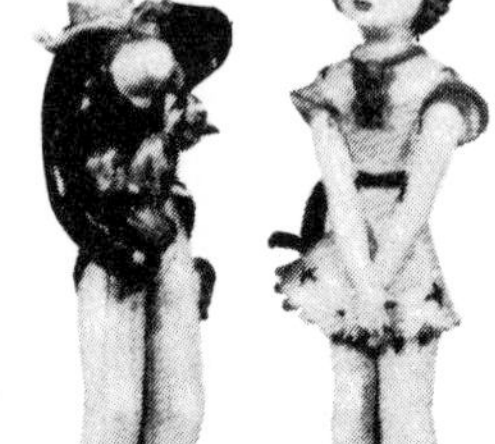

A pair of Goldscheider pottery figures of a young girl and a young man, made in Austria, 15in. high. £400

A Goldscheider pottery figure of a batgirl, designed by Lorenzl, the ivory coloured girl walking with outstretched arms, designer's and maker's marks, 46.5cm. (Bonhams) £1,500

GOSS

The Goss factory was established in 1858 by William Henry Goss, who had learned his trade at the Copeland Works, where he rose to become chief artist and designer. When he set up on his own, he continued to produce the parian busts and figures which he had worked on at Copelands, and also brought out a small amount of terracotta ware. Another early line was jewelled scent bottles and vases, made from pierced and fretted parian and inset with cut glass jewels. No more of these were made after 1885.

The advent of his son Adolphus into the company revolutionised production. Adolphus realised that a huge market existed among the new Victorian day-trippers for souvenirs of the places they had visited, and he hit on the idea of producing small china ornaments bearing the towns' coats of arms. William Henry did not appreciate this inspiration at first, but his son finally persuaded him and soon the factory's bust and figure output had been completely replaced by the new heraldic ware.

It was Adolphus too who arranged the marketing and distribution of his idea, and he became the firm's principal salesman. One agent per town was appointed as sole distributor, and they could only sell pieces bearing their own town's coat of arms, though after 1883 they were allowed to select from a wider range of shapes. Despite Adolphus' success, relations with his father were very strained, and when William Henry died in 1906 he was excluded from a share in the business. It fell finally to a fourth son, Huntley, in 1913, who was no business man. He tried to survive and capitalise on the Great War by introducing a range of

Preserve jar and lid with grapefruit decoration, 110mm. (Goss & Crested China Ltd.) £75

Nut Tray with South Africa 1900 commemorative decoration, 145mm. diam. (Goss & Crested China Ltd.) £75

A very rare W. H. Goss porcelain figure of the Trusty Servant, decorated in bright enamels, 20cm. high. (Henry Spencer) £1,300

Little girl Goss doll with real hair, porcelain arms, head and legs. £400

A Goss parian bust of Queen Victoria, for Mortlock's of Oxford Street, 236mm. high. (Phillips) £225

Shakespeare leaning on a lectern, parian, 175mm. high. (Goss & Crested China Ltd.) £275

battleship and military designs, but eventually failed and sold the firm in 1929. The new owners continued to make heraldic ware for four more years, during which time all pieces were marked *Goss*, *Goss England* or *Made in England*. Harold Taylor Robinson tried to revive the company in 1931 as W H Goss Ltd, but failed and went bankrupt in 1932.

After this, throughout the 30s a colourful range to match the Art Deco mood of the times was produced. Cottage ware was a particularly successful line, and commemorative mugs and beakers were produced for coronations and jubilees. Production ended in 1940 and the Goss site is now owned by Portmeirion Potteries.

A number of marks were used during the production period, some of which have already been mentioned. A Goshawk with outstretched wings was in continuous use from 1862, and indeed, the factory was known locally as the Falcon Works.

Goss Oven, printed mark and legend.
(Christie's S. Ken) £275

Goss commemorative vase for the death of Edward VII *Edward the Peacemaker*, 1910.
(The Crested China Co.) £80

Gretna Green, The Old Toll Bar, printed mark and legend.
(Christie's S. Ken) £1,430

Goss cruet set and stand.
(The Crested China Co.) £75

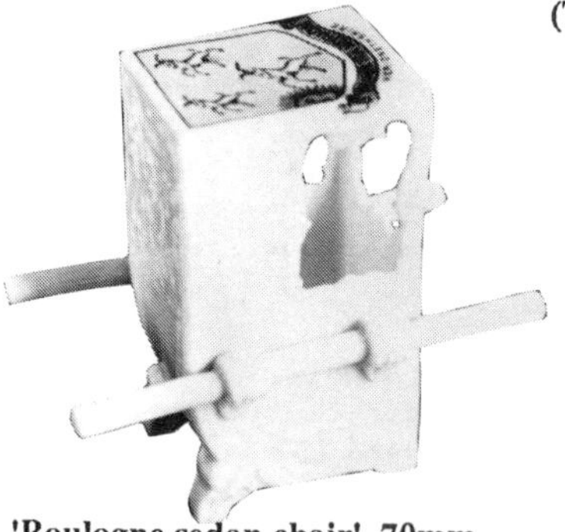

'Boulogne sedan chair', 70mm long.
(Goss & Crested China Ltd) £40

'London Stone', 110mm. high.
(Goss & Crested China Ltd) £140

Goss Bettwys y Coed kettle with arms of Dunkerque.
(The Crested China Co.) £20

'First and last house in England', small, 65mm. long.
(Goss & Crested China Ltd) £120

Large three handled loving cup, 120mm. high.
(Goss & Crested China Ltd) £75

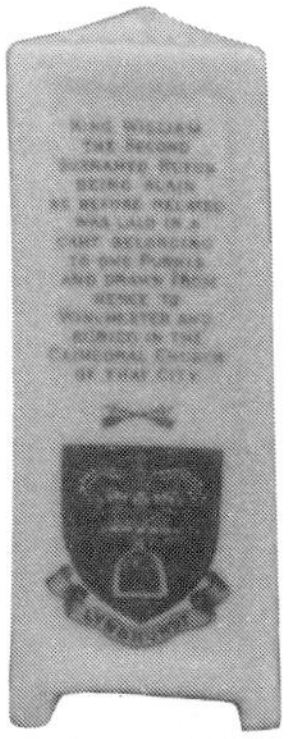

Goss Rufus stone with matching arms and *Lyndhurst*.
(The Crested China Co.) £18

Goss Bagware teapot with crest of sailing ship and *God speed Greenock*.
(The Crested China Co.) £60

Goss England Edyth.
(The Crested China Co.)
£225

Goss Welsh Picyn with matching arms of Llanberis.
(The Crested China Co.) £20

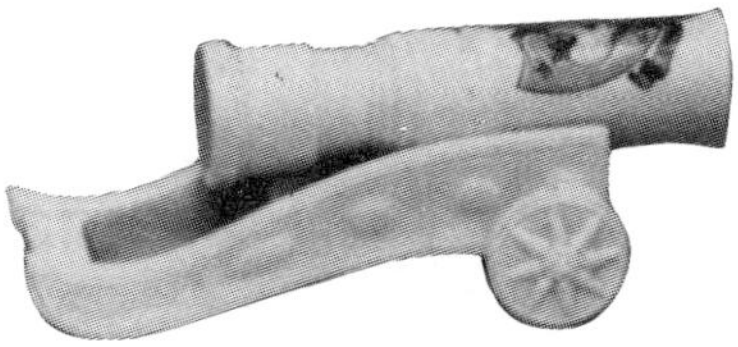

Model of 'Mons Meg, Edinburgh Castle', 120mm. long.
(Goss & Crested China Ltd)
£35

'Guillemot egg', 90mm. long.
(Goss & Crested China Ltd)
£80

Goss Ludlow sack bottle with matching arms.
(The Crested China Co.) £30

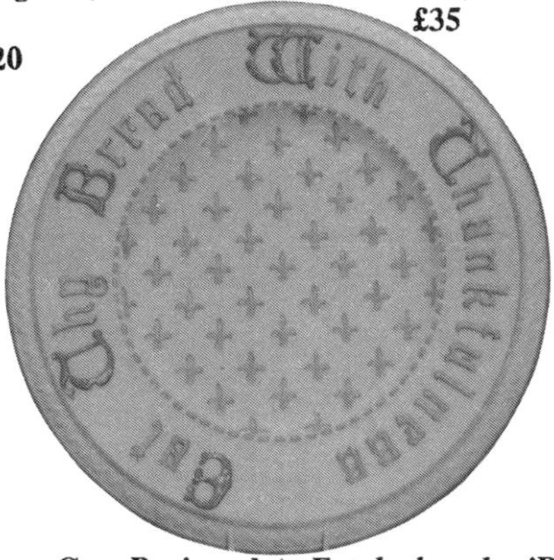

Goss Parian plate *Eat thy bread with Thankfulness*, 345mm. diameter.
(The Crested China Co.) £250

'Rye cannon ball on plinth', 105mm. high.
(Goss & Crested China Ltd) £80

'Las Palmas ancient earthen jar', 60mm. high.
(Goss & Crested China Ltd) £10

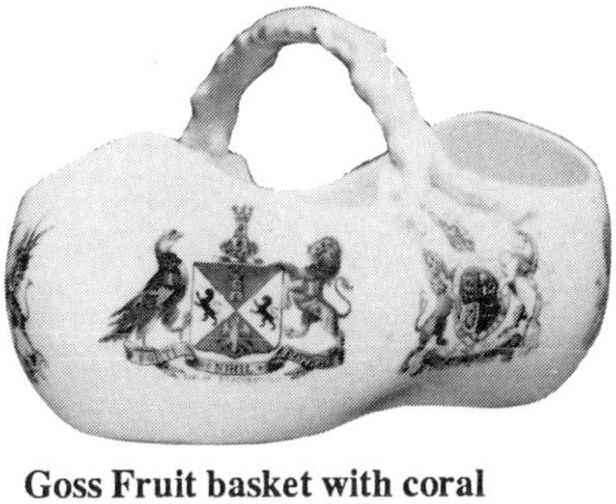

Goss Fruit basket with coral handle, first period, 200mm. long.
(Goss & Crested China Ltd) £225

Goss bust of The Earl of Beaconsfield, 154mm. high.
(Goss & Crested China Ltd) £150

William Wordsworth's Home, Dove Cottage, Grasmere, 100mm. long. (Goss & Crested China Ltd) £500

Whitby Pillion Stone, 70mm. long, with Arms of Knares–borough. (Goss & Crested China Ltd) £30

Toby Jug, 100mm. Coloured, third period. (Goss & Crested China Ltd) £125

First Period Dr. Keneally Spill And Match Holder, 190mm. high. (Goss & Crested China Ltd) £350

A Goss Agent's Change Tray, 140mm. diam. (Goss & Crested China Ltd) £300

GRAYS POTTERY

The firm of A E Gray & Co was a Staffordshire pottery operating at Hanley between 1912–33 and then at Stoke between 1934–61. Susie Cooper designed for them between 1925–32. In the 1960s they amalgamated with the firm of W Kirkham and from then on traded as Portmeirion Potteries.

Their marks, which are usually printed incorporate versions of a galleon and *Grays Pottery England.*

A Gray's Pottery Art Deco spherical lampbase, painted in colours with a stylised scene of golfers, 6in. high. (Christie's S. Ken) £770

A Gray's pottery tea for two, painted with floral sprays in blue, green, yellow and orange on a black ground, height of teapot 4½in. (Christie's S. Ken) £418

GRIMWADE

Grimwade Bros produced earthenware between 1886–1900 at Hanley, Staffs, From 1900 they became Grimwade Ltd. Their marks include *G Bros* on a star within a circle until c. 1900, when it changed to a crown and *Stoke Pottery*. Thereafter many fully named marks were used, including *Winton* (1906) *Vitro Hotel Ware* (c. 1930) *Royal Winton Ivory* (c. 1930) and *Atlas* (c. 1934–9).

Grimwade pottery plate 'Well if you know of a better 'ole go to it'. £35

Grimwade mug 'Well if you know of a better 'ole go to it'. £35

Grimwade vase depicting 'Old Bill', 'At present we are staying at a farm'. £50

Grimwade shaving mug with transfers of 'Old Bill' and Arms of Margate. £40

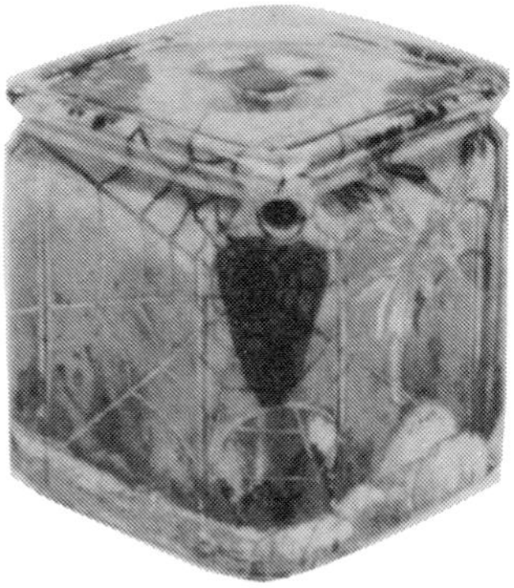

A Grimwades Cube lustre teapot, printed and painted with fairies, cobwebs and toadstools, printed factory mark, 4in. high. (Christie's S. Ken) £110

GRUEBY

The Grueby Faience Co was formed in 1897 by William H Grueby in East Boston, MA, initially manufacturing tiles, Della-Robbia style plaques and vases. From 1898 matt glazes of opaque enamel were used in shades of blue, brown, yellow and sometimes red. The most characteristic of these, however is dark green with a veined effect. Vases were hand thrown, some plain, others decorated with geometrical patterns or plant forms in low relief. From 1904 glazed paperweights were made in scarab form.

Grueby art pottery usually bears the artist's signature incised and often *Grueby Pottery Boston USA* impressed in a circle surrounding a lotus blossom motif. Grueby Faience was declared bankrupt in 1908 and though a new company was formed for architectural ware, vase production had ceased entirely by 1913. The tile manufacture was sold in 1919, and finally ceased operation around 1930.

Grueby Faience Co. vase, Boston, Massachusetts, circa 1902, with bulbous vase moulded design, matte green glaze, 7in. high.
(Skinner Inc.) £338

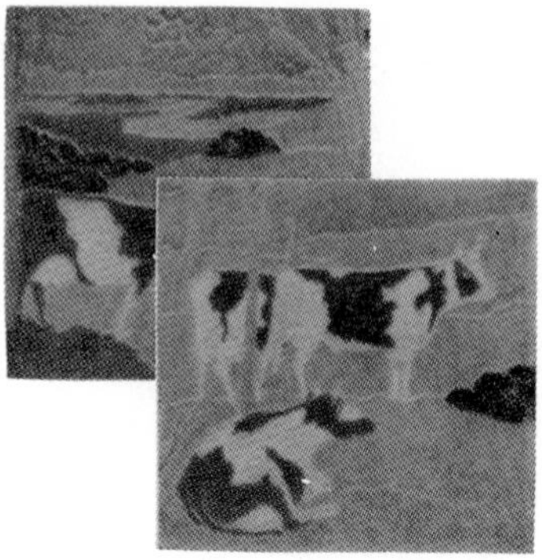

Grueby pottery two tile scenic frieze, Boston, circa 1902, depicting four cows in various states of grazing and repose. (Skinner Inc.)
£3,858

Grueby Pottery wide-mouth vase, Boston, circa 1905, with moulded leaf decoration, matte oatmeal glaze exterior, 3½in. high.
(Skinner Inc.) £195

A Grueby pottery vase, Boston, Mass., circa 1905, 13½in. high. (Robt. W. Skinner Inc.) £2,108

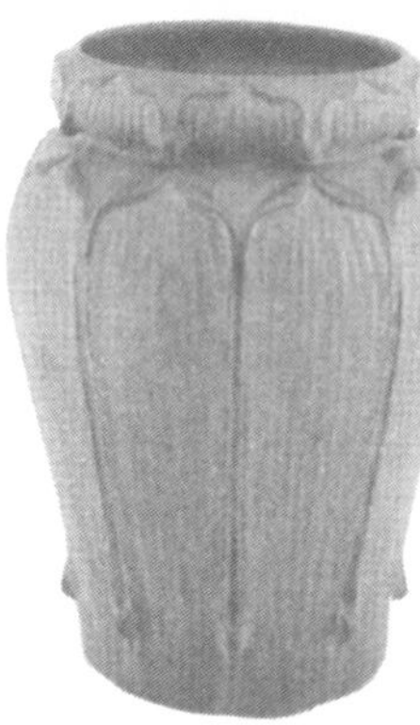

A Grueby Art pottery moulded vase/lamp base, circa 1905, 12¾in. high. £2,140

A Grueby pottery experimental drip glaze vase, Boston, Massachusetts, circa 1905, with wide rolled rim and short neck, 11¼in. high. (Robt. W. Skinner Inc.) £2,285

A Grueby two-colour pottery vase, circa 1905, 13in. high.
£3,610

Early 20th century Grueby pottery vase, Mass., 4¾in. high. (Robt. W. Skinner Inc.) £267

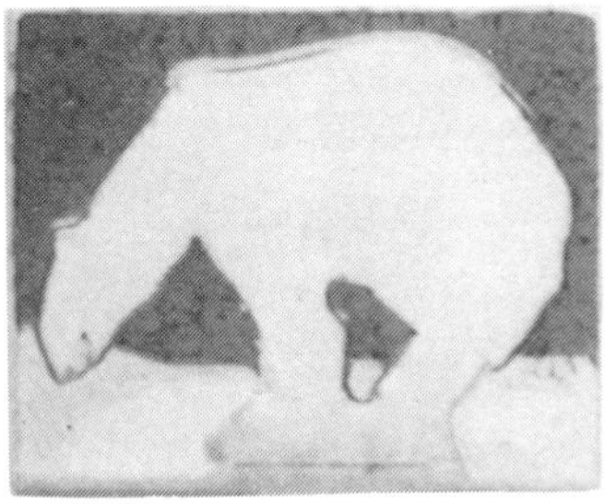

Grueby pottery Polar Bear tile, Boston, rectangular-form with moulded decoration of polar bear, 5⅝in. x 7in. (Skinner Inc) £217

Navy blue Grueby pottery vase, Boston, circa 1910, impressed and artist initialled (glaze imperfection and bubble bursts), 5½in. high. (Skinner Inc.) £1,173

A Grueby pottery vase, signed with logo, circa 1905, 11.7/8in. high. (Robt. W. Skinner Inc.) £1,547

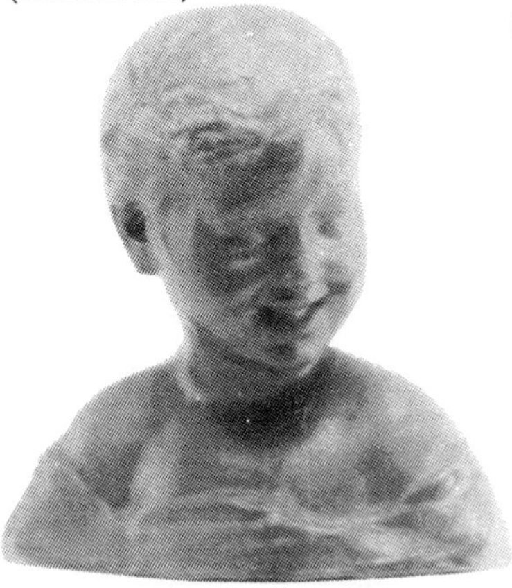

Late 19th century Grueby Faience Co. bust of 'Laughing Boy', based on a statue by Donatello, 11in. high. (Robt. W. Skinner Inc.) £972

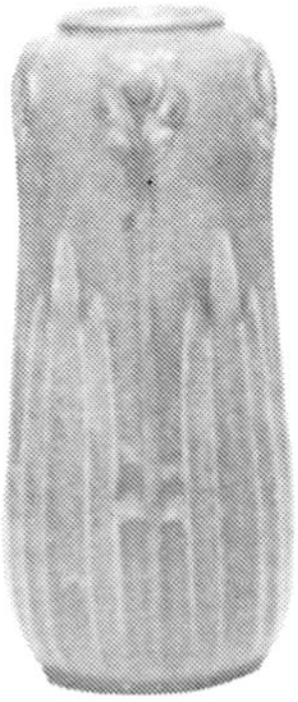

Grueby pottery vase, Boston, Massachusetts, circa 1905, decorated with iris alternating with leaf blades, artist initialled by Ruth Ericson. (Robt. W. Skinner Inc.) £1,142

Grueby pottery monumental floor vase, Boston, Massachusetts, circa 1905, the body with repeating broad thumb moulded and ribbed decoration, 21in. high. (Robt. W. Skinner Inc.) £2,285

Grueby pottery lamp base, Boston, c. 1905, having an elongated neck flaring towards bulbous base, artist signed 'A.L.' for Annie Lingley, 24¼in. high. (Skinner Inc) £2018

Grueby pottery vase, Boston, circa 1905, partial paper label and artists monogram *JE* (minor nicks), 12in. high. (Skinner Inc.) £1,420

HADLEY, JAMES

James Hadley (1837–1903) was an English ceramic modeller who worked at the Worcester factory between 1870–5. He took his inspiration from the Japanese style, producing pieces with reticulated decoration and others in the Shibayama style.

From 1875 he worked independently, supplying models to the Royal Worcester factory until 1896. He also made a series of table figures after Kate Greenaway, carrying baskets and enriched with gilding. His own porcelain, mainly in the form of vases with moulded relief decoration in tinted clay, was marketed as Hadley ware. He was succeeded by his sons, until the firm was sold to the Worcester factory in 1905. His marks include the printed or impressed monogram *JH & S* or *Hadley's Worcester*, later also with a ribbon label.

A figure of a gentleman of George IIIs reign wearing a top hat and tails, by James Hadley, 20.5cm. (Phillips London) £340

James Hadley, a majolica ware model of an elephant carrying a howdah on its back, 22cm. (Phillips London) £420

A pair of shell sweetmeat dishes, attributed to James Hadley, 22cm. wide, impressed and printed marks for 1882. (Phillips) £600

James Hadley, set of five figures of the Down and Out Menu Men, fully coloured, and standing on grey brick bases, approx. 15cm. (Phillips) £1,200

Hadley's porcelain vase and lid with cone finial, 4in. high. (G. A. Key) £170

James Hadley: a very large Cricklight figure of a Grecian water carrier holding an amphora, 79.5cm., date code for 1897. (Phillips London) £1,550

A candle extinguisher in the form of a young lady's head, by James Hadley, 9cm. high, date code for 1892. (Phillips) £400

HAMADA

Shoji Hamada (circa 1894–1978) was a Japanese potter whose early work was influenced by the Korean ceramics of the Yi dynasty. He worked mainly in stoneware, producing vases, bowls etc. in simple sturdy shapes coloured usually in brown, olive, grey and black. In 1920 he came to England with Bernard Leach, and worked with him at St Ives for the next three years. Here, he became fascinated with English medieval pottery and also participated in experiments with lead-glazed slipware. On his return to Japan, he took many ideas with him, and helped found the Japanese Craft Movement in 1929. He became a strong influence in modern Japanese ceramics, and his later pieces, made during the 50s and 60s are characterised by their use of slablike, angular forms.

A stoneware saltglazed deep bowl with flared rim by Shoji Hamada, 28.2cm. diam. (Christie's) £1,320

A stoneware bowl by Shoji Hamada, beige with olive brown vertical stripes and dark brown foliate decoration, 8in. diam. (Bonhams) £1800

A fine slab bottle by Shoji Hamada, tenmoku glaze with abstract design, circa 1960, 8in. high. (Bonhams) £3000

A rare hexagonal vase by Shoji Hamada, tenmoku glaze with three floral motifs, circa 1958, 8in. high. (Bonhams) £3000

A stoneware cut-sided bottle vase by Shoji Hamada, with short neck and shallow foot, circa 1960, 29.1cm. high. (Christie's) £1,650

A stoneware saltglazed press-moulded jar by Shoji Hamada, with paper label inscribed 56, 22cm. high. (Christie's) £1,760

A stoneware elongated oviform vase by Shoji Hamada, 27.9cm. high. (Christie's) £1,100

A small stoneware jar, by Shoji Hamada, circa 1920, 7.3cm. high. £170

A Shoji Hamada stoneware dish, 1960's. £1,650

A small stoneware inkpot, by Shoji Hamada, 1923, 5.4cm. high. £770

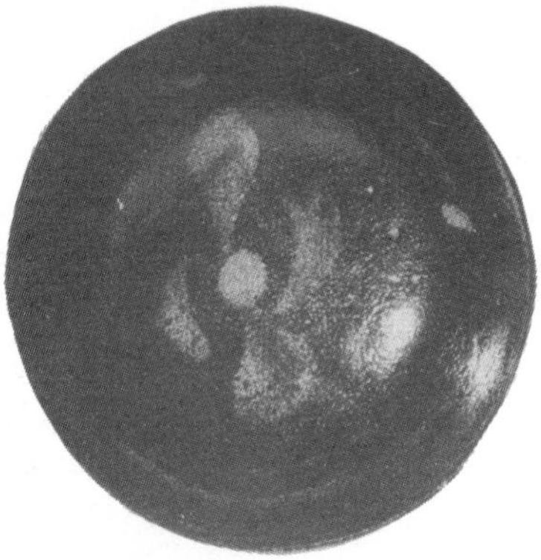

A stoneware bowl on shallow foot, by Shoji Hamada, covered in a tenmoku glaze with brushwork decoration, circa 1921, 18cm. diam. £595

A stoneware press moulded rectangular bottle vase, by Shoji Hamada, circa 1960, 23.5cm. high. £5,185

A stoneware carved jar and cover, by Shoji Hamada, circa 1922, 10.5cm. high. £595

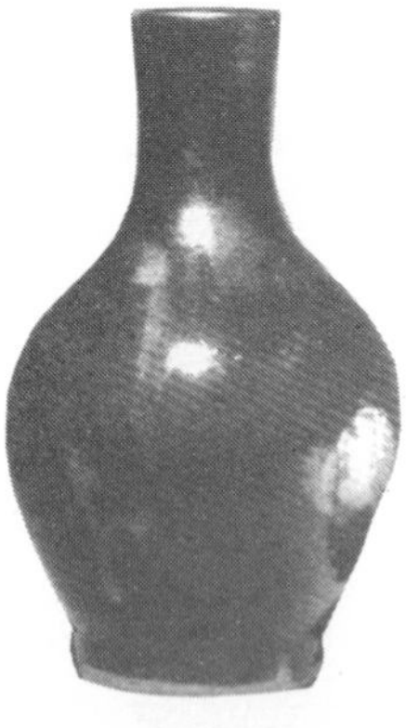

A stoneware bottle vase, by Shoji Hamada, covered in a lustrous black glaze with areas of running iron-brown, circa 1922, 24.6cm. high. £380

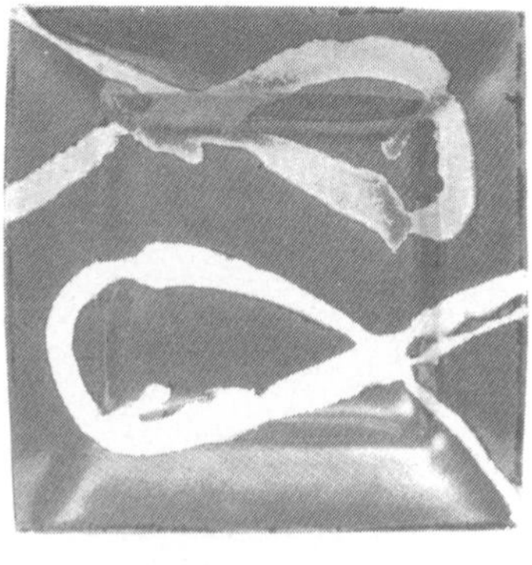

A stoneware moulded rectangular tray, by Shoji Hamada, with printed label Made in Japan, circa 1960. £485

A stoneware bottle-shaped vase, by Shoji Hamada, circa 1930, 37.4cm. high. £1,295

A tenmoku stoneware teabowl by Shoji Hamada, with central ridge, decorated with rust coloured splashes, $4^{1}/_{4}$in. high.
(Bonhams) £1,800

A fine stoneware bottle vase by Shoji Hamada, tenmoku with wax resist floral decoration, in a fitted wooden box with Japanese characters, 8in. high.
(Bonhams) £4,800

A stoneware press-moulded bottle vase by Shoji Hamada, rectangular with square section tapering neck, covered in a mottled metallic brown glaze, 19.5cm. high.
(Christie's) £2,090

A two handled white pot by Shoji Hamada, with a brown rim, $5^{3}/_{4}$in. high.
(Bonhams) £550

A stoneware press-moulded bottle vase by Shoji Hamada, covered in a speckled pale khaki glaze, the neck, shoulder and two side panels with brushed olive-green, 19.8cm. high.
(Christie's) £1,980

A stoneware teabowl by Shoji Hamada, with brushed pale grey hakeme band below rim over sage green, 4in. high.
(Bonhams) £550

A stoneware wax resist decorated dish by Shoji Hamada, with a floral motif, rust, buff rim and motif, 11in. diameter.
(Bonhams) £1,700

An outstanding curved stoneware vase by Shoji Hamada, speckled grey with white vertical lines and brown foliate decoration, in fitted wooden box with Japanese characters, 10in. high.
(Bonhams) £7,500

A stoneware plate by Shoji Hamada, covered in speckled ochre glaze, with iron-brown brushwork to the well, 18.8cm. high.
(Christie's) £396

HAN

The pottery of the Han period (206BC–220AD) is the earliest really attractive Chinese ware, for it was about this time that the ornamental qualities of the medium were realised. Also, at this time there was a certain amount of contact with the near East and even the West, which led to the general introduction of glazes, which had been in use in Egypt from ancient times.

Han pottery is usually either red or slaty grey, depending on the provenance of the clay, and varies in texture from soft earthenware to something approaching stoneware. The bulk of it is glazed, the typical glaze being a translucent greenish yellow, though this is subject to many variations. One of the characteristic features of pottery of this period is the frequent appearance of 'spur marks', usually three in number, around the mouth or base of a piece, which were made by the supports used when the ware was placed in the kiln.

Han pottery is decorated in various ways: either by pressing in moulds with incuse designs, giving a low relief effect, or by the use of stamps or dies, or by applied strips of ornament, all of which would be covered by the glaze.

It was the fortunate custom to bury the dead together with many of the objects which surrounded them in life, and it is to tomb excavations that we owe most of the Han pottery in existence today.

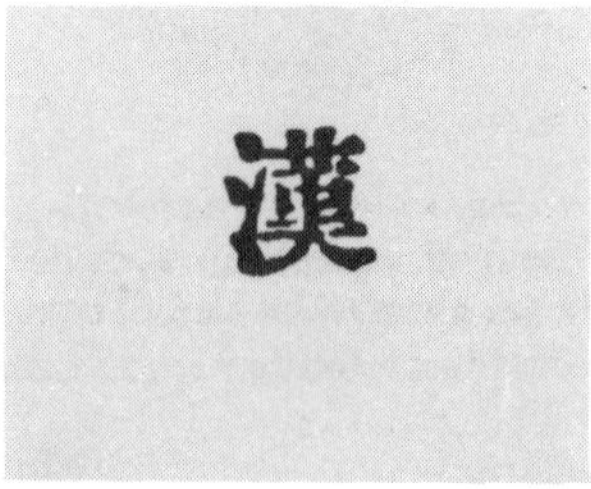

Chinese painted pottery ding, Western Han Dynasty, with swirling red and white design, $6^1/_2$in. high.
(Skinner Inc) £559

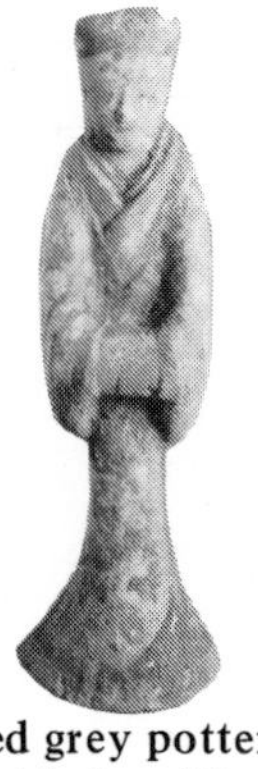

A painted grey pottery figure of a court lady with attenuated silhouette, (firing fissure, minor chips) Han Dynasty, 44cm. high.
(Christie's) £12,100

Two grey pottery rectangular tomb bricks, one impressed to the centre with five parallel rows of lozenge-shaped panels, Han Dynasty, 92cm. x 38.5cm.
(Christie's London) £3300

A green-glazed red-pottery granary jar on three short bear feet, with ribbed mushroom-cap shoulder and short cylindrical neck, Han Dynasty, 25.5cm. high.
(Christie's London) £902

A grey pottery model of a mythical beast standing four-square, the thick tail curling upwards, Han Dynasty, 31cm. long.
(Christie's) £2640

Chinese glazed pottery hill jar, Han style, conical cover with peaked terrain above cylindrical sides, $8^1/_2$in. high.
(Skinner Inc) £931

HIRADO

The Hirado kilns are thought to have been started in the late 16th century by Koreans brought to Japan by the daimyo Hideyoshi. Their early wares were mostly blue and white, and failed to achieve any great recognition until the late 18th and early 19th centuries. They are made of the finest white porcelain and painted in a soft cobalt blue with miniaturist landscapes. In the main they consist of faceted bottles, or narrow necked flasks, while some other vases and utensils have animals or insects moulded on to their sides.

While these were very fine, in the 19th century Hirado wares developed a truly amazing delicacy and perfection.

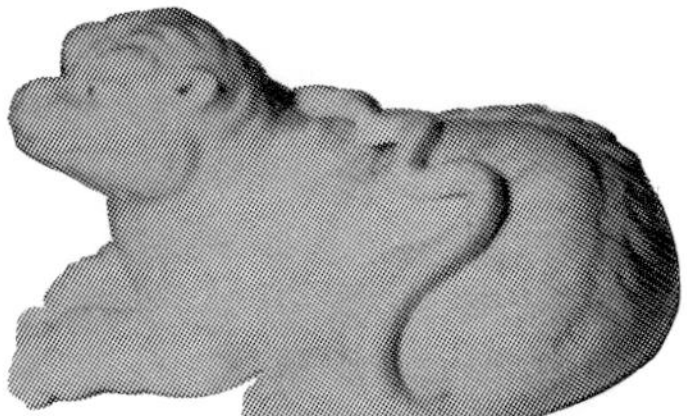

Mid 19th century white glazed Hirado model of a stylised tiger, 20cm. long. £485

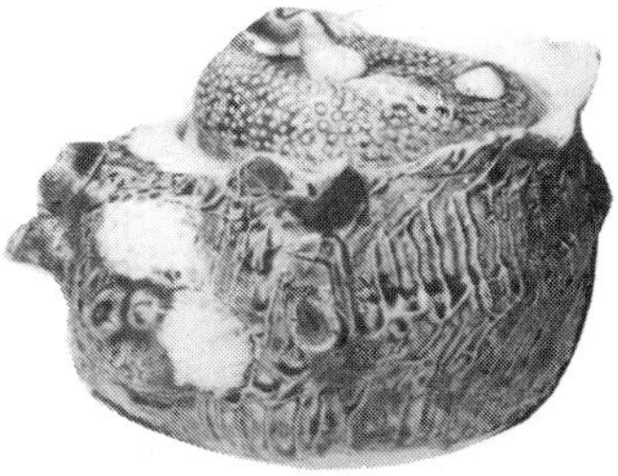

Late 18th century bowl and cover modelled as a seashell with smaller shells, probably Hirado, 14.4cm. wide. £460

A 19th century Hirado circular deep dish, 15.5cm. diameter. £450

Late 19th century well-modelled Hirado blue and white group of five playful karashishi, 18.8cm. high. (Christie's) £518

A 19th century Hirado cylindrical brush pot, 14.3cm. diam. £600

Late 19th century Hirado blue and white oviform vase, 26.2cm. high. (Christie's) £756

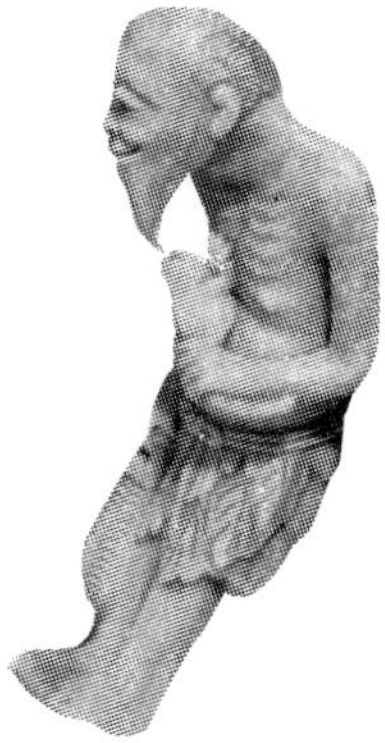

A 19th century Hirado ware netsuke of Gama Sennin, impressed signature Masakazu, 8.1cm. high. (Christie's) £605

One of a pair of late 19th century Hirado saucer-shaped dishes, each decorated in Kutani style, 61.2cm. diam. (Christie's) £3,850

HISPANO MORESQUE

In 711 the Moorish armies of the Caliph of Damascus invaded Spain, where they were to remain until their final expulsion by Ferdinand and Isabella in 1492. Thus for almost 800 years Spain formed the point of convergence of Eastern and Western civilizations, and nowhere is this dual influence seen more clearly than in its pottery.

Islamic potters had learned the art of tin-glazing with the addition of copper and silver oxides from their Mesopotamian counterparts. They brought this knowledge with them, and there are reports of a thriving export trade of lustreware from the Malaga region of Spain dating from as early as the mid 12th century.

Some of the forms of the early wares would be difficult to reproduce even today.

In the 14th century many Muslim potters from Malaga and Murcia moved to the Valencia area, and Manises became the renowned centre of 'golden' pottery. Here it became subject to gothic influence, and the representation of a wide range of birds and animals became popular.

Towards the end of the 15th century came a demand for lighter tablewares, resulting in the introduction of a new range of shapes and more precise techniques similar to those used by Staffordshire potters, such as, for example, the greater use of moulds.

In the early 17th century animal forms take on more stylised forms, and the fine draughtsmanship of earlier pieces is lacking. From the 19th century many reproductions were made. It is worth remembering that no regular marks ever appear on genuine Hispano Moresque ware.

An Hispano-Moresque tapering waisted albarello decorated in blue and copper-lustre with two bands of stylised bunches of grapes, late 15th century, 18cm. high. (Christie's) £2,640

An Hispano-Moresque blue and copper-lustre large dish with a raised central boss with a quartrefoil surrounded by a band of radiating fronds, 16th century, 41cm. diameter. (Christie's) £2,420

An Hispano-Moresque gold-lustre armorial dish, the raised central boss with the Arms of a rampant lion within a spirally gadrooned surround, late 15th century, 48cm. diameter. (Christie's) £8,250

Hispano-Moresque charger decorated in lustre with plant motifs, Valencian, md 16th century. (Christie's Rome) £1,437

An Hispano-Moresque copper-lustre large dish of pale colour and large size, the raised central boss with a swan surrounded by a band of stylised script, 16th century, 41cm. diameter. (Christie's) £2,200

An Hispano-Moresque copper-lustre oviform jar, the short cylindrical neck with four grooved loop handles divided by waisted panels of flowers and loop-pattern, 17th century, 22cm. high. (Christie's) £3,850

HÖCHST

Hard paste porcelain was first produced at Höchst-am-Mein in 1750 by Johann Benckgraff and Josef Jakob Ringler, who had both come from Vienna. The operation was never on a sound financial or administrative footing and the Elector had to make several reorganisations before his successor took over completely in 1778. The factory closed in 1796.

Early wares were characterised by a rather coarse body and a milky glaze, but quality soon improved and there was a large output of figures as well as of tableware. Especially important are the figures from the Commedia dell' Arte, set on high square pedestals. These are similar to those subsequently produced at Fürstenberg (the modeller Feilner may have been responsible for both) but the Höchst models are livelier and less fussy.

Höchst was among the earliest factories to make pastoral groups and arbour scenes. These were mainly by J F Lück. Laurentiis Russinger made rather larger groups in the manner of Boucher. He was succeeded in 1767 by Johann Peter Melchior, whose delightful groups of children gave way in the early 1770s to groups of classical sentimentality.

When the factory closed the moulds passed on to works in Damm and Bonn, both of which made falsely marked reproductions. In the early years of this century further fakes were made at Passau.

From 1750–60 the mark is usually that of a wheel with between four and eleven spokes. Six is the most common, and eight often denotes a fake. These were either incised or impressed. A similar mark in underglaze blue was used between 1760–96; and an Electoral Hat 1760–64.

One of a pair of Höchst teacups and saucers, painted with a girl with an apron full of fish and her companion holding a net, three figures carrying packages through a marsh from a boat, circa 1765.
(Christie's) (Two) £3,520

One of a pair of Höchst teacups and saucers painted with pastoral scenes after engravings by J.E. Nilson, circa 1765.
(Christie's) (Two) £3,520

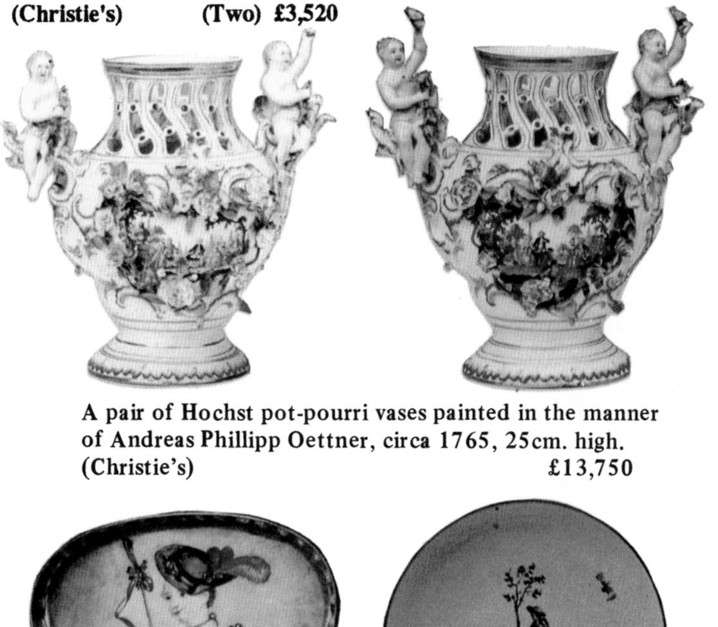

A pair of Hochst pot-pourri vases painted in the manner of Andreas Phillipp Oettner, circa 1765, 25cm. high.
(Christie's) £13,750

A Höchst copper-gilt mounted oval snuff-box painted with scenes of lovers in landscape vignettes beside sheep and a masked figure, circa 1775, 9.5cm. wide.
(Christie's) £5,280

One of a pair of Höchst teacups and saucers, painted with a huntsman and hounds beside a pond, an old woman and a young boy, a gardener planting a tree helped by a girl with a rake and a gallant and companion, circa 1765.
(Christie's) (Two) £1,870

A Hoechst milking group, modelled by J. P. Melchior, she milking a brown marked cow drinking from a pail, her companion holding it by a tether, circa 1770, 18.5cm. wide. (Christie's London) £1,650

A Hochst figure of Harlequin wearing a multi-coloured suit and a conical hat, circa 1755, 16cm. high. (Christie's) £3,520

A Hoechst group of Die erlegte Taube, perhaps modelled by J. P. Melchior as a scantily draped youth, with a distressed maiden kneeling at his feet, circa 1770, 17.5cm. high. (Christie's London) £825

Hoechst china cup and saucer, the cup with eared handle and perching birds of Paradise and gold rim, impressed blue mark, late 18th century. (Kunsthaus am Museum) £311

A Hochst group of 'Der Bekranzte Schlafer', modelled by J. P. Melchior, circa 1770, 19cm. wide. (Christie's) £3,850

A Höchst slender baluster coffee-pot and domed cover with rose finial, applied branch handle and leaf-moulded spout, circa 1755, 22.5cm. high. (Christie's London) £715

A Hoechst figure of Winter, as a youth carrying a bundle of sticks on his shoulder, blue wheel mark, circa 1785, high. (Christie's London) £352

A Hochst group of Wandering Musicians, modelled by J. P. Melchior, underglaze blue wheel mark to base, circa 1770, 23cm. high. (Christie's) £4,400

A Hochst figure of a drummer, modelled by J. P. Melchior, in black hat and pink clothes, circa 1775, 13cm. high. (Christie's) £880

IMARI

The name Imari derives from the port through which the porcelain of 17th century feudal Japan was exported. It has been adopted to describe the palette of underglaze blue and overglaze iron red and gilt of the Arita export wares. Most 17th century Japanese porcelain was blue and white and, due to fluxing of the cobalt with the glaze, the blue decoration characteristically bleeds into the surrounding area. It was to overcome this fault that early workmen painted iron red and gold onto the glaze to conceal the blurred edges.

An Imari moulded teapot, the chrysanthemum-shaped body with chrysanthemum flowerheads and foliage in relief, circa 1700, 13.8cm. high. (Christie's) £1,540

An Imari barber's bowl decorated in iron-red enamel and gilt on underglaze blue with a vase containing flowers and foliage, Genroku period, 27cm. diam. (Christie's) £418

An Imari jar and cover decorated in iron-red and black enamels and gilt on underglaze blue, Genroku period, 63cm. high. (Christie's) £1,870

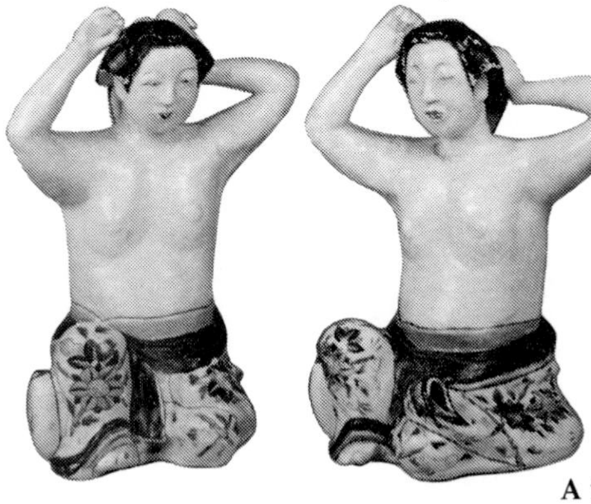

A pair of rare and unusual Imari bijin, the partially clad figures decorated in iron-red, green, aubergine and black enamels and gilt, Genroku period, 31.5cm. high. (Christie's) £13,750

A fine Imari tankard decorated in iron-red enamel and gilt on underglaze blue, the ovoid body with three shaped panels, the loop handle pierced for a mount, Genroku period, 22.5cm. high. (Christie's) £4,180

An Imari polychrome bottle vase, painted with peonies and chrysanthemums amongst scrolling foliage with birds flying above, 30.5cm., late 17th century. (Bearne's) £1,550

A pair of Imari jars of square section, each facet painted with a jardinière of chrysanthemums, 24.5cm. (Bearne's) £1,000

A Chinese Imari tankard of cylindrical form, painted in underglaze blue, iron-red and gilding, 5¼in. high, Kangxi. (Bonhams) £200

An Imari charger, the central roundel depicting a bijin walking up stairs leading to a porch behind which stands a blossoming cherry tree, circa 1700, 54.3cm. diameter.
(Christie's) £3,300

A pair of Imari baluster vases and covers decorated in iron-red enamel and gilt on underglaze blue, the domed covers surmounted by karashishi finials, late 17th/early 18th century, 47.0cm. high.
(Christie's) £6,050

An Imari shallow dish decorated in iron-red and gilt on underglaze blue, the central roundel with a cockerel and a hen and their young standing beside buildings, circa 1700, 27.6cm. diameter.
(Christie's) £1,980

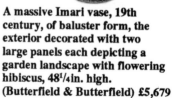

An Imari charger decorated in typical coloured enamels and gilt on underglaze blue, circa 1700, mounted as a Victorian giltwood and composition occasional table on column supports, 58.5cm. diameter. (Christie's) £7,150

An Imari circular tureen, cover and stand decorated in iron-red, green and aubergine enamels and gilt on underglaze blue, lappet handles, kiku mon, circa 1700, dish 27.7cm. diameter, tureen 19.8cm. high.
(Christie's) £8,800

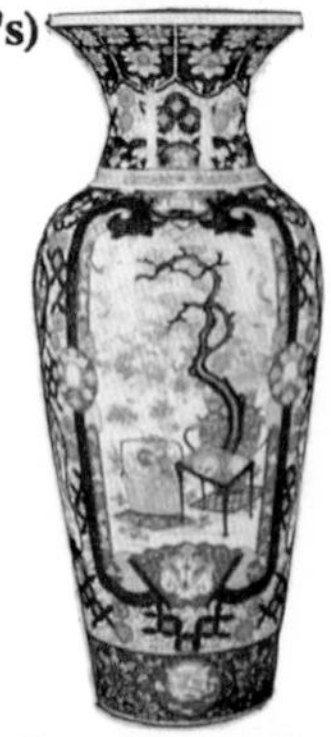

A massive Imari vase, 19th century, of baluster form, the exterior decorated with two large panels each depicting a garden landscape with flowering hibiscus, 48¼in. high.
(Butterfield & Butterfield) £5,679

A pair of hexagonal Imari vases and covers, the body with four lappet panels containing alternate pinks and ho-o among clouds, circa 1700, 52.0cm. high.
(Christie's) £13,200

An Imari charger decorated with lush peonies and bamboo, bordered above and below by panels of geometric design, late 17th/early 18th century, 53.5cm. diameter.
(Christie's) £5,500

A pair of Imari baluster vases and covers with vertical 'S' scroll designs and roundels depicting wave pattern, all interspersed with flower sprigs, circa 1700, 61.6cm. high.
(Christie's) £8,250

An Imari jar decorated with three shaped panels depicting two bijin walking under a parasol in a garden, the panels divided by vivid floral designs, late 17th/early 18th century, 41cm. high.
(Christie's) £6,050

A pair of Imari bottle vases decorated in iron-red enamel and gilt on underglaze blue, the globular body with plants set in roundels and birds on a ground of cloud pattern, late 17th century, 25cm. high.
(Christie's) £2,530

An Imari pierced box decorated in iron-red, black, yellow, green and aubergine enamels and gilt on underglaze blue, late 17th/early 18th century, 9cm. high, approx. 14.6cm. square.
(Christie's) £1,980

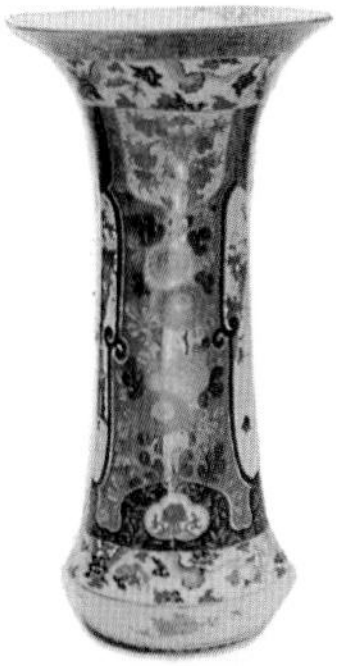

A large Imari vase, finely painted on either side with two ladies strolling in a garden with a cat on a lead, 76.8cm., early 19th century.
(Bearne's) £4,200

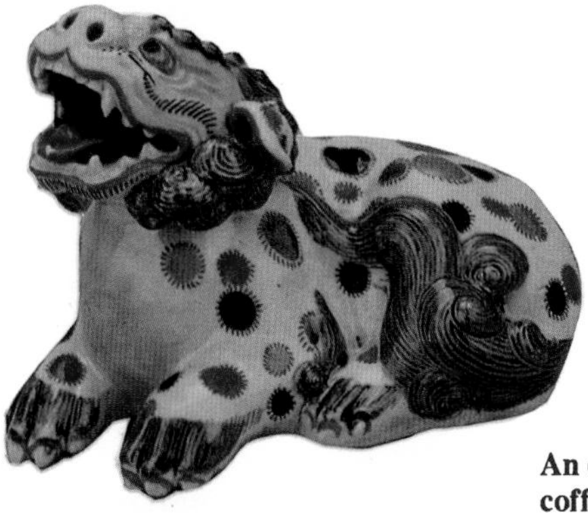

An Imari koro and cover modelled as a seated karashishi decorated in iron-red, green, black enamels and gilt, late 17th/early 18th century.
(Christie's) £6,380

An ormolu-mounted Imari coffee urn and cover, the fluted sides with a continuous design of ho-o birds among flowering and fruiting boughs, the cover similarly decorated, late 17th century, overall height 30.5cm.
(Christie's) £13,200

An octagonal Imari vase and cover, the body with alternate vases of chrysanthemums and cherry blossom, the shoulder with four lappet-shaped panels, circa 1700, 65cm. high.
(Christie's) £7,150

A pair of Imari jars and covers decorated in iron-red, green, yellow, black and aubergine enamels and gilt on underglaze blue, late 17th century, 40.5cm. high.
(Christie's) £4,950

An Imari model of an actor, his kimono decorated with chrysanthemum and cherry blossom flowers and foliage amongst brocaded ribbons, circa 1700, 39cm. high.
(Christie's) £2,860

A foliate rimmed Imari rectangular dish, the central panel with kirin beneath branches of cherry blossom, the sides with floral panels, late 19th century, 30.5cm. long. (Christie's London) £440

An Imari coffee urn on three shaped feet, with a moulded dragon head spout above the base, decorated with shaped panels of floral sprays, circa 1850, 30.2cm. high. (Christie's London) £3,080

An Imari shallow bowl, painted in underglaze blue and enamelled in colours and gilt with a European warship, second half 18th century, hair cracks, 24cm. (Lawrence Fine Arts) £638

An Imari porcelain plaque, of scalloped circular form, decorated with a phoenix perched on a branch, 56cm. diam. (Spencer's) £600

A pair of Imari octagonal jars and covers, each decorated with shaped panels of cranes perched on branches and rocky outcrops, late 17th/early 18th century, 62cm. high. (Christie's London) £26,400

Japanese Imari covered bowl, late 19th century, decorated overall with finely painted carp on a blue ground, 11in. diam. (Skinner Inc.) £750

Late 17th century Ko-Imari jar decorated in iron-red, black, green and yellow enamels, 34cm. high.(Christie's) £60,500

An Imari model of an actor decorated in iron-red, green, aubergine and black enamels and gilt on underglaze blue, Genroku period, 39cm. high. (Christie's) £2,090

An Imari barber's bowl decorated with a vase of peonies and chrysanthemums on a veranda, the wide border with panels of pomegranates, Genroku period, 29.5cm. diam. (Christie's London) £1,980

ITALIAN

The word maiolica came into use about the middle of the 15th century to describe firstly lustred Spanish pottery and then all kinds of tin glazed earthenware. The principal centres for the production of the latter were Orvieto, Tuscany and Faenza. Deruta joined them not long afterwards and featured, from 1501, a golden and a ruby lustre.

Decorative styles and themes were to some extent common, which can make identification difficult, though some characteristic features, such as the blue stained enamel of Faenza and the grey and blue of Castel Durante, did emerge. The istoriato pictorial style was perfected by Pellipario, first at Castel Durante and later at Urbino. Urbino was also the source of a new style of grotesque decoration after Raphael from the mid 16th century.

The 17th and 18th centuries saw imitations of Dutch delft emerging from Savona and elsewhere, while Florence has the distinction of producing the only porcellanous ceramic material to be made in Renaissance Europe. This 'Medici' porcelain is of an artificial soft-paste type.

As far as true porcelain is concerned, the Vezzi factory at Venice was started in 1719 with the help of a Meissen renegade, while Doccia, from 1737, drew its styles from Vienna. French-style soft-paste porcelain was made at Capodimonte from 1742, and production was resumed in Naples in 1770.

Italian porcelain is characterised by its grey colour, and this is common to the products of Nove, Treviso, Doccia and Venice.

An Italian majolica salt modelled as a figure of a woman standing at a table, 18th century, 8in. high. (Christie's S. Ken) £528

A large blue and white Italian dish painted with David, crowned and playing a harp, mid 18th century, 49cm. diam. (Christie's) £825

A North Italian cruet painted with birds perched among scrolling red and yellow flowers with blue berries beneath blue scroll borders, probably Turin, circa 1750. (Christie's) £1,210

A Caltagirone albarello of waisted cylindrical form, painted in ochre and pale green with scrolling foliage on a pale blue ground, 23cm. (Phillips) £380

An early 18th century Siena circular dish painted with two women with children, 31.5cm. diam. (Christie's) £1,100

A Ligurian wet drug jar of globular form with short spout and strap handle, inscribed in manganese with *Syr*Rosar Firr*, 20cm. (Phillips) £650

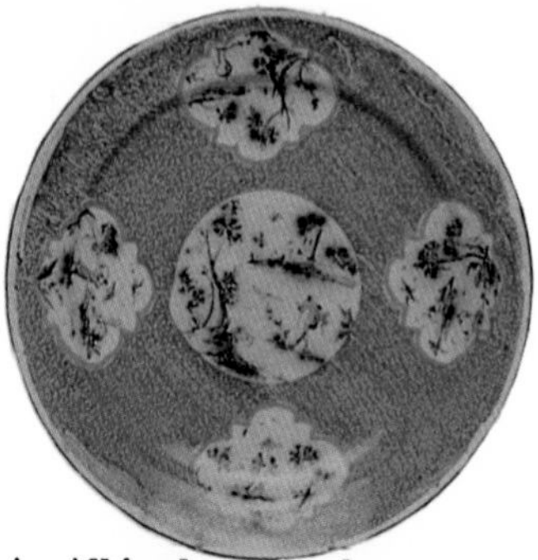

An Albissola sponged-manganese-ground dish, with figures walking among trees and buildings within bright-yellow quatrefoil cartouches, manganese beacon mark, circa 1740, 26cm. diameter. (Christie's) £660

A Faenza waisted portrait albarello named in blue gothic script for *Sangue. drag°* with a portrait of a Turk in profile to the left flanked by the initials *MS*, circa 1550, 27cm. high. (Christie's) £9,900

A Faenza berettino-ground armorial tondino of cardinal's hat form and Casa Pirota type, the central arms suspended from a winged cherub's head, circa 1530, 18.5cm. diameter. (Christie's) £33,000

A waisted albarello painted in dark-blue and ochre with blue-edged ochre diamond-ornament within rectangular panels edged with scrolling grasses, perhaps Faenza or Naples, late 15th century, 21cm. high. (Christie's) £6,050

A pair of Faenza small waisted albarelli named in blue gothic script for *Pill aure* and *Pill eolie* on blue ribbons beneath portrait medallions flanked by foliage, circa 1560, 13cm. high. (Christie's) £6,050

A Tuscan wet-drug jar with short waisted neck, the oviform body decorated in blue and ochre with the sacred *YHS* monogram, circa 1460, 25cm. high. (Christie's) £4,180

A Cantagalli charger, possibly by Farini, the central roundel depicting two putti rowing a galleon across choppy waters, 51cm. diameter. (Phillips) £800

A famiglia gotica slender waisted albarello named in blue gothic script on a ochre and blue-lined manganese scroll flanked by scrolling foliage and peacock feather, perhaps Faenza or Naples, late 15th century, 31cm. high. (Christie's) £12,100

A vaso a palla indistinctly named in gothic script for *rotag*[i] on an oval yellow cartouche held by mermaids, the reverse with three circular portrait medallions, circa 1560, 33cm. high. (Christie's) £16,500

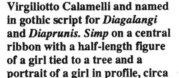

A Faenza armorial rectangular tile painted in blue and ochre with two identical testa di cavallo shields bearing the arms and flanked by the initials *MO*, late 15th century, 15.5cm. x 31.5cm.
(Christie's) £3,300

Two Faenza waisted albarelli decorated in the workshop of Virgiliotto Calamelli and named in gothic script for *Diagalangi* and *Diaprunis. Simp* on a central ribbon with a half-length figure of a girl tied to a tree and a portrait of a girl in profile, circa 1525, 27cm. high.
(Christie's) £22,000

A Lodi shaped oval tray painted in a vibrant palette with Moses striking the rock surrounded by other figures and animals beneath a blue and yellow sky, circa 1720, 48cm. wide.
(Christie's) £6,050

One of a pair of Albissola sponged-manganese-ground plates painted in manganese and lightly enriched in ochre and green with figures walking and on horseback among buildings and trees, circa 1740, about 24cm. diameter.
(Christie's) (Two) £1,540

A finely painted Venetian large oviform jar painted with the forefront of a galloping horse, amongst military and musical trophies, 32.5cm., mid-16th century. (Phillips) £24,000

An Urbania tazza painted in a vibrant palette in the manner of Ippolito Rambaldotti with Christ meeting His Mother on the way to Calvary, mid 17th century, 28.5cm.
(Christie's) £4,950

A Faenza waisted portrait albarello named in blue gothic scipt for *Eu . Forbio* with a portrait of a young woman in profile to the left, circa 1550, 27cm. high.(Christie's) £9,900

A pair of Faenza berettino-ground albarelli, each with the initials *SM* beneath a yellow star surrounded by alla porcellana and strapwork beneath a robianna, circa 1520, about 16.5cm. high.
(Christie's) £16,500

A Deruta waisted albarello named in blue for *DIA. ANISV* on a rectangular label within a green and yellow foliage wreath and flanked by blue grotteschi on a yellow and orange ground, circa 1510, 21.5cm. high.
(Christie's) £18,700

One of a pair of large Italian pottery circular dishes in the majolica style painted with classical figures, 24in. diam. (Christie's S. Ken)
Two £330

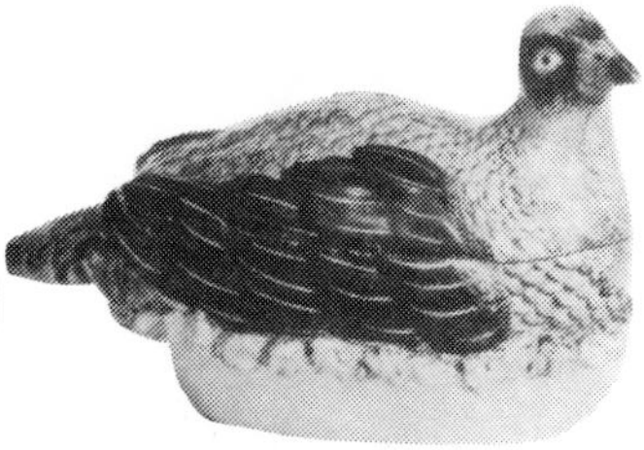

A Milan (Clerici) partridge tureen and cover, the bird seated on a basket painted in colours, the plumage manganese, circa 1750, 17cm. wide. (Christie's London)
£3,850

An Italian istoriato plate with the Judgement of Paris painted in colours, 1544, 27cm. diam. (Christie's)
£11,000

An Italian maiolica waisted albarello painted with a saint, circa 1600, 28cm. high. (Christie's) £990

An Italian moulded dish, the centre with a twin tailed mermaid holding a tail in each of her outstretched arms (rim chip, minor glaze flakes), late 17th/early 18th century, probably Angarano, 47cm. diam. (Christie's London)
£3,300

An Italian majolica drug jar, the knopped cylindrical body on spreading foot painted in blue outlined in manganese, 18th century, 5¾in. high. (Christie's S. Ken) £242

Late 17th century S. Italian maiolica Holy Water stoup painted in colours, 31cm. high. (Christie's) £495

A small pair of 19th century Italian albarello pots, the bases signed R.B., 4½in. high. (Christie's) £198

An 18th/19th century South Italian maiolica plaque painted with Christ, 38cm. high. (Christie's) £462

GEORGE JONES

George Jones (d. 1893) was a Staffordshire potter working at the Minton factory. In 1863 he established the Trent pottery, where he manufactured white and transfer printed earthenware for the domestic market as well as majolica. From 1872, by which time he was trading as George Jones & Sons, he was producing ornamental wares with pâte-sur-pâte decoration, such as wall pockets and vases. Porcelain was introduced in 1876 in the form of basket shaped flower holders etc and around 1880 vases with coloured earthenware body and painted decoration were also being made. The factory was renamed Crescent Pottery in 1907.

A rare George Jones majolica posy holder modelled as a green crested crane with long yellow beak, seated on a blue yellow-lined base, 14cm.
(Phillips) £420

A George Jones punch bowl with Mr. Punch lying on his back supporting the holly-decorated bowl in his arms, circa 1875, 36cm. diam.
£3,130

Pair of George Jones majolica garden seats of cylindrical form, circa 1874, 18.1/8in. high.
£5,935

A George Jones majolica cheese dome and stand.
£360

A George Jones majolica jug moulded in relief with panels of a pointer and its prey reversed with a fox hunting a rabbit, 1872, 10in. high.
(Christie's S. Ken) £550

A George Jones figure of a camel, impressed with monogram GJ and Kumassie, 23.2cm. high. £1,045

A George Jones vase, the handles formed as be-ribboned rams' heads, moulded maker's monogram GJ and Stoke-on-Trent, 34cm. high.
£1,100

KAKIEMON

There is a charming tradition that Sakaida Kizai-emon, an Arita potter, made an ornament in the form of twin persimmons (kaki) for his feudal overlord, who was so pleased with it that he conferred on him the honorary name of Kaki-emon. Sakaida adopted this as his family name and it was thus that the porcelain got its name. Sakaida worked for a merchant named Toshima Tokuyemon, who had learned the secret of enamelling in colours, and together they mastered the art to commence one of the most important ceramic productions.

At first, white glazed pieces were brought to the Kakiemon workshops for colouring, though they later acquired their own kiln. Their vibrant designs and colours made such an impact on the European market that within a few years every European factory was trying to produce direct imitations. Early pieces, dating from 1640–70, use thick bright turquoise and iron red in imitation of the orange–red of ripe persimmons. Additional colours are azure blue, soft orange, primrose yellow, lavender blue and grass green.

Early pieces were for the use of the patron, and were strictly in the Japanese taste. However, in time decoration became more refined, and instead of covering large areas of the piece, became sparser, showing the water-colour quality of the enamelling. Marks rarely appear before the 18th century, and the most common are the *fuku* (happiness) and *kin* (gold) marks. Pieces were made in a wide variety of shapes, from baluster jars to human and animal figures. From the 18th century many designs show a strong European influence.

A Kakiemon bowl, decorated in iron-red, blue, green, yellow and black enamels and gilt, the interior with two birds amongst pine, prunus and bamboo, late 17th/early 18th century, 35.9cm. diameter.
(Christie's) £49,500

A Meissen kakiemon circular two-handled tureen and cover painted with 'The Three Friends', blue crossed swords mark and *Pressnummer* 21, circa 1740, 32cm. wide.
(Christie's) £8,800

A Kakiemon ewer, the body with two panels depicting figures with fans and parasols in a garden where a bough of cherry blossom issues from rockwork, late 17th century, 20.5cm. high.
(Christie's) £7,700

A Kakiemon hexagonal teapot and cover decorated in iron-red, blue, green and black enamels, the pinched sides with panels of mixed flowers and foliage, late 17th century, 15.2cm. long.
(Christie's) £2,200

A Kakiemon octagonal tapering beaker decorated in iron-red, green, blue and black enamels, the exterior with a sarigue leaping amongst brushwood fences and floral sprays, late 17th/early 18th century, 11.1cm. x 7.5cm. (Christie's) £6,600

An early enamelled kraak style dish, decorated in the Kakiemon style in iron-red, blue, green, yellow and black enamels, the centre with a profusely filled flowerpot on a verandah, late 17th century, 31.7cm. diameter.
(Christie's) £6,380

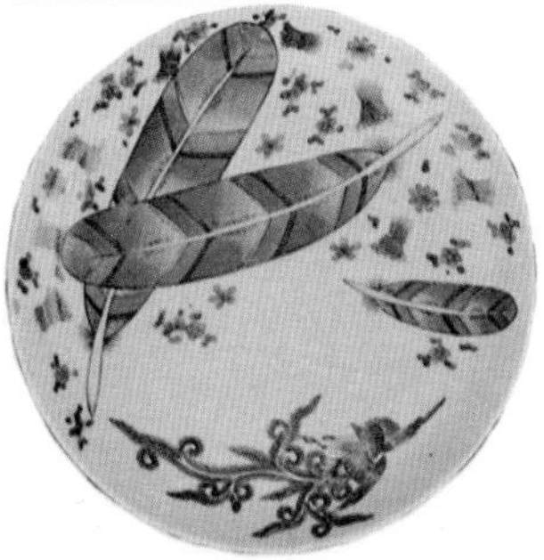

A Kakiemon blue and white shallow dish, the interior decorated with three feathers and a ho-o bird on a background of wild flowers and brushwood sheaves, late 17th century, 21.6cm. diameter.
(Christie's) £3,520

A Kakiemon octagonal deep bowl, the interior with chrysanthemums, peonies and prunus issuing from rockwork within a border of scrolling foliage, late 17th century, 19.5cm. diameter.
(Christie's) £12,100

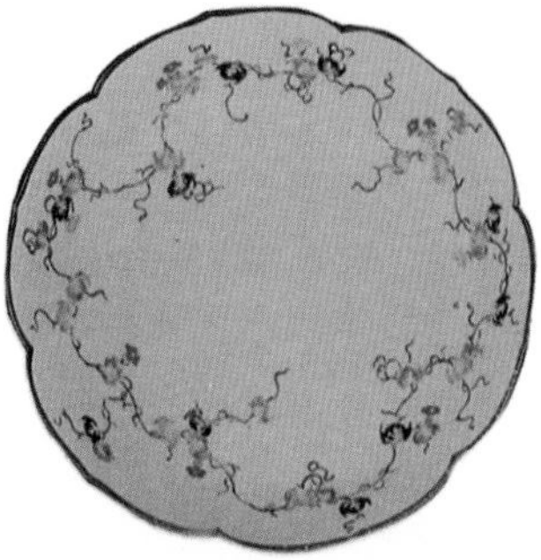

A foliate-rimmed Kakiemon dish decorated with a continuous design of entwined vine to the edge, chocolate rim, late 17th/early 18th century, 26.1cm. diameter.
(Christie's) £8,800

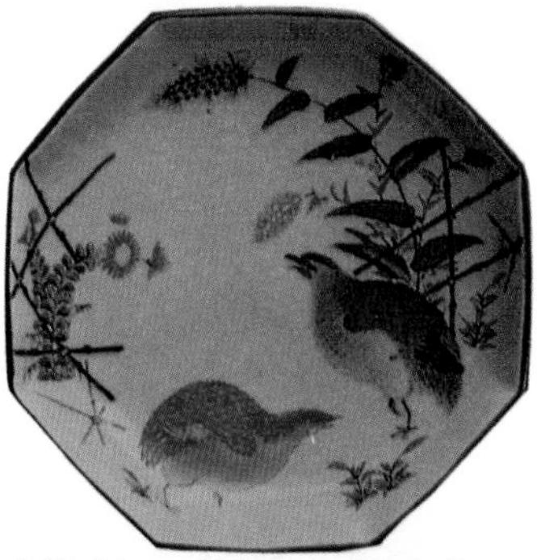

A Kakiemon-style octagonal dish with two quails beside overhanging flowers and foliage on a trellis, the underside with sprays of scrolling foliage, late 17th/early 18th century, 14.4cm. diameter. (Christie's) £7,700

A pair of Kakiemon vases and covers, the hexagonal jars with domed covers surmounted with a knob finial, late 17th century, approx. 38cm. high.
(Christie's) £550,000

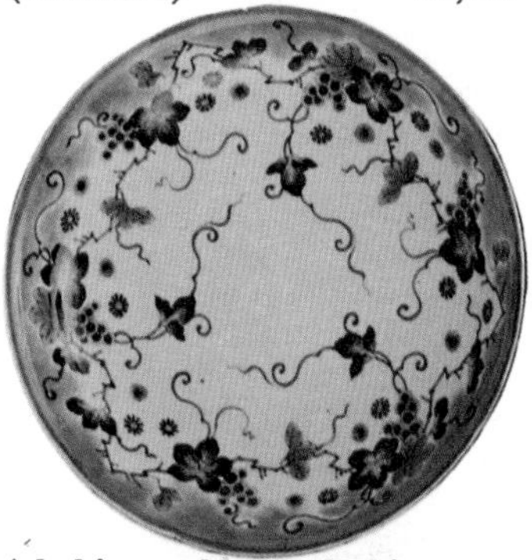

A kakiemon blue and white shallow dish decorated with gourd vine tendrils and leaves, fuku mark, late 17th-early 18th century, 21.4cm. diameter.
(Christie's) £2,200

An early enamelled dish with a ho-o bird among flowers and foliage, bordered by panels of pine and bamboo interspersed among flowerheads and scrolling foliage, late 17th century, 21.5cm. diameter.
(Christie's) £3,300

A Kakiemon model of a seated bijin, her kimono with a design of scattered flowersprays and leaves, her undergarments with splashes of colour interspersed among flowerheads, late 17th century, 27cm. high.
(Christie's) £165,000

A Meissen shallow dodecagonal Kakiemon bowl painted with The Hob in the Well pattern, tall bamboo and flying birds within a border of chrysanthemum and blue foliage alternating with peony and branches of leaves, circa 1730, 25cm. wide.
(Christie's) £27,500

Late 17th/early 18th century Kakiemon type shallow dish, decorated in various coloured enamels and underglaze blue, 24.5cm. diam. (Christie's) £2,420

Late 17th century Kakiemon teabowl with later ormolu mounts, the bowl 6.75cm. diam., fitted box. (Christie's) £1,100

An ormolu mounted Kakiemon porcelain vase of bombe shape, the porcelain late 18th century, 5in. wide. (Christie's) £990

One of a pair of Kakiemon oviform jars and covers, circa 1680, 29.5cm. high. (Christie's) £15,400

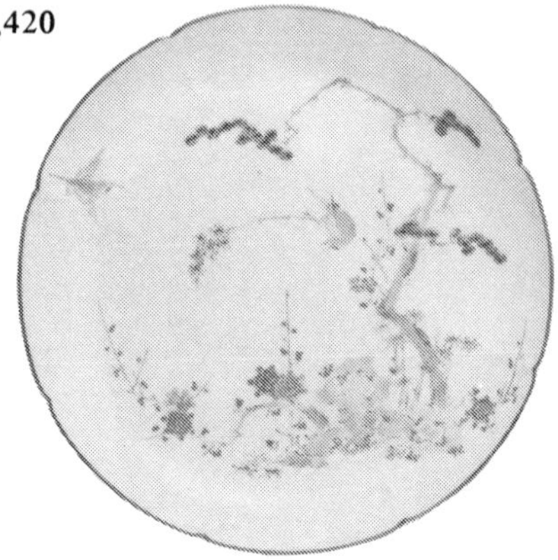

A very fine foliate rimmed, moulded Kakiemon dish decorated with a bird in the bowing branches of bamboo, chocolate rim, circa 1680, 21.5cm. diam. (Christie's London) £24,200

An important oviform Kakiemon vase decorated with three panels each containing figures standing beneath a parasol holding an uchiwa, circa 1680, 39cm. high. (Christie's London) £242,000

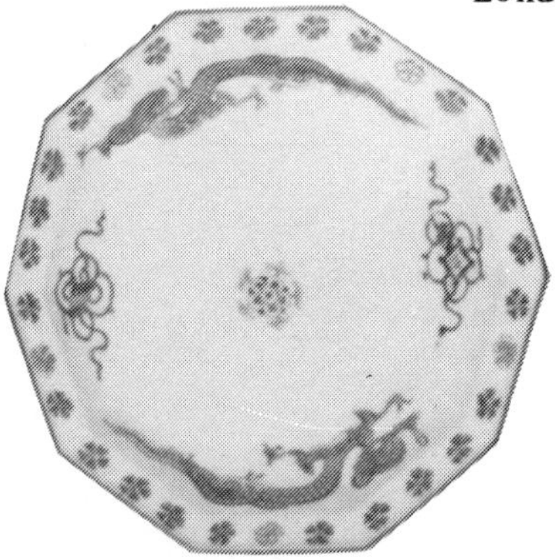

A rare Kakiemon decagonal saucer dish, the centre with a single floret surrounded by two dragons, late 17th century, 11cm. diam. (Christie's London) £2,420

A Kakiemon model of a Bijin decorated in iron red, green, blue, yellow and black enamels (slight damage), circa 1680, 39.5cm. high. (Christie's London) £33,000

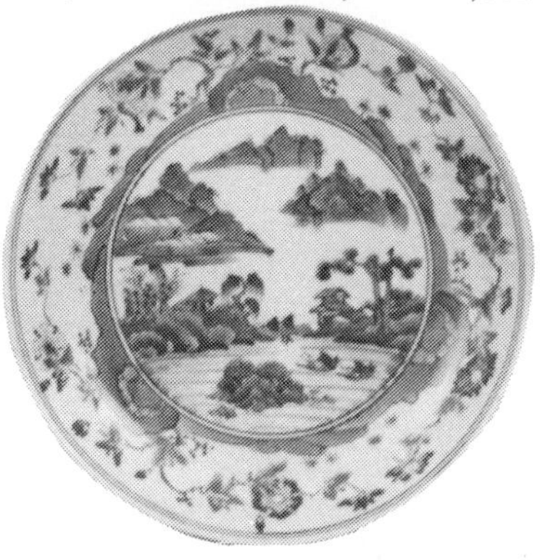

A Kakiemon type shallow dish decorated with a central roundel containing a village in a lakeside landscape, late 17th century, 25cm. diam. (Christie's London) £4,180

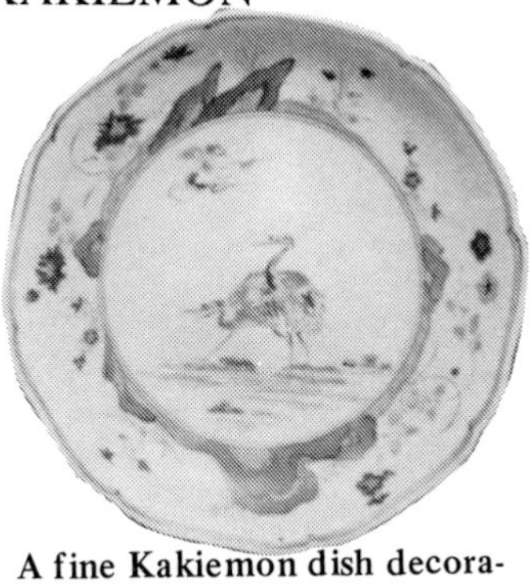

A fine Kakiemon dish decorated with cranes beneath stylised clouds, Ming six-character mark to the base (Chenghua), late 17th century, 20cm. wide. (Christie's) £5,500

A multi-faceted Kakiemon type vase decorated with sprays of peony, chrysanthemum and other flowers and foliage, late 17th century, 19.5cm. high. (Christie's) £7,150

A rare Kakiemon foliate rimmed dish decorated in vivid iron-red, green, blue and black enamels and gilt, late 17th century, 19cm. diam. (Christie's) £7,700

A Kakiemon ovoid jar decorated with a continuous wide band of butterflies hovering among peony, chrysanthemums and other flowers, circa 1660, 21.5cm. high. (Christie's) £44,000

A Kakiemon teapot and cover, the lobed sides with panels of various flowers and foliage, the cover with ho-o birds, circa 1680, 16.5cm. long. (Christie's) £3,850

A fine rare and unusual Kakiemon ewer decorated in iron-red, yellow, blue, green and black enamels, late 17th century, 16cm. high. (Christie's) £5,500

A rare Kakiemon deep bowl decorated in vivid coloured enamels on underglaze blue, the central roundel with two large uchiwa, late 17th century, 26cm. diam. (Christie's) £1,760

A Kakiemon compressed globular kendi or gorgelet with short bulbous spout, decorated in iron-red, blue and green enamels, late 17th century, 20.2cm. high. (Christie's) £4,950

A Kakiemon type underglaze blue dish decorated with two herons in a central roundel, circa 1680, 18cm. diam. (Christie's) £1,210

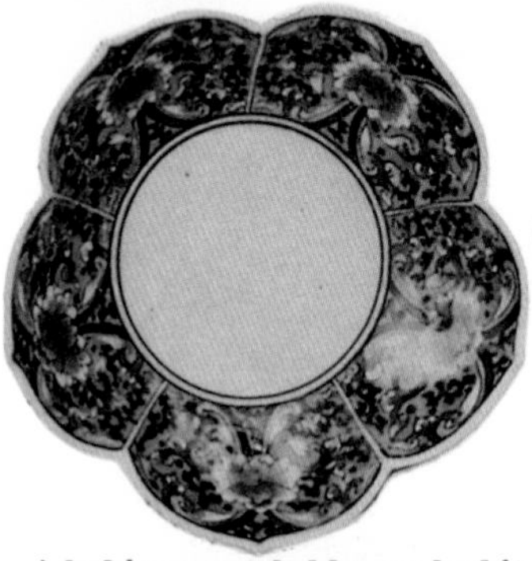

A kakiemon style blue and white six-lobed dish, the plain central roundel bordered by six panels, each containing a flower blossom, late 17th/early 18th century, 13.1cm. diameter.
(Christie's) £935

A kakiemon blue and white four-lobed dish, the central decoration a large Tokugawa mon, the exterior with smaller versions of the same, circa 1700, 15.2cm. long.
(Christie's) £6,050

A kakiemon blue and white foliate-rimmed dish decorated with a goose among reeds on a riverbank, another hovering above, circa 1700, 25cm. wide.
(Christie's) £2,750

A kakiemon blue and white shallow dish with a central roundel containing a pavilion in a lakeside landscape perched on a rocky precipice, fuku mark, seven spur marks, late 17th century, 25.8cm. diameter.
(Christie's) £4,180

A kakiemon style celadon kendi decorated in iron-red, blue, green and black enamels, late 17th century, 19.6cm. high.
(Christie's) £1,870

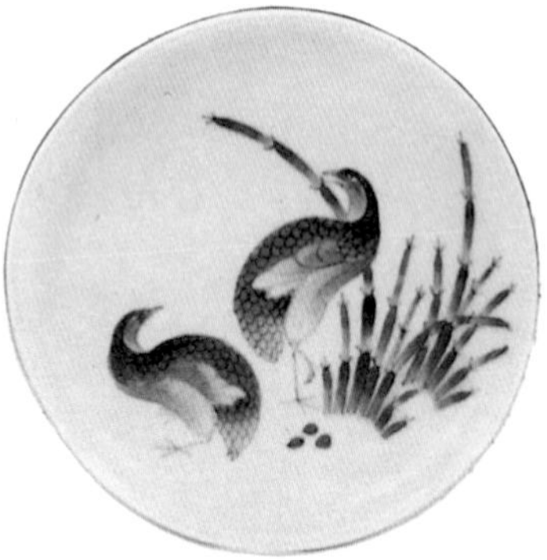

A kakiemon blue and white shallow dish with a pair of quail pecking amongst autumn grasses, late 17th century, 15cm. diameter.
(Christie's) £6,600

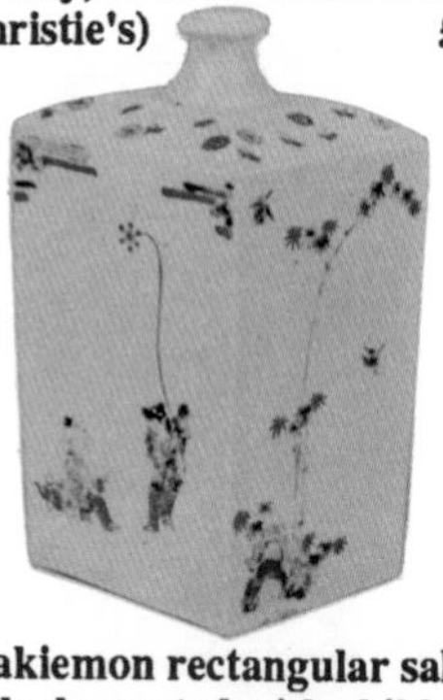

A kakiemon rectangular sake bottle decorated with children playing and flying a kite among plum blossom, bamboo, birds and rockwork, late 17th century, 15cm. high.
(Christie's) £4,180

An early enamelled kakiemon style teapot decorated in iron-red, blue, green, yellow and black enamels, with two shaped panels depicting ho-o birds, late 17th century, 15cm. long.
(Christie's) £22,000

A fine early enamelled kakiemon vase with boats in a lakeside landscape, beneath willows and other trees among rocks, late 17th century, 19cm. high.
(Christie's) £24,200

KANGXI

The Kangxi period in Chinese porcelain follows directly on the so-called Transitional period (1620–82) when there was great unrest and the Dutch, forbidden to continue their activities, turned their attention to Japan.

In 1682, however, the emperor Kangxi appointed Ts'ang Ting-hsuan as director of the Imperial factory, and following this appointment Chinese porcelain was to reach an unprecedented perfection of quality. During Kangxi's reign (1662–1722) porcelain decorated in underglaze blue was produced in ever increasing quantities for the European market. These are usually far superior to late Ming export material.

During the reign of Kangxi many wares for the home market were produced with monochrome glazes including a lustrous mirror black and fine translucent greens and yellows. It was probably during the later years of the reign, too, that the rose crimson enamel derived from gold was first introduced from Europe, and it was this that was to form the basis of the famille rose palette. Wares produced during Kangxi reign rarely bear his reign mark, which makes dating difficult.

A peachbloom-glazed beehive waterpot, taibo zun, Kangxi six-character mark, the well-potted domed sides rising to a narrow waisted neck, 5in. diameter.
(Christie's) £21,484

A blue and red square brushpot, Kangxi six-character mark, painted in underglaze-blue and copper-red on the waisted body, 6½in. square.
(Christie's) £2,005

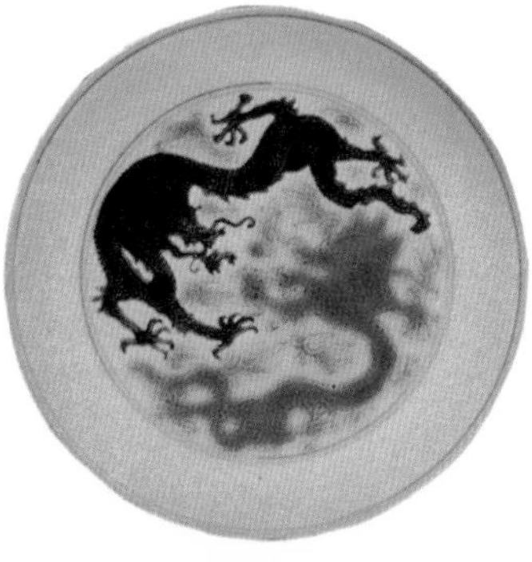

An aubergine and green yellow-ground incised 'dragon' dish, encircled Kangxi six-character mark, the centre of the interior with an aubergine and a green incised five-clawed dragon, 5½in. diameter.
(Christie's) £931

A famille verte 'magpie and prunus' rouleau vase, Kangxi, decorated to the cylindrical body with two magpies perched on a blossoming prunus tree amongst bamboo, 17¾in. high.
(Christie's) £5,729

A blue and white jardinière, Kangxi, painted to the exterior with The Three Friends, pine, prunus and bamboo below a band of key pattern, 17in. diameter.
(Christie's) £716

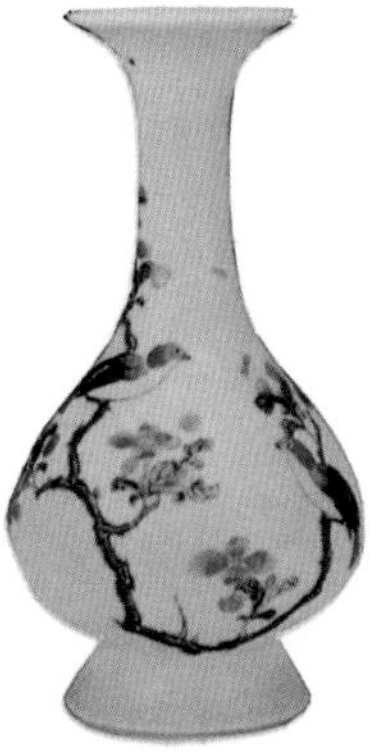

A famille verte pear-shaped vase, Kangxi, brightly enamelled in iron-red, green, turquoise, aubergine and gilt, 9in. high.
(Christie's) £2,507

A fine 'green dragon' dish, Kangxi six-character mark, painted to the centre of the interior with a circular panel of a scaly dragon reaching for a flaming pearl, 7¾in. diameter.
(Christie's) £7,161

A Kangxi famille verte deep bowl, painted in vivid enamels, 23cm. diam. (Christie's) £1,396

A Kangxi rare documentary dated white-glazed stem cup, 10cm. high. (Christie's) £5,673

A blue and white brush-pot of cylindrical form painted with groups of scholars and attendants on a terrace, Kangxi, 18.5cm. diam. (Christie's London) £2,420

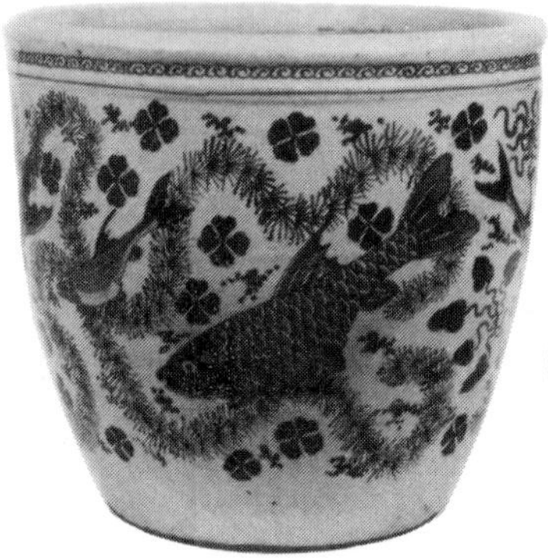

A blue and white and underglaze copper red fish bowl, Kangxi, 40cm. diam. £2,640

A pair of Kangxi Buddhistic lion joss stick holders, 20.5cm. high. £250

A Kangxi blue and white baluster jar, 10.8cm. high. (Christie's) £654

A Kangxi porcelain vase, of inverted baluster form, painted in underglaze blue with a continuous rocky mountainous river landscape, 27.5cm. high. (Henry Spencer) £110

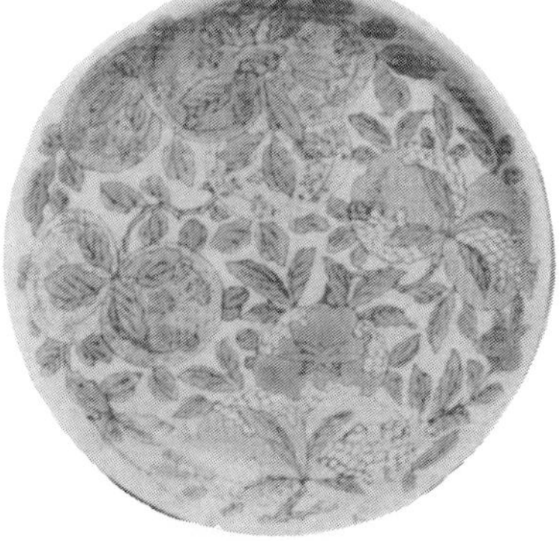

A fine famille verte 'Pomegranate' saucer-dish painted in bright enamels in aubergine, yellow and various tones of green with fruiting peach and pomegranate, encircled Kangxi six-character mark, 25cm. diam. (Christie's London) £66,000

A Kangxi blue and white cylindrical brush holder with slightly everted rim, 5in. high. £210

A Kangxi 'egg and spinach' bowl, a finely mottled glaze of green, yellow and brown splashes, 17.5cm. diam. (Christie's) £1,134

A Kangxi famille verte winepot and cover in the form of a cluster of bamboo. £350

A Kangxi yellow-glazed bowl, sides flaring into an everted rim, all under a lustrous yellow glaze, 19cm. diam. (Christie's) £1,308

A blue and white ginger jar of ovoid form, painted with cartouches enclosing precious objects, wood stand and cover, 10in. high, Kangxi. (Bonhams) £300

A pair of 'egg and spinach' bowls, covered in a lustrous green, yellow, brown and white splashed glaze, 4³/₄in. diameter, Chenghau nianzhi mark, Kangxi. (Bonhams) £700

A blue and white silver mounted jar and cover, painted with panels of Long Eliza and prunus blossom below a band of cloud scrolls, 5¹/₄in., Kangxi. (Bonhams) £220

A large green-glazed 'Blue and Yellow Dragon' saucer-dish painted at the centre with a striding dragon chasing a flaming pearl, Kangxi period, 32.2cm. diam, fitted box. (Christie's) £25,300

A pair of famille verte figures of The Laughing Twins, Hehe Erxian, Kangxi, 27cm. high. £755

A Kangxi famille verte foliate dish, painted in the Kakiemon style, 8¾in. diam. (Christie's) £785

A fine blue and white cylindrical brushpot, Bitong, Chenghua six character mark, early Kangxi, painted around the exterior with a continuous scene illustrating scholarly pursuits, three observers watching two scholars playing go, 6½in. diameter.
(Christie's) £4,297

A pair of Wucai saucer dishes, encircled Kangxi six-character marks and of the period, with a floral roundel of dense torn-off sprays of daisy, magnolia, lotus, prunus, camellia and peony, the underside with five torn-off sprays, 6½in. diameter.
(Christie's) £18,620

A peachbloom beehive waterpot, taibo zun, Kangxi six-character mark and of the period, the exterior incised with three archaistic dragon roundels, 5in. diameter.
(Christie's) £5,729

A Doucai 'shou' dish, ençircled Kangxi six-character mark, the central medallion painted with a crane in flight within a peach-shaped panel reserved on a shou character, 8¼in. diameter.
(Christie's) £2,488

One of a pair of cafe-au-lait-glazed bowls with rounded sides rising steeply to the rim from a slightly tapering foot, under an even brown glaze, Kangxi six-character mark and of the period, 10cm. diameter.
(Christie's) £5,500

A blue and white 'hibiscus' dish, painted to the centre of the interior with four stylised hibiscus blossoms issuing from leafy stalks within a circular panel, 8⅛in. diameter.
(Christie's) £2,332

A fine small Kangxi famille verte rouleau vase, delicately enamelled with seven exotic butterflies in flight amongst scattered flower-sprays and small insects, 7½in. high.
(Christie's) £3,008

A pair of famille verte dishes, each enamelled with magnolia and peony issuing from rockwork, with panels of chrysanthemum and prunus around the well, Kangxi, 35cm. diameter. (Christie's) £3,080

A fine blue and white beaker vase, Jaijing mark, Kangxi, finely painted to the flaring neck with a high official on horseback followed by his attendants and a procession of three female riders, 17¾in. high.
(Christie's) £6,996

An aubergine and green-glazed incised circular 'dragon' bowl, encircled Kangxi six-character mark, spiritedly carved on the exterior with two five-clawed dragons above breaking waves, 11.2cm. diameter.
(Phillips) £3,000

A pair of Wucai and Doucai 'dragon' saucer-dishes, encircled Kangxi six-character marks and of the period, each interior painted with a blue five-clawed dragon striding in pursuit of another green-bodied dragon, 5¾in. diameter.
(Christie's) £17,187

A fine blue and white cup, encircled Kangxi six-character mark, finely pencilled to the exterior with a continuous mountainous landscape and huts obscured behind willow, 3in. high. (Christie's) £25,000

An iron-red 'dragon' dish, encircled Kangxi six-character mark, painted at the centre with a five-clawed dragon chasing a flaming pearl amidst fire-scrolls, surrounded by two dragons chasing flaming pearls around the well, 8½in. diameter.
(Christie's) £1,866

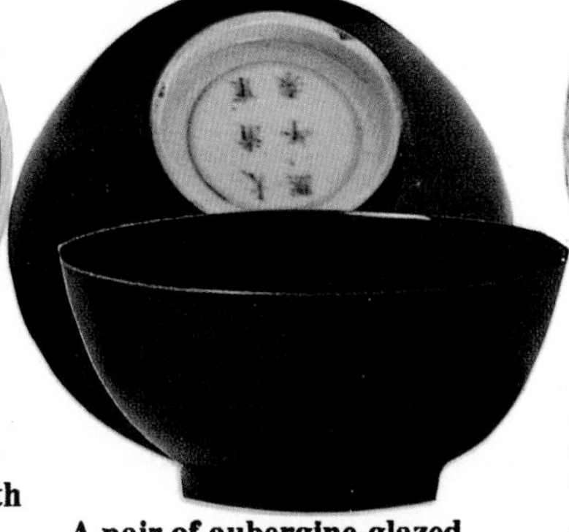

A pair of aubergine-glazed bowls, the rounded sides rising to a straight rim, encircled Kangxi six-character marks and of the period, 12.4cm. diameter.
(Christie's) £4,070

A rare large foliated blue and white charger painted in the Yuan style with a central design of a quatrefoil enclosing floral sprays around a floral roundel on a fretted ground, Kangxi, 21.9cm. diameter.
(Christie's) £2,860

A fine blue and white slender baluster vase, Chenghua six-character mark, Kangxi, finely painted in various tones of blue wash to the body with two officials in an interior, 17½in. high.
(Christie's) £6,996

Two blue and white 'month' cups, encircled Kangxi six character marks and of the period, one painted with ducks in a lotus pond beside a four-line poem, the other with a gnarled tree issuing from lingzhi and grass beside another four-line poem, 2⅜in. diameter.
(Christie's) £9,310

A blue and white brushpot, Chenghua four-character mark, early Kangxi, finely painted with the scene of a scholar on a donkey followed by an attendant, departing from a lady on a cart with a male and female attendant in front of a city gate, 5⅛in. high. (Christie's) £716

KLOSTER VEILSDORF

Of all the many small factories which flourished in the Thuringian forests in the 18th century, the best known is probably that of Kloster Veilsdorf.

It was established in 1760 by Prince Friedrich Wilhelm von Hildburghausen and employed many specialists from other factories, such as Abraham Ripp, a kiln worker, Nikolaus Paul, the arcanist, Caspar Schumann, a painter, and most famous of all, Wenzel Neu, the modeller. With such a collection of talent, it was not surprising that they produced practical wares of excellent quality, skilfully decorated by such painters as Schumann and Döll.

Wenzel Neu is probably responsible for most of the figure output between 1760–65. The quality is not particularly high, but the style is very typical of Thuringian ware in general. Many groups were made using the same models in various guises. In about 1780 allegorical figures of the four Continents were produced, which was a completely new departure. These were probably modelled by Franz Kotta, who subsequently worked at the Volkstedt factory. He also produced a fine bust of Prince Friedrich, the factory's founder.

The factory was purchased in 1797 by the sons of Gotthelf Greiner, who then used the clover leaf mark from their Limbach factory. The earlier mark consists of *CV*, sometimes in monogram, sometimes with a shield of arms between the two letters, and sometimes drawn to look like Meissen crossed swords.

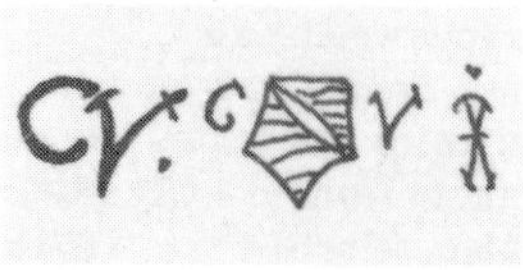

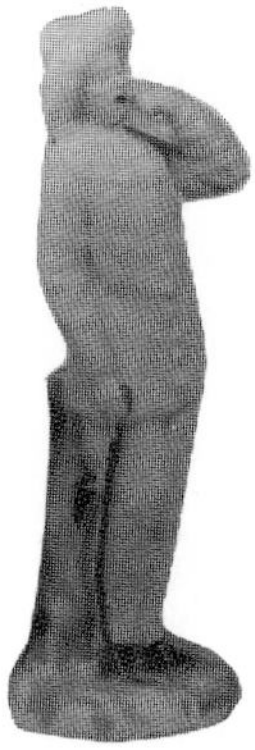

A Kloster Veilsdorf figure of Capitano Spavento modelled by Wenzel Neu, 1764-65, 16cm. high. £1,080

A Kloster Veilsdorf figure of Pierrot modelled by Wenzel Neu, 1764-65, 15.5cm. high. £5,400

A Kloster Veilsdorf figure of a crouching leopard, probably modelled by Pfranger snr., circa 1775, 12cm. long. £450

A Kloster Veilsdorf cane handle, formed as a bearded old man, circa 1770, 7.5cm. high. £540

A Kloster Veilsdorf figure of Cadi-Leskier, modelled by Pfranger, circa 1770, 14cm. high. £3,490

A Kloster Veilsdorf figure of Pantalone modelled by Wenzel Neu, 1764-65, 14.5cm. high. £2,160

KUTANI

Kutani wares, in contrast to Kakiemon, were directly derived from late Ming coloured pieces. They are the most highly prized of all Japanese porcelains and are very difficult to date, as no records of the old factories survive. Broadly speaking, the early pieces are referred to as Ko- (old) kutani, as opposed to the Ao- (new) Kutani revivalist stonewares of the 19th century.

Ko-kutani pieces usually have a whitish grey body with a milky white glaze. The colours are rich and harmonious and include vivid green, egg yellow, aubergine, Prussian blue and iron red. Decoration is mainly representative of birds and insects among flowering trees and shrubs, and rarely features animals, while figures are Chinese in conception. They were probably made during the latter part of the 17th century for the use of the overlord and his court.

As the 18th century wore on the power of the Shogunate, the main patrons of such kilns, began to wane, and the Kutani kiln, which had been under the protection of the daimyo Maeda, collapsed in the last years of the century, following his fall from favour. In 1816 Yoshidaya Denyemon revived the kiln, and production continued until the 1860s. These Ao-kutani pieces lack the vitality and originality of the earlier products. They are often heavily enamelled, with green or yellow grounds, and the decoration is outlined in black. They also bear a small two character mark which was lacking on the earlier pieces.

The Arita kilns, which fared much better during the early 19th century, continued to produce pieces in the Ko-kutani style.

**A Kutani koro amusingly modelled in the form of a Shishi, the rounded body raised on four legs, the tail forming the handle, Meiji period, 7¾in. high.
(Bonhams) £200**

**A Kutani koro and cover of typical form, painted all over in iron-red and gilt with Shishi and cash symbols, 11¾in., Meiji period.
(Bonhams) £500**

**A garniture of three Kutani vases, the central covered jar with Buddist lion knop, each painted on one side with a woman and children in a garden, 30cm.
(Bearne's) £660**

**One of a pair of Kutani vases, painted in iron-red and gilt with cockerels amongst peony between ho-o, 14in. high, Meiji period.
(Bonhams) £600**

A late Kutani (Kaga ware) box and cover formed as a chest attended by three karako, signed *Takayama ga,* late 19th century, 25cm. high. (Christie's London) £3,080

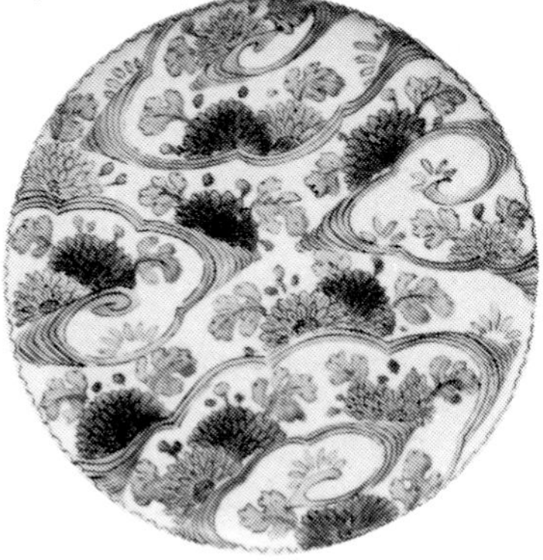

An important Ko-Kutani dish decorated with chrysanthemum flowerheads and foliage scattered among stylised waves, late 17th century, 21cm. diam.
(Christie's) £33,000

A ko-Kutani dish with a redbreast perched on a branch of plum blossom, the reverse with two flower sprays, Fuku mark, late 17th century, 14.7cm. diameter.
(Christie's) £2,200

A Kutani elephant with tasselled saddling decorated with ho-o bird, carrying on its back an elaborate cage resting on an ornately fenced base, 19th century, 50cm. high. (Christie's London) £7,150

A Kutani style shallow dish, depicting a farmstead, the upper section with lozenge diaper design, the reverse with cherry blossom sprays, fuku mark, circa 1700, 14.5cm. diameter.
(Christie's) £3,520

A rare Kutani double gourd shaped bottle, the wide lower section with sprays of chrysanthemum amongst rockwork, circa 1670, 19.5cm. high.
(Christie's London) £6,600

A pair of hexagonal late Kutani (Kaga ware) vases decorated with six oval panels, surrounded by various designs including ho-o birds and clouds, late 19th century, 37cm. high.
(Christie's London) £2,200

A Kutani bottle vase, the body with a continuous decoration of tassels hanging down from an ornate pelmet, the neck with vertical and horizontal bands of wave, late 17th century, 20.8cm. high.
(Christie's) £7,700

An important Ao-Kutani deep dish, with two fans interspersed on a ground of chrysanthemum flowerheads, late 17th century, 28cm. diam.
(Christie's London) £39,600

A pair of 19th century Kutani-style shaped vases, with Oriental figure decoration to complete body in burnt orange and charcoal grey colour, 14in.
(Giles Haywood) £1,150

A ko-Kutani dish decorated in various coloured enamels, the central roundel containing two overlapping panels, one depicting a bird perched on bamboo, late 17th century, 21.5cm. diameter.
(Christie's) £4,400

KYOTO

Kyoto was both the seat of the Japanese Imperial court and an important area of ceramic production in the Edo period (1615–1868). In the 17th century, the potter Ninsei had developed an enamelled and gilt pottery, which continued to be manufactured in the 18th century onwards, principally by Kenzan and his successors. Individual potters thrived all over the city, making not only faience, but porcelain in blue-and-white, kinrande and three-colour Ming styles. Notable among them were Y Seifu in the Meiji period and later K Kawai and M Ishiguro.

A Kyoto type circular bowl with foliate rim, signed, Meiji period, 24.2cm. diam. £1,295

A Kyoto tapering rectangular vase painted with panels of a daimyo and his retainers, signed Nihon Yozan, Meiji period, 12.7cm. high. £670

A Kyoto compressed globular koro, signed Kinzan, Meiji period, 8.2cm. diam. £865

Pair of late 19th century almost life-sized stoneware models of a courtier and a courtesan, probably Kyoto ware, 149cm. high. £7,150

Late 19th century Kyoto chrysanthemum-shaped deep bowl decorated in colours and gilt, signed Kizan kore o tsukuru, 29.8cm. diam. £920

Late 19th century Kyoto hexagonal vase decorated in colours and gilt on a royal blue ground, signed Kinkozan zo, 43.6cm. high. (Christie's) £2,160

Late 19th century Kyoto square dish with canted corners, 15.7cm. sq. £660

A Kyoto trumpet-shaped beaker vase decorated in coloured enamels and gilt, signed Kinkozan, Meiji period, 17.8cm. high. £1,025

BERNARD LEACH

Born in 1887, Bernard Leach was brought up in Japan, and Japanese influence predominates in his work. After studying under Frank Brangwyn in the UK, he returned to Japan in 1909 and began to develop influences which let to the Japanese folk art movement. In 1920 he settled in St Ives in Cornwall where, initially with the help of Shoji Hamada, he made stoneware and raku, using local materials. Throughout his life he returned frequently to the East, and he is noted not only for his own output but also as a teacher and a writer. His pottery is remarkable for the carefully planned relationship of body and glaze and by the variety of decorating techniques which he employed. He died in 1979.

A large stonewar jar by Bernard Leach, with lobed sides, circa 1965, 19.3cm. high. (Christie's) £770

A Bernard Leach stoneware jar and cover, circa 1943, 28cm. high. £1,210

A Bernard Leach stoneware St Ives four inch tile painted with a weeping willow tree, 10.2cm. square. (Phillips London) £260

A tall stoneware jug by Bernard Leach, with incised strap handle, circa 1970, 27cm. high. (Christie's) £550

A tall stoneware jug by Bernard Leach, covered in green running glaze, the body decorated with a series of indented studs, impressed BL and St. Ives seals, circa 1961, 12¹/₄in. high. (Bonhams) £1,100

A rare stoneware plate by Bernard Leach, decorated with a painted mountain goat, impressed BL and St. Ives seals, circa 1955, 9³/₄in. diameter. (Bonhams) £1,500

A stoneware vase by Bernard Leach, decorated with brush strokes and spots, in brown and blue, impressed St. Ives, circa 1938, 4³/₄in. high. (Bonhams) £400

A stoneware punch bowl by Bernard Leach, with curved ridged conical lid and two handles, circa 1960, 12½in. wide.
(Bonhams) £320

A porcelain preserve pot and cover decorated by Bernard Leach, covered in a mushroom glaze decorated with grey blue band with iron brown scrolling brushwork, 12cm. high.
(Christie's London) £308

A fine stoneware lidded bowl by Bernard Leach, with conical pagoda lid, impressed BL and St. Ives seals, circa 1967, 9in. diam.
(Bonhams) £3,500

A large stoneware bowl by Bernard Leach, the interior a celadon glaze with foliate painted decoration, circa 1960, 12¼in. diam.
(Bonhams) £1,050

A large stoneware 'fish' vase by Bernard Leach, circa 1970, 37.5cm. high.
(Christie's) £6,050

A blue and white porcelain circular box and cover by Bernard Leach, the domed cover with cobalt blue bands and red enamelled birds, 7cm. high. (Christie's London)
£1,320

A rare porcelain sake bottle by Bernard Leach, with stopper, off-white with decoration of leaping fish in olive brown, circa 1960, 7½in. high.
(Bonhams) £1200

A porcelain plate by Bernard Leach, blue and white with three fishes, circa 1958, (repair to rim), 7½in. diam.
(Bonhams) £700

A superb stoneware 'pilgrim' bottle by Bernard Leach, tenmoku with orange markings, impressed BL and St. Ives seals, 14in. high.
(Bonhams) £3800

A stoneware slab bottle by Bernard Leach, tenmoku glaze, black and rust, impressed BL and St. Ives seals, circa 1966, 7½in. high.
(Bonhams) £850

A fine stoneware slab bottle by Bernard Leach, covered in a pitted mushroom coloured glaze, the front and back faces quartered, 19.5cm. high.
(Christie's) £1,980

An important tall vase by Bernard Leach, light greenish speckled glaze with incised and combed willow tree decoration, impressed BL and St. Ives seals, circa 1955, 14½in. high.
(Bonhams) £2,700

A stoneware jar and cover by Bernard Leach, with domed cover, the dark ground covered in a translucent celadon glaze, impressed BL with St. Ives Pottery seal, 15.5cm. high.
(Bonhams) £1,045

An outstanding stoneware vase by Bernard Leach, glazed in tenmoku, this 'bottle form' would have been thrown on the wheel then beaten and shaved to a square section, impressed BL and St. Ives seals, circa 1963, 14in. high.
(Bonhams) £3,800

A stoneware vase by Bernard Leach, a celadon glaze with tenmoku raised rim, impressed BL and St. Ives seals, circa 1930, 7¼in. high.
(Bonhams) £440

A fine porcelain dish by Bernard Leach, pale celadon, with an embossed deer surrounded by two circles, impressed BL and St. Ives seals, circa 1967, 7½in. diameter.
(Bonhams) £1,200

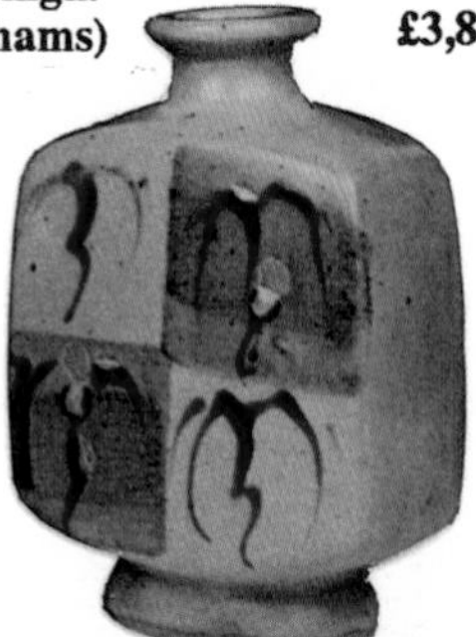

A fine stoneware slab bottle by Bernard Leach, covered in an oatmeal glaze, the front and back faces quartered, each panel with iron-brown brushed decoration of a willow tree, impressed BL with St. Ives Pottery seal, 18.7cm. high.
(Bonhams) £2,640

A magnificent stoneware Pilgrim dish by Bernard Leach, with the figure of a pilgrim, rust, khaki and black tenmoku, impressed BL and St. Ives seals, circa 1970, 13in. diameter.
(Bonhams) £5,200

A stoneware flask, by Bernard Leach, circa 1957, 33cm. high. (Christie's) £3,520

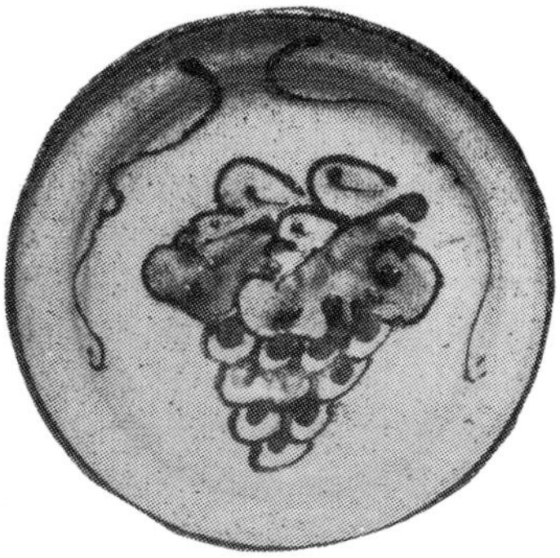

A slip-trailed soft raku bowl by Bernard Leach, impressed BL and St. Ives seals, circa 1920, 23.2cm. diam. £800

A Yingqing porcelain globular vase by Bernard Leach, covered in a bluish white glaze with blue black rim, circa 1965, 15cm. high. (Christie's) £308

A stoneware rectangular slab bottle by Bernard Leach, covered in a tenmoku glaze with shiny black and rich russet areas, circa 1962, 19.4cm. high. (Christie's) £286

A stoneware pilgrim plate with everted rim, decorated by Bernard Leach, 32.2cm. diam. £4,535

A stoneware pear-shaped vase by Bernard Leach, covered in a blue-grey glaze over which brushed hakeme is incised with bell flowers, circa 1960, 26cm. high. (Christie's) £352

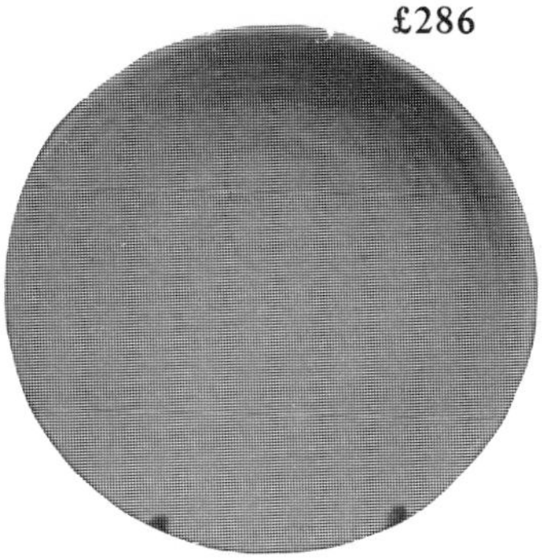

A Yingqing porcelain bowl by Bernard Leach, the exterior covered in a pale greenish white glaze, circa 1970, 17.5cm. diam. (Christie's) £440

A tapering stoneware cylindrical vase by Bernard Leach, covered in an olive-green and pale green ash glaze with areas of russet brown, circa 1965, 30.4cm. high. (Christie's) £880

A stoneware 'leaping deer' plate with everted rim decorated by Bernard Leach, circa 1965, 23.9cm. diam. (Christie's) £2,200

LEEDS CREAMWARE

Very fine Leeds creamware was made under the proprietorship of Hartley Green & Co between 1780–1800. A perforated ware was typical of the output, each opening being made with a separate punch, and not, as was later the case at Wedgwoods, by a multiple tool.

Marks are *Hartley Green & Co* and *Leeds Pottery*, either alone or repeated in a cross. The old moulds were reused at Slee's pottery in Leeds from 1888 and were marked like the originals.

A Leeds creamware cylindrical teapot and cover, with floral terminals and spiral moulded spout, 12cm. (Phillips London) £1,700

A Leeds creamware plate, the centre painted with the portraits of the Prince and Princess William V of Orange, 24.7cm. (Bearne's) £170

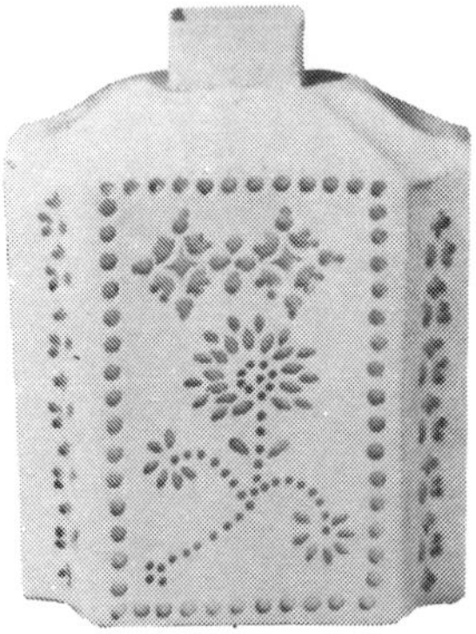

A Leeds creamware tea canister of octagonal shape, 12.5cm. high, incised no. 25. (Phillips) £1,250

A Leeds creamware baluster coffee-pot and domed cover, the green striped body with entwined strap handle, circa 1775, 22.5cm. high. (Christie's) £2,860

A Leeds creamware teapot and cover with 'beaded' edges, brightly painted with Chinese figures in a garden, 17cm., late 18th century. (Bearne's) £230

A Leeds creamware baluster jug, boldly painted below the spout with a portrait of the Princess of Orange, 14cm., late 18th century. (Bearne's) £115

A creamware punch-kettle and cover, painted in a famille rose palette with Orientals among furniture, vases and shrubs, probably Leeds, circa 1775, 21cm. high. (Christie's) £660

A Leeds creamware figure of a bird, with green splashes to its neck, tail and breast, standing astride a slender quatrefoil base, circa 1780, 21cm. high. (Christie's) £2,420

LENCI

The Lenci pottery was active in Turin during the 1930's, and produced three distinctive types of wares. The first, consisting of wall plaques in the form of female heads in scarves, as if going to Mass and figures of the Madonna and Child, were aimed at the domestic market. In stark contrast was the second group, made up of female figures, either nude or clad in contemporary costumes.

The third, and less well-known type, consists of vases and dishes decorated with Cubist-style painted scenes.

A Lenci earthenware box and cover, cover modelled with a dozing elf, dated 4.2.32, 21cm. £330

A Lenci centrepiece modelled as a young naked girl, 46cm. high. (Christie's) £880

A Lenci ceramic figure, of a nude girl wearing a chequered cap kneeling on the top of a globe, with a book in one hand and a dog by her side, with painted signature *Lenci, Made in Italy, Torino*, 48cm. high. (Christie's) £3,960

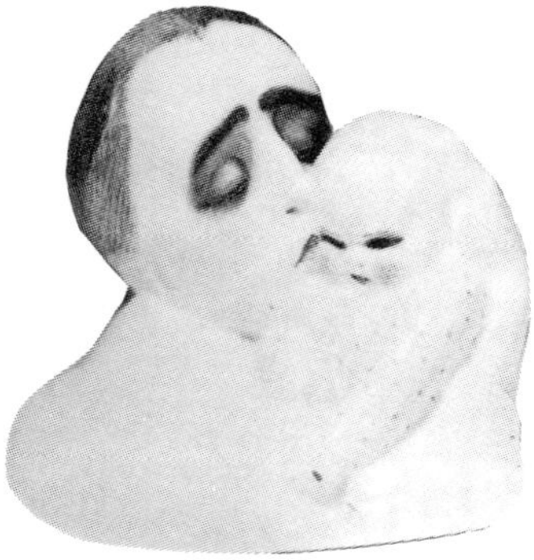

A Lenci bust of a father and baby, the sleekly groomed, dark-haired man clasping and kissing a rosy-cheeked, fair-haired and somewhat reluctant baby, 18cm. high. (Phillips) £680

A Lenci figure group, of a bare-breasted native woman wearing an abstract patterned wrap-around skirt in yellow, green and black, 44cm. high. (Phillips) £900

A large figure of a native girl, marked 'Lenci Torino Made in Italy', 1930's, 55.5cm. high. £440

A Lenci figure of a rooster, painted marks Lenci 1936 S.P., 29cm. high.(Christie's) £1,080

A Lenci pottery wall mask modelled as a young girl wearing a head scarf, 11½in. wide. £200

A Lenci Art Deco ceramic figure, modelled as a girl wearing an orange hat, black jacket and black, white and grey chequered skirt, 37.5cm. high.
(Phillips) £2,000

L Cacio Selle Colombe, a Lenci pottery figure modelled as a girl sitting with her floral and striped skirts spread out around her, 24.5cm. high. (Phillips London) £580

A Lenci ceramic figure of a young peasant woman wearing black skirt, maroon floral shirt and yellow print scarf, 12½in. high.
(Christie's) £640

A good Lenci ceramic group modelled as a mer-child holding a fish aloft, she kneels on the back of two open-mouthed fish, 51cm. high.
(Phillips) £3,000

A Lenci ceramic group, modelled as a seated figure of a girl wearing a black dress, a coloured and patterned cape and a purple scarf, 34.8cm. high. (Phillips London) £950

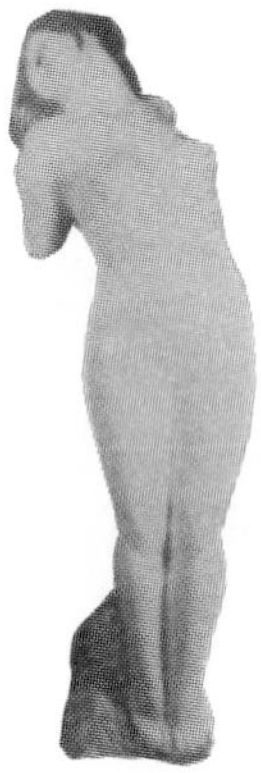

A monumental Lenci ceramic figure, the stylised female nude standing on a rock, covered in a cream slip, 99.2cm. high. (Christie's London) £6,600

A Lenci Art Deco ceramic figure with box and cover, moulded as the head, shoulders and torso of a young woman, 21.4cm. high. (Phillips London) £1,100

A Lenci polychrome ceramic figure of a mermaid and her baby astride a giant turtle, painted in shades of green and brown, 12¾in. high. (Christie's S. Ken) £1,265

A Lenci ceramic head of stylised form, the hair and eye sockets painted in shades of blue and green, 14in. high.
(Christie's) £990

LIBERTY

Arthur Lazenby Liberty was the archetypical Victorian entrepreneur. Starting life as an assistant in a London emporium, he rose to be the manager of a firm called Farmer and Rogers which sold Oriental imports to the rapidly increasing clientele of customers in search of beautiful things for their homes. Recognising the magnitude of the new market, Liberty took a chance and opened his own shop in Regent Street in 1875. Within five years it had proved to be a huge success and it is still thriving on its original site. His success was due to the fact that he had a discriminating taste and knew exactly what his customers wanted to buy.

With regard to pottery, Liberty sold art pottery made by Charles Brannam of Barnstaple (Barum ware) and also the Aller Vale Pottery of Newton Abbot. Liberty was, in addition, a close friend of William Moorcroft, and sold his work with the printed mark *Made for Liberty & Co.*

LIMBACH

The Limbach factory was established in the mid 18th century by Gotthelf Greiner, who had previously been a glass maker. It turned out simple, cheap tablewares, which had the unique distinction of being almost over marked, some bearing the marks of the painter, workshop, factory, and date!

Figures were also made in the style of Meissen and though the quality is inferior, they do have a pleasing simplicity. Again, as if to underline their relation to that factory, they often bear the marks of crossed hayforks! Limbach marks were applied in iron red or purple The factory is in existence to this day.

A pair of Liberty jardinières on pedestals, each with shallow hemispherical bowl decorated with entrelac border in relief. 80cm. high. (Christie's) £2,090

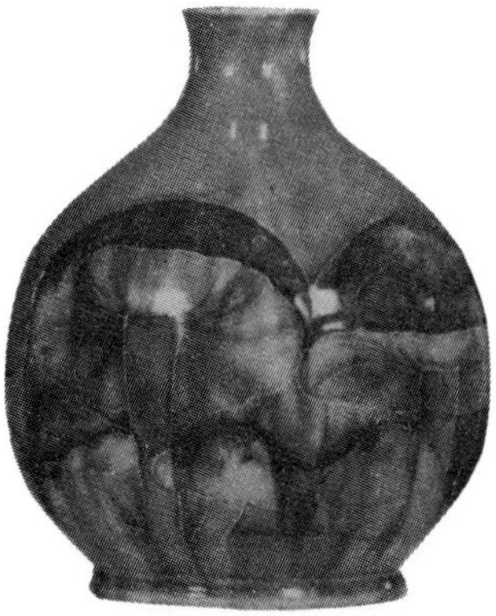

A Moorcroft pottery oviform vase made for Liberty & Co., in the Toadstool pattern, 10in. high, signed in green. (Christie's) £715

A Limbach figure of a girl emblematic of Summer in a yellow hat, orange bodice and puce skirt under a yellow-flowered apron filled with a sheaf of corn, circa 1770, 13cm. high. (Christie's) £330

A Limbach group emblematic of Winter, he wearing a puce and blue hat, she with a puce and black hat, circa 1780, 16cm. high. (Christie's London) £715

A Limbach bird nesting group, modelled as a boy climbing a tree and handing birds from a nest to his companion below, circa 1780, 20cm. high. (Christie's London) £1,320

A Limbach figure of a fisherman leaning against a tree-stump, one bare foot raised, holding a large fish in his arms, circa 1770, 14cm. high. (Christie's) £660

LINTHORPE

The Linthorpe Pottery was established in 1879, near Middlesborough, with Henry Tooth as manager, and, until 1882, Christopher Dresser as art director and designer. Their early wares were designed on simple, flowing lines with equally flowing glazes in two or more rich colours, while later sgraffito or pâte-sur-pâte decoration was introduced. It ceased production in 1890. Pieces are marked with *Linthorpe*, sometimes over the outline of a squat vase. Some are signed by Dresser, and or initialled with Tooth's monogram.

A Linthorpe pottery bowl with electroplate cover, mount and swing handle, designed by Dr. Christopher Dresser, 5½in. diam.
(Christie's S. Ken) £110

A Linthorpe earthenware jug, shouldered tapering form with flared neck, with facsimile signature *Chr. Dresser* 19.5cm. high. (Christie's London) £176

A Linthorpe pottery jug, designed by Dr. Christopher Dresser, with everted rim continuing to form an angled handle, terminating in a rippled design, covered in a streaky caramel, green and crimson glaze, 21cm. high.
(Christie's) £1,980

A Linthorpe twin-handled pottery vase designed by Christopher Dresser, the vessel of flattened oviform with bulbous neck, 20.8cm. high.
(Phillips) £120

A Linthorpe vase, designed by Dr. Christopher Dresser, the gourd-shaped body with double angular spout and curved carrying-bar, streaked glaze of green and brown.
(Christie's) £1,100

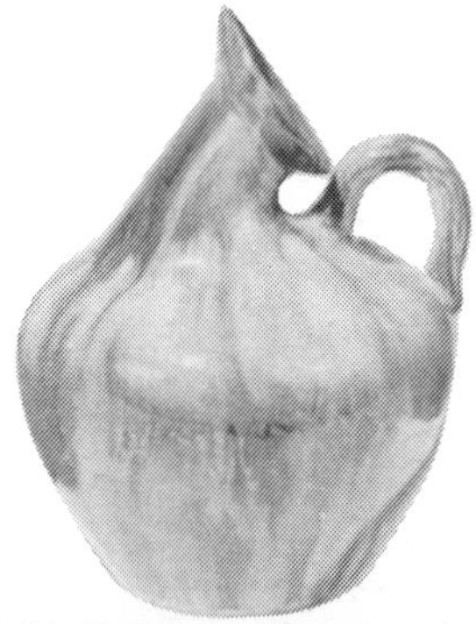

A Linthorpe earthenware jug designed by Dr Christopher Dresser, covered in a thick predominantly green and brown glaze, (slight restoration to lip rim) 16.7cm. high. (Christie's) £176

A Linthorpe vase, designed by Dr. Christopher Dresser, the streaky glaze in tones of green and brown, with incised decoration of a single fern encircling the gourd, 19cm. high.
(Christie's) £1,045

A large Linthorpe Pottery vase designed by Christopher Dresser, of almost egg shape, covered with a brown, milky green, milky blue and amber glaze, 43.5cm. high. (Phillips London) £1,150

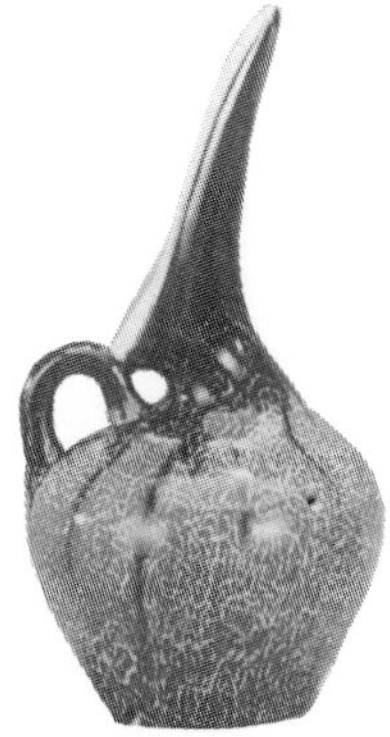

A Linthorpe vase, designed by Dr. Christopher Dresser, glazed in streaky pale and dark brown with a white crackelé effect, 25cm. high
(Christie's) £495

A Linthorpe vase, designed by Dr. Christopher Dresser, formed as a cluster of five pointed gourd shapes encircling a central funnel-shaped neck, 11cm. high.
(Christie's) £1,430

A Linthorpe pottery vase, designed by Dr. Christopher Dresser, the centre decorated with pierced flower bud design, 20cm. high.
(Christie's) £715

A Linthorpe jug, designed by Dr. Christopher Dresser, humped shape with vertical spout and carved handle, incised geometric pattern, 18cm. high.
(Christie's) £605

A Linthorpe face vase, designed by Dr. Christopher Dresser, domed cylindrical shape with double angular spout, decorated with a stylised face on one side, 15.5cm. high.
(Christie's) £660

A Linthorpe vase, designed by Dr. Christopher Dresser, glazed in streaky pale and dark green, with moulded maze patterns and linear designs, 22.5cm. high.
(Christie's) £528

A Linthorpe goat's-head vase, designed by Dr. Christopher Dresser, double gourd shape, decorated with four goats' heads, 28cm. high.
(Christie's) £3,190

A Linthorpe vase, designed by Dr. Christopher Dresser, with frilled lug handles and incised decoration of a bearded face on one side, 22cm. high.
(Christie's) £2,860

A Linthorpe vase, designed by Dr Christopher Dresser, decorated with four grotesque heads, each forming a handle, covered in a streaky green glaze, 22.5cm. high.
(Christie's) £990

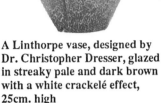

LIVERPOOL

There were seven porcelain factories in Liverpool in the 18th century, of which three, Chaffers, Christians and Penningtons, are generally regarded as forming the mainstream tradition from 1754–99.

The Chaffers' factory (1754–65) made a bone ash and a soapstone porcelain which are often difficult to tell apart as most of the standard shapes were identically produced in both.

Blue and white made up the bulk of production and showed a strong Worcester influence in terms of both shape and decoration, being painted in a free and pleasant style. Distinctive characteristics are the upturned lips of jugs and the fact that cream and sauceboats are often moulded.

The decoration of the polychrome pieces was also of a high quality, often featuring Chinese figure and floral subjects.

The Christian factory (1765–76) produced examples which were well potted but on which the decoration was competent rather than outstanding. Blue and white teawares are very common but flatware is rare, while the polychrome output was again decorated with floral or Chinese mandarin subjects. Christian's specialised in garniture sets of vases, decorated with floral reserves on a gros bleu ground.

The output of the Pennington factory (1769–99) consisted largely of imitations of Christian's wares but was generally of inferior quality as regards both potting and painting. Again, blue and white predominates, and among the finest examples are ship's bowls, which were sometimes named and dated.

A Liverpool blue and white moulded oval sauceboat, attributed to Wm. Ball's factory, circa 1758, 14.5cm. wide. (Christie's) £2,420

A Liverpool tin-glazed stoneware small cylindrical mug, circa 1760, 6.5cm. high. (Christie's) £1,980

A Pennington Liverpool ship bowl painted in blue with a ship in full sail, inscribed *Success to the Perseus, Capt. Gibson, 1790,* **25cm. (Phillips London) £3,400**

A Liverpool creamware oviform jug printed in black with figures on a quayside, 10½in. high, circa 1797. (Christie's) £682

Liverpool creamware pitcher, England, circa 1800, black transfer printed three-masted ship flying the American flag, 10in. high. (Skinner Inc.) £981

A Liverpool delft transfer-printed tile by John Sadler, circa 1760, 13cm. square. (Christie's) £330

A Liverpool tin-glazed stoneware blue and white oviform teapot and cover painted with bamboo and foliage beside fences, circa 1750, 12.5cm. high.
(Christie's) £1,210

A Liverpool delft spirally fluted cornucopia wall vase, 8in. high, circa 1760.
(Christie's) £495

Liverpool creamware platter, Herculaneum pottery, circa 1800, transfer printed medallion of Liberty and Washington's tomb, 11¼in. wide.
(Skinner Inc.) £2,544

Liverpool creamware pottery pitcher, England, 1807–09, transfer printed cartoon depicting cow pulled by Bunopart and John Bull and milked by Jefferson, 8¼in. high.
(Skinner Inc.) £4,607

A Liverpool delft blue and white dated bowl, the interior with a man holding an axe, with the date 1769, 18.5cm. diam.
(Christie's) £1,650

Liverpool creamware presentation pitcher, early 19th century, black transfer decorated with portrait of Benjamin Franklin, 9½in. high.
(Skinner Inc.) £2,493

A Liverpool mug, painted in underglaze blue, iron-red and gold with flowers and rocks and a bridge over a river, 9.5cm. (Lawrence Fine Arts)
£990

A Liverpool Delft blue and white bottle painted with chrysanthemum and other flowers, 9¾in. high, circa 1750. (Christie's)
£350

A Liverpool delft polychrome coffee-cup, painted in blue and green with a building flanked by trees, circa 1760, 6cm. high.
(Christie's) £715

LONGTON HALL

Longton Hall was one of the first porcelain factories in the entire United Kingdom, and production commenced around 1750. Unsurprisingly, in these circumstances, initial output was somewhat primitive in quality, but the standard of both potting and decoration rapidly improved. Early pieces consisted mainly of the so-called 'Snowman' figures and mugs, plates, dishes etc. decorated in 'Littler's' blue. The underglaze was often runny and uneven, but has a brightness which was no doubt in imitation of Vincennes. The reserves were often left unfilled, giving the pieces a somewhat unfinished appearance.

William Littler had joined the venture in 1751 and by 1753–4 there was an improvement in the standard of potting, though decoration was still quite primitive. At this time the scarce Longton Hall powder blue vases, teapots and bottles were made. Between 1754–7 some really beautiful pieces were produced, including a range of leaf-moulded wares in the Meissen style. A large proportion of the output of that time was in fact moulded in remarkable shapes with leaf, fruit and vegetable motifs.

Decoration was carried out by, among others, the 'Castle' painter who specialised in European scenes, and the 'Trembly rose' painter whose floral motifs bear a resemblance to Red Anchor Chelsea. Bird painting was often really superb.

The polychrome wares produced between 1758–60 are also finely decorated, and the products transfer printed in black by Sadler were made at this time.

From 1754 blue and white was also made, but examples of this are now fairly rare.

A Longton Hall leaf dish, painted in the manner of the Trembley Rose painter, circa 1755, 22.5cm. wide. (Christie's) £396

Rare Longton Hall tureen and cover of lobed circular shape, circa 1755, 12in. wide. £3,250

A Longton Hall mug of cylindrical shape with a spurred handle, painted in blue with an Oriental style landscape, 6.5cm. (Phillips) £700

A rare Longton Hall pierced leaf basket of deep circular shape, the overlapping leaves with light puce ribs, 25.5cm. wide. (Phillips) £3,600

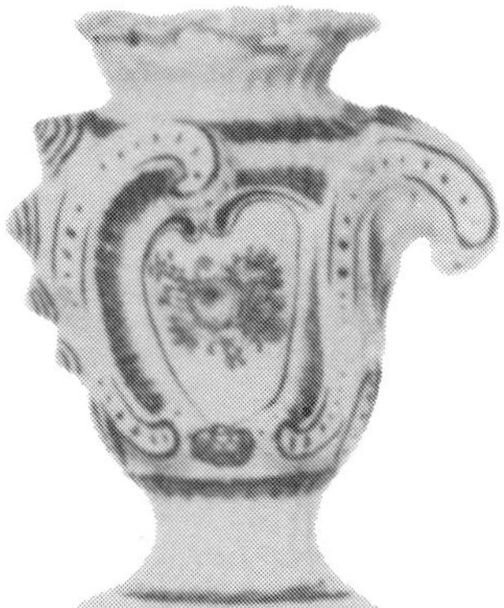

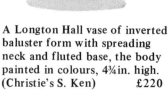

A Longton Hall vase of inverted baluster form with spreading neck and fluted base, the body painted in colours, 4¾in. high. (Christie's S. Ken) £220

A Longton Hall figure of a milkman with two pails, one on his head the other by his side, circa 1755, 27cm. high. (Christie's London) £2,750

LONGTON HALL

The wares are characterised by low footrings and the slight tears in the paste which become clear when they are held to the light. Most have Chinese decoration and twig form handles are common.

The factory failed in 1760, but after a break, William Littler recommenced production at West Pans, near Musselburgh, where he continued until around 1777. The wares produced here were generally of inferior quality to the earlier pieces. *LL* appears on them in blue underglaze, whereas there are no marks on the first period Longton Hall pieces.

A Longton Hall cabbage-leaf moulded teapot and cover, circa 1755, 11cm. high. (Christie's) £12,100

A Longton Hall white figure of a turkey of so-called 'Snowman' type, circa 1750, 18.5cm. high. (Christie's) £1,760

A Longton Hall figure emblematic of Plenty, seated on a mound in a plummed hat blue pink lined coat and pink dress, circa 1755, 5¼in. high. (Christie's S. Ken) £500

A pair of Longton Hall pigeon-tureens and covers, the naturally modelled birds to left and right with purple feather markings, circa 1755, 22cm. long. (Christie's) £6,600

A Longton Hall figure of a flower seller, seated on a tall scroll-moulded base, wearing a yellow coat with fan collar, 4⅝in. high, circa 1755. (Tennants) £650

A Longton Hall mug of flattened bell shape, with pointed 'broken' handle, 16cm. high. £400

A Longton Hall group of Hercules and the Nemean Lion, circa 1755-56, 5¼in. high. £605

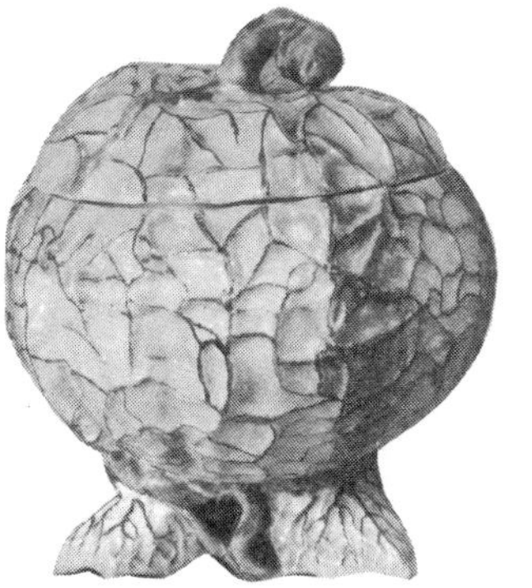

A Longton Hall circular melon tureen and cover, puce W mark, circa 1755, 11.5cm. high. £10,800

LOWESTOFT

Lowestoft did not really set out to become a top-class manufacturer of porcelain, and the proprietors' diffident approach can be seen in their original description of themselves as 'China Manufacturers and Herring Curers'! The factory was established by four partners in 1757, with the humble purpose of producing useful wares for the local inhabitants, and it leapt to spurious fame when some 19th century ceramic writers wrongly ascribed to it a hard paste Chinese porcelain being made expressly for the European and American market.

The earliest Lowestoft pieces were decorated only in a soft underglaze blue in the style of Nanking and no coloured enamels were introduced before 1770. The blue and white ware was often relief moulded and often, too, associated with the modeller James Hughes.

The 1770s saw the introduction of enamelled pieces in Imari type designs, but as the porcelain remains of the soft-paste European variety they are quite distinctive. It is mostly tea wares which received this sort of treatment. There followed a more sophisticated type of decoration in the European style, with bold flowers and no distracting borders, and some Chinese type designs were also adopted.

From about 1790 a sparse and simple sprig motif became popular, often in enamel colours but sometimes only in gold. The factory at this time also made some of the earliest seaside souvenir porcelain in the form of mugs and inkwells bearing inscriptions such as *A Trifle from Lowestoft*, for by now the town was a fashionable watering place.

An 18th century Lowestoft porcelain miniature sparrow-beak jug, 3½in. high. (Hy Duke & Son) £60

A Lowestoft miniature teapot and cover of globular shape, printed in blue with a version of the 'Three Flowers' pattern, 8.5cm. (Phillips) £480

A rare Lowestoft custard cup painted in colours with a 'Redgrave' pattern beneath an egg and flower border, 6cm. (Phillips) £320

A late 18th century Lowestoft porcelain sparrow beak jug of baluster form, painted with Long Elizas, 9cm. high. (Spencer's) £360

A Lowestoft blue and white bell shaped tankard painted with Oriental buildings among trees, circa 1764, 4¾in. high. (Christie's) £715

A rare Lowestoft model of a pug dog with a green collar and a brown coat, seated on a green rectangular base, 9cm. (Phillips) £1,500

LOWESTOFT

Though the bulk of Lowestoft production consisted of 'useful' wares, in keeping with the partners' original intentions, some purely decorative pieces were made, such as small animal figures. It is probable that the factory closed in 1799, by which time Staffordshire competition would be very fierce, and it is on record that a number of Lowestoft craftsmen were taken on by Chamberlains at Worcester in that year.

A Lowestoft circular sugar bowl and flat cover painted with scattered cornflowers, circa 1795, 11.5cm. diam. (Christie's London) £1,100

A Lowestoft bell-shaped mug, painted in colours, in the manner of the Tulip Painter, 14cm. high. (Phillips) £1,100

A Lowestoft blue and white fluted baluster coffee pot and cover transfer printed with loose bouquets, circa 1780, 26.5cm. high. (Christie's London) £990

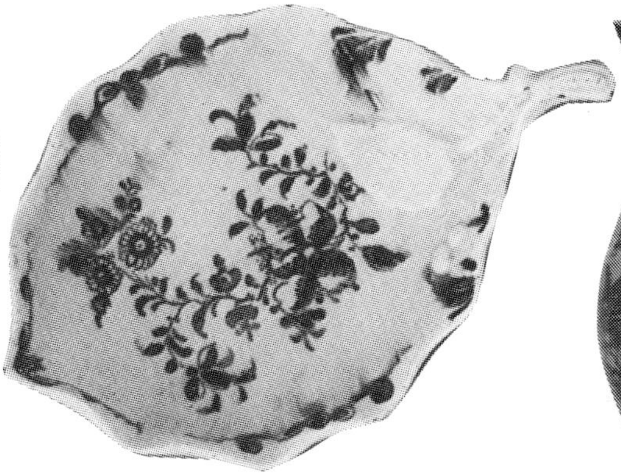

A Lowestoft blue and white leaf-shaped pickle dish with moulded stalk handle and veins, circa 1765, 6in. wide. (Christie's) £480

Lowestoft jug, blue and white chinoiserie pattern of landscapes and figures, approx. 7in. (G. A. Key) £160

A Lowestoft cylindrical mug, the scroll handle with thumb rest, 15cm. high. (Phillips) £1,900

A Lowestoft oviform punch-pot and cover painted in a famille rose palette with Oriental figures at various pursuits, circa 1780, 22cm. high. (Christie's) £2,640

A Lowestoft blue and white rectangular octagonal tea caddy, circa 1765, 13cm. high. £1,190

A Lowestoft teapot and cover, printed in underglaze blue with the ‘Pagoda and Man Crossing a Bridge’ pattern, the cover with the ‘Wolf and Exotic Bird’, 10.5cm. high. £550

A Lowestoft square inkwell, the base inscribed in black, ‘Eliz,th. Buckle 1775’, 5cm. high. £2,970

A Lowestoft feeding cup, painted in blue with a five petalled flower with two sprays and a moth, 7.5cm. (Phillips) £600

A Lowestoft blue and white patty pan, blue crescent mark, circa 1768, 10.5cm. diam. £170

An inscribed Lowestoft ‘trifle’ mug with single-spur handle, 14cm. high. £5,000

An unrecorded Lowestoft ship bowl inscribed *Success To The Cruizer Cutter/Henry Major Master,* 27cm. (Phillips London) £2,300

A Lowestoft blue and white baluster mug with scroll handle, painted with a three storey pagoda, circa 1765, 14.5cm. high. (Christie's London) £308

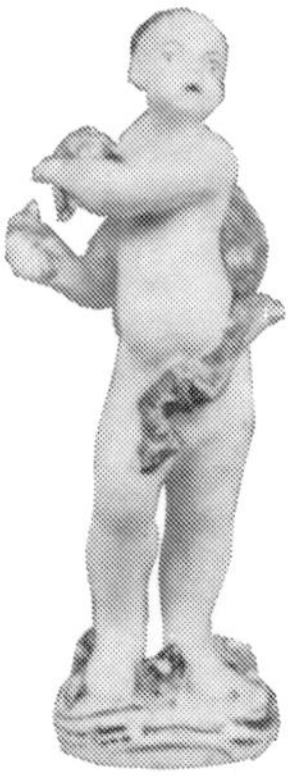

A Lowestoft figure of a putto, his brown hair tied in a top-knot, a puce scarf trailing from his shoulder, circa 1770, 13.5cm. high. (Christie's London) £1,870

A Lowestoft blue and white moulded globular jug with cylindrical neck and loop handle, painted with Orientals at discussion, circa 1765, 26cm. high. (Christie's London) £1,870

LUDWIGSBURG

In 1758 Johann Jakob Ringler established a porcelain factory for Duke Carl Eugen of Württemberg. Ringler had arrived there via Vienna, Höchst and various other centres, but it was at Ludwigsburg that he remained until his death in 1802.

The factory produced a distinctive smoky brown body, which, if the exquisite detail on some of the figures is anything to go by, was nevertheless excellent for modelling. Tablewares and vases really show little originality, but some fine modellers were employed on figure production. Among the earliest were groups of dancers, reflecting the Duke's interest in ballet, probably by Jean Louis, who also is credited with having designed the tiny Venetian Fairs series. Both of these were subsequently the subjects of many inferior reproductions. Other modellers include J C W Beyer, who composed 'lean and hungry' figures, and Johann Göz.

The Duke was generous with money for the factory, but after his death in 1793 it rapidly declined, and closed in 1824.

The most common mark is two interlaced back to back *C*s below a ducal crown. After the accession of Duke Ludwig in 1793 the Cs were replaced by an *L* and from 1796–1816 an *FR* monogram for King Frederick. In 1816 Frederick was succeeded by William, and the mark became *WR*. Three stag's horns in a shield were sometimes used around 1800.

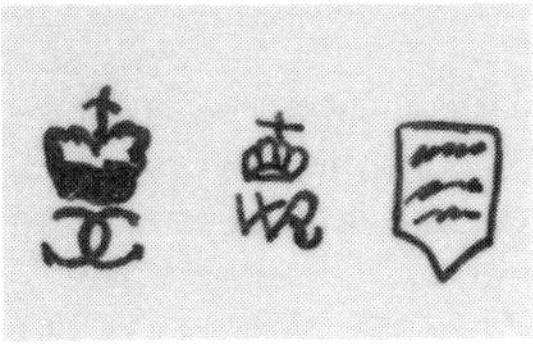

A Ludwigsburg teabowl and saucer, painted with birds on branches, circa 1760.
(Christie's) £495

A Ludwigsburg rococo oval two-handled tureen and cover, blue crowned interlaced C mark and impressed IP, circa 1765, 32cm. wide. £2,640

**Four Ludwigsburg putti emblematic of the Senses, after models by Johann Heinrich Schmid, Taste eating fruit, Smell with a basket of flowers, Hearing listening to a watch and Touch holding fruit, circa 1780, 24cm. high overall.
(Christie's) £2,090**

**A Ludwigsburg group of Bacchus and a Bacchante modelled by Johann Christian Wilhelm Beyer, the naked figures embracing and she squeezing a bunch of grapes into his bowl, circa 1765, 24cm. high.
(Christie's) £2,750**

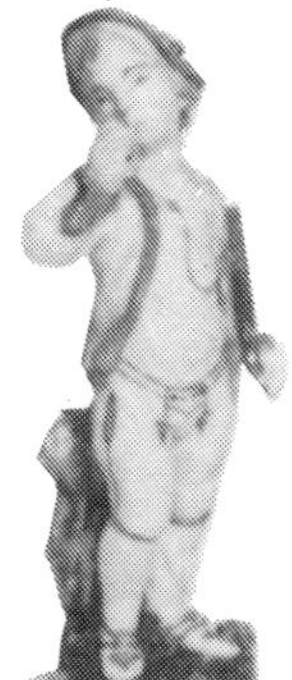

A Ludwigsburg figure of a Tyrolean boy playing a pipe, standing on a shaped rectangular base (stick missing, damage to extremities), circa 1770, 10.5cm. high.
(Christie's London) £308

A Ludwigsburg group of dancers modelled by Franz Anton Bustelli, blue crowned crossed-C mark and incised UM 3 to base, circa 1760, 16cm. high. (Christie's) £12,100

A Ludwigsburg figure of Columbine from the Commedia dell'Arte modelled by Franz Anton Bustelli, circa 1760, 10.5cm. high. £2,180

A Ludwigsburg group of a boar being attacked by three hounds, blue interlaced C mark, circa 1765, 17cm. long. £1,080

One of a pair of Ludwigsburg rococo two-handled pot pourri vases and pierced covers, circa 1770, 28cm. high. £1,620

A Ludwigsburg figure of a youth seated on a rocky outcrop, circa 1770, 19cm. high. £460

A Ludwigsburg chinoiserie group, modelled by J. Weinmuller, incised Geer mark, circa 1770, 34cm. high. £1,760

A Ludwigsburg figure of Arion, blue interlaced L mark and impressed I.L.F. 53. and with iron-red painter's mark of Sausenhofer, circa 1765, 15cm. high. £265

A Ludwigsburg miniature group of three figures rolling dice, blue interlaced C mark, circa 1775, 8cm. wide. £1,510

A Ludwigsburg figure of a lady with a muff modelled by Pierre F. Lejeune, circa 1760, 12.5cm. high. (Christie's) £825

A Ludwigsburg group of two putti, blue interlaced C's and impressed IO marks, circa 1765, 17cm. high. £385

MAJOLICA

Majolica is a glazed or enamelled earthenware often decorated in relief, and it was 16th century Italian mastery of this medium which provided the inspiration for its revival some three centuries later. In this country, Minton in particular made a wide range of objects in majolica, from garden ornaments to small figures, from 1850 onwards, under the guidance of Leon Arnoux. Some of his work was shown at the Great Exhibition in 1851. Wedgwood too revived its own 18th century green glazed ware with decoration of relief-moulded leaves, using a white earthenware body. Elsewhere, in Italy production centred mainly round the Cantagalli workshop in Florence and the Ginori family in Doccia, while Scandinavian and American factories also jumped on this popular bandwagon.

**An English majolica tobacco-jar and cover in the form of a pug dog, glazed in shades of brown and with a pink interior, circa 1860's, 8in. high.
(Christie's S. Ken) £308**

A majolica spill-vase group of a squirrel seated on its haunches nibbling a nut beside a hollow tree-trunk, circa 1870. 4¼in. high. (Christie's S. Ken) £88

A pair of Majolica blackamoor figures of a man and woman, each standing by a tree stump, damaged, 70cm. high.
(Bearne's) £800

**A Spanish maiolica dish painted in blue, yellow and ochre with a portrait of the Virgin in profile to the left within two bands of flowerheads, 18th century, 30.5cm. diameter.
(Christie's) £990**

A pair of siena maiolica vases by Bartholomeo Terchi, one vase signed Bar: Terc(h)i: Romano: 1726, 56cm. high overall. (Phillips) £2,400

**A Brown, Westhead, Moore & Co. majolica group of two kittens, one climbing up the front of a lady's boot, the other chasing a ball of wool, circa 1880's, 6¼in. high.
(Christie's S. Ken) £462**

Early 17th century Netherlands majolica syrup jar, painted in blue with scrolling foliage and plant pods, 23.5cm. high. (Phillips) £500

MARBLEHEAD

The Marblehead pottery was established in 1905 with the view of providing occupational therapy for patients in a local Massachusetts sanatorium. After a short while, however, it was operating as a separate commercial venture. The pottery produced earthenware vases and bowls, in simple, often straight-sided shapes, and covered in muted matt glazes. Characteristic decoration includes animal and flower motifs and also features of the Massachusetts coast such as seaweed, fish, ships etc. Its produce was sold from 1908 onwards. The Marblehead mark consists of an impressed *M* and the emblem of a sailing ship, with the potter's initials incised.

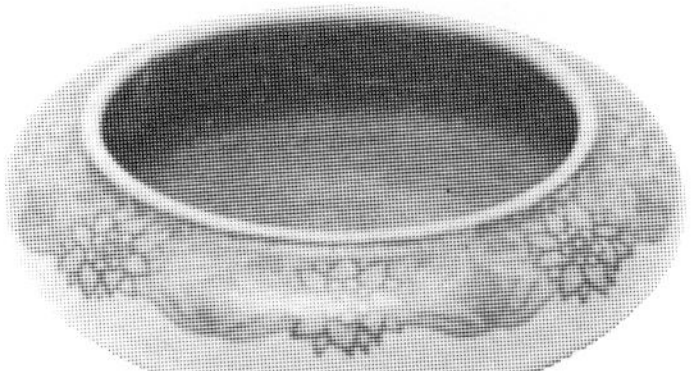

Decorated Marblehead pottery bowl, Massachusetts, circa 1905, squat shallow form, initialled *HT* for Hannah Tutt, 7½in. diam. (Robt. W. Skinner Inc.) £399

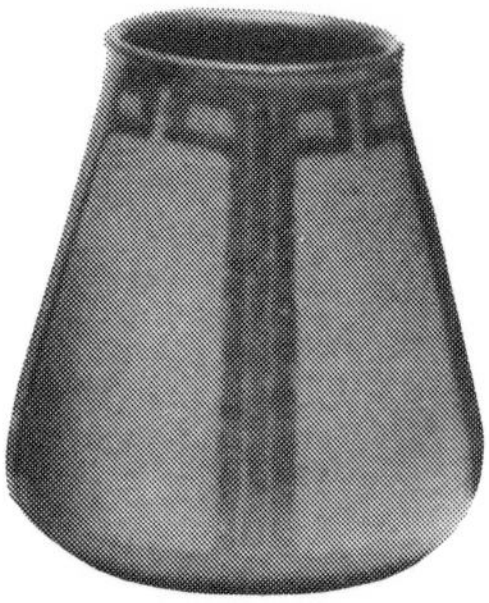

Decorated Marblehead pottery vase, Massachusetts, circa 1905, stamped with logo and incised with early *MP* mark, 5¾in. (Skinner Inc.) £988

Marblehead Pottery decorated vase, Massachusetts, early 20th century, with design of alternating elongated trees, 6⅜in. high. (Skinner Inc.) £623

Marblehead pottery experimental landscape vase, executed by Arthur E. Baggs, circa 1925, 7¼in. high. (Skinner Inc.) £1,975

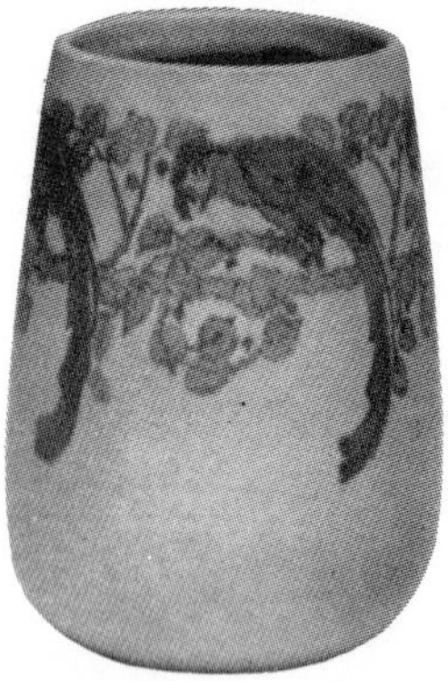

Marblehead Pottery decorated vase, Massachusetts, early 20th century, with repeating design of parrots on branches, 7in. high. (Skinner Inc.) £831

Marblehead Pottery decorated vase, Marblehead, Massachusetts, early 20th century, with incised and painted repeating design of flowers, 3¾in. high. (Skinner Inc.) £1,039

A decorated Marblehead pottery four-colour vase, Mass., circa 1910, 6in. high. £1,300

MARSEILLES

Marseilles faience was made by a number of factories in the 18th century, but the name most often associated with it is that of Pierrette Caudelot, la Veuve Perrin.

After the death of her husband in 1748, she ran the factory until her own death in 1793. Until 1764, when he set up his own concern, she was in partnership with Honoré Savy who claimed to have invented the style of decoration where a translucent green enamel is applied over black painting. Other popular forms of decoration include chinoiserie scenes in the style of Pillement and scenes after the artist Teniers, while Mediterranean fish were often used to decorate large soup tureens.

Another of her former employees who set up on his own was Joseph Robert. He was responsible in no small degree for the high quality of the decoration at the Perrin factory and he set up his own factory in 1766 to produce porcelain. His products have a highly distinctive style, and the decoration is quite different from the mainstream of French production of the time. It often features individual flower painting and landscape scenes strongly reminiscent of the Meissen style of the late 1730s. The factory did not survive the Revolution and closed in 1793. While Perrin and Savy may also have manufactured porcelain, no confident ascriptions of their pieces can be made.

One of a pair of Marseilles (Veuve Perrin) shaped circular plates painted en camaieu vert with bouquets of flowers, circa 1765, 25cm. diam. (Christie's) £462

A French faience holy water stoup, painted in colours with St Louis kneeling before an altar in a landscape vignette, third quarter of the 18th century, probably Marseilles 44cm. high. (Christie's London) £825

A Marseilles faience pear-shaped ewer and two-handled oval basin, 14¾in. wide, circa 1765. £295

A Marseilles faience casket in the form of an armoire, late 18th century, 14½in. high. £700

One of a pair of Marseilles circular dishes painted en camaieu verte, Savy's factory, circa 1770, 28.5cm. diam. £1,620

MARTINWARE

The Martin Brothers cooperative, which set up in 1873, consisted of Robert Wallace Martin, who had worked for the Fulham pottery, and his brothers Walter and Edwin, who had previously been employed by Doulton. Walter was thrower, and Edwin decorator, while a further brother, Charles, became the business manager and ran a shop in Brownlow Street, London.

Martinware comes in a wide variety of shapes. The decoration is mainly incised, with the colours reminiscent of Doulton stoneware. The most common motifs are plants, birds, animals and grotesques, of which perhaps the most notable are R W Martins 'wally birds'. These are often found as tobacco jars, with the heads forming the lids, and generally have a somewhat menacing air. Some of the later production tended more towards the abstract, relating it to later studio pottery. The works closed in 1914.

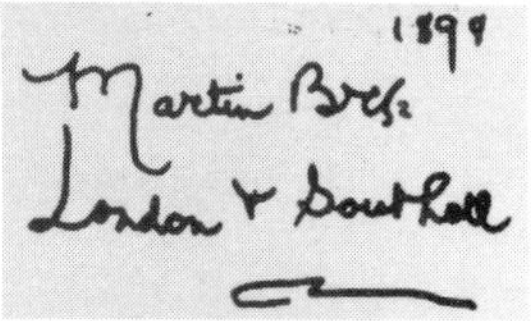

A Martin Bros. stoneware two-handled spirit flask, 9½in. high, London and Southall, 1901. £700

An early Martin Brothers vase, incised with birds and leafy branches in green, blue and brown, 23.3cm. high. (Phillips) £85

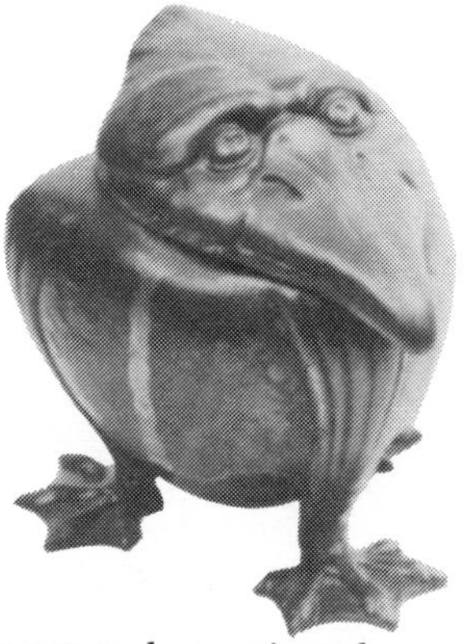

An unusual ceramic and pewter inkwell, cast in the style of a Martin Brothers bird with the head forming the hinged cover, 4¼in. high. (Christie's S. Ken) £220

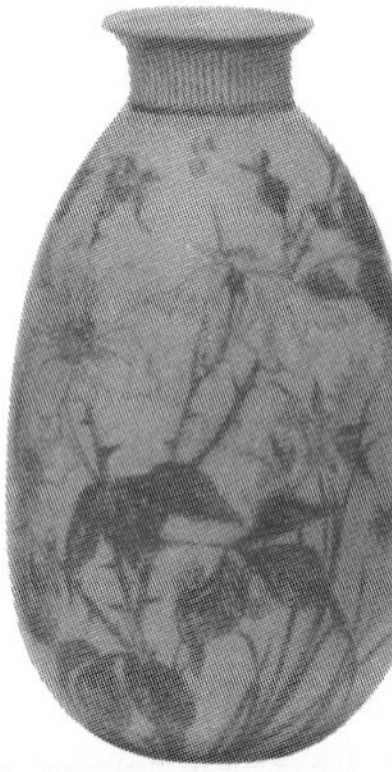

A Martin Brothers stoneware vase, incised with a pattern of wild roses in a cream glaze with briers and leaves in green on an oatmeal ground, 25.50cm. high. (Phillips) £620

A Martin Bros. stoneware jug, moulded and painted with a 'knobbled' design in blue and brown enamels, 23.3cm., inscribed *Martin Bros, London & Southall, 10–1895.* (Bearne's) £420

A Martin Brothers stoneware vase, swollen form with flared neck, decorated with caricatures of fish and eels swimming amid underwater plants, dated 6-1890, 18.9cm. high. (Christie's) £660

A Martin Brothers grotesque bird, the head incised *Martin Bros., 3–1902, London & Southall,* mounted on circular ebonised wooden base, 25cm. high. (Christie's) £3,740

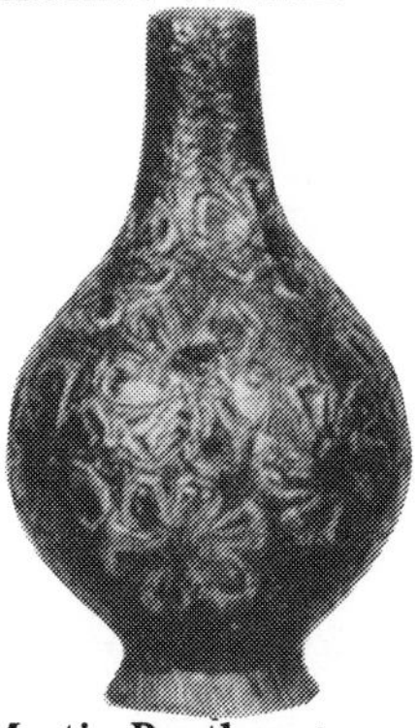

A Martin Brothers brown-glazed stoneware vase of swollen form with tapering cylindrical neck and flared base, with incised decoration of flowerheads, 15.7cm. high. (Christie's) **£110**

A Martin Bros. stoneware jug, the bulbous body suggesting a sea-creature, 21.8cm. high. £430

A large Martin Brothers stoneware bird, having broad brown beak and large slightly protruding eyes, 36.5cm. high. (Phillips) £5,200

A Martin Bros. stoneware tobacco jar and cover, modelled as a grotesque grinning cat, 1885, 22cm. high. £7,560

Two Martin Brothers stoneware jugs of rounded rectangular section, the body incised and painted in blue and green with flowering branches and stylised monogram CH&EA. (Christie's) £198

A Martin Bros. stoneware jug painted with fish and sea monsters on mottled blue ground, 10¼in. high, London and Southall 1897. £700

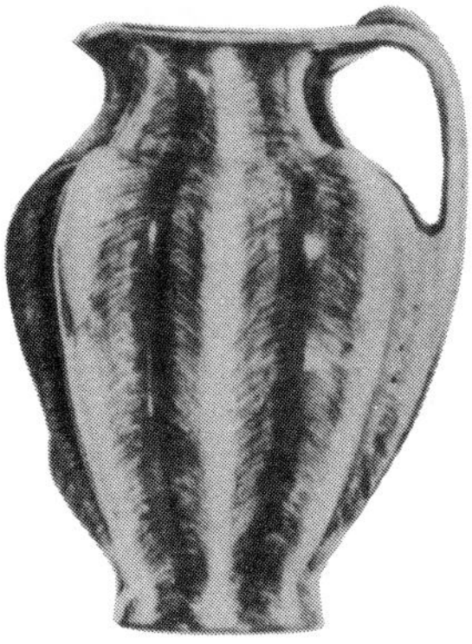

A Martinware 'gourd' single-handled lobed pottery jug, London Southall, circa 1900, 10in. high. £380

A Martin Brothers jug, with incised decoration of a stork-like creature with a long pelican bill on two of the three sides, 1898, 24cm. high. (Christie's) £990

A stoneware Martin Bros. grotesque double-face jug, dated 1903, 19cm. high. £1,190

An unusual Martin Brothers stoneware twin handled loving cup, with twin snake handles and incise-decorated with winged griffins having foliate tails in browns and beige. (Phillips London) £320

A Martin Brothers stoneware salt modelled on the corners with the heads of four comical horned beasts, 10cm. high. (Phillips) £220

A Martin Brothers stoneware double face jug, each side of the globular vessel modelled in high relief with a grinning visage, 16.5cm. high. (Phillips London) £720

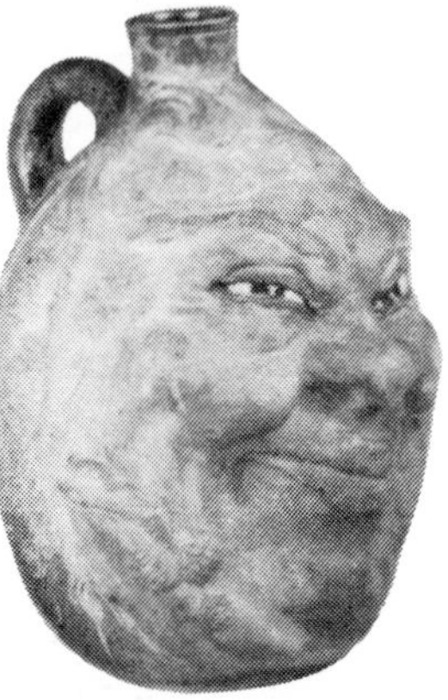

A Martin Brothers John Barleycorn jug, the ovoid body modelled with grinning face, 18cm. high, incised mark and 6-1911. (Lawrence Fine Arts) £550

A Martinware grotesque bird tobacco jar, the detachable head with long drooping beak, the incised plumage decorated in typical shades of brown and blue, 11in. high (excl. stand). (Christie's S. Ken) £6,160

A Martin Brothers stoneware vase, painted with grotesque fish, eels, a starfish and aquatic foliage in browns, white, black and blue, 21.5cm. high. (Phillips London) £620

A Martin Brothers stoneware vase, decorated with white clematis and marguerites on a dark brown ground, 1889, 21.4cm. high. (Christie's London) £264

A Martin Brothers stoneware vase, painted in browns, white, black and blue with grotesque fish, an eel, a crab and a jellyfish, 23cm. high. (Phillips London) £600

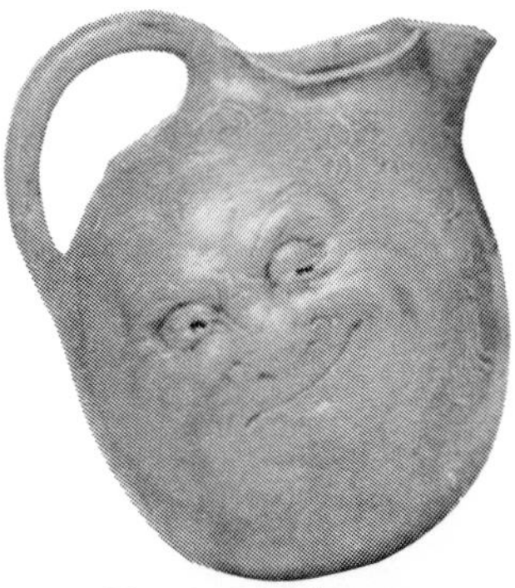

A Martin Brothers stoneware double face jug, with a broad spout and overhead loop handle, 19.5cm. high, signed *Martin Bros., London & Southall.* (Phillips London) £2,000

A Martin Brothers vase, the writhen globular body with four handles modelled as snakes biting the rim of the vase, 1899, 27.5cm. high.
(Christie's) £2,420

A Martin Brothers vase, the body glazed in dark green with an incised cellular pattern, incised *Martin Bros., London & Southall*, 18.5cm. high.
(Christie's) £462

A Martin Brothers character jug, modelled as a grotesque seal-like creature holding its sides, its gaping mouth forming the spout, greeny-blue body glaze, 24.5cm. high.
(Christie's) £462

A Martin Brothers stoneware vase, decorated with magnolia blooms and insects nearby, against a textured ground glazed in brown and white, 23.60cm. high.
(Phillips) £360

An amusing Martin Brothers stoneware model of a baby owl, the creature has a pale brown round body resting on a circular base above ebonised stand, 27.50cm. high, signed *Martin Bros. London & Southall* and dated *10–1895*.
(Phillips) £3,000

An unusual Martin Brothers stoneware timepiece, formed as a tower with domed and floral decorated top, foliate and beaded decoration flanking the face and panels of birds, London 1875.
(Phillips) £620

A Martin Brothers stoneware jug, covered in a brown and mottled green-blue glaze, decorated with incised grotesque sea creatures and lines of verse, dated 12–1888, 23.5cm. high.
(Christie's) £1,320

A large Martin Brothers jardinière, the swollen form with everted pie-crust rim, on short ridged foot, incised decoration of scrolling plants and foliage, 1888, 50cm. high.
(Christie's) £2,420

An amusing Martin Brothers stoneware bird, having a removable head with bushy brows and a broad brown beak, 33cm. high, signed on head and base *R.W. Martin & Bros. London & Southall*, dated 1892.
(Phillips) £2,600

MASON

Miles Mason was a dealer in Chinese porcelain who in around 1800 set up his own manufactory at Lane Delph, to replace stock which he could no longer obtain from the East. There, he produced both bone china and 'hybrid' hard paste porcelain, mostly decorated with underglaze blue printing in simple Chinese patterns. Their teaware and dessert ware shapes were mostly unique of their type and so are readily recognisable. Later, however, the factory moved on to produce ironstone pottery, with such success that Mason's Ironstone is a leading name to this day.

Mid 19th century Mason's ironstone toilet set. (British Antique Exporters) £200

One of a pair of Mason's ironstone soup tureens, covers and stands, circa 1825, 13in. £750

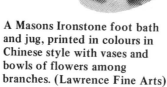

A Masons Ironstone foot bath and jug, printed in colours in Chinese style with vases and bowls of flowers among branches. (Lawrence Fine Arts) £1,760

Part of a mid 19th century Mason's ironstone dessert service of nine pieces, plate 9in. diam. £550

A Miles Mason sugar bowl and cover painted with 'The Dragon in Compartments' pattern, 16cm. wide, with two others, 15cm. and 19cm. wide, 1810-15. (Christie's) £429

Mason's style jug and foot-bath. £850

Mason's ironstone jug decorated with Imari pattern, 8in. high. (G. A. Key) £78

A Mason's ironstone circular jardiniere, the handles in the form of bears, 42cm. diam. £800

A Mason's ironstone bowl, 27.2cm., 1820's. £460

A Mason's bird of paradise pattern canted rectangular meat dish, circa 1850, 17in. long. £100

One of a pair of Mason's blue and gilt two handled vases and covers, 20in. high. £1,000

A very rare garniture of Mason vases, 19.5cm and 17cm. high., two vases impressed M. Mason. (Phillips) £1,200

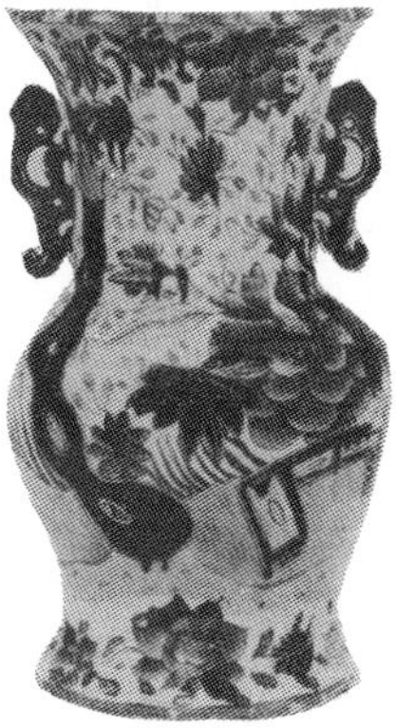

One of a pair of Mason's ironstone baluster vases with fluted trumpet necks, circa 1820, 14½in. high. £725

Mason's pottery jug painted and stamped mark, with lizard handle and Imari pattern, 8in. high. (G. A. Key) £110

A pair of Mason's ironstone baluster shaped octagonal vases with high domed covers, 20in. high. £340

A massive Mason's ironstone ewer of vase shape with double scroll handle, circa 1820, 67cm. high. (Christie's) £700

MEISSEN

At the beginning of the 18th century the race was on in Europe to find the secret of the manufacture of Chinese-type porcelain. The winner was Augustus the Strong, Elector of Saxony, thanks to his sequestration of a young alchemist, J F Böttger, whom he originally employed to turn base metal to gold. When Böttger failed at this, Frederick set him the alternative task of porcelain manufacture under the eye of Ehrenfried Walther von Tschirnhaus, a Saxon physicist who was also fascinated by this challenge. Success finally came in 1710, and a new red and white porcelain manufactory was set up in the Albrechtsburg at Meissen.

Production problems persisted, however, and it was not until 1713 that the first pieces were offered for sale, the decoration of which was largely influenced by the court silversmith Johann Irminger, and featured moulded and applied vine leaf and foliage reliefs and modelled and applied rose sprays.

The king wanted colour, but Böttger was never really successful in finding enamels which would withstand the firing temperatures required to fuse them into the glaze, and much of his output remained white.

Poor Böttger never enjoyed his triumph. He was still under guard until 1714, and at the mercy of a capricious ruler who refused to entertain his plans for improved kilns etc. In 1719 the factory's arcanist, Stölzel, smuggled its secrets out to Vienna enabling a rival establishment to be set up there, and when Böttger died in March of that year, at the early age of 37, the factory was in disarray.

Immediately however a turn-round occurred. The king made instant reforms,

A Meissen KPM baluster teapot and domed cover, painted by P. E. Schindler, circa 1724, 15cm. wide. (Christie's) £7,700

A Meissen group of two vintagers on a rocky outcrop, a young woman by their side filling a bottle from a barrel, 21 cm. (Bearne's) £760

A Meissen figure of the Courtesan from the Cries of London series, modelled by J. J. Kandler and P. J. Reinicke, circa 1754, 14cm. high. (Christie's) £1,760

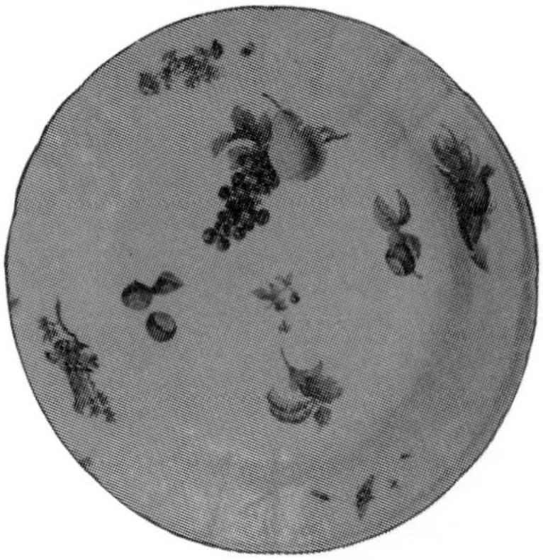

One of a pair of Meissen circular dishes, blue crossed swords marks, Pressnummern 20 and 21, circa 1745, 30.5cm. diam. (Christie's) £2,420

A Meissen powder purple ground milk jug and cover with bud finial painted in colours with Watteau figures, crossed swords mark, circa 1745, 14cm. high. (Christie's London) £1,210

A Meissen group of a Mother and Children modelled by J. J. Kandler and P. Reinicke, circa 1740, 23.5cm. high. (Christie's) £1,650

installed the new kilns he had denied Böttger, and underglaze blue was achieved. From Vienna too came the repentant Stölzel, bringing with him the enamel painter Gregorius Höroldt, who quickly perfected a superb range of overglaze enamels and used them to create fine copies of oriental wares as well as his own chinoiserie inventions. Through Höroldt, Meissen finally came to fame and fortune, and the first marks were introduced. For 15 years painted decoration remained paramount, and was only superseded by J J Kaendler's relief moulding and figurines in the late 1730s.

From 1740 Kaendler's output was phenomenal. In addition to a constant supply of naturalistic figures, he designed new relief patterns for tablewares, and it is to him more than anyone that Meissen owes its long triumph, which started to wane only after the peace of 1763, when the victorious Frederick the Great of Prussia was successful in luring several fine modellers (though not Kaendler) to his new factory in Berlin.

The rococo Meissen style came to look increasingly out of date in the new Neo Classical age. Throughout the late 18th and early 19th century the factory struggled for survival in the face of disappearing markets (as imports were forbidden by several countries to protect their domestic products), and the new dominance of English creamware. Though the Napoleonic Wars temporarily cut off the supply of English goods, other German potters had learned to imitate Wedgwood cream and Jasperware, and finally Meissen too came to manufacture imitations, both of this, and their own earlier pieces.

A Meissen figure of a thrush, modelled by J. J. Kandler, circa 1745, 18cm. high. (Christie's) £3,080

A Meissen two-handled silver-shaped jardiniere, the fluted body painted with sprays of Manierblumen, circa 1755, 17cm. wide. (Christie's) £880

A Meissen deckelpokal, blue crossed swords mark to the base, and gilder's mark c to both pieces, circa 1725, 18cm. high. (Christie's) £8,250

A pair of late Meissen figures of a gallant and a lady, each standing on a shaped grassy base moulded with gilt scrolls, 10½in. high. (Christie's) £1,760

A Meissen figure of a recumbent pug dog on a baroque stool, modelled by J. J. Kandler, 11cm. high. (Christie's) £6,600

A Meissen hexagonal baluster teacaddy painted in the manner of P. E. Schindler with Orientals taking tea, circa 1725, 9cm. high. (Christie's) £1,980

A Meissen group emblematic of Water, modelled as Neptune and Venus scantily clad in puce and yellow flowered robes, crossed swords mark, circa 1750, 16.5cm. wide. (Christie's London) £440

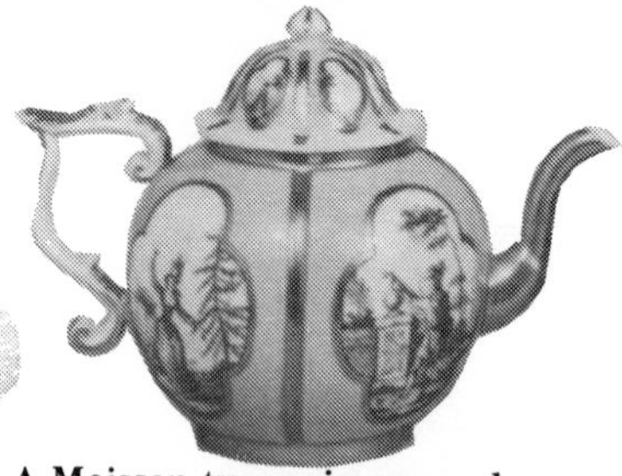

A Meissen turquoise ground quatrefoil teapot and cover with a wishbone handle, painted in Purpurmalerei with theatrical figures and women in landscapes, circa 1735, 17cm. wide. (Christie's London) £1,100

A Meissen figure of a recumbent lion, modelled by J. J. Kaendler, painted with a brown coat, traces of crossed swords mark, circa 1745, 22cm. wide. (Christie's London) £1,320

19th century Meissen Zwiebelmuster centrepiece, 39cm. high. (Auktionshaus Arnold) £932

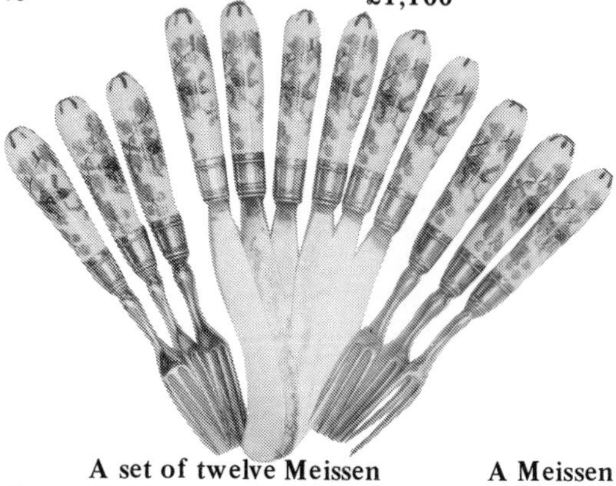

A set of twelve Meissen Kakiemon knives and forks painted with two birds perched on a branch, circa 1735, silver tines and blades, the handles 7cm. long. (Christie's London) £8,800

A Meissen figure of a bagpipe player modelled by J. J. Kaendler, in green and yellow waistcoat and pink cloak with yellow stockings, circa 1740, 23cm. high. (Christie's London) £1,980

A fine Meissen chinoiserie arbour group modelled by Reinicke, the young lovers seated closely together, 18.5cm. crossed swords mark, circa 1755. (Phillips London) £2,700

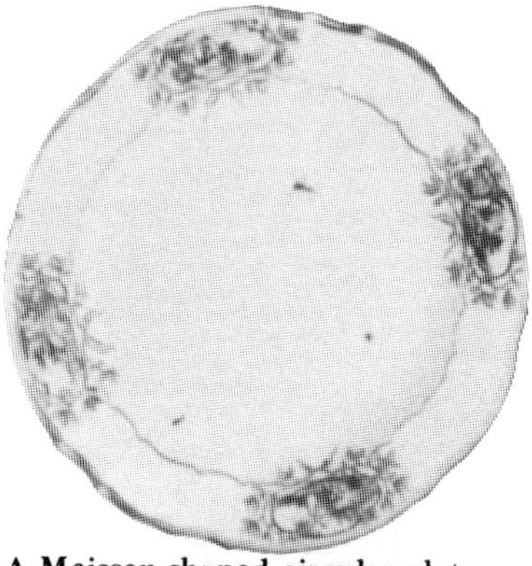

A Meissen shaped circular plate moulded with Gotzkowsky erhabene Blumen, the rim painted in colours with four quatrefoil cartouches, circa 1738, 23.5cm. diam. (Christie's London) £935

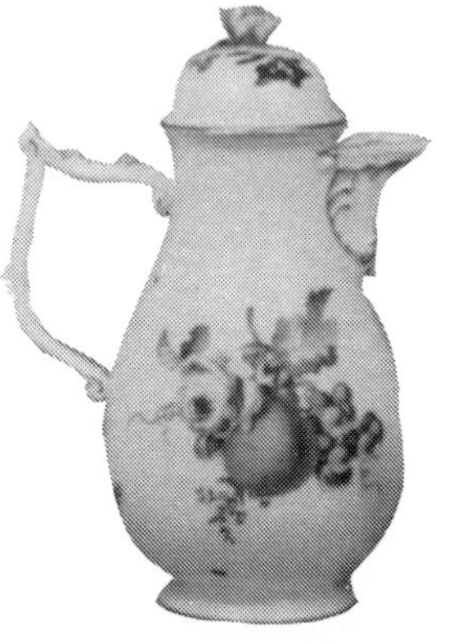

A Meissen baluster coffee pot and domed cover, painted with fruiting vine and cut peaches, roses, a pear, wild strawberries and a butterfly, 22.5cm. (Christie's London) £1,650

A late Meissen group of three dogs, one a pug standing with black face and paws and wearing a green collar, 21cm. (Phillips London) £1,100

A Meissen Flaeschenhalter from the Swan service modelled by J. J. Kaendler and J. F. Eberlein for Count Bruehl, circa 1740, 24cm. wide. (Christie's London) £41,800

A late Meissen group after the painting by Francois Boucher entitled *Pensent-ils au raisin?* 19.4cm. (Phillips London) £440

A rare Meissen figure of a cellist, dressed in a puce striped jacket, yellow waistcoat and puce breeches, 12.5cm. (Phillips London) £400

A pair of Meissen models of doves modelled by J. J. Kaendler, the naturalistically modelled and coloured birds sitting on shaped round bases, circa 1745, both about 16cm. wide. (Christie's Geneva) £5,577

A Meissen candlestick from the Swan service modelled by J. F. Eberlein and J. J. Kaendler, for Count Bruehl, and his wife Anna von Kolowrat Kratkowska, circa 1739, 24cm. high. (Christie's Geneva) £32,175

19th century, Meissen porcelain group of two putti, 17cm. high, restored. (Auktionshaus Arnold) £269

A Meissen circular dish from the Red Dragon service, painted in orange and gold, circa 1740, 29.5cm. diam. (Christie's London) £2,420

A Meissen gardening group, the central figure standing on high rockwork before a tree stump, blue crossed swords and incised numeral marks, late 19th century, 29cm. high. (Christie's London) £2,420

A Meissen model of a carthorse by J. J. Kaendler, standing on a flower encrusted base and tree trunk support, 20cm. (Phillips London) £800

A Meissen blue and white chinoiserie rectangular tea caddy painted with birds in flight above flowering plants and rocks, circa 1730, 10.5cm. high. (Christie's London) £330

A rare Meissen model of Count Bruhl's Tailor, modelled by J. J. Kaendler, the tailor seated astride the goat, 15cm. (Phillips London) £4,200

A Meissen chinoiserie salt from the Bruhlsche plat de menage modelled by J. J. Kaendler as a laughing Chinaman, crossed swords mark, circa 1737, gilt metal cover, 19cm. high. (Christie's London) £7,700

A Meissen plate, the white centre painted with damsons, cobnuts, redcurrants and flowers, 26.5cm. (Phillips London) £900

A rare late Meissen group of two naked young boys playing together on a scroll base, 13cm. (Phillips London) £320

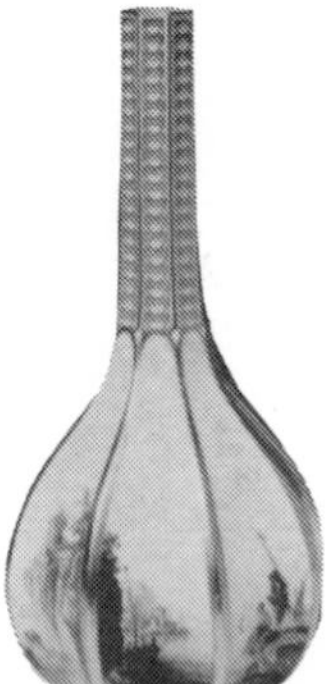

A late Meissen bottle shaped vase, the alternate panels finely painted in purple and red monochrome with coastal scenes, 19.5cm. (Phillips London) £620

Two Meissen blackamoor sweetmeats, the male figure with a feathered skirt and headdress, the female wearing a yellow and puce skirt, crossed swords marks, circa 1760 and 1765, 17.5cm. and 20cm. high. (Christie's London) £1,760

A fine Meissen milk jug and cover, painted within two panels with merchants on a quayside, probably by C. F. Herold, 21cm., crossed swords mark. (Phillips London) £4,600

A Meissen shaped oval bombe snuff box painted in colours with figures conversing on quaysides before Venetian palaces, circa 1740, 7.5cm. wide. (Christie's Geneva) £6,864

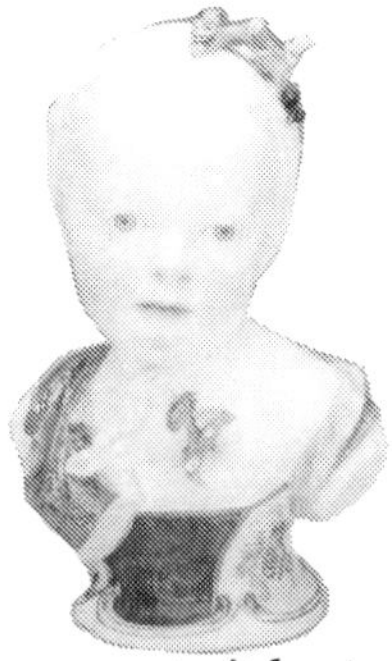

A Meissen portrait bust of Princess Marie Zepherine de Bourbon modelled by J. J. Kaendler , crossed swords mark, circa 1755, 25cm. high. (Christie's Geneva) £8,151

A Meissen chinoiserie teapot and cover with gilt pinecone finial, bird's head spout and shell and scroll handle painted with Chinese figures, circa 1740, 18cm. wide. (Christie's Geneva) £2,789

One of two Meissen figures of Cupid kneeling beside a target centred with a pink heart, 8½in. high. (Christie's S. Ken) Two £715

A Meissen rectangular snuff box painted by Christian Friedrich Herold, with early European scenes within slightly recessed cartouches, circa 1732, 7.5cm. wide. (Christie's Geneva) £27,885

A Meissen figure of a lady holding a letter in her right hand, her left hand in a feather muff, blue crossed swords and incised and impressed numerals, circa 1880, 8½in. high. (Christie's S. Ken) £385

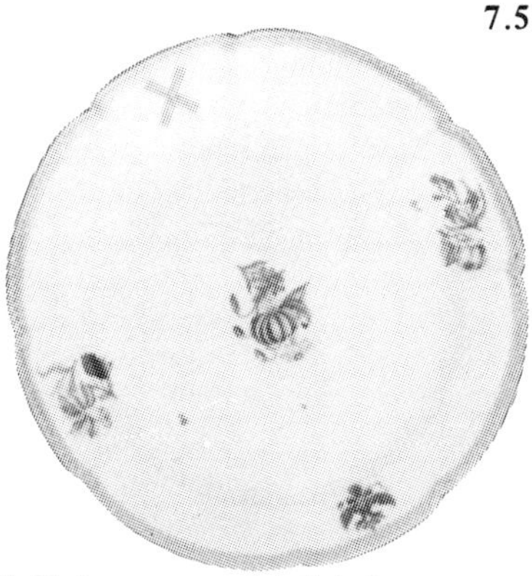

A Meissen armorial dish from the St Andrew the First Called service moulded with Gotzkowsky erhabene Blumen and painted with sprays of Holzschnitt lilies, circa 1742, 28cm. diam. (Christie's Geneva) £5,577

A Meissen figure of a wheelwright from the Handwerker modelled by J. J. Kaendler and P. Reinicke, circa 1750, 21.5cm. high. (Christie's London) £1,210

A Meissen circular powder box and cover, painted in colours with scattered tight sprays of deutsche Blumen, circa 1760, with chased copper gilt mounts, 8cm. diam. (Christie's Geneva) £1,073

Meissen china group of a child kneeling beside a puppy drinking milk, 9cm. high, sword mark, 1905. (Kunsthaus am Museum) £342

Meissen oval-shaped tureen and Cover, Germany, 19th century, with gilded and moulded leaf-shape handles, finial of a young girl simply draped, 14¾in. handle to handle.
(Skinner Inc) £526

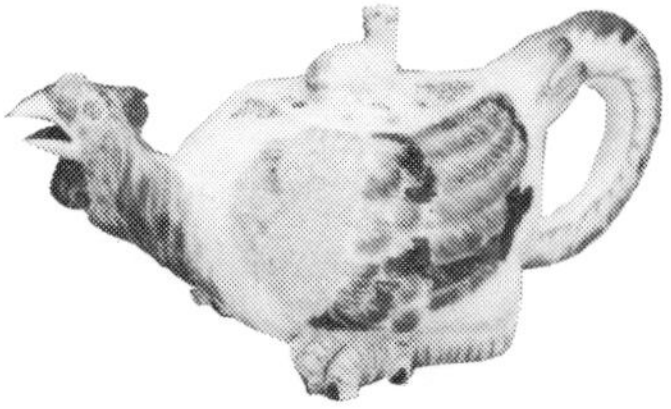

A Meissen teapot and cover modelled as a seated rooster (Hahnenkanne) by J. J. Kaendler, the flat cover with a seated dog finial, crossed swords marks, circa 1735, 19.5cm. wide. (Christie's Geneva) £4,290

Meissen figure group of 'The Apple Pickers', Germany, late 19th century, depicting a man and woman under an apple tree, apples, 10¼in. high.
(Skinner Inc) £657

Meissen group of Cybele, Germany, late 19th century, goddess modelled wearing a crown and seated on the back of a lion, 9in. high.
(Skinner Inc) £921

Rare Meissen bust of a child, Germany, late 19th century, a draping of grapes and vines over the shoulders and about the head, 10in. high.
(Skinner Inc) £789

A Meissen figure of a fish seller modelled by J. J. Kaendler, holding a large orange tailed carp in her arms, circa 1745, 19.5cm. high. (Christie's London) £2,200

Meissen Group 'Silenus on a Donkey', late 19th century, on an oval moulded base, a nude child holding the donkey's tail, crossed swords mark, (chip), 8in. high.
(Skinner Inc) £855

A Meissen figure of an egg seller modelled by J. J. Kaendler standing offering an egg from a basket over her left arm, circa 1745, 18cm. high. (Christie's London) £1,980

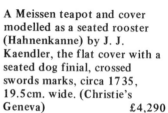

A Meissen chinoiserie teapot and cover of depressed pear shape with curved spout, painted in the manner of Höroldt with Orientals among furniture, shrubs and vases of flowers, circa 1725, 10.5cm. high.
(Christie's) £5,500

A Meissen group of a shepherdess and companion, she wearing a yellow cloak and flowered dress and he in striped jacket and turquoise breeches, circa 1770, 15cm. high.
(Christie's) £1,760

A Meissen Fläschenhalter from the Swan service modelled by J.J. Kändler and J.F. Eberlein for Count Brühl, of compressed oval shape with a gilt undulating rim, 1737–41, 24cm. wide.
(Christie's) £13,200

A Meissen blue-ground campana-shaped vase painted with a lover and companion in a wooded landscape, blue crossed swords marks, circa 1880, 48cm. high.
(Christie's) £3,850

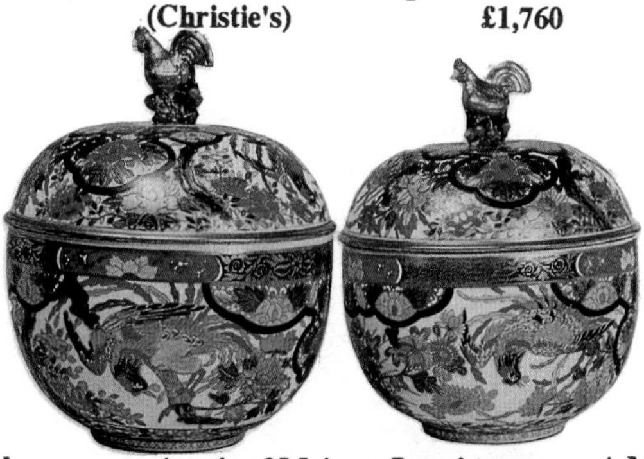

A pair of Meissen Imari tureens and covers, each freely painted in the typical palette enriched with gilding, with two exotic cockerels among flowering peony and chrysanthemum, circa 1735, 34cm. high.
(Christie's) £35,200

A Meissen powdered-purple-ground cream-pot, cover and stand of squat baluster form, painted in the manner of J.G. Höroldt with harbour scenes, circa 1730, the stand 17.5cm. diameter. (Christie's) £12,100

A Meissen group of a nurse and two children modelled by J.F. Eberlein, the nurse seated on a rococo-scroll chair, wearing a puce bodice and yellow skirt with indianische Blumen, circa 1755, 16.5cm. high.
(Christie's) £2,200

A Meissen Purpurmalerei écuelle, a cover and a stand, painted with estuary and landscape scenes, buildings, figures and ships, circa 1740, the stand 23.5cm. diameter.
(Christie's) £5,060

A Meissen group of two maidens and Cupid, one standing wearing a flowered turquoise robe, the other seated on clouds, circa 1880, 8in. high.
(Christie's S. Ken) £1,320

Meissen porcelain bust of a child, Germany, late 19th century, enamel decorated with gilt trim, raised floral corsage, 6in. high.
(Skinner Inc.) £247

A Meissen group of two men in 18th century costume with tricorn hats, a globe and navigational instruments between them.
(Bearne's) £1,050

A Meissen cabinet cup and saucer, the cup painted with a view of the city of Dresden, crossed swords marks.
(Phillips) £700

A Meissen Hausmalerei tapering hexagonal tea-caddy painted by Ignaz Bottengruber with a raven, a long-eared owl and a fabulous bird in black and brown, circa 1725, 9.5cm. high.
(Christie's) £1,650

An extremely large late Meissen group of Count Bruhl's tailor riding on a goat, the tailor dressed as a courtier, 43cm. high, incised numeral.
(Phillips) £3,500

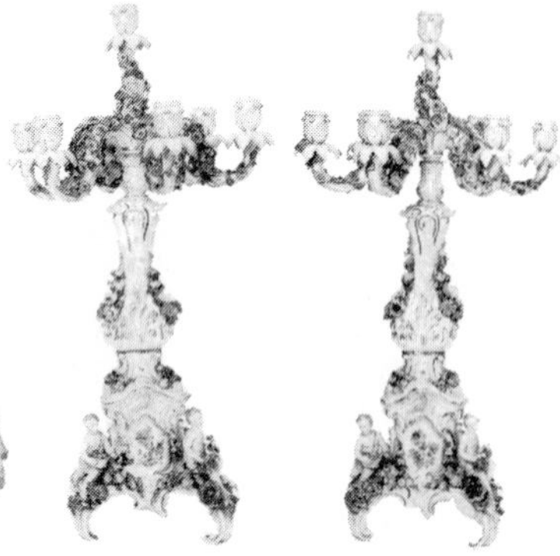

A pair of late Meissen tall six branch candelabra on triangular bases painted and encrusted with flowers in colours and with three seated figures of putti holding garlands, overall height 64cm.
(Phillips) £3,600

Meissen porcelain cherub figure, Germany, late 19th century, seated on a brick oven-like stand, holding a pot in one hand, $5^{3}/_{4}$in. high.
(Skinner Inc.) £351

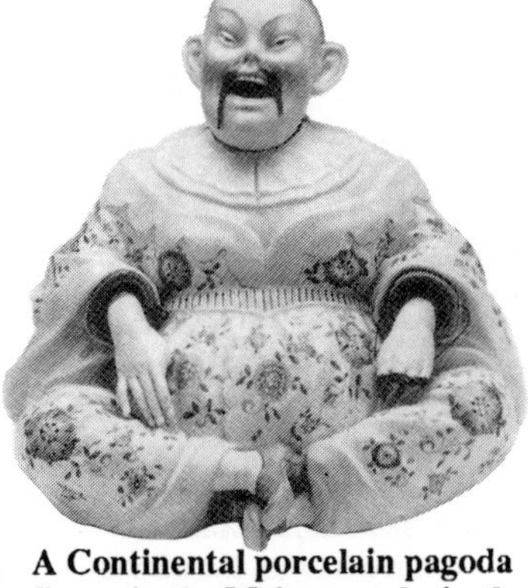

A Continental porcelain pagoda figure in the Meissen style, in the form of a laughing seated Chinaman with nodding head, 28cm.
(Bearne's) £200

A late Meissen group of Harlequin and Columbine modelled by Paul Scheurich, on oval base, 27cm.
(Phillips) £1,500

A Meissen porcelain covered cup and saucer finely painted with deer hunting scenes, late 18th/ early 19th century.
(Bearne's) £400

Meissen porcelain group of children working a wine press, Germany, late 19th century, crossed swords mark, 13in. high.
(Skinner Inc.) £1,350

A Meissen Hausmalerei goldchinesen two-handled beaker and a saucer, gilt at Augsburg in the Seuter workshop with figures at various pursuits, circa 1725.
(Christie's) £880

A Meissen porcelain group of two semi-naked children, the girl with a bird and a cage, her companion with a large mask, 15cm. high.
(Bearne's) £380

A Meissen baluster pot-pourri vase and a pierced cover, the green branch handles with applied trailing fruit and flower terminals, the side of the vase with Cupid, blue crossed swords mark, circa 1870, 59.5cm. overall.
(Christie's) £4,180

A Meissen group of Europa and the bull draped in pink and white, on an oval mound base moulded with gilt scrolls, blue crossed swords mark, circa 1880, 24cm. high.
(Christie's) £550

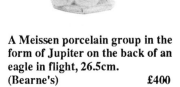

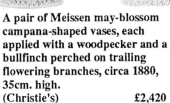

A Meissen porcelain group in the form of Jupiter on the back of an eagle in flight, 26.5cm.
(Bearne's) £400

A pair of Meissen may-blossom campana-shaped vases, each applied with a woodpecker and a bullfinch perched on trailing flowering branches, circa 1880, 35cm. high.
(Christie's) £2,420

Meissen porcelain figure of a lady, Germany, late 19th century, enamel decorated and modelled standing wearing winter clothing, 8in. high.
(Skinner Inc.) £702

A Meissen kakiemon baluster sugar-castor and pierced artichoke cover painted with a winged kylin, a bird in flight and indianische Blumen, circa 1735, 16cm. high. (Christie's) £3,502

A Meissen group of Harlequin and Columbine after the model by J.J. Kändler, Harlequin wearing a mask and a tunic half chequered and half with playing cards, circa 1740, 15.5cm. high. (Christie's) £6,050

A Meissen baluster coffee-pot and domed cover moulded with gadroons enriched alternately with gilding and Böttgerluster, painted in colours with figures chopping wood, circa 1735, 22cm. high. (Christie's) £8,250

A Meissen Augustus rex beaker-vase painted by J E Stadler, divided into three sections, blue AR mark, circa 1730, 39cm. high. (Christie's) £28,600

A pair of Meissen models of quail by J.J. Kändler, on circular mound bases applied with corn and water weeds, circa 1745, 14cm. high. (Christie's) £6,600

A Meissen powdered-pink-ground two-handled beaker and a saucer painted in the manner of B G Hauer with a harbour scene and an equestrian figure in a landscape within ogival gilt ombrierte line reserves, the beaker circa 1730. (Christie's) £825

A Meissen chinoiserie cylindrical tankard painted in the manner of J.G. Höroldt with figures around a table playing mandolins and drinking tea before a palm tree, circa 1730. (Christie's) £11,000

A Meissen shaped oval bombe snuff-box painted with figures conversing on Venetian quays and before palaces with ships, camels and castles within shaped cartouches with gilt scrolls and lustre panels, the underside painted in Purpurmalerei with merchants on a beach, circa 1750, 7.5cm. wide. (Christie's) £5,500

A Meissen group of musicians, a gentleman holding a violin and offering a lady a beaker of wine, below a girl playing a guitar and a boy trying to embrace her, circa 1770, 36cm. high. (Christie's) £4,620

A Meissen gold-mounted oval snuff-box painted with scenes after Teniers, the sides with six cartouches with figures at various pursuits within rococo scroll-moulded puce and pale-blue borders and scattered pink roses, 1750-65, 8cm. wide.
(Christie's) £14,300

A Meissen group of the hand kiss modelled by J.J. Kändler, the gallant wearing a gilt flower and black foliage grey waistcoat over black breeches and yellow shoes with red rosettes, circa 1740, 18cm. high. (Christie's) £4,180

A Meissen two-handled beaker and cover and a saucer painted in Purpurmalerei with a gallant and companion in a shrubbery, the reverse with a gentleman beside an urn, circa 1735 and 1740, 10.5cm. high.
(Christie's) £990

A Meissen clock-case of rococo scroll-moulded outline with turquoise palm fronds and shell moulding enriched with gilding, between moulded panels of Holzschnitt Blumen including lily of the valley, narcissus and roses, circa 1745.
(Christie's) £4,180

**A pair of Meissen cylindrical tobacco-jars and covers painted with soldiers in encampments and with landscape scenes within quatrefoil panels linked by gilt trellis, circa 1740, later French gilt-metal mounts. 14.5cm. high.
(Christie's) £7,700**

**A Meissen equestrian group emblematic of Europe from the series of the Continents modelled by J.J. Kändler, the female figure, sitting on a rearing white horse, wearing a gilt crown, circa 1745, 19cm. high.
(Christie's) £1,980**

A Meissen Group of a nurse and two children modelled by J F Eberlein, the mother seated on a rococo-scroll chair, wearing a dress painted with indianische Blumen, circa 1755, 16.5cm. high.
(Christie's) £2,200

**A pair of Meissen kakiemon baluster oil and vinegar ewers and covers, with dragon and mask-head spouts and terminal, Dreher's marks Z, circa 1735, 16.5cm. and 15.5cm. high.
(Christie's) £2,860**

A Meissen group of the housekeeper modelled by J J Kandler, wearing a white cap, yellow-flowered jacket over a turquoise skirt, sitting at a table with cabriole legs and writing her books, circa 1755, 15.5cm. high. (Christie's) £2,860

MENNECY

The Mennecy factory was set up in 1734 in Paris by Louis François de Neufville, Duc de Villeroy under the directorship of François Barbin. For the first year it produced faience, but then turned to porcelain and in 1748 moved to Mennecy.

For its early products it drew heavily on the shapes manufactured at Rouen, and on St Cloud (blue lambrequins) and Chantilly (Kakiemon) for its decorations. Mennecy soon developed its own style however. Its paste was characterised by its lovely dark ivory colour and its glaze by its wet-looking brilliance. The factory did not have a wide range of shapes, but those it did produce were admirably simple in form, tall, globular teapots with gently curving spouts, and cups and saucers which were either straight sided, tapering down or pear shaped. Among its most characteristic pieces were spirally fluted custard cups and sugar bowls with lids surmounted by a rosebud.

Painted decoration was very beautiful, dominated by cool blues and pinks and often depicting naturalistic flower or bird designs and delicate polychrome landscapes where brown and green predominate. Mennecy also excelled at figure modelling, especially under the sculptor Gouron, who came to the factory in 1753.

Mennecy continued producing rococo style, mainly useful wares into the 1770s, after which quality declined. It continued in production until 1800, by which time porcelain had been abandoned in favour of faience and cream coloured earthenware. Mennecy porcelain is marked *DV* for the Duc de Villeroy. After the factory moved to Bourg la Reine in 1773 the mark *BR*, often incised, was used.

A Mennecy teapot and cover of globular shape with double ogee handle and flower finial, 9.5cm. high, incised DV mark. £720

A Mennecy hen snuff box with silver gilt mount, mark of Eloy Brichard, Paris, 1756-62, 5cm. wide. £1,190

A pair of Mennecy figures of pug dogs, circa 1750, 14cm. long. £4,940

A pair of Mennecy figures of a young man and woman, circa 1740, 17.5cm. high. £1,980

A French white soft paste model of an elephant, free-standing with long tusks and a curling trunk (one ear chipped, firing cracks to underside), circa 1750, probably Mennecy, 20cm. long. (Christie's London) £6,050

A small white Mennecy baluster jug and cover with hinged silver mount, circa 1740, 11.5cm. high. £1,510

METTLACH

The original Mettlach factory was established in 1809 at the Abbey of Mettlach in the Rhineland. In 1836 it merged with the factories of Villeroy and J F Boch and together this group produced earthenwares. Stoneware was also made from 1842 onwards, with a high proportion of the output being exported to America.

Art Pottery, decorated with inlaid clays in contrasting colours (Mettlach ware) was also introduced, and among the top artists working there was J Scharvogel. In the later part of the 19th century terracotta and mosaic tiles were added to the range. Marks include Mettlach castle with the monogram of *VB*, and a circular mark with Mercury looking over *Villeroy & Boch* and *Mettlach.*

A Mettlach plaque of a spring landscape, signed H. Cradl?, stamped Villeroy & Boch, 17½in. diam., Germany, 1910. £720

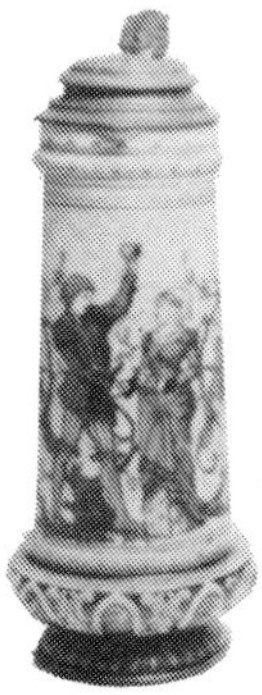

Large Mettlach Stein, circa 1898, etched decoration depicting lovers, signed *Warth,* pewter lid, 14½in. high. (Robt. W. Skinner Inc.) £457

Late 19th century Mettlach plaque, signed C. Warth, 16¾in. high. £150

A Mettlach tankard of tapered cylindrical form with pewter cover, Germany, 1898, 7in. high. £270

A Mettlach pewter mounted 'Castle' stein, impressed marks and numbers, date code for 1898, 40cm. high. £1,100

A Mettlach salt glazed stoneware jardiniere, the continuous central band incised and decorated in colours with gnomes cavorting amongst blossoming branches, 23cm. diam. (Spencer's) £400

A Mettlach stoneware vase, the ovoid body decorated with an encircling pattern of stylized flowers, 41.7cm. high. (Bearne's) £150

MING

When Chu Yuang Chang founded the Ming dynasty at Nanking in 1368, the art of producing high fired porcelain had already been mastered and was being used to make not only small pieces but also huge storage jars. The glaze on these is often cracked, so that it is possible to see clearly how the base, lower body, shoulders and neck were made separately and then stuck together with a watered down porcelain clay before drying and decorating.

Underglaze painting too had already been discovered during the previous Yuan period, and Ming decorators exploited the possibilities of both iron red, and the favoured Burmese cobalt blue to the full.

Ming pieces can often be dated by appearance. Fourteenth century pieces, often painted with brilliant precision in loosely composed designs, were made from a finely mixed white clay with a thin greyish glaze, whereas on those dating from the 15th century, the glaze is often thick and clear and has allowed the blue to bleed into it during the firing, giving an effect of enhanced depth and richness.

Celadons had been produced during Sung times, and their use was continued during the Ming period, but they were used for heavily potted wares, storage jars, lanterns etc which were carved or applied with a premoulded design and covered with a thick celadon glaze. These proved extremely popular in the near East, Burma and India, perhaps because it was believed that poison would boil if it touched a celadon surface!

The enamel painting of porcelain was first successfully introduced at the end of the fifteenth century.

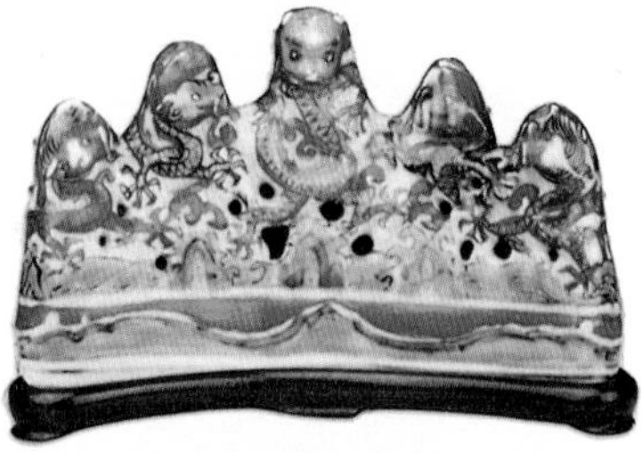

A rare late Ming Wucai brushrest, Wanli six-character mark, moulded and reticulated with an ascending yellow dragon at the centre flanked by four smaller dragons in brown, red, blue and green, 6½in. wide. (Christie's) £47,266

A Ming blue and white pear-shaped vase for the Islamic market, Zhengde, the globular body painted with six roundels containing Islamic script divided by vertical flanges and amidst clouds and a flaming pearl, 10in. high. (Christie's) £8,551

An early Ming blue and white dish, Yongle, painted to the centre of the interior with a lotus arabesque comprising a central flower-head surrounded by five smaller flower-heads, the well with a continuous foliate lotus scroll below a band of classic scroll at the rim, 11in. diameter. (Christie's) £12,891

A large Ming blue and white 'Hundred boys' jar, painted to the exterior with a continuous scene of boys at play, with a group acting out the scene of a high official flanked by advisers in audience and a kneeling subject, 15¾in. diameter. (Christie's) £27,986

A Ming blue and white baluster vase, 15th century, painted around the body in inky-blue tones with a foliate lotus-scroll between double lines, 5in. high, box. (Christie's) £1,862

A rare early Ming blue and white baluster vase and cover, guan, painted around the body in inky tones with 'heaping and piling' to depict a continuous lotus meander, Yongle, 27cm. wide. (Christie's) £49,500

MING

This was done by applying the colours to clear glazed pieces and then refiring them in a low temperature 'muffle kiln'.

The late Ming period saw the opening up of an export trade extending far beyond the traditional markets of the near East and Southeast Asia. In 1595 the Dutch established a trading post at Canton, and it was the Dutch East India Company who first brought back the Kraak porselyns which were to provide the inspiration for European porcelain manufacture.

It is worth remembering that the marks on Ming pieces should not be taken as gospel. If a potter were successful in reproducing an earlier style to the same standard as the original, he would apply the mark of the emperor of the period of the original. This was done for honorific reasons, and not, then at least, from any desire to deceive.

A Ming blue and white bowl, the deep rounded sides flaring at the rim, the exterior painted in bright blue tones with Buddhistic lions, the interior with a flaming ruyi motif centering a cash symbol, Jiajing six-character mark, 15cm. diameter.
(Christie's) £2,750

A Ming 'green and yellow' dish, Jiajing six-character mark, the interior with five ruyi connected by a leafy vine, all in olive-green enamel reserved on an ochre-yellow ground, $6\frac{3}{4}$in. diameter.
(Christie's) £2,507

A rare pair of celadon-glazed candlesticks, early Ming Dynasty, formed probably in three parts with small petal-moulded sconces, $9\frac{1}{4}$in. high.
(Christie's) £8,594

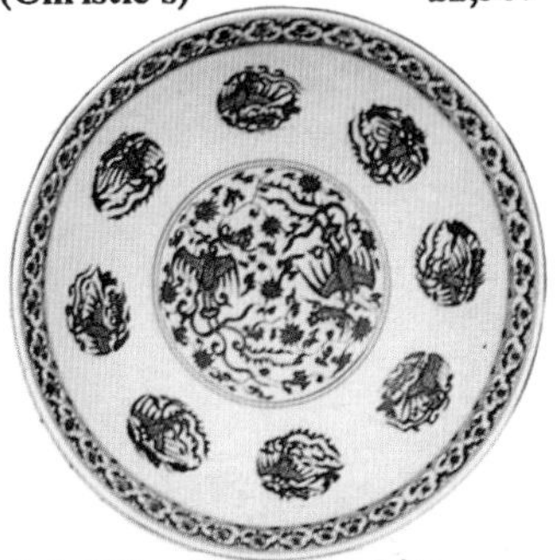

A late Ming blue and white 'phoenix' bowl, the centre of the interior painted in bright blue tones with an ascending and a descending phoenix, Wanli six-character mark and of the period, 20cm. diameter.
(Christie's) £3,300

A Ming blue and white zhadou, zhengde four-character mark and of the period, the lower bulbous body, interior and exterior of the flaring neck similarly painted with two scaly five-clawed dragons striding amid dense leafy vines, 6in. diameter.
(Christie's) £34,982

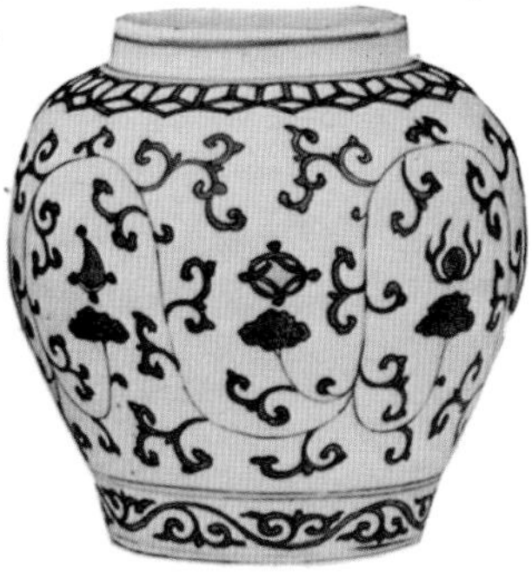

A late Ming blue and white baluster jar, encircled Wanli six-character mark and of the period, painted around the broad body with large, looping leafy meanders of peony, each flower-head beneath a Daoist emblem, 5in. high.
(Christie's) £1,432

A fine and rare Ming yellow and red-glazed jar, painted in reserve on a pale mustard-yellow ground with two five-clawed scaly dragons emitting fire scrolls in a lively motion amongst cloud scrolls, $5\frac{7}{16}$in. high.
(Christie's) £68,410

Chinese Doucai porcelain dish, late Ming Dynasty, raised on four bracket feet, central scene depicting a figure in an ox drawn cart, 7½in. wide.
(Skinner Inc.) £625

A very rare and important Ming blue and white large deep bowl, the shoulder with eight horizontal rectangular flanges, painted in vibrant blue tones, Yongle/Xuande, 36.8cm. wide.
(Christie's) £209,000

A 15th/16th century Ming fahua oviform jar, 15cm. high. £1,295

An early 16th century large Ming blue and white baluster jar, Guan (minor restoration), 36.5cm. high. (Christie's) £4,364

An fine early Ming blue and white dish, the medallion painted with a ribboned bouquet of lotus flowers, leaves, a seed pod, sagittaria and aquatic plants, Yongle, 40.3cm. diameter.
(Christie's) £132,000

A fine Ming Wucai square baluster jar painted on the body with scrolling underglaze-blue lotus below the eight Buddhist emblems, wood stand, fitted box, 18cm. high. (Christie's London) £66,000

Chinese Longquan celadon plate, Ming Dynasty, ribbed and floral incised decoration in centre, 13in. diam. (Skinner Inc.) £255

A blue and white ewer, of double gourd form, painted with a panel of a ferocious kylin, the reverse with a phoenix, late Ming, 9½in. high.
(Lawrence Fine Arts) £1,760

A late Ming Wucai barrel-shaped jar and cover, the base with Wanli six-character mark and of the period, 15cm. diam., fitted box. £34,560

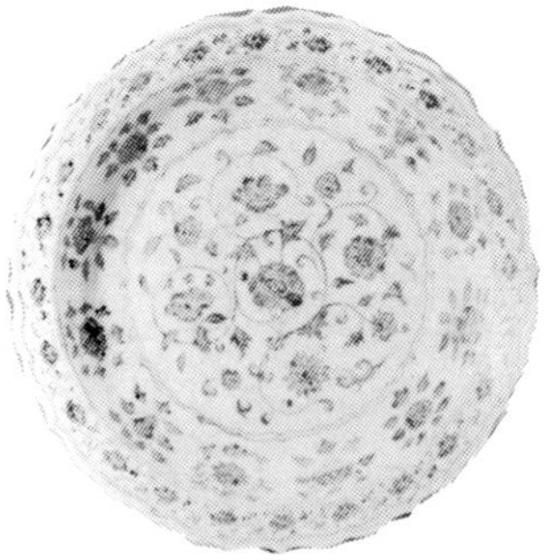

An early Ming blue and white foliate-rim dish painted with a composite floral arabesque, 15in. diam. (Christie's) £27,898

A Ming blue and white square box and cover, the sides painted in bright blue tones with a lotus scroll, Longqing period, 11cm. square. (Christie's) £12,100

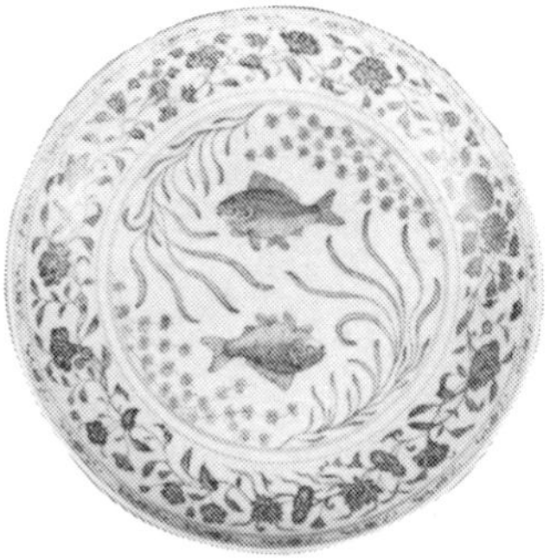

An important large early Ming blue and white dish, vividly painted, with two carp swimming amongst aquatic fern and weeds at the centre, Yongle, 53.6cm. diam. (Christie's) £209,000

A fine late Ming blue and white small jar painted in bright blue tones with three peacocks, 5¼in. high. (Christie's) £11,956

Late 17th/early 18th century shield-shaped Arita dish, the base with three spur marks and a Ming Chenghua mark, 12.4cm. £650

A fine and rare Ming blue and white vase for the Japanese market, the lower section formed as a cube, 12¼in. high. (Christie's) £67,753

A very rare early Ming underglaze-blue yellow-ground saucer-dish, painted in strong cobalt tones with a spray of flowering pomegranate, Xuande period, 29.4cm. diam. (Christie's) £220,000

A late Ming blue and white baluster jar, encircled Wanli six-character mark and of the period, 34cm. high. £10,450

A Ming 'Green Dragon' saucer-dish, the interior incised and painted in bright green enamel, Hongzhi period, 20cm. diam. (Christie's) £715

MINTON

Thomas Minton was born in 1765 and apprenticed at the Caughley Works where he was trained in the art of engraving copper plates for underglaze-blue painted designs. In 1793 he established his own works at Stoke on Trent, where it traded as Minton & Co from 1845 and Mintons Ltd from 1873. It was noted from the first for the high quality and diversity of its output, which at first consisted mainly of blue printed earthenware, though porcelain was added to the range in 1797, The original pattern book of that period survives today.

From 1847 large quantities of parian ware were produced, and figures were made by a number of eminent modellers. Various partners took responsibility for various branches of the firm, and by 1868 these separated. Minton, Collins & Co specialised in tile manufacturing, while C H Campbell became responsible for earthenware.

Minton had a strong presence at the Great Exhibition of 1851 where they displayed Sèvres style porcelain vases, terracotta and majolica garden ornaments, parian figures and tiles, all of which attracted much favourable comment. Pâte-sur-pâte decoration was introduced by the Sèvres-trained decorator and modeller Marc Louis or Miles Solon, who worked for Minton between 1870 and 1904. Dinner services were commonly painted or printed in the Japanese taste with flowers, chickens or butterflies.

Art Nouveau vases, again decorated by Solon, were popular around the turn of the century, and were usually decorated with coloured glazes contained by raised lines of trailed slip.

A pair of majolica wall-brackets each modelled as three loosely draped children flanked by eagles on columns, possibly Minton, circa 1865, 14in. (Christie's) £770

A Minton majolica ewer in the form of a heron, after a model by Hugues Protât, the handle spout modelled as the body and gaping mouth of a pike caught in the beak of the bird, date code for 1878, 21¼in. high. (Christie's) £1,540

Two Minton majolica models of boys steering rowing-boats each figure seated at the stern of the twin-sectioned vessel and holding the tiller, date code for 1866, 6¾in. long. (Christie's) £605

A pair of Minton four-light candelabra after a model by A. Carrier de Belleuse, the stems modelled with figures emblematic of Night and Day, date code for 1866, 25¼in. high. (Christie's) £2,200

A Minton majolica group of a putto riding a hippocamp after a model by A. Carrier de Belleuse, incised ermine mark, date code for 1859, 15½in. high. (Christie's) £638

A Minton majolica centre-dish in the form of a putto dragging a cart behind him, clad only in a wreath of vine and a blue drape tucked into an orange sash, date code for 1873, 15in. high.
(Christie's) **£825**

A Minton majolica oyster-stand modelled with four tapering circular tiers of oyster shells with white-glazed interiors and brown exteriors, date code for 1862, 11in. high.
(Christie's) **£2,090**

A Minton majolica bacchanalian group of three putti with a ram, the ram drinking from a goblet proffered by one putto, another putto seated on its back holding reins, date code for 1862, 15in. high.
(Christie's) **£1,411**

Twelve Minton porcelain plates with bright turquoise grounds, painted in colours with exotic birds perched on blossoming branches, some with insects, within gilt rims enriched with black zig-zags, with date code for 1872, 9½in diameter.
(Christie's) **£2,640**

A Minton majolica jug, the mottled manganese and blue body moulded in high relief with two pairs of peasants drinking and dancing flanking a seated figure, code for 1873, 10½in. high.
(Christie's) **£750**

A Minton majolica teapot and cover in the form of a seated Chinaman, holding a grotesque mask, his detachable head forming the cover, circa 1874, 7in. high.
(Christie's) **£990**

A Minton royal-blue-ground porcelain and parian flower-basket centre-dish from a dessert-service modelled as four parian figures emblematic of the Seasons, circa 1851, 24¼in. high.
(Christie's) **£3,300**

One of a pair of Minton Art Pottery Studio pilgrim vases painted with portraits of young girls, 20cm., 1871. (Phillips London) Two £320

A Minton plate with pierced gilt border, painted by James Rouse, depicting three children and a robin, 25cm., 1871. (Phillips London) £380

One of an impressive pair of Minton vases in Sevres style, painted with scenes of rustic lovers, after Boucher, within scrolling tooled gold borders, 31cm. (Phillips London) Two £650

A large Mintons art pottery circular wall plate by William Stephen Coleman painted in naturalistic colours with a pubescent young girl depicting an allegory of Leda and the Swan, 49.5cm. diam. (Phillips) £3,800

A magnificent Minton pate sur pate vase by Louis Marc Solon, of Greek amphora shape, 56cm., gold mark and date code for 1886. (Phillips London) £950

A rare and interesting Minton majolica ware Lindsay platter, probably painted by Thomas Allen, the oval centre painted in bright colours with Venus kneeling in a shell boat, 46cm. (Phillips London) £420

A Minton rectangular plaque by Louis Solon, signed, decorated with Cupid stealing flowers from a basket held by a maiden, 19 x 10.5cm. (Phillips London) £380

A pair of brightly coloured Minton figure candlesticks, the candlestick columns in green with gilt bulrushes, 21.5cm. (Phillips London) £1,500

Art Nouveau Minton majolica glazed jardiniere and stand, with stylistic blue flowers and green foliage, 36in. in height overall. (G. A. Key) £750

A large and important Minton majolica wine cooler and cover, moulded in low relief with military scenes below fox's masks and drapery, 64cm. (Phillips London) £5,100

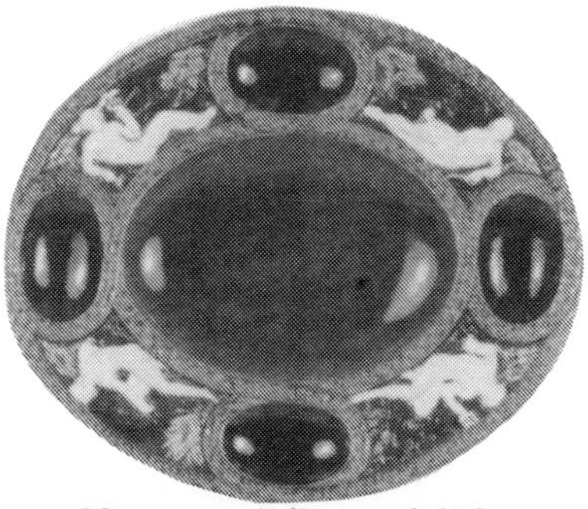

A Minton majolica oval dish with green glazed depressed centre, the border moulded in relief with reclining Classical nude figures, impressed date code for 1856, 38cm. wide. (Christie's London) £495

A rare Minton figure of Lord Byron, wearing a claret coloured jacket and blue striped trousers on a rectangular base, 15.5cm. (Phillips London) £400

A Mintons ceramic charger, the beige glazed ground decorated with painted floral reserves in turquoise and charcoal, 43.4cm. diam. (Christie's London) £330

A Minton model of a cat wearing a black collar and sponged in green and yellow (ears restored), circa 1830, 12.5cm. high. (Christie's London) £330

Minton porcelain plate painted by Joseph Smith, inscribed *The Bohemian Wax Wing* on the back, circa 1846. (G. A. Key) £165

One of a pair of Minton pot pourri vases, each side painted with a circular landscape panel framed in gold on a pink ground, 13cm. (Phillips London) Two £650

A Minton blue ground pate sur pate tapering oviform vase, decorated in white relief by L. Solon, with a nymph in a diaphanous dress, date code for 1893, 40cm. high. (Christie's London) £3,300

A Minton majolica jardiniere and stand, the pink glazed basketweave moulded sides decorated in relief, date code for 1870, 21cm. high. (Christie's London) £990

A Minton's art pottery eight inch tile, hand painted with the head of a girl, 20.4cm. square. (Phillips London) £140

One of a pair of Minton majolica-ware figures of boys leaning on tall vine baskets, 23cm. high, model no. 421, date codes for 1868. (Phillips) £340

A Minton shaped rectangular basket of 'Clarence' shape, blue crossed swords mark, circa 1835, 18.5cm. wide. (Christie's) £352

A Minton blue and gilt vase modelled as a kneeling cherub supporting a leaf pattern vase on a circular base. (Greenslades) £210

A pair of Minton 'Dresden Scroll' vases and pierced covers in neo-rococo style, 29cm. high. (Phillips) £1,100

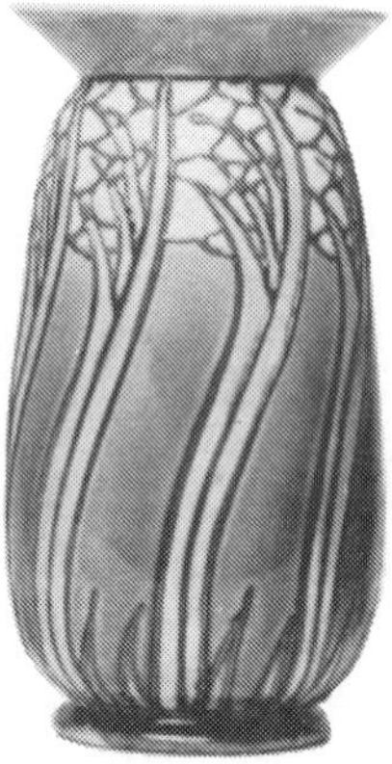

A Minton Secessionist vase, covered in mustard-yellow and turquoise glazes, with green and brown piped slip decoration of stylised trees, 22.8cm. high. (Christie's) £187

A Minton vase and cover by Louis Jahn, 50cm. high, impressed and printed marks. (Phillips) £1,000

One of a pair of Minton porcelain plates each painted with scenes of country seat with several figures, 9in. wide. (Dacre, Son & Hartley) Two £1,250

A Mintons Kensington Gore pottery moon flask, 34.2cm. high. (Phillips) £300

A Minton majolica two-handled jardiniere, the handles modelled as entwined snakes, their heads resting on the shoulder, date code for 1869, 38cm. wide. (Christie's) £1,045

One of a set of three good Minton encaustic pictorial eight-inch tiles, moulded marks. (Phillips) £176

A Minton majolica sweetmeat dish supported by a seated Bacchanalian figure wearing a garland of vine leaves. (Greenslades) £253

A Minton Pilgrim vase, painted probably by A. Boullemier after W. S. Coleman, 20cm. high, date code possibly 1873. (Phillips) £260

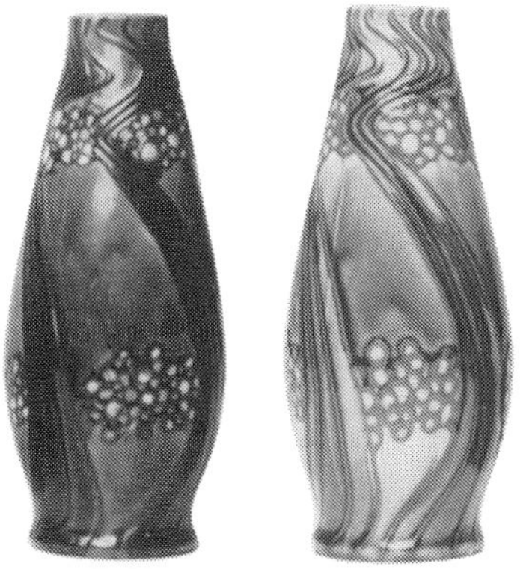

Two Minton Secessionist vases each of inverted baluster form, one covered in violet and blue glazes, the other in red and brown, 23.8cm. high. (Christie's) Two £220

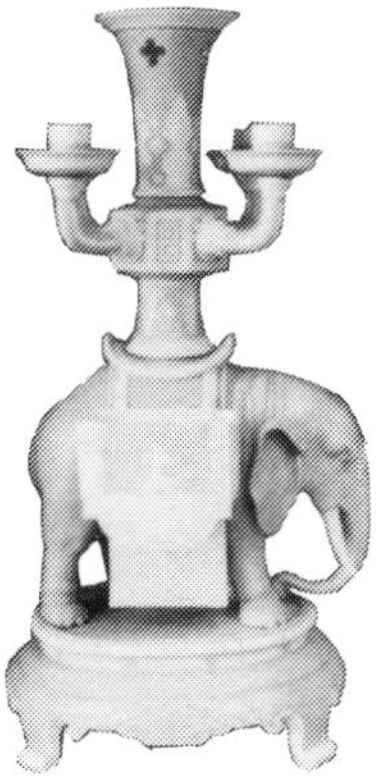

A Minton porcelain elephant centrepiece with four candle holders. (Hobbs Parker) £750

A pair of Minton candlesticks with cherubs supporting the candle holders. (Hobbs Parker) £400

A fine Minton pate-sur-pate plate, signed Louis Solon, 24cm. high., printed Minton and A. B. Daniell & Sons retailer's mark. (Phillips) £750

A fine pair of Minton porcelain figures of Red Riding Hood and boy woodman, on green and gilt rococo bases, 6½in. high. (G.A.Property Services) £800

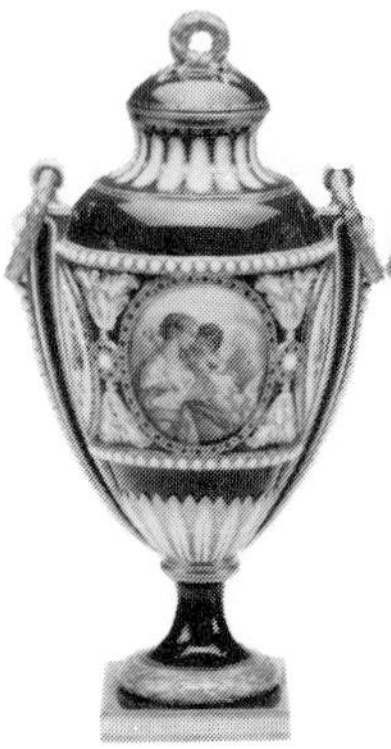

A fine pair of Minton porcelain pedestal jars and covers in the Sèvres manner, 41cm., circa 1860.
(Bearne's) £3,400

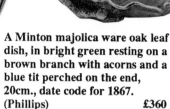

A Minton majolica ware oak leaf dish, in bright green resting on a brown branch with acorns and a blue tit perched on the end, 20cm., date code for 1867.
(Phillips) £360

A pair of Minton style porcelain candlesticks brightly painted with flowers on a gold decorated green and white foliate ground, 24.4cm., late 19th century.
(Bearne's) £1,350

A Minton slipware jardinière, the inscription commemorating the 1911 Coronation, 16cm.
(Phillips) £180

Two Minton parian groups of putti riding on sea horses, with wings and curling fish tails, 34cm., impressed date symbols possibly for 1851 or 1855.
(Phillips) £650

A Minton style majolica jardinière, decorated with basket weave moulding and colourful bands of flower heads, 37cm.
(Bearne's) £360

A Mintons porcelain rectangular plaque painted with a young woman sitting in an arbour, 35.5cm. x 21cm.
(Bearne's) £420

A pair of Minton candle-snuffers modelled as ladies wearing brightly coloured and gilt eighteenth century dress, circa 1830, 9.5cm. high.
(Christie's) £935

A Minton majolica lavender-ground garden seat, moulded in relief with stylised honeysuckle alternating with passion-flowers, date code for 1869, 18½in. high.
(Christie's S. Ken) £935

A Minton biscuit figure of Hannah Moore seated in an armchair on scrolling base, 17cm.
(Phillips) £200

A Minton majolica oval jardinière, the two handles modelled as a scantily clad cherub kneeling on a scroll, 1868, 18in. wide.
(Christie's S. Ken) £968

A Mintons blue-ground vase and cover in the Art Nouveau style, the body and stem painted with swags of pink roses, date code for 1919, $10^{1}/_{2}$in. high.
(Christie's S. Ken) £385

A Minton style majolica jardinière and stand, the rims moulded with petal-like designs, painted in typical green, brown and cream enamels, total height 25cm.
(Bearne's) £300

A pair of Minton majolica cornucopia vases, circa 1872, modelled as putti astride cornucopiae issuing from dolphins, 27in. high.
(Christie's East) £2,798

A Mintons majolica jardinière, the blue ground moulded in relief with vertical flat ribs, terminating in paw feet, circa 1870's, $10^{3}/_{4}$in. high.
(Christie's S. Ken) £330

A pair of finely painted Minton vases and covers, the pointed ovoid bodies painted within oval panels with shipping scenes, 38cm.
(Phillips) £1,300

A Minton majolica garden-seat in the form of a seated monkey eating fruit and wearing a lugubrious expression, date code for 1867, $19^{1}/_{2}$in. high.
(Christie's S. Ken) £935

A pair of Minton candleholders modelled as a youth and companion wearing broad-brimmed hats and striped and flowered dress, circa 1835–36, 9in. high.
(Christie's S. Ken) £935

MOCHAWARE

Mochaware was produced from about 1780 until 1914 and was named from mocha quartz. It is characterised by its decoration , by which tree, moss and fernlike effects were introduced by means of a diffusing medium, which was described as 'a saturated infusion of tobacco in stale urine and turpentine'! It was inexpensive to make, and was first made of creamware and subsequently of pearlware and cane ware. It was designed mainly for domestic use, for public house serving jugs and mugs for measures used to serve shrimps, nuts etc.

Mochaware pitcher, England, early 19th century, with four large brown, rust and white tobacco leaves, 9½in. high. (Skinner Inc.) £3,681

Mochaware pitcher, England, 19th century, decorated with bands of "worming" on ecru and siena grounds, 8in. high. (Skinner Inc.) £774

MONTELUPO

In the 17th and 18th centuries a coarse, heavy earthenware was produced at Montelupo, near Florence. It was characterised by the somewhat rough and ready painting of caricature figures of soldiers and men dressed in curious contemporary Italian costumes and bristling with weapons, striding across the plates.

In the mid 17th century, marks are found referring to Rafaello Girolamo and Jacinto or Diacinto Monti of Montelupo. Helpfully, the date also appears on these.

A Montelupo wet drug jar, the flat handle and the spout painted green, the pharmacy sign of a crescent beneath the terminal of the handle, circa 1560, 25cm. high. (Christie's London) £1,540

A Montelupo crespina boldly painted in ochre, yellow, blue and green with a central circular medallion of a fox surrounded by radiating panels of stylised foliage, mid-17th century, 25cm. diameter. (Christie's) £1,210

A Montelupo crespina, the centre with the bust portrait of a girl draped in a green shawl and inscribed *VESTRO* within a border of radiating panels, early 17th century, 23.5cm. diameter. (Christie's) £1,760

A Montelupo wet-drug jar, with strap handle painted a foglie in blue, ochre and yellow, third quarter of the 16th century, 24.5cm.high. (Christie's) £880

A Montelupo à Quatieri crespina painted in blue, ochre, yellow and green with a putto in a landscape, 27cm. (Phillips) £1,100

MOORCROFT

When Macintyre's art pottery department closed in 1913, Moorcroft established his own pottery at Cobridge, employing his old colleagues. There, they made a wide range of items from pen trays to toastracks, from vases to brooches.

His flambé glazes were developed in the 1920s, and by the 1930s his range of motifs included fruit, birds, fish and boats. Matt glazes were introduced and his designs became increasingly simple. Moorcrofts signature always appears on his products, often painted in green until the 1920s and thereafter mainly in blue.

An octagonal bowl with everted rim, the interior decorated with alternate panels of peacock feathers and tulips, 10in. wide.
(Christie's) £308

An ovoid vase with everted rim decorated with a band of frilled orchids, in pastel tones on a cream ground, 8½in. high.
(Christie's) £275

A twin-handled square biscuit barrel and cover decorated in the 'Hazledene' pattern, in shades of green and blue, 6½in. high.
(Christie's) £495

A pair of cylindrical candlesticks decorated in the 'Pomegranate' pattern, in shades of pink, ochre and green on a mottled green and blue ground, 8in. high.
(Christie's) £990

A spherical vase decorated with stylised fish among waterweeds, in shades of red and ochre on a speckled salmon pink ground, the interior blue, 6in. high.
(Christie's) £1,210

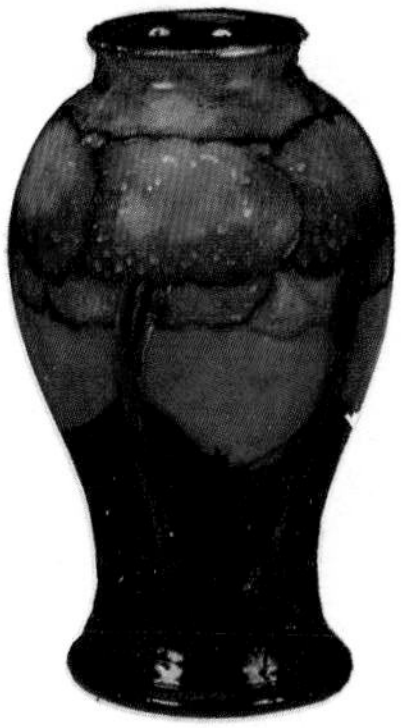

A baluster vase decorated in the 'Eventide' pattern, in shades of ochre, pink, green and blue, 13in. high.
(Christie's) £682

A twin-handled tapering cylindrical jardiniere, made for Liberty, decorated in the 'Hazledene' pattern, in shades of blue and green, 8¼in. high.
(Christie's) £550

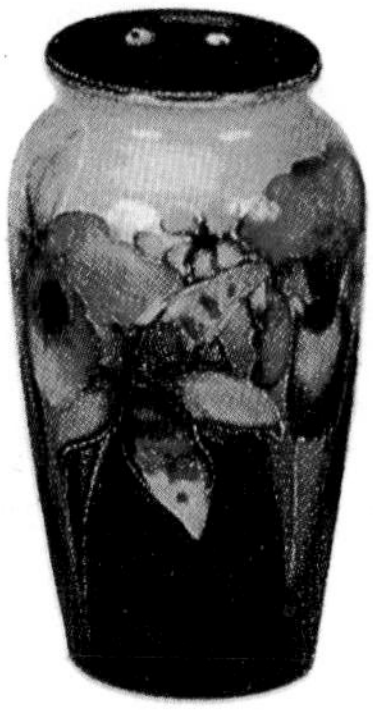

A tapering cylindrical vase decorated with a bland of orchids, in shades of yellow, pink and purple on a graduated blue ground, 5in. high.
(Christie's) £275

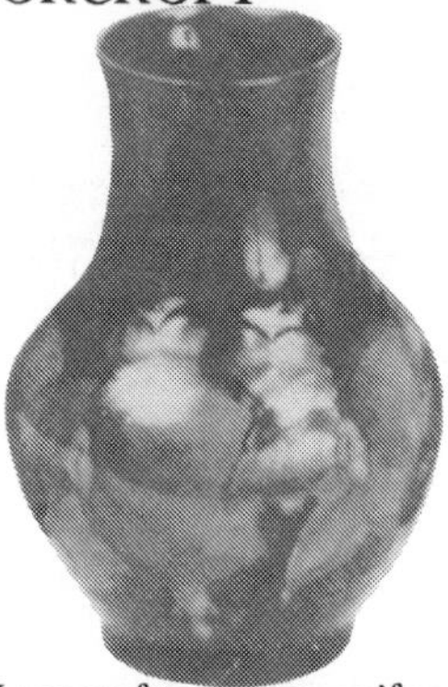

A Moorcroft pottery oviform vase with short cylindrical neck, decorated in the Pomegranate pattern of fruit and foliage, 6½in. high. (Christie's S. Ken) £209

A Moorcroft pottery bowl, decorated in the Claremont toadstool pattern, on a mottled green ground, 27cm. diam. (Bonhams) £280

A Moorcroft Cornflower pattern three handled cylindrical vase, with white piped decoration of cornflowers, covered in a yellow, blue and green glaze against a cream ground, 19cm. high. (Christie's London) £1,320

A Moorcroft Pomegranate pattern tall cylindrical vase, with white piped decoration of fruit and berries, covered in puce, blue, green and amber glaze, circa 1914, 27.7cm. high. (Christie's London) £715

A Moorcroft Hazeldene pattern bowl with incurved rim, decorated in the centre with a large central tree and smaller trees at the side, 24cm. diam. (Phillips London) £300

A Moorcroft tall cup shaped vase, incised with horizontal bands, the green piped decoration of scrolling leaves, covered in a blue and white glaze, 26.4cm. high. (Christie's London) £660

A Moorcroft Florian ware Lilac pattern baluster vase, with white piped decoration of lilac branches, covered in a pale and dark blue glaze with splashes of crimson, circa 1900, 30.2cm. high. (Christie's London) £2,090

A Moorcroft Chrysanthemum pattern urn shaped vase, the white piped decoration of chrysanthemums amongst scrolling foliage, covered in a puce, green and amber glaze, 1913, 21.6cm. high. (Christie's London) £1,650

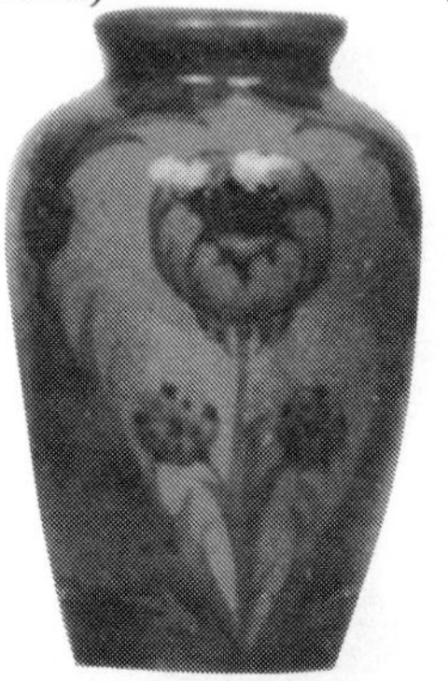

A Moorcroft baluster vase, the green piped decoration of poppies in scrolling leaf cartouches, covered in pale green and blue glaze, circa 1935, 20.9cm. high. (Christie's London) £418

A Moorcroft pottery 'Claremont' pattern jardinière decorated with mushrooms and coloured in streaked red, blue and yellow glaze against a green ground, 12.5cm. high.
(Phillips) £500

A large Moorcroft Pomegranate pattern vase, white piped decoration of fruit and berries, covered in a puce, green, red and blue glaze, 31.6cm. high.
(Christie's) £1,870

A Moorcroft pottery bowl in the 'Pomegranate' pattern, centred with a band of large red fruit with leaves and purple berries, 21cm. diameter.
(Phillips) £240

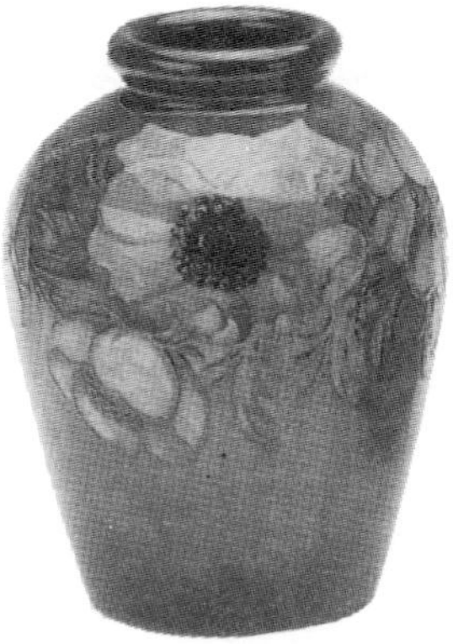

A Moorcroft pottery vase, the ovoid body painted with the anemone pattern on a red ground, 16.5cm.
(Bearne's) £240

A Moorcroft pottery fruit bowl of circular form, painted with fish, seaweed and sea anemones in shades of red, blue, yellow and green, 24.5cm. diameter.
(Spencer's) £500

Moorcroft potpourri and cover, England, circa 1905, pomegranate and pansy design in green, blue, red, yellow and blue, 5in. high.
(Skinner Inc.) £540

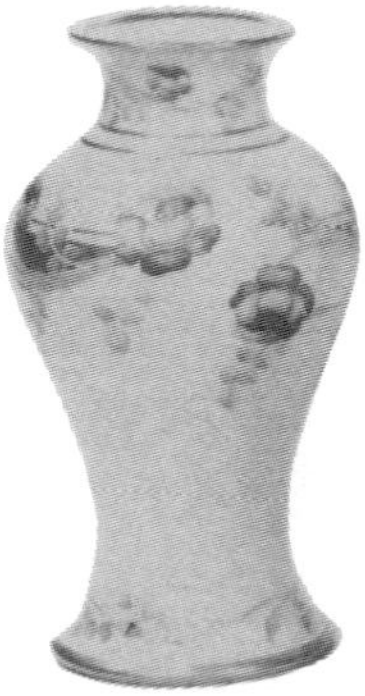

A pair of Moorcroft vases, designed for James Macintyre & Co., circa 1904–1913, the white ground decorated with a rose garland design, 20cm. high.
(Christie's) £1,760

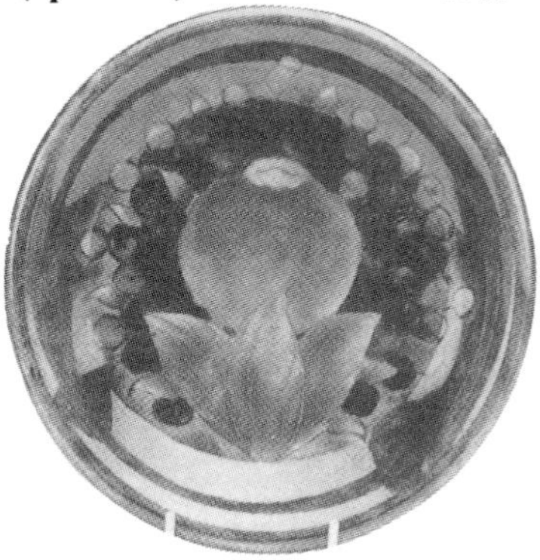

A Moorcroft plate, the cavetto decorated with the pomegranate and grape pattern, 22.3cm.
(Bearne's) £130

A Moorcroft 'Florian Ware' vase, designed for Liberty & Co., circa 1903–1913, the olive green ground decorated with a dark green and blue poppy design, stamped mark *Made for Liberty & Co.*, 31cm. high.
(Christie's) £2,310

A twin-handled vase, decorated in Florian Ware cartouches of pink roses and green foliage on a blue ground, 8in. high.
(Christie's) £3,080

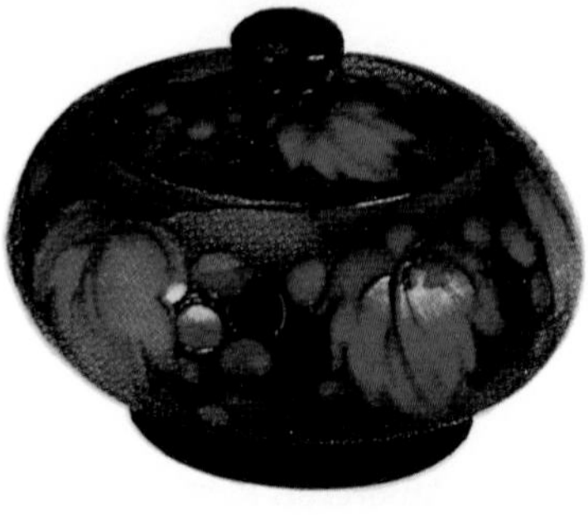

An oviform powder bowl and cover decorated with pansies, in shades of mauve and green on a deep blue ground, 3½in. high.
(Christie's) £286

A Florian Ware twin-handled vase, decorated with scrolling cartouches of peacock feathers and flowerheads, in shades of pale and dark blue, 8in. high.
(Christie's) £902

A twin-handled square biscuit barrel and cover, decorated in the 'Pomegranate' pattern, in shades of pink and blue on a sage green ground, 6¼in. high.
(Christie's) £440

A pair of Florian Ware baluster vases, decorated with scrolling cartouches of poppies and foliage, in shades of pale and dark blue, 12in. high.
(Christie's) £990

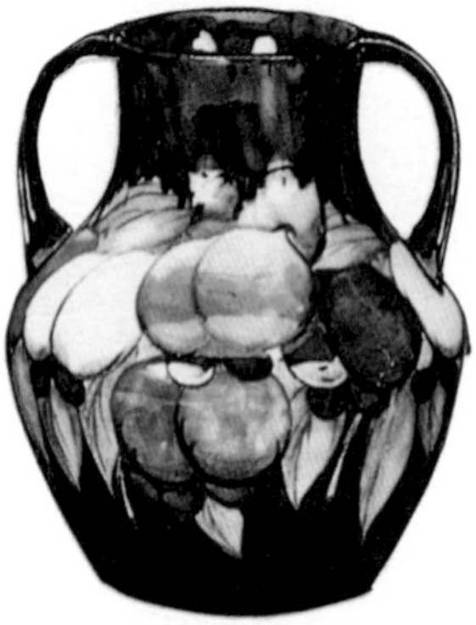

A large twin-handled vase, decorated with a band of plums and foliage, in shades of pink, mauve and green on a dark blue ground, 12½in. high.
(Christie's) £1,430

An oviform vase, decorated with a band of vine leaves and berries, in shades of yellow, pink and green on a deep blue ground, 12in. high.
(Christie's) £385

A pierced oval soap dish decorated in the 'Moonlit Blue' pattern, in shades of blue and green, 7¾in. long.
(Christie's) £308

A Flamminian vase made for Liberty, embossed on the shoulder with three foliate roundels, covered in a rose pink glaze, 6½in. high.
(Christie's) £187

MOORCROFT MACINTYRE

William Moorcroft (1872–1945) was a Staffordshire potter who trained as an art teacher, but became designer for Jas. Macintyre & Co at Burslem. He designed vases, bowls etc. decorated with plant forms and scale patterned borders and panels mainly in blue, red and gold (Aurelian ware). His Florian ware (1898–1904) was decorated with violets, poppies and cornflowers in underglaze colours. His flowers were often stylized and depicted in darker shades of the base colour. Landscape patterns, toadstool and pomegranate motifs were introduced later and Flammarion ware was produced from around 1905 with lustre glazes, often red or green and again slip decorated with plant forms.

A Macintyre cup and saucer, decorated in the 'Eighteenth Century' pattern of floral swags and ribbons, in shades of blue, green, pink and gilt.
(Christie's) £352

A Macintyre Gesso Faience biscuit barrel with electroplate mount and cover, incised with alternate spirals of flowers and foliage, 6½in. high.
(Christie's) £462

A pair of Macintyre Green and Gold Florian Ware vases, decorated in shades of green and gilt with cartouches of poppies and curvilinear foliage, 10¼in. high.
(Christie's) £572

A Macintyre oviform pot decorated with yellow poppies and cartouches of forget-me-nots, in shades of yellow, green and blue, 3in. high.
(Christie's) £275

A Macintyre Green and Gold Florian Ware twin-handled coupe, with cartouches of curvilinear poppies and tulips, in shades of blue, green and gilt, 7½in. high.
(Christie's) £528

A Macintyre plate decorated with three swirling sprays of irises, in shades of green and blue, 8in. diameter.
(Christie's) £682

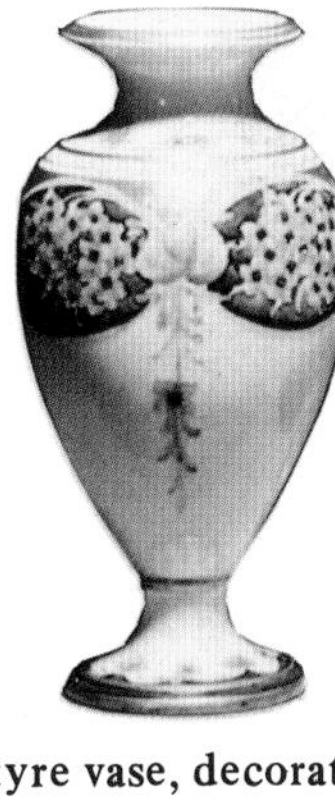

A Macintyre vase, decorated in shades of yellow, blue and gilt with oval cartouches and pendant trials of flowers and foliage, 9¼in. high.
(Christie's) £825

MOORE

Bernard Moore (1853–1935) was a Staffordshire artist potter who, with his brother Samuel, succeeded to his father's porcelain factory at St Mary's Works, Longton in 1870. Trading as Moore Bros. they made high quality tableware, which was sometimes highly ornamental, together with lamps, baskets etc. They used a clear turquoise glaze and metallic colours and favoured decorative motifs were modelled cupids, animals, especially dogs, and plant forms. Chinese cloisonné imitations were also produced and pilgrim bottles with pale pâte-sur-pâte decoration and gilding.

The Moore Bros. factory was sold in 1905. Thereafter, at Wolfe St, Stoke, in conjunction with C Bailey of Doulton, Moore tried out flambé glazes. The pieces he produced here tended to be based on simpler earthenware forms and were sometimes decorated by leading contemporary pottery artists such as Beardmore and Billington.

Marks include *Moore*, and from 1880 *Moore Bros* impressed or incised. The name painted with a printed globe mark also occurs after 1880.

MORRIS WARE

Morris ware was produced from the 1890s into the early 20th century by the firm of S Hancock and Sons, an earthenware company in Stoke on Trent. The pieces were decorated by George Cartlidge (b. 1868) in plant forms outlined in trailed slip in the style of William Moorcroft, and usually also signed by him.

A Bernard Moore red flambe jardiniere of flared cylindrical form, 29cm. high. £450

A flambe pottery bowl, by Bernard Moore, 8¼in. diam., and a Chinese carved wood stand. £230

A Bernard Moore flambe baluster vase, decorated in gilt with a Japanese lady sitting at a table, 18cm. high. (Phillips) £190

A large Bernard Moore lustre pottery jardiniere, 11½in. high. £720

A Morrisware pottery vase, decorated with peonies in mauve, crimson and olive-green against a sea-green ground, 16.5cm. high. (Phillips) £280

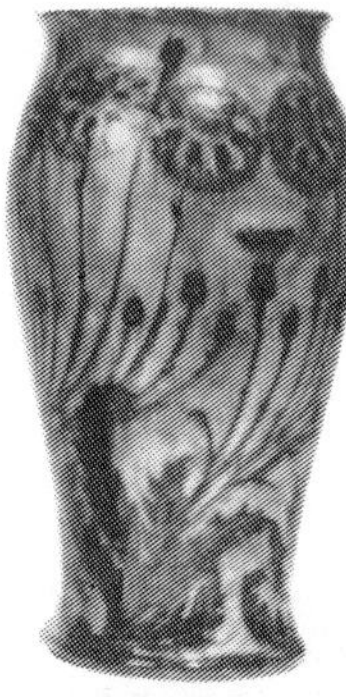

A large S. Hancock & Sons Morrisware baluster vase, decorated with mauve and inky blue thistles on a greeny yellow ground, 32.9cm. high. (Christie's London) £990

MOUSTIERS

The Moustiers factory was established in around 1670 in a remarkably remote corner of France, about 60 miles north east of Marseilles. Early wares were in the blue and white made popular by Rouen, and many fine dishes with pictorial scenes were made. Pierre Clerissy took over in 1679 and started a business that under his grandson Pierre II, was to flourish until 1757.

In about 1710 designs ere adopted based on the engravings of Jean Berain, who as designer to the King in the Department of Occasional Expenses had been responsible for the backgrounds for court galas and entertainments at Versailles.

Polychrome wares were also designed at Moustiers by Jean-Baptiste Laugier and Joseph Olerys, which often depicted mythological or biblical scenes surrounded by elaborate festoon borders. They also designed some with fantastic human and animal figures, sometimes indulging in less than decorous pursuits. Their monogram *LO* is common and often faked. Genuine Moustiers is very light, finely potted and has a smooth, milky white glaze.

A Moustiers shaped oval dish painted in shades of manganese with Berainesque dwarfs, birds and a fox, circa 1740, 33cm. diam. £1,310

A French faience oval basket and cover, Moustiers, circa 1740, 8½in. wide. £585

A Moustiers shaped circular plate, manganese GOL and cross mark of Olerys and Laugier, circa 1740, 25cm. diam. £785

One of a pair of Moustiers (Ferrat) shaped circular plates painted with pairs of parrots, circa 1770, 25cm. diam. (Christie's) £385

A Moustiers (Olerys and Laugier) shaped dish painted with garlands and the armorial device of three boots with the motto 'Forward'. £330

A Moustiers faience 'Seau a Rafraichir' with double plumed mask handles, attributed to Olerys and Laugier, circa 1740, 21cm. diam. £850

A Moustiers faience tazza with lobed rim, painted with the fable of the 'Fox and Goose', 30cm. wide. £600

NANKIN

'Nankin' is the name given to blue and white porcelain of the late eighteenth and nineteenth centuries, which was shipped through the port of Nanking.

'Nankin yellow', on the other hand is used to describe a lustrous, pale golden brown glaze used together with Kangxi underglaze blue decoration. It was used particularly for export wares to the near East.

A blue and white oval tureen, cover and stand, heavily encrusted, circa 1750, the stand 41cm. wide. £3,015

One of two blue and white spittoons, the interior with a border of trellis pattern, circa 1750, 12.6cm. diam. £2,125

One of two blue and white dishes, the borders each with three clusters of flowering branches, circa 1750, 42cm. diam. £9,930

A copper red and celadon glazed figure of a standing dignitary, circa 1750, 18.3cm. high. £19,510

A large blue and white deep dish painted with four fan-tailed fish, circa 1750, 45cm. diam. £7,095

Large mid 19th century Chinese Nanking ashet, 16½in. wide. (Peter Wilson) £410

A blue and white 'piggy-back' group formed as a standing lady and a small boy, circa 1750, 19.8cm. high. £9,225

Early 19th century Chinese Nankin porcelain decoration with Shi Shi dog and punt in a lake setting centre, 17 x 13in. (G. A. Key) £210

NANTGARW

The history of the Nantgarw pottery began in 1814 when William Billingsley and his son-in-law Samuel Walker arrived there. Billingsley had been a painter at Derby and had also experimented with porcelain bodies in the hope of modifying the Derby paste to resemble that of Sèvres.

At Nantgarw, a useful site both for the proximity of coal supplies and a link with the Bristol Channel in the form of the newly opened Glamorgan canal, they succeeded in making a soft paste porcelain which was of amazing quality and translucence. To do so however had cost them all their capital, and they were lent further funds by a local surveyor, W W Young. Also, the President of the Royal Society sent the proprietor of the Swansea works, L W Dillwyn, to have a look. Dillwyn was greatly excited by what he saw at Nantgarw and arranged for Billingsley and Walker to move to Swansea. There, Billingsley oversaw the painting, while Walker experimented with a more reliable body than that which had been produced at Nantgarw.

In 1819, both returned there and the second Nantgarw period began.

Due to financial problems, Billingsley and Walker left Nantgarw again in 1820, and Young was left with the pottery. He employed Thomas Pardoe, a Derby-trained potter who had worked at Swansea, to decorate the remaining stock. Pardoe's free, slightly naive style was in stark contrast to London decorated Nantgarw. He painted birds, landscapes and figure subjects, using often broader strokes and heavier colour than other painters. The pieces were sold at two auctions in 1821 and 22.

A Nantgarw coffee cup and saucer with pierced heart-shaped handle, painted by Thomas Pardoe, circa 1820. (Christie's) £330

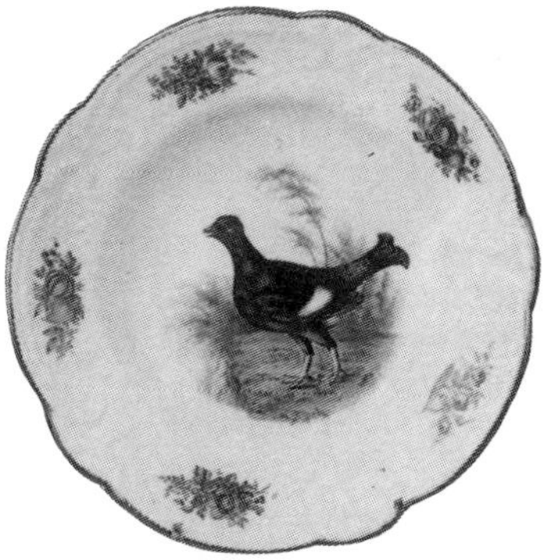

A Nantgarw (London-decorated) ornithological soup-plate, the centre painted with Black Grouse, named on the reverse, circa 1820, 24cm. diameter. (Christie's) £1,980

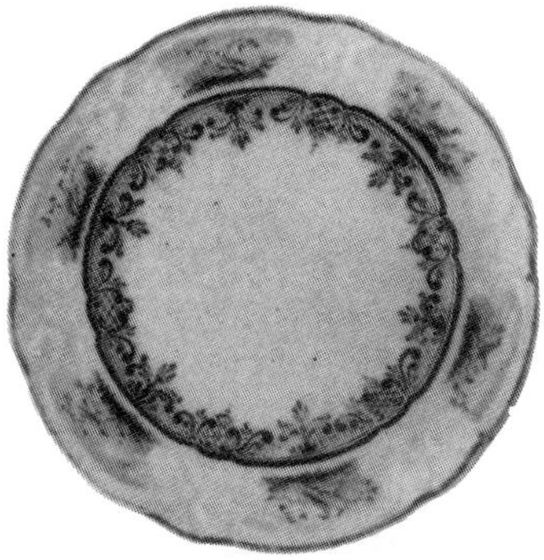

A Nantgarw plate painted by Thomas Pardoe, the border with exotic birds perched on trees in landscape vignettes within moulded foliage-scroll cartouches, circa 1820, 21.5cm. diameter. (Christie's) £495

A Nantgarw London-decorated gold-ground circular two-handled sauce tureen and stand, the body and stand painted with garden flowers on a gilt band, circa 1820, the stand 18.5cm. diam. (Christie's) £2,860

A Nantgarw armorial cabinet-cup and saucer, the central arms within a garter with the motto *Deus et Patria*, circa 1820. (Christie's) £2,090

A Nantgarw plate painted by Thomas Pardoe, the centre with two pheasants perched on a tree in a landscape vignette, circa 1820, 22cm. diameter. (Christie's) £1,540

NAPLES

The Royal Factory of Naples was established in 1771 by Ferdinand IV, son of Charles III, and employed many of the ex-workers of the latter's Capodimonte factory.

Domenico Venuti was made Director in 1779. He engaged skilled modellers etc from other factories and the first really successful pieces produced at Naples were huge services, used as Royal gifts, and often featuring a biscuit figure centrepiece.

The decoration often drew heavily on themes from the new discoveries at Herculaneum and Naples and books were published explaining the various classical allusions. Commoner today are tablewares decorated with a central medallion showing peasants in traditional garb, with borders of wreaths or Pompeian fret.

With regard to body, early pieces tend to be rather yellow, but a fine white or creamy body was developed during the 1780s. Early painting shows a marked resemblance to Capodimonte of the later rococo period.

Some figures were produced, usually off white, either glazed or in biscuit. Some, of individuals strolling along alone or in pairs, are interesting for having no base, but are balanced on their own feet.

Naples, of course, first employed the much copied crowned *N* mark. Unless the piece is soft paste porcelain however the mark is fraudulent. *FRF* is also used in blue black or red enamel, under a crown.

A Naples figure of a lady dressed as an Oriental wearing a plumed hat, yellow shawl and pink coat over a long dress with blue spots, circa 1790, 16cm. high. (Christie's London) £7700

A Naples two-handled ecuelle, cover and stand painted with vignettes of five dated nocturnal eruptions of Vesuvius, circa 1794, stand 23.5cm. diam. (Christie's) £13,200

A pair of Naples armorial waisted albarelli, the central quartered Arms in ochre, yellow and blue within a beaded cartouche, mid-16th century, 23cm. high. (Christie's) £7,700

A Naples (Real Fabbrica Ferdinandea) group of a gallant and companion, he in a black top hat, she in a black shawl over a purple patterned skirt and yellow shoes, circa 1790, 18.5cm. high. (Christie's) £8,800

A Naples creamware white group of the Madonna with the Infant Christ and St. John, inscribed Laudato Fecit 1794, 35cm. high. (Christie's) £4,400

A Naples (Real Fabbrica Ferdinandea) Royal portrait medallion with the heads of King Ferdinando IV and Queen Maria Caroline, circa 1790, 6.5cm. diameter. (Christie's) £1,760

NEVERS

When the Duke Luigi Gonzaga of Mantua became Duke of Nevers in 1565, he brought with him from Italy some leading faienciers, notably Domenico Conrado and his brothers from the Savona area. The Conrados prospered and were to hold a virtual monopoly of faience manufacture in Nevers until around 1630. Through the influence of Guilio Gambini, an Italian potter from Lyon, who was in partnership for some time with Augustino Conrado, much early production was in the late Urbino pictorial style, with designs of biblical and mythological scenes. Some large figures were also made at Nevers and were probably made by Daniel Lefebvre, who worked there between 1629-49.

Given the brothers' origin it is unsurprising that much Nevers faience was decorated in the Savona style though both the clay and glaze were harder than those used there. Because the firing was done at unusually high temperatures, the colours sometimes have a faded look, and the final protective covering of a glassy lead glaze normally found on Italian maiolica was also omitted.

The Conrados also introduced a new painting technique, whereby cobalt was added to the basic tin glaze to make blue, and designs were painted on this base in a thick white enamel paste. It is called the 'Persian' style, but probably owes more to Limoges enamels. Pseudo oriental designs in time superseded those of Italian inspiration as the potters copied Chinese inspired Dutch faience.

Early marks often include the decorator's name with *A Nevers* or *DF* and a date incised for Lefebvre's work.

A French faience figure of an Oriental lady standing in a classical pose, her long plaited hair tied by a blue top knot, circa 1730, possibly Nevers, 37cm. high. (Christie's London) £4,180

A French istoriato tazza painted with Diana and Acteon, the alarmed Diana and her attendants covering her with drapes, probably Nevers, last quarter of the 16th century, 28cm. diam. (Christie's London) £1,540

Late 17th century garniture of three Nevers bleu persan vases, 37cm. and 59cm. high. £4,950

A pair of faience bucket-shaped jardinières, the sides painted in yellow, green, iron-red and underglaze blue with an Oriental by shrubs in a garden, probably Nevers, circa 1680, 13.5cm. high. (Christie's) £3,300

A Nevers (Conrade) armorial blue and white tondino, the centre painted with a huntsman blowing a horn accompanied by his hound, circa 1680, 30cm. diam. (Christie's London) £1,045

A massive Nevers bleu persan bucket-shaped jardinière, the strapwork and foliage handles with bearded mask terminals, circa 1680, 47cm. high. (Christie's) £2,200

NEWCOMB POTTERY

This American pottery was set up in 1895 at Newcomb College, New Orleans, a women's section of Tulane University, Louisiana. Essentially, the work of professional potters was bought in to be decorated by the students and the emphasis was on local materials and decorative motifs, such as indigenous trees like magnolia or palms. The products were mainly low fired earthenware painted in underglaze colours, predominantly blue, green and yellow. These were given a glossy glaze at first, but after 1910 softer colours and matt glazes were brought in and decoration became more naturalistic, with some motifs being modelled. The pottery continued in existence until 1930.

NEWHALL

The Newhall or New Hall factory at Shelton, Stoke on Trent, made hard paste porcelain from 1782-1812 and bone china thereafter. Their product however was quite different from the true porcelain of China and Germany; in reality it was somewhere between a hard and soft paste, and the term 'hybrid paste' has been coined to try and describe it.

Newhall produced exclusively useful wares, and specialised in tea services. Although the overall output was huge, catering for the middle rather than the upper classes, early pieces are still quite rare. Usually these were simply painted, and sometimes had the spiral wreathing found also at Bristol and Plymouth. Handles are usually of clip form and cream jugs helmet shaped.

After about 1790 forms became more standardised and somewhat lost their individuality.

A Newcomb College pottery high glaze mug, New Orleans, signed by Ada W. Lonnegan, circa 1901, 4¼in. high. £950

Early 20th century Newcomb College pottery vase, Louisiana, stamped and initialled KS, 5in. high. £435

A Newcomb pottery floral vase, New Orleans, circa 1928, initialled by Henrietta Bailey, 5¼in. high. (Robt. W. Skinner Inc.) £486

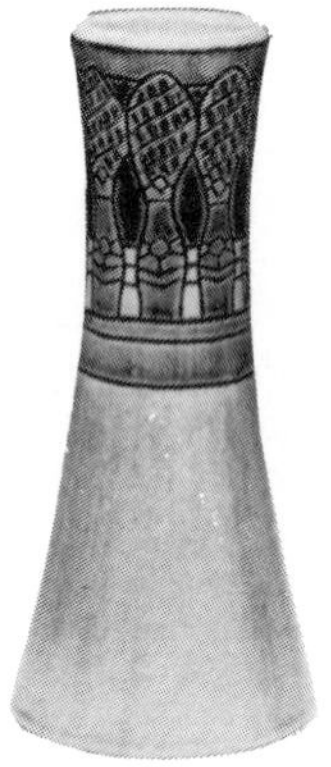

Newcomb College Pottery vase, New Orleans, Louisiana, circa 1905, the flaring cylindrical form with incised and painted decoration, 9¾in. high. (Skinner Inc.) £1,351

Newhall porcelain tea pot, oval panel shape with sprig flower decoration, complete with cover. (G. A. Key) £100

Newhall three piece tea service, printed with landscape views, comprising teapot, sugar and cream jug. £400

NEWPORT POTTERY

The Newport pottery was a subsidiary of A J Wilkinson Ltd operating in the 1930s, and is distinguished by having among its designers the legendary Clarice Cliff.

A large Newport pottery Bizarre wall mask, 1930's, 37cm. high. £330

A Newport pottery 'Archaic' Bizarre vase, 1930's, impressed number 373, 17.75cm. high. £660

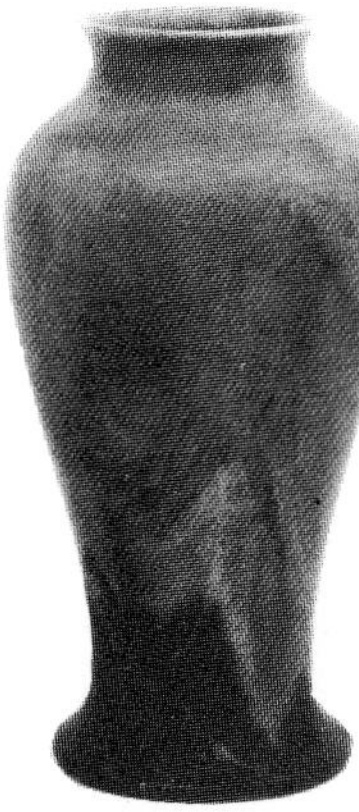

A Newport pottery Bizarre vase, deep inky blue at base, printed marks, 1930's, 36cm. high. £880

An amusing Newport pottery model of an owl wearing a suit, signed *M. Epworth*, 18.5cm. (Bearne's) £110

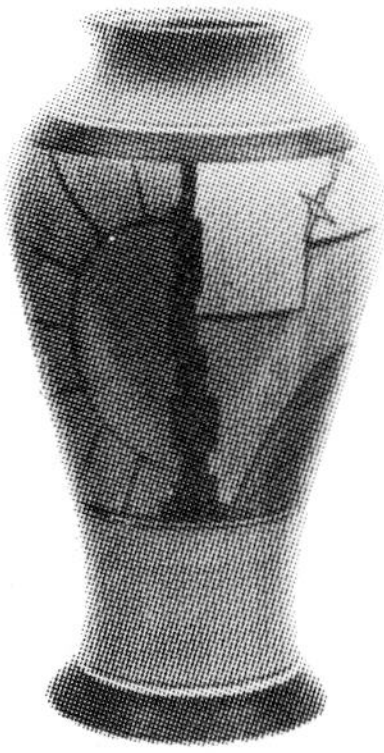

A large Newport pottery Bizarre vase, 1930's, 36.75cm. high. £2,750

A Newport pottery Bizarre 'Delicia' jar and cover, 1930's, 21cm. high. £440

A Newport pottery Bizarre charger, 1930's, stylised foliate design in blue, orange and green with blue border, 33.5cm. diam. £190

A Bizarre single-handled 'lotus' vase, 29.3cm. high. Newport, late 1930's. £350

NIDERVILLER

The manufacture of hard paste porcelain began at Niderviller in 1765 and continues today. The factory was originally opened in 1754 by Baron Jean Louis de Bayerlé to make faience. In 1770 it was purchased by the Comte de Custine and passed on his death to Claude Francois Lanfrey.

For its styles, it drew heavily on the wares of Strasbourg, turning out vases, clocks and large tablewares in the high rococo taste, Forms and decoration were almost identical for both its faience and porcelain output, the latter comprising mainly oriental or European flowers, sprigs or landscapes.

Figures were produced, the majority being left unglazed. Many were modelled by Charles Sauvage, known as Lemire. When Paul Louis Cyfflé's Lunéville factory was sold in 1780 many of his moulds also passed to Niderviller.

Marks are *BN* in monogram, *CN* in monogram, two interlaced *C*s or *N Nider* or *Niderviller*.

NOVE

In 1728 Giovanni Batista Antonibon established an earthenware and hard paste porcelain factory at Nove near Bassano. He was succeeded there by his son and grandson, and it continued in the family until the late nineteenth century.

It is noted for its tureens in the form of fish, and for practical rococo tablewares painted in high temperature colours. The mark of a star with a tail is common on 19th century pieces.

Good quality cream coloured earthenware was also made at Nove from about 1780 by Giovanni Maria Baccin and others such as Baroni, Bernardi, Viero and Cacchetto. Most of these are clearly marked.

A Niderviller faience shaped hexafoil dish, circa 1775, 25cm. diam. £5,675

One of a pair of Niderviller covered vases and covers, 15¼in. high, circa 1780. £1,500

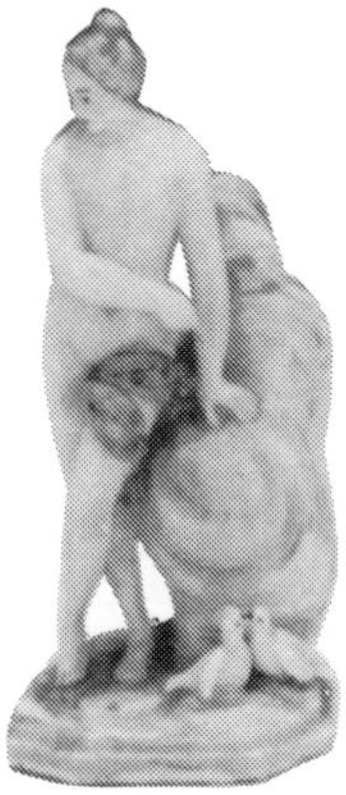

A Niderviller miniature group of Venus scantily clad in a puce cloth leaning against billowing cloud scrolls, circa 1780, 8.5cm. high. (Christie's Geneva) **£300**

A Niderviller figure of 'La Jardiniere', on a circular base, 20.5cm. high. (Phillips) £240

Two Nove pistol-shaped handles painted with fruit and flowers, fitted with a steel four-pronged fork and a blade, 19th century, 7.5cm. and 8cm. long. (Christie's) £176

A Le Nove two handled ecuelle cover and stand, painted in colours with scattered sprays of flowers, iron red star marks, circa 1770, the stand 22cm. diam. (Christie's London) £1,870

NYMPHENBURG

Following the establishment of the porcelain factory at Meissen, the rulers of the other German states were anxious to set up their own ventures. One of the most successful was at Nymphenburg in Bavaria, where production began in 1753 and continues to the present.

The original factory was situated at Neudeck, under the patronage of the Bavarian Elector, who had married a granddaughter of Augustus the Strong, and it was transferred to Nymphenburg itself in 1761.

Throughout its early history a galaxy of talent was employed there, but financially things ran far from smoothly and a succession of managers were engaged to try to make it profitable. The fame of the Nymphenburg factory, however, rests essentially on the work of one man, the modeller Franz Anton Bustelli, who is to rococo what Kaendler was to baroque.

Nymphenburg porcelain is of the true hard paste variety, fairly white in colour and covered with a fine and brilliant glaze. Early pieces were delicately coloured and many left in the white. Flat washes of red-blue, black, pink and gold were used for colouring dresses. Small pieces, such as snuff boxes, and tablewares were also produced in profusion during this period.

Early Neudeck-Nymphenburg pieces often bear the diamond paned shield from the arms of Bavaria, and from 1765 a hexagram mark was additionally used. A lively 'seconds' market existed from the beginning, and defective pieces were sold in the white with the factory mark cancelled by an engraved stroke.

A Nymphenburg oil and vinegar stand with two bottles and hinged covers, circa 1765, the bottles 18cm. high. £8,730

A well-painted Nymphenburg topographical cup, and a saucer, the cup with a view of Marsbach. (Phillips) £420

A pair of Nymphenburg figures designed by Prof. J. Wackerle of stylised 18th century fops. £2,375

A Nymphenburg baluster coffee pot and domed cover painted in colours to both sides with birds roosting in trees and perching on terraces, indistinct incised mark, circa 1760, 23cm. high. (Christie's London) £2,200

A Nymphenburg shaped circular dish from the Hof service painted with a large spray of roses, chrysanthemum and tulips, further flowers and a butterfly, circa 1762, 23.5cm. diameter. (Christie's) £2,750

A Nymphenburg figure of a parrot modelled by Dominicus Auliczek, its plumage painted naturalistically in green, yellow, iron-red and blue, circa 1765, 15.5cm. high. (Christie's) £3,960

OHR

George Ohr (1857–1918) was an American artist potter who was based in Missouri. His work was characterised by being of very thin porcelain, which was then distorted by being squeezed or folded into weird forms with handles then applied. His glazes were notable for their flowing colours, such as green and plum.

Most of his pieces are marked with *G E Ohr, Biloxi, Miss.*

George E. Ohr Pottery vase, Biloxi, Mississippi, circa 1904, fluted top on cylindrical form, midnight blue over cobalt glossy glaze, 5in. high.
(Skinner Inc.) £442

A G. E. Ohr pottery vase, the concave-shaped mouth with elongated folded handles, circa 1900, 10in. high. £2,360

George E. Ohr Pottery vase, Biloxi, Mississippi, circa 1898, mottled olive green iridescent glaze, 4in. high.
(Skinner Inc.) £208

A 20th century moulded pottery 'steamboat' pitcher, cast after the original by George E. Ohr, 9in. high. £200

Late 19th/early 20th century George Ohr art pottery vase, Mississippi, 4in. high. £445

PALERMO

The maiolica manufactured at Palermo in the 16th and 17th centuries has much in common with the style of Castel Durante. Blue and yellow grounds predominate with profuse decoration. The forms are common to those being produced elsewhere at the time, i.e. albarelli, drug jars etc.

Marks are rare. One of the few which has been found, on an albarello of good quality is Fatto in Palermo 1606.

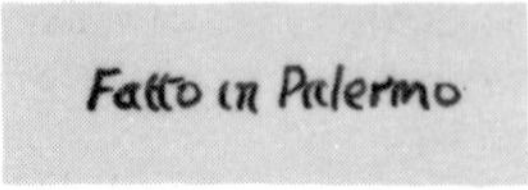

A Palermo wet drug jar with pointed ovoid body painted with flowerheads and leaves in yellow and green, on a blue ground, 20cm., 17th century.
(Phillips) £650

A Palermo majolica albarello of waisted cylindrical form, painted with a yellow ground oval panel of a bishop saint, 17th century, 11½in. high.
(Christie's S. Ken) £1,100

PARIAN

In the early 19th century, Staffordshire potters were experimenting with formulae for unglazed white porcelain which could be modelled into statuary in imitation of the finest Greek marble sculptures found on the island of Paros. The firms of Copeland and Garrett and Minton were front-runners in the race, and it was Copeland who in 1842 released the first piece of 'parian' statuary, entitled Apollo as the Shepherd Boy of Admetus. Their success was due to the high quantity of feldspar in the formula and a firing process which permitted a large amount of air in the kiln. The result was a lustrous transparency and delicacy of moulding.

Minton, who were the first to use the name Parian, contested Copeland's claim of a 'first', and the jury at the Great Exhibition produced a soothing statement which declared in effect a draw.

Copeland commissioned figures from many of the finest sculptors of the day, while Minton's principal modellers were John Bell and Albert Carrier Belleuse.

Wedgwood, Worcester and Coalport all produced parian ware, including some impressive tableware, where glazed and decorated bone china was successfully combined with lightly gilt statuary.

Standard parian was found to be excellent for relief moulded fancy ware, with smear glazing. Coloured backgrounds were achieved by tinted slip brush-applied to the appropriate parts of the mould, and the main colours were blue, sage and brown. Standard parian was criticised because the fine granular surface was easily soiled, though this was to some degree overcome from 1860 by the use of a thin coating of lead glaze.

A Bennington Parian teapot with domed cover, squirrel finial, 5in. high. £280

A Copeland Parian bust of a young woman with flowing hair, 23in. high. £500

A Parian figural group of sleeping children 'Le Nid', circa 1875, signed 'Croisy', 15in. high. (Robt. W. Skinner Inc.) £418

A Copeland Parian group of 'The Sleep of Sorrow and the Dream of Joy', after the original sculpture by Rafaelle Monti, circa 1875, 18½in. high. £500

A Bates, Brown-Westhead and Moore parian bust of Apollo after a model by Delpech, Art Union stamp and dated 1861, 14in. high. (Christie's S. Ken) £330

A Minton Parian group of Ariadne and the Panther on rectangular base, year cypher for 1867, 13.7in. high. £300

PARIS

During the Neo-Classical period many small porcelain factories were scattered in and around Paris, most of which were under some form of noble patronage. Mainly they produced tableware and there was very little figure production.

Despite their numbers however, the porcelain they produced was surprisingly uniform in both shape and decoration, and it is often very difficult to tell the output of one from another unless they are marked. The severer neo-Classical style did not, of course, lend itself to the wilder flights of imagination in the same way as did Baroque and Rococo. Plates were usually plain and unmoulded, coffee and teapots cylindrical or vase shaped, cups cylindrical and bowls often raised on feet.

One new form which did emerge at this time however was the semicircular bulb or flower pot, the fronts of which were divided into three panels with pilasters, and decorated with neo-Classical motifs.

Decoration of the period was not generally elaborate in content, consisting mainly of formal motifs, but its technical brilliance was truly amazing. There was much use of gilding and chased decoration which, together with coloured grounds and borders, often matt, gave a remarkably rich effect.

Napoleon's expedition to Egypt and his elevation to Emperor saw the beginning of the Empire period, during which the Paris factories continued to thrive. In many aspects the Empire style is merely an extension of neo-Classicism, but wares now began to show a greater variety of form, with greater use of modelling for the handles and spouts of teapots etc. Vases, too, while retaining their basic shape,

Paris Porcelain Figural Desk Set, France, late 19th century, the cover modelled as three young girls, the oval base with mounted inkwell and sander, 8in. high. (Skinner Inc) £330

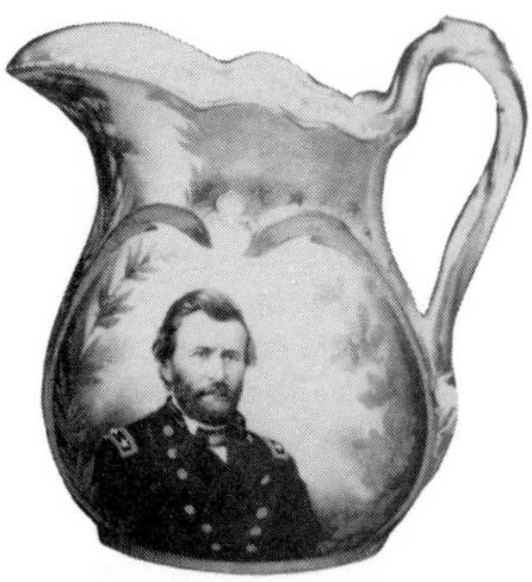

Paris porcelain American historical pitcher, France, circa 1862, enamel decorated portraits of Grant and Farragut in military dress, 8 3/8in. high. (Skinner Inc.) £11,339

A pair of ormolu-mounted Paris pale blue-ground campana-shaped vases, one painted with a stag-hunt, the other with a boar-hunt, circa 1810–20, 38in. high. (Christie's) £5,060

A Paris (Stone, Coquerel et le Gros) plate transfer-printed in sepia with a view of Chateau de Houghton, Comté de Norfolk, circa 1820, 23.5cm. diameter. (Christie's) £495

A Paris tea kettle, cover and stand, iron-red monogram mark of Louis-Stanislas Xavier, circa 1780, 30cm. wide. £1,660

A Paris porcelain veilleuse, the globular teapot and cylindrical holder painted with peasant lovers in landscape vignettes, circa 1830, 24cm. high overall. (Christie's) £275

PARIS

had more interesting handles, which were often of biscuit, or gilt unglazed porcelain. Their matt surface contrasted with the highly polished gilding on the bodies. Egyptian motifs were understandably common.

Another new form of the time was the cabinet cup, not part of a service but as an entity in itself. The saucers for these tended to be fairly plain and decorated only with gilding and they acted as a foil for the highly elaborate cups. These were often flared in shape with ornate modelled handles, richly decorated with fine enamel painting of topographical scenes, portraits etc. in panels. They were often so lavish and extravagant that it seems unlikely they were ever designed for any practical use.

Theodore Deck (1823–91) was a French artist potter from Alsace who from 1856 onwards was making ornamental earthenware in Paris. His early work was often decorated with scenes commissioned from artists, and he was greatly influenced by middle Eastern, notably Iznik styles.

PAUL REVERE

The Paul Revere pottery was established in the early years of the 20th century in Boston, for the purpose of training girls from poor immigrant backgrounds, the profits to be used for their education in other subjects. It produced earthenware nursery and breakfast bowls and dishes etc. decorated with stylized floral motifs, mottoes etc, with the decoration often confined to the borders. Pieces were marked with initials or with *SEG* for Saturday Evening Girls (q.v.)

A Dagoty Paris ewer and basin, the ewer with matt blue ground, decorated in white relief with acanthus leaf borders and swan neck griffins, 31cm. high. (Phillips London) £2,875

A Paris pink-ground barrel-shaped coffee-cup and saucer painted with a chinoiserie figure smoking a pipe, fabulous trees and plants, circa 1810. (Christie's) £330

A Paris gold-ground baluster coffee-pot and cover painted at Naples each side with figures watching a puppet-show and spaghetti vendors, circa 1800, 18.5cm. high. (Christie's) £1,980

A Paris biscuit roundel of Napoleon, the head of the Emperor moulded with a laurel wreath, pierced for hanging, circa 1810, 15.5cm. diameter. (Christie's) £418

Paul Revere Pottery decorated tea tile, Boston, Massachusetts, early 20th century, with central decoration of a cottage, 5¾in. diameter. (Skinner Inc.) £195

Paul Revere Pottery decorated vase, Boston, Massachusetts, early 20th century, with incised and painted band of tree design, 8½in. high. (Skinner Inc.) £1,195

PEARLWARE

Pearlware was the name given in 1780 by Josiah Wedgwood to a whitened version of his celebrated creamware which he had just developed successfully.

This was made by adding a touch of blue colouring to the body. It could be just as thin as porcelain, and formed an excellent background for blue printing, enabling it to compete favourably with Chinese wares. It was quickly adopted by many other potteries, and became extremely popular in the late 18th/19th centuries.

A pearlware oval plaque moulded in high relief and coloured with two recumbent lions, circa 1790, 28.5cm. wide. (Christie's) £715

A Yorkshire pearlware model of a show horse, with an ochre and green saddle-cloth tied with a blue girth, circa 1800, 14.5cm. high. (Bearne's) £1,250

A pearlware globular teapot and cover, printed with two circular panels of female archers, circa 1800, 7½in. wide. (Christie's S. Ken) £176

An unusual Victorian bargeman's pearlware smoking companion, the tobacco jar with an antique slavery portrait and a biblical reference, 38cm. high overall. (Henry Spencer) £220

A pearlware shallow bowl on a small foot, the interior printed in blue with a double portrait busts of George III and Charlotte inscribed '*A King Rever'd, A Queen Belovd, Long May They Live*', 19cm. (Phillips) £400

A dated Staffordshire pearlware globular jug, inscribed 'Samuell Piggott 1799' and flanked by the farmer's arms, 7¼in. high. (Christie's S. Ken) £110

A pearlware group depicting the marriage of John Macdonald, he and his companion flanking an anvil with a priest attending, circa 1810, 8½in. high. (Christie's S. Ken) £550

A pearlware figure of a hound seated erect with a dead bird at its feet, on a shaped base, Staffordshire or Yorkshire, circa 1785, 10.5cm. wide. (Christie's) £506

A pearlware toby-jug holding a frothing jug of ale, in blue, yellow and manganese jacket, circa 1790, 10in. high.
(Christie's S. Ken) £1,100

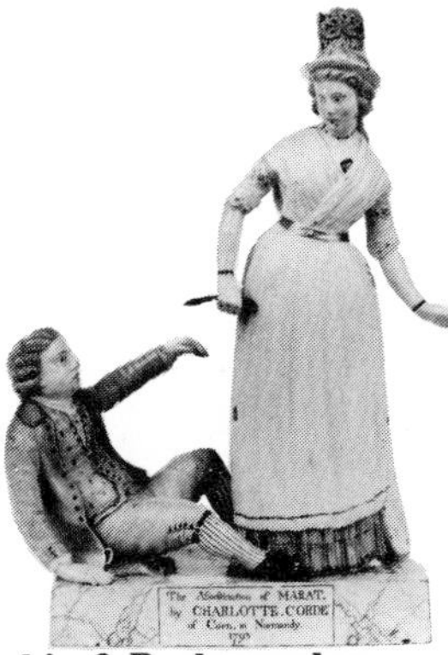

A Lakin & Poole pearlware group of the assassination of Marat, Charlotte Cordé standing holding a metal knife in her right hand, her bonnet embellished with a green bow, impressed mark, circa 1794, 35cm. high.
(Christie's) £2,090

A Hall pearlware group of a ewe and lamb, their coats splashed in iron-red, the ewe standing before a flowering bocage, circa 1820, 15.5cm. high.
(Christie's) £418

A 19th century pearlware slops jar and cover, of baluster form with grotesque animal mask handles, 11in. high.
(Spencer's) £880

A Staffordshire pearlware figure of Ceres of Pratt type, holding a sickle and sheaf of corn, circa 1800, 21.5cm. high.
(Christie's) £330

A John Meir blue and white pearlware plate, the centre printed with a portrait of Queen Caroline wearing a coat and feathered hat, 21.5cm.
(Bearne's) £360

A Staffordshire pearlware figure of the Prophet Jeremiah, his robe painted in iron-red with flower-sprays and wearing a pale-lilac-lined mottled blue cloak, circa 1820, 28cm. high.
(Christie's) £1,210

A Staffordshire pearlware shaped rectangular plaque, moulded in relief with a bust portrait of Queen Victoria, circa 1845, 8¾in. high.
(Christie's S. Ken) £187

A pearlware figure of Amphitrite and the dolphin, in red robes on a green base, perhaps Scottish circa 1800, 6in. high.
(Christie's S. Ken) £143

A Staffordshire pearlware teapot and cover of lozenge section with leaf moulded handle, the body painted in colours with birds, 6¾in. high. (Christie's S. Ken) £209

A Yorkshire pearlware figure of a sportsman in green-brown hat, blue jacket, spotted waistcoat and yellow breeches, circa 1800, 26.5cm. high. (Christie's) £4,400

A rare pearlware water jug and bowl, probably London, decorated with embossed GR IV monograms within grooved bands, 22cm. and 29.5cm. (Phillips) £320

A Staffordshire pearlware yelow-ground Bacchus jug, moulded in relief with a grinning face, 7½in. high. (Christie's S. Ken.) £200

A Staffordshire pearlware group of a dandy and companion wearing their finest clothes, circa 1820, 21cm. high. (Christie's) £550

A pearlware inscribed oviform jug with loop handle, painted in the manner of Absolon of Yarmouth, circa 1790, 18.5cm. high. £1,980

A pearlware toby jug and cover, probably Yorkshire, the seated man with a pipe by his side and a foaming jug of ale on his knee, 26.5cm. (Bearne's) £640

A Staffordshire pearlware model of a roaring lion with brown mane and black muzzle, circa 1790, 33cm. long. (Christie's London) £1,650

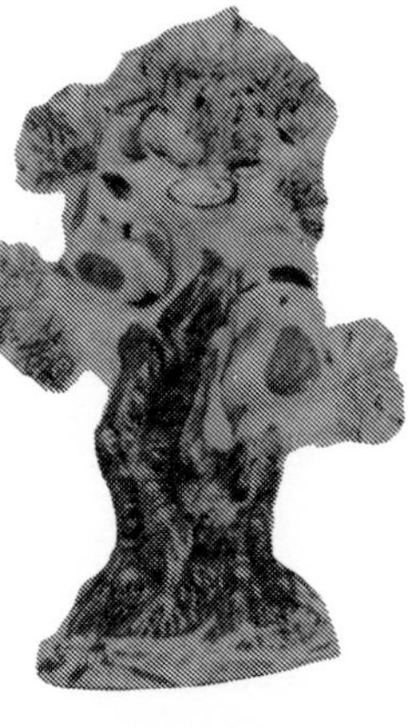

A pearlware 'Birds in Branches' group, probably Staffordshire, circa 1790, 19.5cm. high. (Christie's) £660

PESARO

Pesaro was another of the towns in the Duchy of Urbino with a strong potting tradition, and maiolica was made there during the late 15th and 16th centuries.

In 1462 mention was made of a loan of a large sum of money for the enlargement of a manufactory of vessels, and it is to this date that the commencement of maiolica manufacture is generally ascribed.

In 1546, Jean Sforza passed an edict in favour of Pesaro, forbidding the introduction from other factories of any but common vessels for oil and water and a similar edict was passed in 1552, naming the potters Bernardino Gagliardino, Girolamo Lanfranchi and Mo. Rinaldo as engaging to supply the town and country with vases and pieces painted with historical subjects. Girolamo Lanfranchi was succeeded by his son Giacomo, who in 1562 invented the application of gold to maiolica, fixed by fire.

A notable patron of the pottery was Guido Ubaldo II, who became Duke of Urbino in 1538, but on his death in 1572 the pottery began to decline and by 1718 there was only one potter still there who made ordinary vessels.

The manufacture of pottery was revived in the middle of the century, when Antonio Casali and Filippo Caligari from Lodi set up again to make practical wares such as drug jars, lamps and cups. These were decorated in the later French, imitation Sèvres style, with low fired enamel colours, probably by Pietro Lei, who came to the factory from Sassuolo in 1763. Favourite motifs were gold arabesques, medallions of flowers, and landscapes.

Imitation Urbino ware was made by Magrini & Co of Pesaro from 1870.

A documentary Pesaro trilobed jug, inscribed in Greek, circa 1790, 22cm. high. (Christie's) £2,200

A Pesaro istoriato tondo painted in colours after Sforza Marcantonio with the legend of Perseus and Andromeda, circa 1570, 25.5cm. diam. (Christie's London) £24,200

A Pesaro fluted crespina painted with the Sacrifice of Isaac, circa 1570, 24.5cm. diam. (Christie's) £5,500

A Pesaro fluted crespina painted with Christ on the road to Calvary, circa 1570, 23.5cm. diam. (Christie's) £3,630

A Pesaro istoriato tazza painted in colours by Sforza di Marcantonio with Anchises and Aeneas arriving at Pallanteum, circa 1550, 27cm. diam. (Christie's) £3,080

A Pesaro cylindrical albarello boldly painted with manganese, blue and orange flowers, oranges and scrolling foliage between blue concentric bands, circa 1780, 22cm. high. (Christie's) £1,000

PETIT

Jacob and Mardochée Petit purchased their factory at Fontainebleu in 1830 and it remained in the family until well into the second half of the century. It was Petit perhaps more than any other who recaptured the spirit of the true rococo during its 19th century revival, and the clocks, lavish inkstands, vases and tea warmers which he modelled in the form of personages or figures are among the most popular of his works.

Many French factories of the time made products in styles attributed to Petit but those bearing the underglaze blue mark *JP* are obviously better quality and command a premium.

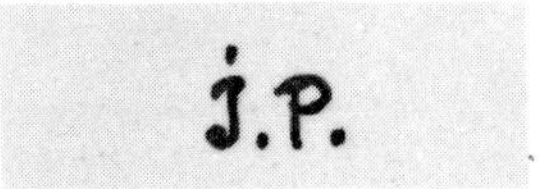

A Jacob Petit garniture of a clock and a pair of candlesticks all moulded with rococo scrolls, shells and leaf motifs, 39.5cm. (Phillips) £900

A pair of early 19th century Jacob Petit baluster vases on square bases with gilt mask handles, 71cm. high. (Wellington Salerooms) £4,000

A Jacob Petit pot-pourri in the form of a fish, painted in iron-red and apricot and gilt scales, 19th century, $7\frac{1}{2}$in. long. (Christie's S. Ken.) £200

An attractive pair of early 19th century Jacob Petit porcelain taper holders, modelled as a Turkish sultan and his sultana, 16.5cm. high. (Henry Spencer) £1,500

A Jacob Petit tapering oviform vase and domed cover with two blue rope-twist handles, blue JP monogram, mid 19th century, 20in. high. (Christie's S. Ken.) £550

A pair of Jacob Petit vases of ogee shape with flared rims, painted in colours with bouquets on both sides, 18cm. (Phillips) £400

A Paris (Jacob Petit) clock-case and stand of scroll outline, blue JP marks, circa 1835, 37cm. high overall. (Christie's) £825

A Jacob Petit porcelain figural vase, as a lady seated on a rocky mound encrusted with flowers, 27.5cm. high. (Henry Spencer) £300

PILKINGTON

Pilkington's Tile and Pottery Co. was set up in 1892 at Clifton Junction Lancashire, to manufacture tiles, but from 1897 the production range was extended to include buttons, vases etc. Shortly afterwards the decoration of bought-in biscuit vases also began.

Opalescent glaze effects were discovered in 1903 and from then on the production of glazed earthenware known as Lancastrian pottery began. These wares, which consisted of vases, bowls, trays etc. were usually simple in shape, but decorated in a wide palette of colours often with a crystalline or opalescent effect.

The company was run by two brothers, William and Joseph Burton, who were both ceramic chemists and who were instrumental in developing the lustre, decorated pottery which formed the bulk of the factory's 20th century production. Modelled, moulded or incised decoration appears on these pieces, while the decorator R Joyce modelled animals and birds. Lapis ware was introduced in 1928, and tile production continued throughout.

The factory ceased production in 1937, midway between the deaths of the two brothers, though it started up again in a limited way ten years later, when potters were encouraged to produce individual pieces which were then decorated and signed with the artist's monogram.

Until 1904 the mark *P* was sometimes used, followed until 1913 by *P* and *L* and two bees. The Tudor rose was a later mark, and *Royal Lancastrian* is another variation.

A Pilkington Lancastrian lustre vase and cover decorated by Richard Joyce with a frieze of antelopes and stylised trees, 15.5cm. high. (Christie's) £550

A Pilkington Lancastrian deep bowl designed by Walter Crane and decorated by Wm. S. Mycock, date code for 1913, 21.6cm. high. £865

A Pilkington's Royal Lancastrian lustre vase decorated by Gordon Forsyth, painted in red and gold lustre with bands of tudor roses, 1915, 8½in. high. (Christie's S. Ken) £352

A Pilkington's Royal Lancastrian twin-handled vase decorated by Gordon Forsyth, 1908, 30.2cm. high. £190

Pilkington's Royal Lancastrian lustre two-handled baluster vase decorated by William S. Mycock, 8.25in. high. (Prudential Fine Art) **£200**

A Pilkington's Lancastrian moulded ovoid lustre vase decorated by Richard Joyce, the body embossed with wild animals amongst grassland, 1915. (Christie's S. Ken) £770

A Pilkington Royal Lancastrian lustre vase decorated by W. S. Mycock, with short cylindrical neck, decorated with vertical bands of Tudor roses, dated 1927, 30cm. high high. (Christie's London) £880

A Pilkington Royal Lancastrian lustre charger decorated by William S. Mycock, decorated with a flamboyant armorial crest, dated 1924, 30.6cm. diam. (Christie's London) £352

A massive Pilkington Royal Lancastrian lustre vase, decorated by Gordon Forsyth, decorated in gold with griffins passant on an iridescent greeny-blue ground, dated 1911, 63cm. high.
(Christie's) £3,740

A Pilkington's Lancastrian lustre moonflask by Walter Crane and Richard Joyce, decorated with the coat of arms of the City of Manchester, 27cm. high.
(Spencer's) £1,600

A Pilkington Royal Lancastrian lustre vase and cover decorated by William S. Mycock, decorated in gold with a double headed eagle, date code for 1913, 23.5cm. high. (Christie's London) £440

A Pilkington Royal Lancastrian lustre vase and cover decorated by Gordon Forsyth, with two central reserves each surrounded by laurel leaves and flanked by two lions, 29cm. high.
(Christie's) £3,300

A Pilkington 'Royal Lancastrian' lustre vase by Richard Joyce, painted in golden lustre with two mounted knights in armour 26.5cm. high.
(Phillips) £950

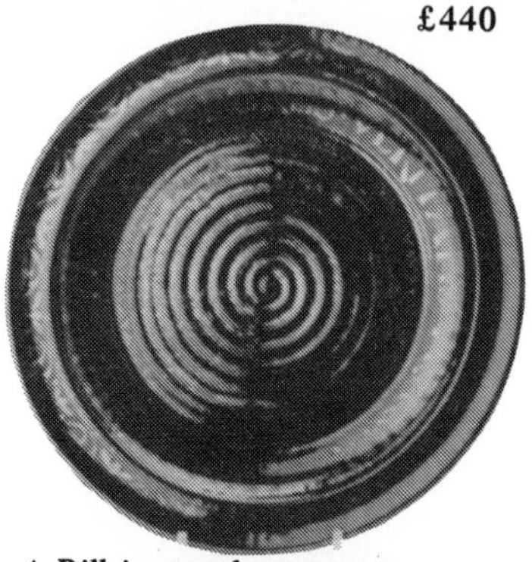

A Pilkington lustre pottery charger, by W. S. Mycock, with concentrically ribbed interior, with foliate border, dated 1918, 33cm. diam. (Bonhams) £150

A Pilkington's lustre vase decorated by Gordon M. Forsyth, with gold lustre rampant lion with a cartouche, code for 1908, 28cm. high.
(Christie's) £396

PLYMOUTH

The first pottery in England to make hard paste porcelain was William Cookworthy's factory at Plymouth, where production started in 1768. There were enormous technical difficulties to overcome, with a huge amount of kiln wastage, and this made it difficult to turn the project into a commercial success.

The Plymouth paste was very hard and white, and the glaze tended to be heavily smoked. Spiral wreathing, a pattern of fine grooves which appeared on the surface of the vessels as they twisted in the kiln, is also common. However, some quite elaborate shapes were achieved, such as large vases and intricate shell salts. More common are the useful tablewares, with pickle leaf dishes, for example, often painted in underglaze blue and overglaze iron red. The decoration was often in the Chinese Mandarin or famille verte style. Most successful of all were the bird decorated mugs by the French painter Mons Saqui.

Most of the polychrome production was unmarked, and is often difficult to distinguish from early Bristol. With the blue and white output, however, this is easier, as Plymouth produced a very blackish underglaze blue, due to the high temperature at which it was fired. It is rarer than the polychrome, but a greater proportion is marked.

Marks usually comprised the chemical sign for tin with a combined 2 and 4 in underglaze blue, and naturally add greatly to the value of a piece.

After less than three years, Cookworthy transferred the whole operation to Bristol in 1770.

24

A Plymouth cream jug, painted in underglaze faded sepia or blue with flowers, trees and rocks, 9cm. (Lawrence Fine Arts) £418

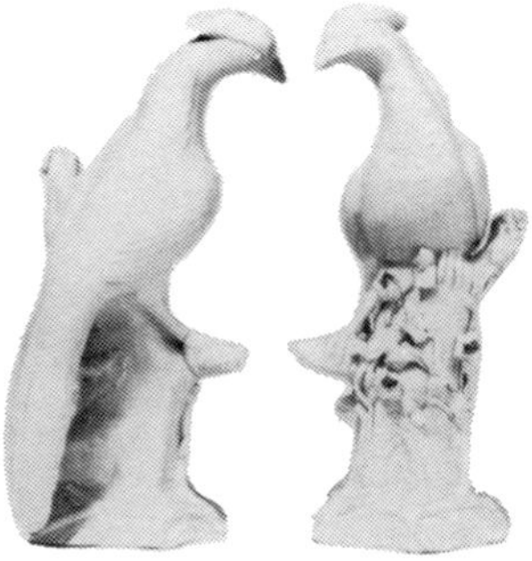

Two Plymouth white figures of pheasants, Wm. Cookworthy's factory, circa 1768, 20cm. high. £1,405

A pair of Plymouth figures of musicians wearing pale clothes, he playing the recorder and his companion the mandolin, Wm. Cookworthy's factory, circa 1770, 14.5cm. high. (Christie's) £715

Rare Plymouth figure of a lady on scroll moulded base, 6in. high. £800

A rare Plymouth figure of 'Winter' in the form of a naked boy with a robe, in mint condition. £800

A Plymouth group of two putti emblematic of Spring, 14.5cm. high, impressed letters S & D (flower festoon R). (Phillips) £360

POOLE POTTERY

The firm of Carter & Co was established in Poole, Dorset in 1873 to manufacture earthenware and tiles. The latter it often supplied for subsequent decoration, by, among others, William De Morgan. In 1895 they took over the nearby Architectural Tile Co.

Their range of earthenware, notably ornamental pottery, was developed principally by Owen Carter, the son of the proprietor. His experiments with glazes led to the creation of the matt, cream glaze which came to be associated with Carter Stabler and Adams. This amalgamation took place in 1921, when Owen Carter went into partnership with Harold Stabler and John and Truda Adams.

It was out of this partnership that the Poole Pottery, as it was renamed in 1963, grew. Poole Pottery products from all periods are much in vogue as collectables today.

A pottery oviform jug, shape no. 304, painted by Marjorie Batt with bluebirds and foliage in typical colours, impressed *CSA Ltd* mark, 5in. high.
(Christie's S. Ken) £220

A pottery biscuit barrel and cover with wicker handle painted by Sylvia Penney, with stylised flowers and foliage, impressed *Poole,* 5½in. high.
(Christie's S. Ken) £132

A pair of Pheobe Stabler earthenware figures modelled as a boy and girl, each draped with a garland of flowers, impressed *Hammersmith Bridge* mark, 7in. high.
(Christie's S. Ken) £550

The Bull, a pottery group designed by Phoebe and Harold Stabler, modelled as two infants astride a bull in ceremonial trappings of swags and garlands, impressed *CSA* mark, 13in. high. (Christie's S. Ken)
£2,310

A pottery charger painted by Nellie Blackmore with a view of the ship the Harry Paye, by Arthur Bradbury, 15in. diam. (Christie's S. Ken)
£605

A Phoebe Stabler plaster bust of a young girl with pigtails, painted yellow, inscribed *Phoebe Stabler 1911,* 15in. high. (Christie's S. Ken) £242

A Phoebe Stabler 'Piping Faun' roundel, modelled as a young faun with pan pipes tripping through a circular garland of flowers and reeds, 40cm. diameter.
(Phillips) £500

A Carter red lustre flambé vase, with compressed base and lobed cylindrical neck, incised *Carter Poole 1905*, 11in. high.
(Christie's S. Ken) £110

A terracotta sculpture of a fully rigged galleon modelled by Harry Stabler, glazed in shades of blue, green, yellow and white, $20^{1}/_{2}$in. high.
(Christie's S. Ken) £770

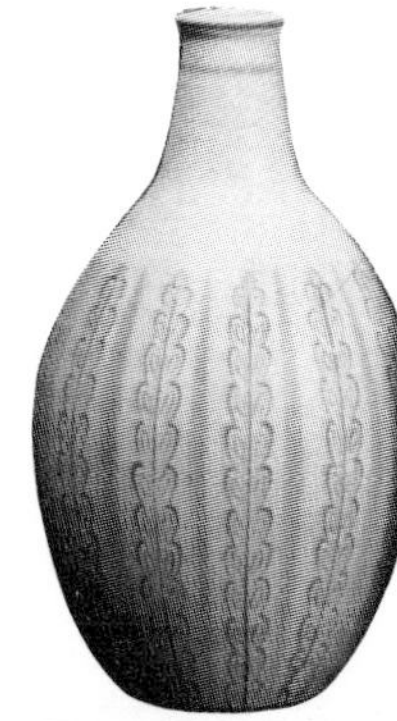

A Free Form Ware vase, shape No. 691, designed by A.B.Read, decorated with vertical lines of stylised foliage, printed *Poole Dolphin* mark, $11^{1}/_{2}$in. high.
(Christie's S. Ken) £242

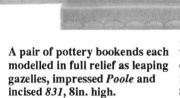

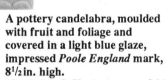

A pottery vase, shape No. 466, painted by Rene Hayes with a band of geometric pattern in typical colours on a white ground, impressed *CSA Ltd* mark and painted insignia, $5^{1}/_{2}$in. high.
(Christie's S. Ken) £94

A pair of pottery bookends each modelled in full relief as leaping gazelles, impressed *Poole* and incised *831*, 8in. high.
(Christie's S. Ken) £440

A pottery candelabra, moulded with fruit and foliage and covered in a light blue glaze, impressed *Poole England* mark, $8^{1}/_{2}$in. high.
(Christie's S. Ken) £66

A pottery vase, decorated with scrolling flowers and foliage, in typical colours on a white ground, impressed *CSA Ltd.* mark, 7in. high.
(Christie's S. Ken) £121

A pair of pottery doves designed by John Adams and modelled by Harry Brown, impressed *Poole England*, $8^{1}/_{4}$in. high.
(Christie's S. Ken) £275

A terracotta two-handled oviform vase shape No. 973, painted with flowers and foliage below geometric border, impressed *CSA Ltd.* mark, 7in. high.
(Christie's S. Ken) £440

A pottery wall decoration modelled as a yacht in full sail, glazed in yellow on grey base, impressed *Poole England* mark, 4in. high.
(Christie's S. Ken) £39

A pottery vase, shape No. 334, decorated with a leaping stag amongst flowers and foliage, impressed *Poole England* mark, 5in. high.
(Christie's S. Ken) £165

'Buster Boy', a pottery figure by Phoebe Stabler of a putto seated on a rock with floral garland draped around his body, incised *Stabler Hammersmith London 1916*, 7in. high.
(Christie's S. Ken) £198

A pottery nursery rhyme jug, designed by Dora Batty and painted by Ruth Pavely, depicting a scene from 'Ride a Cock Horse to Banbury Cross', impressed *Poole England* mark, 7½in. high.
(Christie's S. Ken) £88

A collection of Poole pottery tiles painted in colours with fishing and pastoral scenes, comprising sixteen pictorial tiles, 5in. square.
(Christie's S. Ken) £385

A pottery twin-handled vase, decorated by Eileen Prangnell with a leaping stag amongst foliage, impressed *Poole England*, painted insignia and *TZ*, 5in. high.
(Christie's S. Ken) £187

'The Bathrobe', a pottery figure modelled by Phoebe Stabler of a standing young girl with a large bathrobe wrapped round her, impressed *CSA* mark, 7in. high.
(Christie's S. Ken) £121

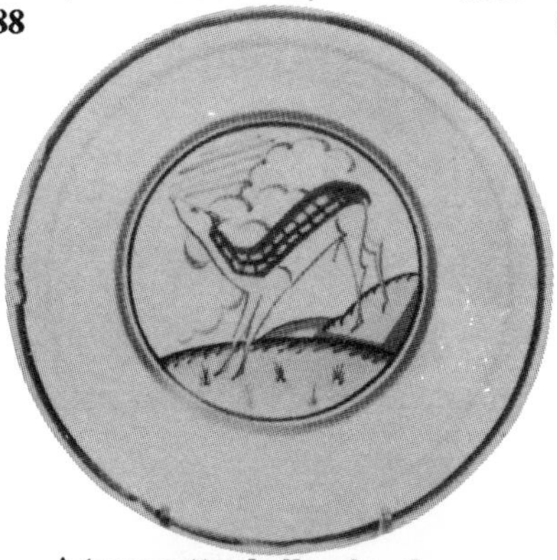

A terracotta shallow bowl, decorated by Anne Hatchard painted with a deer in an open landscape, impressed *CSA* mark, painted insignia and *RG*, 9½in. diameter.
(Christie's S. Ken) £242

A terracotta vase, painted with flowers and foliage in shades of green, yellow, blue and black on a white ground, 5½in. high.
(Christie's S. Ken) £105

POTSCHAPPEL

The porcelain made at Meissen must surely be one of the most forged and copied artefacts of all time. One of the host of factories which sprang up in the 19th century precisely to do this, was situated at Potschappel near Dresden, the major centre for Meissen copies.

The Potschappel factory was established in 1875 and traded as the Sächsische Porzellanfabrik Carl Thieme. It produced exclusively Meissen type pieces, such as the crinoline groups which had been made from the mid 18th century. Carl Thieme, the founder, was also the chief designer.

Various marks were used. Some pieces were clearly marked *Dresden* or *Potschappel*, while others have simply a cross and a *T*. Crossed *Ls* with a coronet and a flower with leaves or a bee on a hive are further variations.

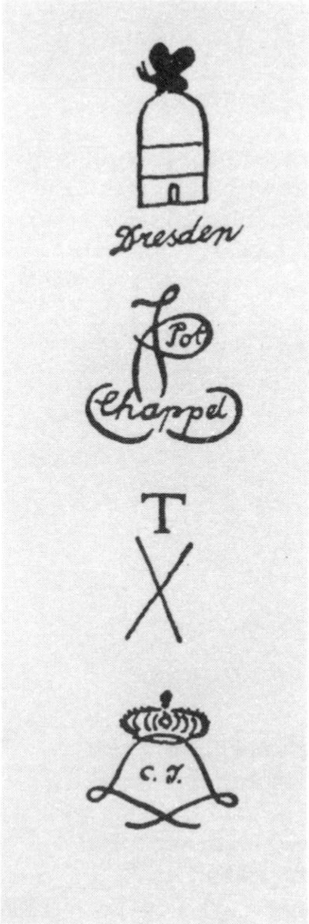

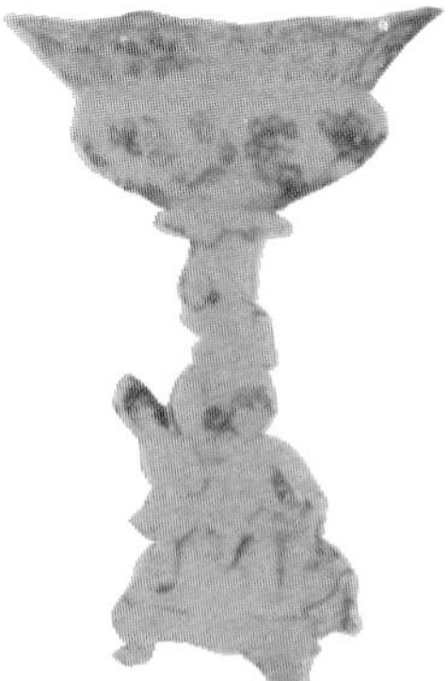

19th century porcelain comport by Potschappel, circa 1872, with a rococo stem supported by two young Cupids, approx. 18in. (G. A. Key) £300

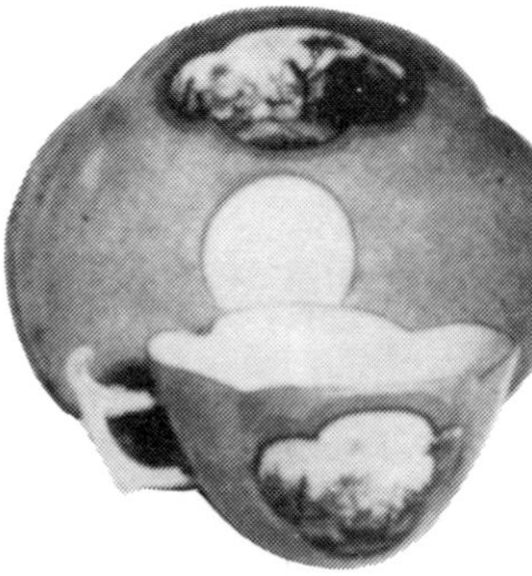

Potschappel porcelain cabinet cup and saucer by Carl Thieme, with a pink ground with a landscape decoration. (G. A. Key) £90

A pair of Potschappel pierced two-handled vases, painted in colours with Classical figures in landscape within borders, 22½in. high. (Christie's S. Ken) £1,430

A Carl Thieme Potschappel pierced centrepiece applied with flowers, the base with four figures, 12½in. high. (Christie's S. Ken) £385

A Carl Thieme Potschappel porcelain table centrepiece, the shaped base with an 18th century lady with two suitors, 55cm. high. (Henry Spencer) £880

A Potschappel two-handled vase and an armorial cover, the vase with crossed T mark, the stand with blue beehive mark, circa 1900, 84cm. high. £920

PRATTWARE

Blue printed ware proved enormously popular in the early 19th century, with just about every English pottery turning out vast quantities of the stuff.

In the 1840s however the firm of F & R Pratt of Fenton achieved a breakthrough when they introduced multi-colour printing. This they did by engraving each colour, using a palette of red, blue, yellow, black or brown, on a separate copper plate. When carefully arranged and engraved in stipple, the result was a full range of colours, which decoration was sometimes further enhanced with gilding.

Initially this was used mainly for decorating potlids, where even great paintings by famous artists were sometimes reproduced. Soon everyone was imitating Prattware, and the range of wares so decorated extended to include tea and dessert services, vases, ceramic picture frames and bread plates.

Pratt was blessed with a highly skilled engraver, Jesse Austin, who sometimes signed or initialled his work. His mark adds great cachet to a piece.

Pratt's pieces usually carry the mark *F & R Pratt Fenton* impressed, or more rarely, a crown with *Manufacturers to HRH Prince Albert/F & R Pratt.*

A Pratt pottery sauce boat moulded in the form of a dolphin, painted in green, brown and ochre enamels, 15.5cm. long.
(Bearne's) £300

A Prattware relief-moulded jug decorated in colours, depicting Admiral Duncan in profile flanked by two ships, 17cm.
(Phillips) £360

A Prattware group of Saint George slaying a dragon, flanked by two female figures in ochre dress, 25cm.
(Phillips) £580

18th century Pratt figure of a cat with blue, green and ochre splashed decoration, 3in. high. (Prudential)
£260

A Prattware watch holder of a longcase clock decorated in Pratt colours and moulded in relief with various Classical figures, 27cm.
(Phillips) £750

A Prattware George IV commemorative plate with a profile head of the King wearing a laurel wreath and naval uniform, 22cm.
(Phillips) £380

A Prattware duck sauce boat, the cream body picked out in blue and ochre, the eyes circled in blue, 19.5cm. (Phillips London) £650

Exceptional Prattware Postilion Toby Jug, England, 18th century, crisply modelled and decorated in underglaze blue, green, orange and ochre enamels, 7 1/4in. high. (Skinner Inc) £1,447

A very rare 'C. Gresley' Prattware teapot and cover, moulded in relief on both sides with three women at various domestic pursuits, 12cm. (Phillips London) £1,200

A Pratt bottle vase, printed in colours with the exterior view of the Crystal Palace Exhibition, 6¾in. high. (Christie's S. Ken) £198

A pair of Prattware oval plaques moulded in relief with classical profile heads of a man and a woman, 26.5cm. (Phillips London) £1,000

A Prattware portrait bust of Admiral Earl St Vincent wearing a brown wig, ochre jacket with yellow frogging, 20cm. (Phillips London) £480

An amusing Prattware model of a bear seated on its haunches, with head turned to face spectator, 13.5cm. (Phillips London) £1,900

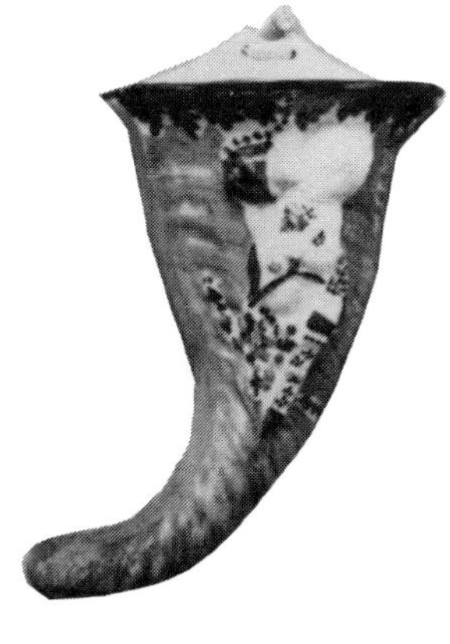

Prattware Cornucopia Wall Pocket, England, c. 1810, moulded in high relief with a figure of a child, (slight chips), 9in. long. (Skinner Inc) £394

A Prattware Grey Goose jug moulded in relief with Old Mother Slipper-Slapper releasing the ochre coloured dog, 16cm. (Phillips London) £280

A Pratt ware cow creamer, the animal with ochre sponging on a white body, the milkmaid wearing a blue bodice and spotted yellow skirt, 22cm. long. (Phillips) £420

A Prattware plaque, "Felix Edwards Pratt", olive green background. (Phillips) £500

A Prattware cottage money box in the form of a two-storeyed house with blue tiled roof, 12.5cm. high. £420

A Prattware model of a young woman wearing a deep-ochre bodice and green skirt, circa 1790, 8in. high. (Christie's S. Ken) £385

A Pratt-type pearlware group, circa 1790, 15cm. high. £900

A Prattware oval jug moulded with two bust portraits of The Miser, 5½in. high, circa 1795. £175

A Prattware oval plaque, modelled in bright colours in relief with The Vicar and Moses, Saturday Night, 13.5cm. high. £190

A Prattware model of a Gothic Chapel with central tower and spire, 24cm. high. £580

A Prattware flask of circular form with a portrait of The Duke of York and the reverse Louis XVI and Marie Antoinette, 5in. high, circa 1794. £120

QIANLONG

The Emperor Ch'ien Lung held sway for 60 years between 1736–95 and his peaceful reign marked a high point in the history of Chinese ceramics. T'ang Ying had supreme control of the Imperial Porcelain Manufactory from 1743 and he brought the Imperial wares to a peak of perfection, introducing to them many new 'foreign' colours, and the use of double glazes.

Blue and white was still made; the vases were often of archaic bronze forms decorated with bronze patterns or a pattern of floral scrolls. The blue, however, was usually a dullish indigo in tone, and the character of Kangxi ware is lacking.

On-glaze painting in famille rose enamels was widely extended in the Qianlong period, and tints were now mixed to produce the European effect of shading. Designs were taken from nature or copied from the antique, featuring brocade designs etc.

Much Qianlong ware was exported, notably 'Mandarin' wares, ewers, punch bowls and vases painted with panels of figure subjects with the surrounding space filled with composite designs of blue and white with passages of pink scale diaper or scrolls broken by small vignettes. Table ware often has elaborately moulded and pierced ornament in famille rose colours. Gilding, too, was freely employed.

In Ch'ien Lung's time the art of porcelain reaches a technical apogee, but later in the period it is already beginning to lose freshness and spontaneity. The pieces are marvellous examples of neatness and finish, but there is a cold sophistication about them, and they lack the fire and vigour which characterised the Ming and Kangxi periods.

A Chinese famille rose tobacco leaf, shaped oval dish, 18¼in. wide, Qianlong. £4,175

A Woucai bowl, the exterior painted with dragons in green enamel and iron-red below a border of flowers and Buddhist symbols, 13cm., Qianlong mark. (Bearne's) £300

A pair of large Mandarin palette vases, each painted with panels of officials and ladies on terraces, 18⅞in. high, Qianlong. (Bonhams) £2,400

A fine underglaze-blue and copper-red garlic-head vase, Qianlong seal mark, the compressed globular sides vividly painted with three Buddhistic lion cubs pawing and playing with ribboned brocade balls, 10½in. high. (Christie's) £32,227

A blue and white stemcup, Qianlong seal mark, the flaring sides of the cup painted to the exterior with lanca characters divided by arches formed by lotus sprays, 3¼in. high. (Christie's) £2,865

A Qianlong export mug, of cylindrical form, with entwined strap handle, decorated with scattered sprays of flowers, 14cm. high. (Henry Spencer) £260

REDWARE

Redware is the original pottery of the American colonies. Its manufacture began in the early 1600s, lasting well into the 19th century, with a potshop in just about every village.

Redware was cheap and easy to make. Its basic colour came from the presence of iron oxide in the clay, which, when fired produced various red tones. It could however be given various other colours by additions to the glaze. While imperfections in the clay often provided interesting natural decorations, the prevalent form of intentional decoration was the use of slip.

One of the earliest recorded potteries was at Jamestown, Virginia, which was operating in 1625. Carolina and Georgia were other states with a strong pottery tradition. Most important of all, however, was Pennsylvania, where the Amish carried slip decoration one stage further to make intricate sgrafitto designs.

The disadvantages of redware are that is brittle, easily broken, and porous, making it unsuitable for a number of domestic uses.

RIDGWAY

Job and George Ridgway set up in business together about 1792 at the Bell Bank Works in Hanley, but Job left in 1802 to set up a factory at Cauldon Place, Shelton, making bone china. His two sons, John and William, succeeded their uncle at Bell Bank, but John left in 1830 to follow his father at Cauldon Place.

William and his son E J extended the Bell Bank works, where they made blue printed earthenware as well as stone china, notably with the 'Indian Temple' pattern. They also pioneered the application of photography and lithography on pottery.

A 19th century Redware deep platter, with squiggle decoration, 17½in. long. (Robt. W. Skinner Inc.) £774

Brown-glazed Redware mantel ornament, America, 19th century, 12in. high. (Skinner Inc.) £129

A 19th century Redware covered jar, Gonic pottery, New Hampshire, 11½in. high. (Robt. W. Skinner Inc.) £387

One of two 19th century slip-decorated Redware dishes, American, 9¼in. and 11¾in. diam. (Christie's) £217

A pair of John Ridgway two-handled flared oval vases, covers and stands with gilt scroll handles, painted with loose bouquets and gilt with stylised ornament, circa 1845, 27cm. high. (Christie's) £1,650

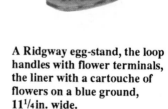

A Ridgway egg-stand, the loop handles with flower terminals, the liner with a cartouche of flowers on a blue ground, 11¼in. wide. (Christie's S. Ken) £209

LUCIE RIE

Lucie Rie (b.1902) is an Austrian artist potter who trained under Powolny in Vienna. In 1938 she came to the UK as a refugee from Nazism and opened a button factory in a London mews, where she was joined by fellow refugee Hans Coper.

Her early pre-war work had consisted of simple, thinly potted stoneware, sometimes polished or covered with rough textured glazes, her style influenced both by functionalist ideals and by Roman pottery. Her mark at this time was a painted *LRG* over *Wien*.

After the war she made porcelain decorated with unglazed bands of cross-hatched decoration coloured with manganese oxide, and stoneware in elegant simple shapes.

She used colour sparingly, and developed a number of glazes, notably a yellow one containing uranium. Others were characterised by their rough uneven texture.

The significance of her work was recognised when she was made a Dame of the British Empire and she still flourishes today. Her mark now is an impressed monogram *LR* within a rectangle.

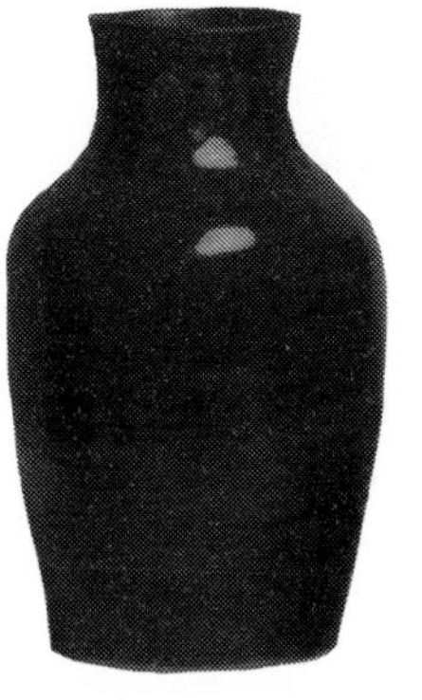

A stoneware baluster vase by Lucie Rie, covered in a shiny deep-blue glaze with run matt-manganese rim, circa 1955, 31.7cm. high. (Christie's) £1,650

A stoneware bottle vase by Lucie Rie, with flared waves rim, flattened cylindrical neck, circa 1975, 27.2cm. high. (Christie's) £1,320

A stoneware bowl by Lucie Rie with compressed flared sides, the exterior carved with fluted decoration, impressed LR seal 14cm. high. (Christie's) £1,980

A stoneware salad bowl with pulled lip by Lucie Rie, covered in a finely pitted bluish-white glaze with iron-brown flecks, circa 1954, 14.3cm. high. (Christie's) £880

A porcelain bottle vase by Lucie Rie, covered in an off-white glaze, with grey veining and a mottled pinkish-green spiral, circa 1965, 27.5cm. high. (Christie's) £2,640

A small stoneware bowl by Lucie Rie, covered in a mirror-black manganese glaze with white rim, circa 1953, 10cm. diam. (Christie's) £462

A stoneware vase by Lucie Rie, covered in a grey-lavender pitted glaze with iron-brown flecks, circa 1970, 17cm. high. (Christie's) £605

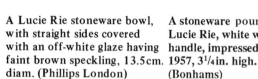

A Lucie Rie stoneware bowl, with straight sides covered with an off-white glaze having faint brown speckling, 13.5cm. diam. (Phillips London) £1,750

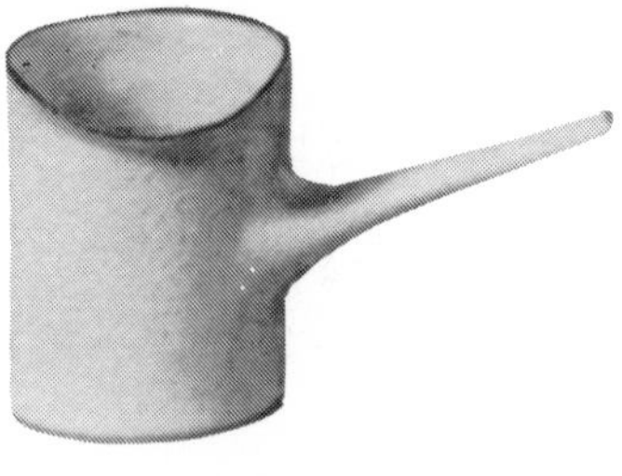

A stoneware pouring vessel by Lucie Rie, white with pulled handle, impressed LR seal, circa 1957, 3¼in. high. (Bonhams) £400

A stoneware cream pot by Lucie Rie, covered in an unusual yellow glaze with running bronze rim, circa 1960, 2¾in. high. (Bonhams) £450

A rare porcelain bowl by Lucie Rie, the white glazed exterior inlaid with small brown circles each with a dot, circa 1968, 5in. diam. (Bonhams) £3,800

An exceptionally fine bronze porcelain Vase by Lucie Rie, with reddish brown shoulder and inner rim, LR seal, circa 1972, 9½in. high. (Bonhams) £2,800

A rare porcelain bowl by Lucie Rie, bronze with a sloping white band inlaid with diagonal lines, circa 1958, 4⅜in. diam. (Bonhams) £1,800

A fine stoneware flared bowl by Lucie Rie, covered in a pale lemon, olive green and speckled pink spiral glaze, impressed *LR* seal, circa 1960, 32cm. diam. (Christie's London) £6,050

A stoneware salad bowl by Lucie Rie, white with speckling and unglazed ring within, circa 1955, 9½in. wide. (Bonhams) £700

A fine porcelain golden bronze bowl by Lucie Rie, the deep terracotta foot and well surrounded by a circular ring of turquoise, circa 1986, 9¼in. diam. (Bonhams) £4,500

A porcelain inlaid sgraffito bowl by Lucie Rie, covered in a pink glaze between two bands of turquoise, the rim and foot covered in a lustrous bronze glaze, circa 1980, 18.2cm. diameter.
(Christie's) £2,860

A fine stoneware 'knitted' bowl by Lucie Rie, inlaid with concentric dark circles from the well, impressed LR seal, circa 1982, 9in. diameter.
(Bonhams) £3,000

A porcelain footed bowl by Lucie Rie, 'American' yellow glaze, impressed LR seal, circa 1970, $6^{1}/_{8}$in. diameter.
(Bonhams) £1,300

A porcelain beaker by Lucie Rie, with four inlaid circular lines, impressed LR seal, circa 1975, $4^{3}/_{4}$in. high.
(Bonhams) £600

A rare stoneware bowl by Lucie Rie, covered in a translucent white glaze with a bronze rim running into the white body, impressed LR seal, circa 1955, $4^{1}/_{4}$in. high.
(Bonhams) £750

A stoneware coffee pot by Lucie Rie, brown with cane handle, impressed LR seal, circa 1952, $7^{1}/_{4}$in. high.
(Bonhams) £110

A rare stoneware vase by Lucie Rie, dolomite glaze, the body slightly flattened, impressed LR seal, circa 1965, $8^{1}/_{4}$in. high.
(Bonhams) £850

A superb porcelain bowl by Lucie Rie, uranium yellow with deep bronze running band at rim, impressed seal, circa 1975, 7in. diameter.
(Bonhams) £6,000

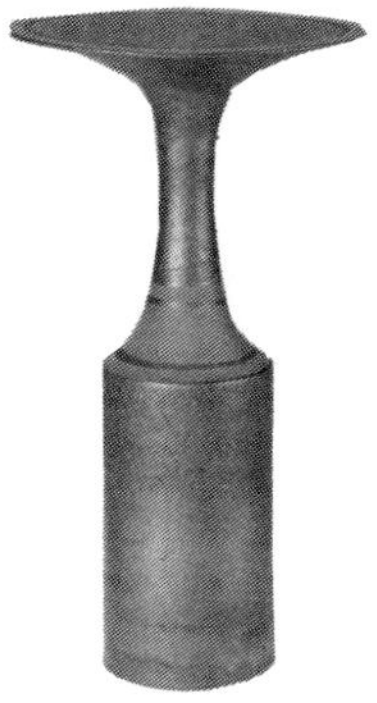

A superb porcelain vase by Lucie Rie, cylindrical with slender neck and widely flaring rim, impressed LR seal, circa 1978, $9^{1}/_{2}$in. high.
(Bonhams) £10,500

ROBJ

Robj was a French dealer who in the 1920s and early 30s commissioned small decorative porcelain items, such as inkwells, ashtrays, preserve pots etc, for sale in his Paris showroom. Lamps, bottles and incense burners often in the form of the human figure were popular as were Cubist inspired statuettes in cream coloured porcelain with a crackle glaze. Robj sponsored annual competitions until 1931, and winning designs were sometimes produced in limited editions at the Sevres factory.

ROCKINGHAM

Pottery manufacture began at the Rockingham factory near Swinton in Yorkshire in the mid 18th century. During the early 19th century high quality pottery was produced mainly for export to Russia. From 1826-42, however, when the factory was run by the brothers Thomas, George and John Brameld, its porcelain became highly acclaimed at home. In quality, Rockingham's output was second only to Nantgarw, while its superior strength meant that it could be used for an astonishing diversity of forms.

It is perhaps most famous for its brown glazed ware. This glaze was applied very thickly, the object being dipped three times, to give a streaked chocolate coloration. It was used for such objects as toby jugs, tea and coffee pots, as well as the famous Cadogan pots. These were teapots shaped as a peach with foliage and fruit decoration. They were lidless, the liquid being poured in through a hole at the bottom to which was attached a tapering, slightly spiralled tube which finished just short of the top. They were thus unspillable.

A Robj earthenware bowl and cover, formed as a Red Indian's head, with dark red glazed feather headdress, 20cm. high. (Christie's) £440

A Robj porcelain jug, modelled as a rotund lady wearing a plum coloured dress, the spout modelled as an apron, 19.5cm. high. (Phillips London) £240

Pair of Rockingham figures of a young boy and a girl, inscribed no. 36, 4¾in. high. £415

One of a pair of early Rockingham primrose leaf moulded plates, painted with flowers in vases on marble tables, probably by Edwin Steele, 24.5cm. (Phillips) £950

A Rockingham cabinet cup and stand with two gilt scroll handles, circa 1835, the stand 11.5cm. diam., the cup 10cm. high. (Christie's) £528

Rockingham-type brown glazed figure of a lion, England, mid 19th century, (chips under base rim), 11in. wide. (Skinner Inc) £180

ROCKINGHAM

Blue and white ware was also produced in the common Willow pattern and some designs peculiar to Rockingham. Rarer are green glazed and cane coloured wares, the latter often decorated with raised classical or floral ornament in blue, white, chocolate or green.

Rockingham also produced a staggering diversity of ornamental ware, from baskets and scent bottles and toys down to bedknobs and door handles – the list is virtually endless, and some outstanding artists were engaged to decorate these.

Their useful ware comprised dinner and dessert services, which fall into two basic designs, one featuring coronet knobs and scrolled handles and the other rustic handles and twig finials. Several famous services were made for the nobility and royalty – William IV paid £5,000 for a Rockingham dinner service. The company, however, lost money on virtually all of these commissions, and with their huge diversity of output the factory was never really on a sound financial footing. The Bramelds relied heavily on their patron Earl Fitzwilliam, whose successor in 1841, in justifiable exasperation, refused to plough any more money into the enterprise. By the next year the factory had closed.

There is a diversity too of Rockingham marks. On pottery *Brameld* is generally found together with a + and a numeral. On cane ware this is usually in an oval plaquette. After 1826 *Rockingham* becomes more common, most often found on brown ware, and until 1830 the Earl Fitzwilliam griffin arms are found with *Rockingham Works Brameld.* After 1830 the colour of the mark changes to puce.

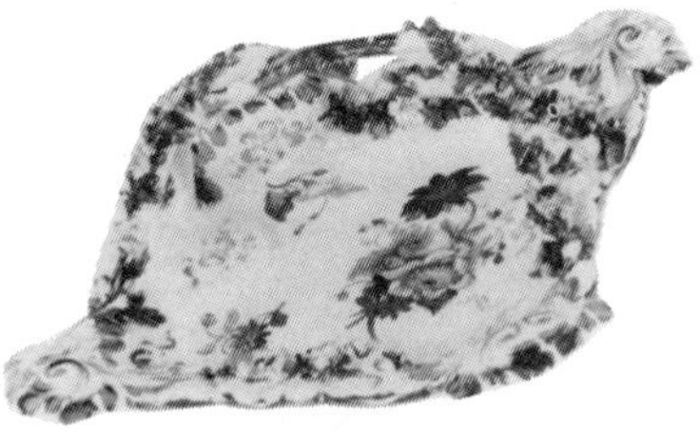

A fine and impressive Rockingham porcelain basket, of shaped rectangular form with double entwined twig handle, griffin mark, 30cm. long. (Spencer's) £900

A Rockingham cylindrical patch box and screw-on cover painted in the manner of Edwin Steele, 1826-30, 10cm. diam. (Christie's) £825

A Rockingham porcelain neo rococo style teapot and sucrier and covers, painted in colours probably by John Randall with exotic birds. (Spencer's) £850

A Rockingham spill vase painted with a church in a mountainous wooded river landscape, C8 in gold and puce griffin mark, circa 1835, 11.5cm. high. (Christie's) £440

A Rockingham flower encrusted circular basket with overhead handle, the exterior applied with flower heads, circa 1830, 11.2cm. (Bearne's) £460

A Rockingham porcelain octagonal plate, decorated in famille verte enamels, 35cm. diam. (H. Spencer & Sons) £250

ROOKWOOD

The foundation of the Rookwood pottery in 1880 received enormous publicity because it was established by a Cincinnati society lady, Maria Longworth Nichols. Its initial aim was to produce a better art pottery rather than commercial success, but in 1883 William Taylor, a friend of Mrs Nichols, was appointed manager, and he both extended the range of designs and organised a distribution network on sound commercial lines.

Though some utility wares were made in the early years, the emphasis was mainly on art pottery which was made using various techniques. The results were often characterised by carved, incised or impressed designs in high relief, often with gilt decoration and overglaze painting or slip painting under the glaze. This last, in which rich warm colours were airbrushed to give an evenly blended background, became known as 'Standard' Rookwood.

Tinted glazes and coloured bodies were introduced and in 1884 an aventurine glaze was developed by accident, in which bright gold crystals appeared deep under the surface. This became known as 'Tiger Eye'.

When Mrs Nichols remarried in 1886, her interest in the pottery waned, and in 1889 she transferred the ownership to Taylor. Under his direction, floral decoration on rich brown, orange and yellow backgrounds and on pink and white 'Cameo' pieces predominates. He moved the business to larger premises at Mount Adams, Cincinnati in 1892, and 'Iris' 'Sea Green' and 'Aeriel blue' designs appeared.

Besides floral decoration, Rookwood pieces now were also adorned with portraits of

Rookwood pottery Spanish water jug, Cincinnati, Ohio, 1882, cobalt blue glaze on strap handled, double spout round pitcher, 10in. high. (Robt. W. Skinner Inc.) £260

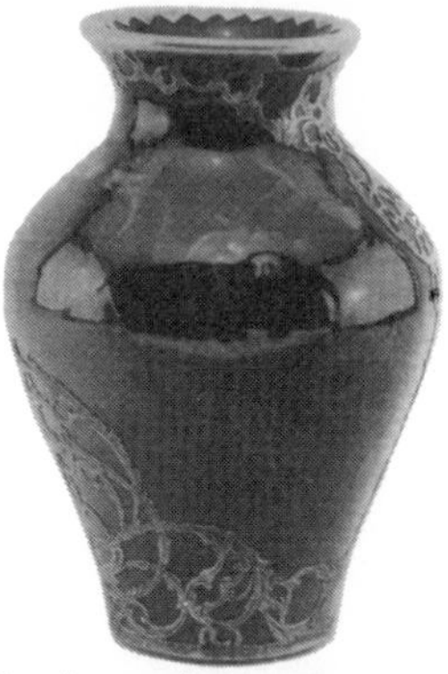

A Rookwood pottery vase with sterling silver overlay, circa 1899, signed by J. Zettel, 8½in. high. £1,595

Rookwood pottery scenic plaque, 'The End of Winter', Cincinnati, Ohio, 1918, original frame, 12¼in. x 9¼in. (Skinner Inc.) £1,708

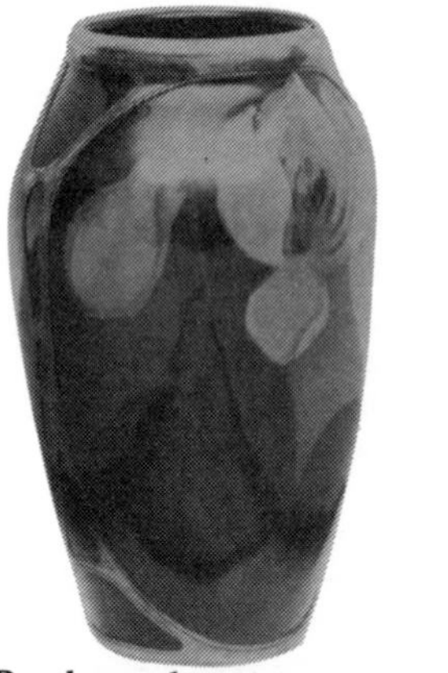

A Rookwood pottery vase with sterling silver overlay, initialled C.C.L., for Clara C. Linderman, 1906, 7¼in. high. (Robt. W. Skinner Inc.) £952

A Rookwood pottery Indian squaw portrait vase, circa 1899, 11in. high. £450

A Rookwood pottery decorated pitcher, artist's initials MLN for Maria Longworth Nichols, 1882, 6in. high. (Robt. W. Skinner Inc.) £446

ROOKWOOD

American Indians, Negroes, animals, and figures from Old Master paintings.

The pottery was outward looking in that it sent several of its leading designers to study in Europe. Among these was Artus van Briggle, who came back with the idea of a matt glaze, and this was incorporated into regular production from 1901. Following this, the production of architectural ware, tiles and medallions etc. began.

Taylor died in 1913, and the factory continued to live on its reputation for almost thirty years. Its earlier successes were never repeated, however, and it closed through bankruptcy in 1941.

Early Rookwood art pottery was confined to pieces individually decorated by the artist, and they commonly signed or initialled their works. Often, too these were dated. From 1886 a reversed *R-P* was officially adopted, with a flame point added for each year up to 1900. A Roman numeral was then added after the new century.

Rookwood iris glaze pansy vase, Cincinnati, Ohio, 1901, decorated with white pansies on lavender and blue ground, 6¾in. high. (Robt. W. Skinner Inc.) £228

One of a pair of Rookwood stoneware bookends, modelled as sphinx holding books, light brown glaze, 18cm. high. **£275**

Three Rookwood pottery standard glaze mouse plates, Cincinnati, Ohio, circa 1893, each depicting a mischievous mouse, 7in. diam. (Robt. W. Skinner Inc.) £371

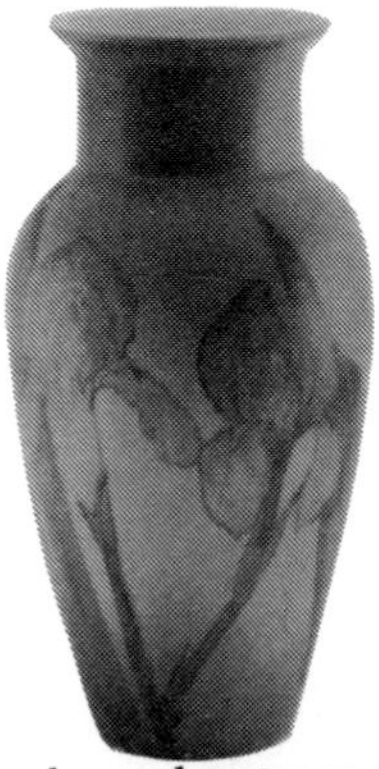

A Rookwood pottery wax-resist floral vase, Ohio, 1929, artist initialled LNL for Elizabeth N. Lincoln, 17in. high. (Robt. W. Skinner Inc.) £593

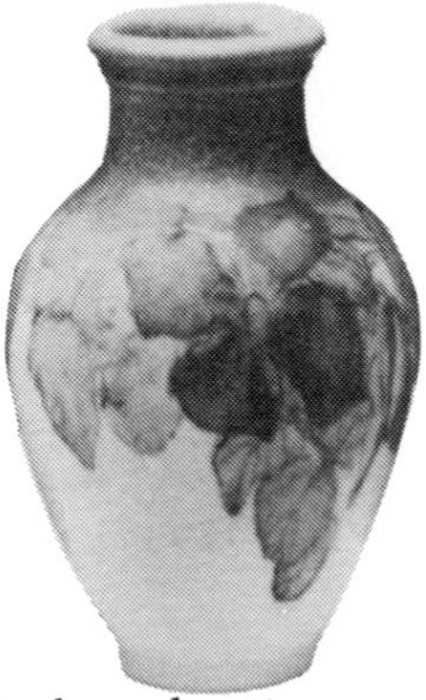

Rookwood pottery wax resist vase, Cincinnati, 1929, decorated with blue and green dogwood blossoms, 11¾in. high. (Skinner Inc.) £185

Rookwood pottery silver overlay mug, Cincinnati, Ohio, 1891, marked 'Gorham Mfg. Co.' 6¼ in. high. (Robt. W. Skinner. Inc.) £638

A Rookwood standard glaze pottery Indian portrait vase, decorated by Grace Young, date cypher for 1905, 30.5cm. high. £3,000

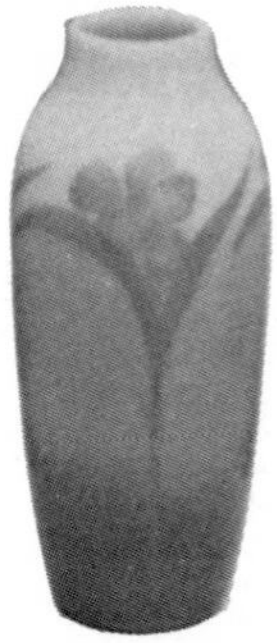

Rookwood Pottery Vellum vase, Cincinnati, Ohio, 1907, executed by Elizabeth Neave Lingenfelter Lincoln (1892-1931), 8in. high.
(Skinner Inc.) £117

Rookwood Pottery vase, Cincinnati, Ohio, 1887, executed by Kataro Shirayamadani in his first year with the pottery, 12in. long.
(Skinner Inc.) £779

Rookwood Pottery vase, Cincinnati, Ohio, circa 1883, with silver glaze neck, three impressed gold bands over body, 10½in. high.
(Skinner Inc.) £979

Rookwood decorated vellum vase, Cincinnati, Ohio, 1910, executed by Edward Diers (1896–1931), 8¾in. high.
(Skinner Inc.) £201

Rookwood Pottery scenic vellum plaque, Cincinnati, Ohio, 1914, executed by Edward George Diers, (1896–1931), 10¾in. high.
(Skinner Inc.) £831

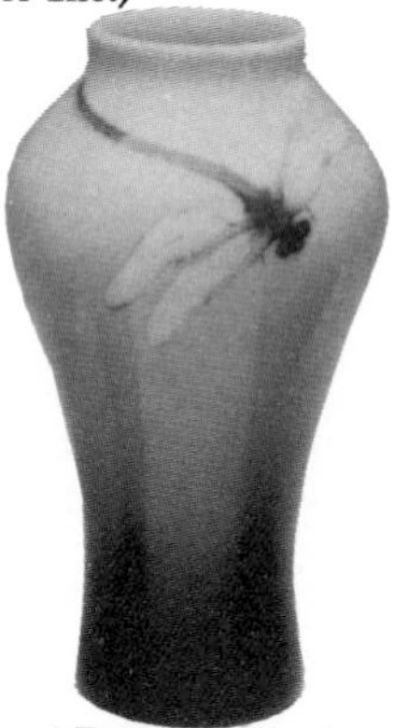

Rookwood Pottery iris glaze vase, Cincinnati, Ohio, 1906, executed by Charles Schmidt (1896–1927), 9⅝in. high.
(Skinner Inc.) £2,286

Rookwood Pottery wax resist vase, Cincinnati, Ohio, 1928, executed by Elizabeth Neave Lingenfelter Lincoln (1892–1931), 11in. high.
(Skinner Inc.) £156

Two Rookwood Pottery tiger eye vases, Kataro Shirayamadani, Cincinnati, Ohio, (1887–1915 and 1925–1948), 14½in. high.
(Skinner Inc.) £1,558

Rookwood Pottery porcelain vase, Cincinnati, Ohio, 1925, executed by Kataro Shirayamadani (1865–1948), 8in. high.
(Skinner Inc.) £623

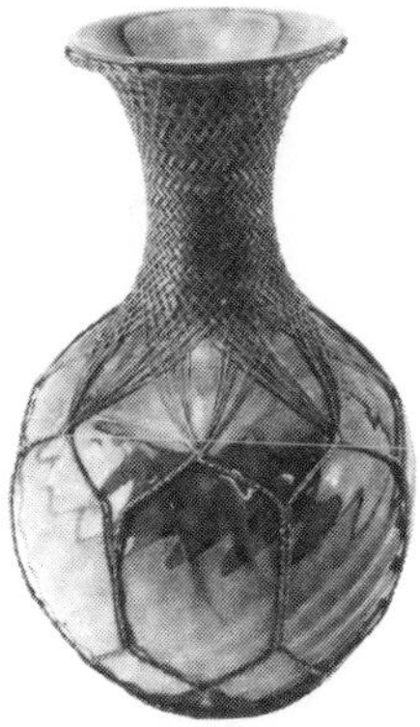

Rookwood Pottery vase with sterling silver mesh, Ohio, 1893, 11¾in. high. £1,250

Rookwood standard glaze jug, with Palmer Cox figure, Ohio, 1891, artist's initials H.E.W., 6in. high. £665

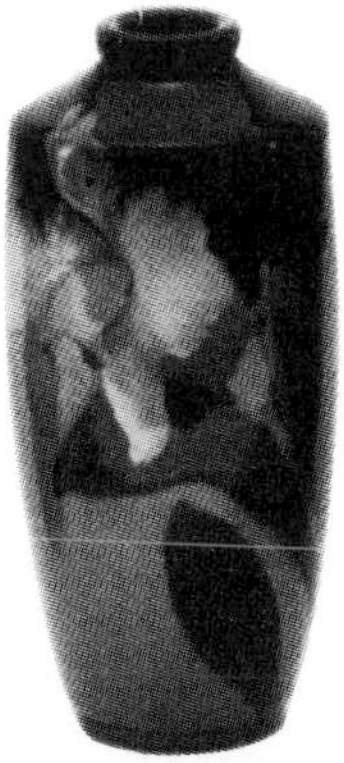

A Rookwood Pottery iris glaze vase, initialled by Olga G. Reed, circa 1902, 7¼in. high. £265

Rookwood Pottery standard glaze pitcher, Cincinnati, Ohio, 1890, decorated with clover and grasses, 12¼in. high. (Robt. W. Skinner Inc.) £514

Rookwood Pottery scenic vellum plaque, signed C. Schmidt, 1921, 12½ x 8½in. £560

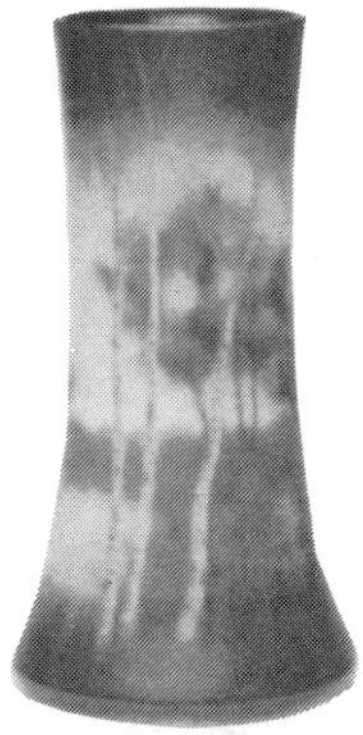

Rookwood Pottery scenic vellum vase, Cincinnati, 1913, decorated with landscape scene in gray-blue on shaded yellow to peach background, 13⅝in. high. (Skinner Inc) £1,242

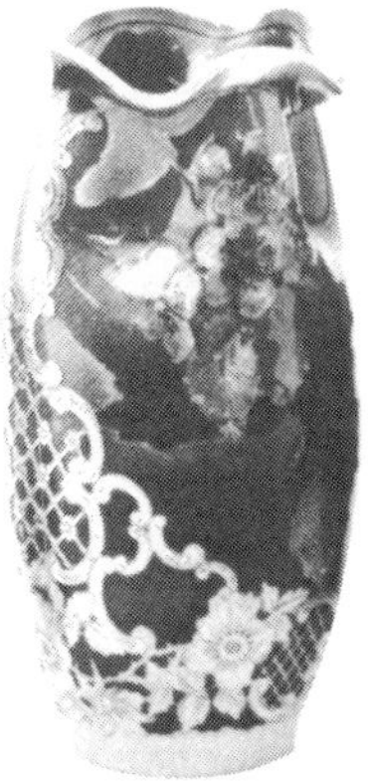

Rookwood standard glaze vase with sterling silver overlay, Ohio, 1892, initialled K.C.M. for Kate C. Matchette, 6½in. high. £1,610

A Rookwood silver overlay vase, impressed artist's monogram SS, 12.5cm. high. £550

A Rookwood Pottery scenic vellum vase, Ohio, initialled by artist Harriet E. Wilcox, 1918, 8in. high. (Robt. W. Skinner Inc.) £505

ROSENTHAL

Philip Rosenthal opened his porcelain factory in 1879 in Selb, Bavaria. It was noted from the first for the high quality of its products. He designed three major services, Darmstadt (1905), Donatello (1907) and Isolde (1910) which at first were left undecorated, but later painted under the glaze in various styles.

From the 1920s figures in Art Deco style were also produced, including theatrical characters and subjects in modern dress, many of which were signed by the artist. Philip Rosenthal died in 1937 and was succeeded by his son, also Philip, who appointed independent artists to work in studios in Selb on pieces which were sold in the Rosenthal studio houses. The firm continues in business today.

Marks include a crown over crossed lines and *Rosenthal*, or over crossed roses.

ROSEVILLE

The Roseville Pottery was established in 1892 in Roseville, Ohio, but moved in 1898 to Zanesville, where the general manager, George F Young, began making art pottery in 1900.

Their early Rozane ware was characterised by slip painting on a dark ground, finished with a high glaze, and closely resembled other art pottery being made in Zanesville at the time by the Weller and Owens pottery companies. It was renamed Rozane Royal to distinguish it from subsequent styles.

With competitors in such close proximity, however, it was necessary to develop new styles very quickly, and Roseville soon had a wide and rapidly changing range, which tended more and more towards matt glazing over relief modelling.

A Rosenthal ceramic sculpture by Gerhard Schliepstein, circa 1930, 50.8cm. high. £1,405

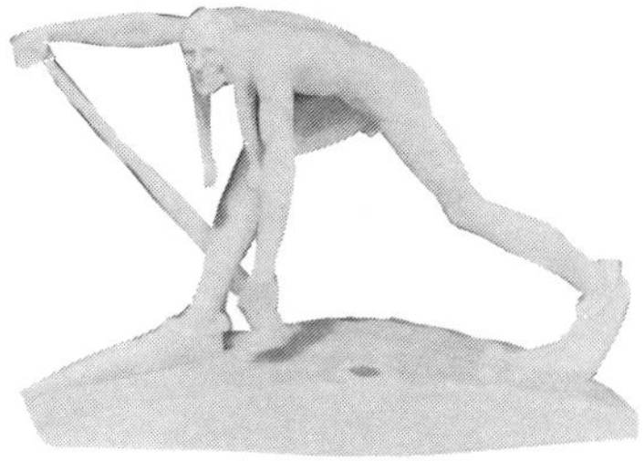

An unusual Rosenthal white porcelain figure by Rosanowski modelled as a lean Jester with exaggerated limbs, 15.5cm. high. (Phillips) £260

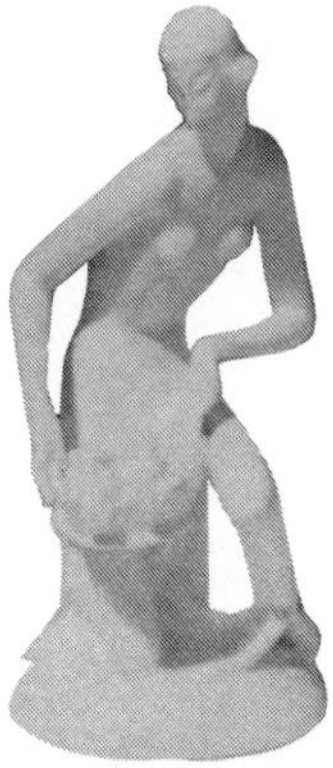

A Rosenthal porcelain figure of Autumn, modelled by Gerhard Schliepstein, design as a kneeling, attenuated barely clad maiden holding a basket of fruit, 18cm. high. (Phillips) £520

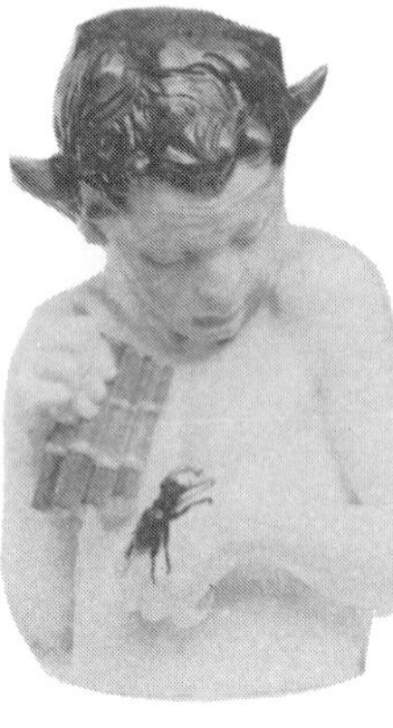

'Fright'. A Rosenthal porcelain bust of a faun by Ferdinand Liebermann, modelled as a young bare-chested faun holding a set of pan pipes, 39.4cm. high. (Phillips) £800

Roseville pottery jardiniere on stand, Zanesville, Ohio, early 20th century, listed as the Artcraft line, 24in. high. (Robt. W. Skinner Inc.) £230

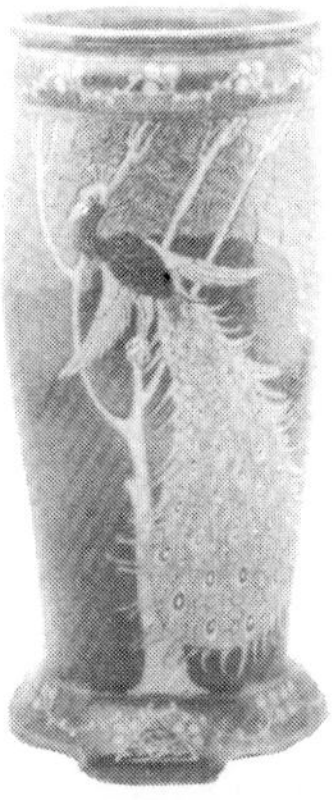

Roseville decorated matt umbrella stand, Ohio, circa 1910, no. 724, 20in. high. £910

ROYAL COPENHAGEN

As its name suggests, the Royal Copenhagen Porcelain Factory was established under the auspices of the Danish Royal family in 1775, and continued under their patronage until it was bought by Aluminia in 1867. In 1884 it was moved to the Aluminia works in the city, under the direction of Philip Schou.

A number of notable artists worked for the company, including G Rode and C F Liisburg, who painted in coloured porcelain slip from the 1880s. The factory was notable for its smooth shaped figures decorated in pale colours under a smooth glaze. In the 1890s some abstract elements emerged, but naturalism reasserted itself again later in the work of G Henning and A Malinowski.

There was some experimentation with glazes, with sang-de-boeuf and crystalline glazes being introduced in the 1880s.

From the 1930s figures were almost exclusively of stoneware and relief decorated stoneware vases were also produced. Some styles and decorations also show a strong Chinese influence.

Marks are generally a crown and motif over three waves, sometimes in conjunction with *Denmark, Danmark* or *Royal Copenhagen.*

A Royal Copenhagen porcelain vase of compressed shape, decorated with a slightly abstract frieze of lilies and foliage, 11.5cm. diam. (Phillips) £160

A Royal Copenhagen group by Gerhard Henning, depicting an 18th century courting couple, 24cm. high. (Christie's) £720

A fine Copenhagen botanical campana vase brilliantly painted with a broad register of specimen flowers, roses, dahlias, asters and lilies, blue wave mark, circa 1810, 43.5cm. high. (Christie's Geneva) £27,885

A Copenhagen pale pink ground two handled oviform vase, painted with a view of a Royal residence, blue waved line mark, late 19th century, 26.5cm. high. (Christie's London) £528

A Copenhagen snuff box and cover modelled as a pug's head, circa 1780, contemporary silver reeded mount, marked for Hamburg, 6cm. wide. (Christie's Geneva) £3,089

A Royal Copenhagen porcelain figure of the Gronland girl, dressed in national costume, holding two bunches of flowers, 6in. high. (Spencer's) £360

ROYAL DUX

Royal Dux is the tradename of the Duxer Prozellanmanufaktur, which was established in 1860 in Dux, Bohemia, now Duchov, Czechoslovakia. It was noted at first for its portrait busts and extravagantly decorated vases, many of which were destined for the American market. From the 1920s onwards it produced Art Deco style figures, of single ladies, dancing couples etc. Marks include an *E* (for the proprietor Eichler) in an oval surrounded by Royal Dux Bohemia set on an embossed pink triangle.

A whimsical Royal Dux porcelain group modelled as small boy in swimming costume squatting down to fondle his devoted pet dog, 6¼in. high. (Christie's) £99

A Royal Dux ceramic centrepiece, with two classical maidens modelled in full relief, 15½in. high. (Christie's S. Ken) £715

Large Royal Dux group with camel and Bedouin seated on its back, 19¾in. high. £580

Pair of Royal Dux figurines, flower girl carrying flower basket and boy with apron carrying basket, signed F. Otto, pink triangle to base. (Giles Haywood) £350

A Royal Dux twin-handled porcelain urn, on square pedestal base, the cylindrical body moulded in full relief with two infants embracing above the head of an old man, 14½in. high. (Christie's) £330

A Royal Dux centrepiece, the trefoil base with column modelled as three bare breasted girls kneeling and supporting lily-form bowl, 6½in. high. (Christie's S. Ken) £198

A Royal Dux bust, the young Art Nouveau maiden gazing to the left, raised pink triangle mark, 20in. high. £660

A Royal Dux ceramic centrepiece, the base modelled as roots and foliage supporting maiden in flowing robes perched between two shells forming the bowls, 16¼in high. (Christie's) £880

A Royal Dux porcelain bottle vase with applied rustic handle, 44.5cm. high. £200

A Royal Dux porcelain posy holder in the form of a rustic cart being drawn by a donkey, 27.5cm. long. (Bearne's) £160

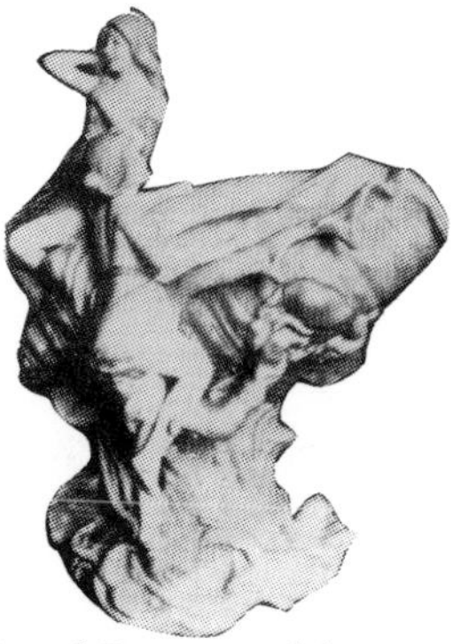

A Royal Dux porcelain ornament formed as two Sirens near conch shell on a stemmed base, 18in. high. (G. A. Key) £250

A large Royal Dux figure group, modelled as two embracing lovers, applied pink triangle marks, 69cm. high. (Lawrence Fine Arts) £550

A pair of Royal Dux porcelain figures in the form of a shepherd wearing a wolf skin, his companion with goats at her feet, 38cm. high. (Bearne's) £700

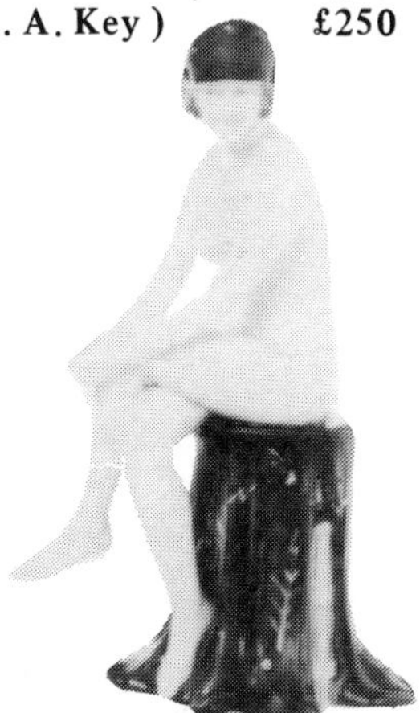

A Royal Dux Art Deco porcelain figure, modelled as a girl with red hair, naked except for a blue cap tied with a ribbon at the side, 27.25cm. high. (Phillips) £250

Royal Dux-style centrepiece designed as a young lady holding water lily, impress mark 8335, 12in. high. (Giles Haywood) £55

A Royal Dux porcelain figure group of a Roman charioteer, the chariot drawn by two rearing horses, 46cm. overall. (Henry Spencer) £780

A Royal Dux porcelain lamp base modelled as an Egyptian slave girl wearing only a loin cloth, applied factory seal, 12½in. high. (Christie's S. Ken) £385

A Royal Dux group in the form of Pierrot kissing the hand of a young woman wearing a flowing ball gown, after a design by Schaff, 28.5cm.
(Bearne's) £560

A pair of Royal Dux bisque porcelain figures of a rustic boy and girl, the young boy wearing a green hat, the girl wearing a décolleté pink blouse, 17in. high.
(Spencer's) £480

A Royal Dux porcelain figural posy holder, in the form of a young girl in Kate Greenaway type dress, 25cm. high.
(Spencer's) £340

A Royal Dux bisque porcelain figure group of a traveller on a camel, the traveller wearing flowing robes, an attendant at the camel's feet, 17in. high.
(Spencer's) £600

A Royal Dux bisque porcelain figure of a bathing belle, seated wearing a green head scarf, and brown bathing costume, 16in. high.
(Spencer's) £750

A Royal Dux bisque porcelain Art Nouveau style flower holder, as a maiden draped in a brown robe seated upon a rocky outcrop, 27cm. high.
(Spencer's) £430

A pair of Royal Dux figures, one of a goat-herd wearing a bear skin over his tunic, his companion feeding a lamb from flowers, 52cm.
(Bearne's) £900

A Royal Dux bisque porcelain figure group, of a young boy wearing a hat, open shirt and rolled-up trousers leading a pair of harnessed oxen, 15in. long.
(Spencer's) £500

A pair of Royal Dux bisque porcelain figures of harvesters after F. Otto, the young boy wearing a sou'wester, the young girl wearing a white blouse and purple bodice, 21in. high.
(Spencer's) £600

A Royal Dux porcelain group of a lion, lioness and dead gazelle on rustic base, 19in. wide, no. 1600. £250

Royal Dux figure of Harlequin and female companion, on oval base, 19in. high. (Phillips Manchester) £250

A fine Royal Dux group of a classical Grecian horseman with his charges, 43cm. high, circa 1900. £500

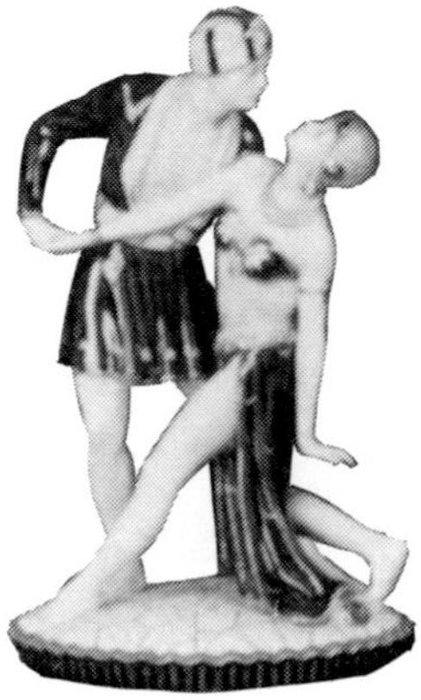

A Royal Dux porcelain group of a dancing couple in blue glazed and gilt Eastern costume, 12¼in. high. (Christie's S. Ken) £352

A pair of Royal Dux book ends in the form of clowns, cream, green and brown designs with gilt work. (G. A. Key) £290

A Royal Dux figure of a peasant boy leaning on a wooden pitcher, 59cm. high. (Abridge Auctions) £385

A pair of Royal Dux figures in the form of a farmer carrying a sickle, his lady companion carrying a ewer, 33cm. high. (Bearne's) £320

A colourful Royal Dux group in the form of a young woman alighting from a sedan chair, two grooms in smart uniforms and tricorn hats at her side, 38cm. high. (Bearne's) £280

A pair of Royal Dux figures of Eastern water carriers, 29cm. high. (Bearne's) £270

RUSKIN

The Ruskin Pottery was founded at West Smethwick, Birmingham, in 1898 by William Howson Taylor (1876–1935) who had trained at the Birmingham School of Art. Throughout his career he was constantly experimenting with glazes and it is these which give his work its principal interest.

Initially, he made 'Soufflé' ware, where the predominant colours were blues, greens, purples, greys and celadons with a glaze in a single colour or mottled, clouded or shaded with a harmonising tone.

Lustre wares were also made in a wide range of colours and shades, and a pearl lustre was introduced, sometimes with a blistered texture and often with a kingfisher blue glaze. Flambé glazes with scattered viridian spots derived from the use of copper salts were produced, and after 1929 matt and crystalline glazes were added to the range. Taylor's High Fired wares featured dramatic colour contrasts, for example purple and black streaking on sea green, or black and green on cream.

With regard to the wares produced, many vases were made, some of which could be heavily potted and covered with blue, green, orange or crystalline blue with a frosted effect. The shapes were often based on Chinese styles. Other products included useful tableware, buttons, hatpins and cufflinks, some silver mounted.

Unfortunately Taylor took the secrets of his glazes with him to his grave, determined that his work should not be imitated. Production stopped at the factory in 1933.

Marks include Taylor's name up to 1903, after which *Ruskin* becomes usual, and the pieces are often dated.

A Ruskin high-fired stoneware scent bottle, with hexagonal 'pointed' screw-fitting cover, the clouded flecking in green, yellow and red, 1927, 15.7cm. high. (Christie's) £715

A Ruskin high-fired stoneware vase, on short everted foot, pale ground overlaid completely with mottled blue, purple and red glaze fragmented by 'snake-skin' patterning, 1913, 26cm. high. (Christie's) £1,500

A Ruskin high-fired stoneware vase, the ivory ground covered with clouds of liver-red, grey, blue and purple glaze, impressed *England 1920*, 30.5cm. high. (Christie's) £1,650

A Ruskin low-fired stoneware vase and cover, with short cylindrical neck, the domed cover with pointed finial, covered in a mottled apple and bottle green iridescent lustre glaze, 26.5cm. high. (Christie's) £500

A Ruskin high-fired stoneware vase, the tall tapering cylindrical form with four prominent drawn shoulders, covered in a red glaze, shading to purple towards the base, with mottled green flecking, incised W Howson Taylor, 1932, 42.2cm. high. (Christie's) £2,000

A Ruskin high-fired stoneware vase, the cream ground overlaid with swirling clouds of red, purple and pale green glaze pooling towards the foot, England 1920, 37.8cm. high. (Christie's) £1,980

A Ruskin high-fired stoneware dish, covered in a rich mottled purple and green over deep red, circa 1920, 24.3cm. diameter.
(Christie's) **£715**

A Ruskin high-fired stoneware vase, the even purple-red glaze irregularly flecked in green, incised *W Howson Taylor, 1932*, 34.2cm. high.
(Christie's) **£1,980**

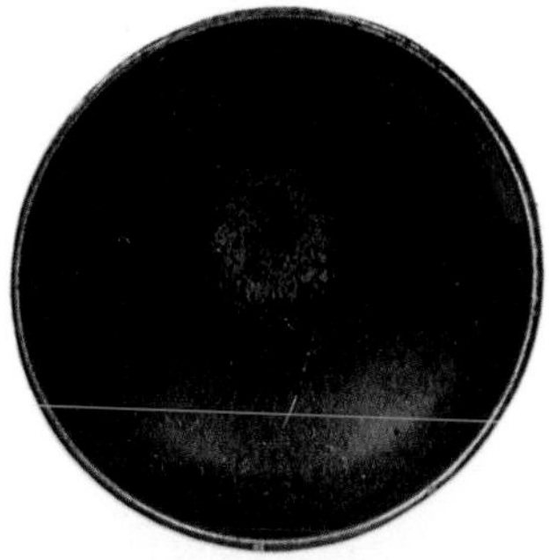

A Ruskin high-fired stoneware bowl, the exterior glazed in deep red clouding over grey, the interior red speckled with purple and green, 1933, 24.5cm. diameter.
(Christie's) **£880**

A Ruskin high-fired stoneware vase, the oatmeal ground clouded with green and speckled with irregular areas of purple and blue, 1915, 21.cm. high.
(Christie's) **£1,100**

A Ruskin high-fired stoneware bowl, the oatmeal ground mottled overall in dove-grey overlaid with red and purple clouding, with green speckling, 31cm. diameter.
(Christie's) **£1,980**

A Ruskin high-fired stoneware vase, pale ground mottled overall in purples and greens fragmented with random 'snake-skin' patterning, 1914, 32.3cm. high.
(Christie's) **£1,650**

A Ruskin high-fired stoneware vase, the liver-red glaze clouding in areas over a mottled dove-grey ground, impressed *Ruskin, England, 1926*, 37.5cm. high.
(Christie's) **£1,320**

A Ruskin high-fired egg-shell stoneware bowl, with dark mottled red glaze clouding to green and purple towards the foot, 21cm. diameter.
(Christie's) **£1,100**

A Ruskin high-fired stoneware vase, the mottled grey ground overlaid with a cloudy red, purple and grey, breaking into grey speckling, 1926, 31.5cm. high.
Christie's) **£1,320**

Ruskin circular footed dish, mottled blue fading to oatmeal, impress to base beneath feet, 6in. diam.
(Giles Haywood) £55

Ruskin iridised circular footed bowl, being mottled yellow fading to pale-green, 1923, 7in. diam.
(Giles Haywood) £110

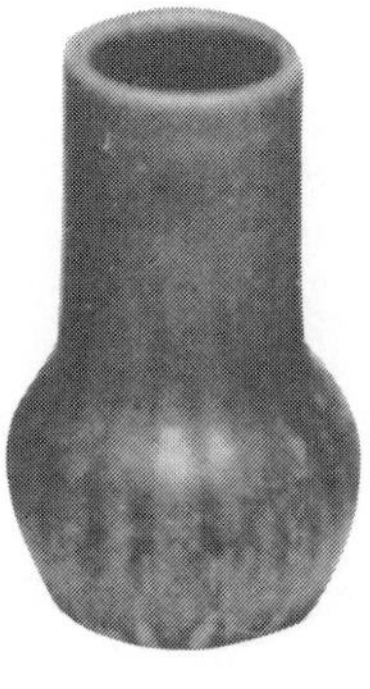

Ruskin matte cylinder-shaped bulbous vase, pale-blue varying to cloud-effect orange and green, 1932, 9in. high.
(Giles Haywood) £55

A Ruskin high fired stoneware vase, the grey ground covered in a speckled sang-de-boeuf and lustrous royal blue glaze, dated 1907, 32.2cm.m. high. (Christie's London) £825

Ruskin matte circular footed vase with flared top, blue varying to orange/oatmeal, 8in. diam.
(Giles Haywood) £80

A Ruskin high fired twin handled shouldered oviform vase, covered in a streaked lavender glaze flecked with green, 13¾in. high. (Christie's S. Ken) £385

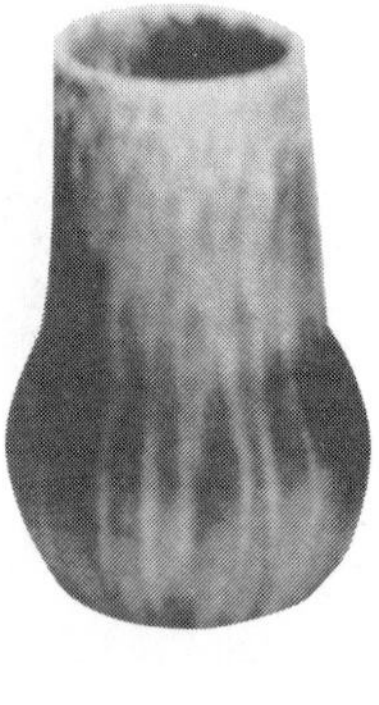

Ruskin matte cylinder-shaped bulbous vase, blue varying to orange/oatmeal, 3in. diam.
(Giles Haywood) £42

A Ruskin high fired stoneware vase, the grey ground covered in mottled sang-de-boeuf, royal and sky blue and turquoise streaked glazes, dated 1908, 29.8cm. high. (Christie's London) £605

A Ruskin crystalline glazed vase, with jade green, pale blue and cream glazes beneath two bands of sky and royal blue crystalline glazes, 21cm. high. (Christie's London) £132

ST CLOUD

Although porcelain seems to have been made at Saint Cloud as early as 1667, it was the faience factory of Pierre Chicaneau which first turned out Chinese-style soft-paste porcelain. When Chicaneau died, his widow remarried one Henri-Charles Trou in I679, but kept the secret of soft-paste manufacture from her new family until her death, when a renewed patent in 1722 mentions the names of Henri and Gabriel Trou. It was this Henri Trou, her stepson, who eventually took over the Paris factory in the rue de la Ville l'Eveque which had been established in 1722 by the widow of Pierre Chicaneau's son!

The factory greatly benefited from the patronage of the Duc d'Orleans (Monsieur) brother of the king, and had as its mark a fleur de lys or a sun face, which latter is much more common. The body of St Cloud porcelain tends to be heavily potted, suggesting it was difficult to work with, and the paste varies in colour from blue-white to ivory. Decoration was usually in the style popularised by Rouen faience with lambrequins much in evidence, from designs inspired by contemporary silver. Meissen influence was also strong, particularly in the latter period of the factory's production, though St Cloud designers were not devoid of their own ideas, and it is probable that the first trembleuse saucer came from there.

Most enamel painting was in imitation of Japanese Arita porcelain decorated in the Kakiemon style. The factory closed in 1766.

A St. Cloud white teapot and cover with flower finial, circa 1720, 16.5cm. high. £215

A St Cloud snuff box and cover modelled in the shape of a crouching cat, silver mounts with a decharge mark, circa 1735, 5.5cm. long. (Christie's London) £990

Twelve Saint Cloud blue and white knife handles, painted with bands of lambrequin and scrolls, circa 1715, the handles 8cm. long. (Christie's) £715

A St Cloud white seau a demi-bouteille with mask handles, circa 1730, 11cm. high. (Christie's) £1,320

One of a pair of St. Cloud blue and white spice-boxes and covers, each with four compartments and standing on three paw feet, circa 1710, 14cm. wide. (Christie's) (Two) £1,760

A St. Cloud snuff box and cover modelled as a Chinese man, circa 1740, 5.5cm. high. £1,030

SALTGLAZE WARE

A saltglaze effect is achieved by glazing during the firing with salt thrown into the kiln at a temperature above 2,000°F, where it combines chemically with the silicate in the clays to form a durable sodium silicate glaze which has the orange-peel appearance associated with Chinese porcelain.

Most early saltglaze ware is coarse and brown, but after the 1740s, when Staffordshire potters had achieved a light white stoneware body comparable in delicacy and durability with Chinese porcelain, the process was also used very successfully with this.

Later it was also coloured with enamels.

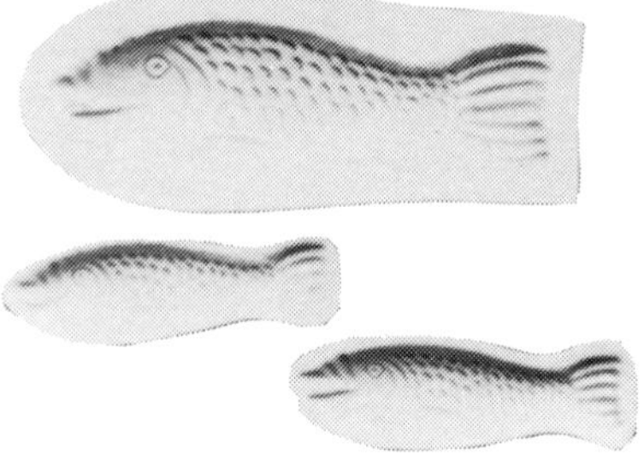

Three Staffordshire saltglaze white fish-moulds naturally modelled with incised scales, fins and tails, circa 1760, 12.5cm. and 9cm. long. (Christie's) £505

A Staffordshire saltglaze sugar sifter, moulded in relief with ozier and diaper panels, 14cm. (Phillips London) £850

A Staffordshire saltglaze polychrome oval sauceboat, the exterior crisply moulded and painted in natural colours with trailing vine, circa 1755, 18cm. long. (Christie's) £3,520

A Staffordshire saltglaze polychrome baluster jug, painted with a figure and buildings in a landscape vignette within a lobed puce feuilles-de-choux and foliate cartouche below, circa 1760, 22cm. high. (Christie's) £6,600

A Staffordshire saltglaze white teapot and cover in the form of a camel, with moulded bird's head and foliage spout, circa 1755, 15cm. high. (Christie's) £7,700

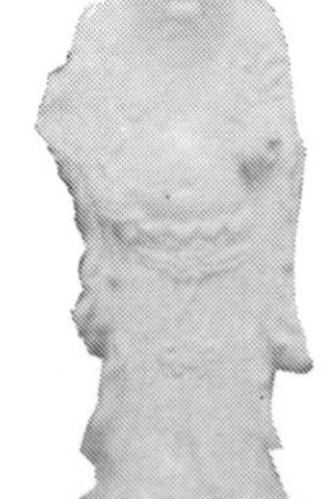

A Staffordshire saltglaze white figure of Chung-li Ch'uan, the bearded Immortal, holding a fan and a peach, circa 1750, 18.5cm. high. (Christie's) £6,600

A Staffordshire saltglaze bear-jug and cover of conventional type, covered in chippings and clasping a dog, circa 1750, 26.5cm. high. (Christie's) £3,960

A Staffordshire saltglaze white snuffer figure, modelled as a lady wearing a peaked bonnet, (two cracks to skirt) circa 1745, 9.5cm. high. (Christie's) £1,980

A Staffordshire saltglaze white miniature teapot and cover with crabstock-moulded spout and handle, circa 1750, 9.5cm. high. (Christie's) £880

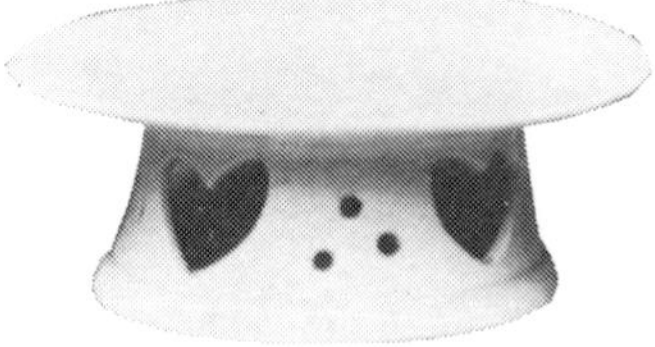

A Staffordshire saltglaze white teapot-stand, on a circular spreading base pierced with hearts, circa 1760, 13.5cm. diam. (Christie's) £880

A Staffordshire saltglaze polychrome globular punch pot, with green crabstock handle and foliage moulded spout, circa 1760, 19cm. high overall. (Christie's) £4,620

A Staffordshire saltglaze white miniature pear-shaped coffee pot and cover with angular loop handle, circa 1760, 11.5cm. high. (Christie's) £495

A Staffordshire saltglaze Admiral Lord Vernon commemorative mug, the cylindrical body with slightly spreading foot moulded in relief with the Royal Arms of England, circa 1740, 19cm. high. (Christie's) £8,800

A Staffordshire saltglaze white heart-shaped pickle dish, moulded with anthemion and scrolls (restored), circa 1760, 10.5cm. wide. (Christie's) £330

A Raeren brown saltglaze Krug, the waist moulded with arcades enclosing figures of soldiers, 17th century, contemporary pewter cover, 28cm. high. (Christie's London) £715

A rare Staffordshire white saltglaze camel teapot and cover, the seated animal with a buckled saddlecloth and a howdah, 14.5cm. (Phillips) £2,300

A Staffordshire saltglaze white miniature conical chocolate-pot and domed cover, circa 1760, 14.5cm. high. (Christie's) £3,300

A Staffordshire saltglaze white bucket-shaped piggin, with ropetwist carrying handle, circa 1755, 7cm. high. (Christie's) £638

A Staffordshire saltglaze bear jug and cover, circa 1740, 24cm. high. (Christie's) £6,050

A Staffordshire saltglaze small leaf dish with green stalk handle, circa 1755, 15cm. wide. (Christie's) £286

A Staffordshire saltglaze polychrome baluster pepper pot, painted in a famille rose palette with Orientals, circa 1755, 12cm. high. (Christie's) £5,280

A Staffordshire saltglaze baluster coffee pot and cover, painted with loose bouquets and flower-sprays within puce and iron-red loop and foliage rims, circa 1755. (Christie's) £5,280

A rare enamelled saltglaze figure of a lady in Turkish dress, after a Meissen model, standing and wearing a long yellow lined blue cloak, 20.2cm. (Phillips London) £6,400

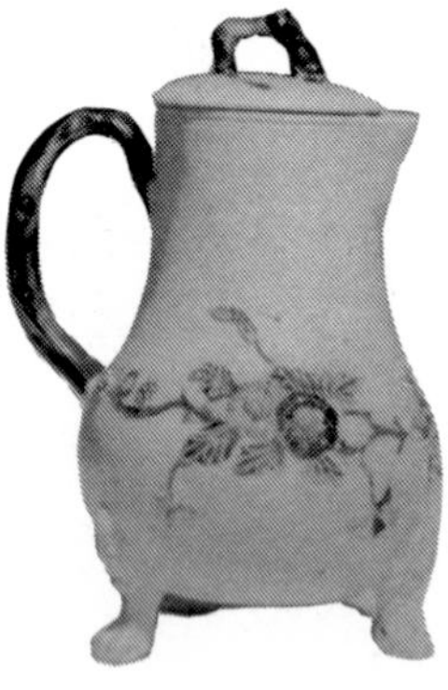

A Staffordshire saltglaze baluster milk jug and cover, circa 1755, 15.5cm. high. (Christie's) £2,200

A Staffordshire saltglaze small mug of cylindrical form with loop handle, painted in colours with a trailing flower spray, 7cm. (Phillips) £340

An extremely rare English saltglazed coffee pot and cover of silver shape, the tapered cylindrical body with tall straight spout, 20.5cm., circa 1700. (Phillips) £1,200

SAMSON

Edmé Samson set up his porcelain factory in Paris in 1845 with the intention of making reproductions of the most popular pieces produced by other makers in both China and Europe.

Samson's pieces were made mainly from a greyish-hued hard paste porcelain, even where the originals had been in soft paste, and a bluish tinged glaze is found particularly on Chinese inspired examples. In fact, it can be very difficult to tell these Chinese reproductions from the originals. The body used is very similar, though Samson's wares have a smooth finish as opposed to the 'orange-peel' texture of Chinese porcelain. In the main, the Chinese wares which were imitated were 'Export' pieces decorated in the European style in famille rose and famille verte palettes, and they often featured armorial decoration. English production was not so popular on the Continent at the time. Bow, Chelsea and Derby figures were, however, produced in considerable numbers.

Reproductions of St Cloud and Chantilly pieces were very popular however, in particular their celebrated cachepots, the originals of which were already beyond most purses. Meissen was another favourite source on inspiration, and here again it is sometimes difficult to tell the original from the copy, although the Samson pieces tend to have a light speckling on the body and a blackening of the base. Their appearance overall is somewhat glassier, and the colours harsher. Strangely, Italian porcelain escaped Samson's attentions almost entirely, though many copies of tin-glazed earthenwares such as Deruta and Gubbio were made. Iznik pottery was another prime target.

An ormolu-mounted Samson porcelain vase, decorated overall with foliage, flowers and birds, late 19th century, 17½in. high. (Christie's) £825

A pair of Samson figures of Autumn and Winter, on rococo bases highlighted in gilt, 14in. high. (Christie's S. Ken) £352

A pair of Samson white figures of Saints Andrew and John, the former standing before his cross, the latter holding the Book of Revelation, circa 1880, 15½in. high. (Christie's) £1,320

A Samson gilt metal mounted pot pourri vase and cover, painted with peasant figures in rural landscape vignettes, on a shaped square gilt metal base, late 19th century, 58cm. high. (Christie's London) £2,420

A Samson porcelain and ormolu-mounted two-handled potpourri vase and cover, with high ormolu pineapple and foliage finial, blue cross mark, circa 1880, 53cm. high. (Christie's) £2,750

Pair of Samson porcelain figure ornaments, 'Presentation of Ribbons' and 'The Hairdresser', 7in. high. (G. A. Key) £380

SATSUMA

From the 16th century pottery was made at Kagoshima (formerly Satsuma) prefecture in Japan. Korean potters provided the early inspiration - the main kilns at Naeshirogawa and Ryumonji were developed under them, and early pieces are notably Korean or Chinese in style.

From the 18th century however, Satsuma ware is essentially a hard, grey-white or vellum coloured earthenware with a crackle glaze, which is embellished with extravagant gilding and enamelling. It was introduced to the West at the Universal Exhibition in Paris in 1867.

A small deep Satsuma bowl, the central hexagonal roundel containing the word renchu (a company), beneath which numerous figures converse merrily, the reverse decorated with dense chrysanthemum blossoms and butterflies, signed Shizan, Meiji period (1868-1912) 9.9 cm. diameter. (Christie's) £1,540

A Satsuma beaker, the exterior with a continuous decoration of three levels from the heavenly to the terrestial, with Kannon, birds, students and bijin, signed *Inkinzan zo*, late 19th century, 8.6cm. high. (Christie's) £1,320

A Satsuma shallow dish with a lobed rim decorated in various coloured enamels and gilt with a central roundel depicting Tadazumi slaying the nue watched by Yorimasa, signed Kozan, late 19th century, 11.8cm. wide. (Christie's) £550

A Satsuma model of Kannon, the standing goddess wearing an elaborate headdress and holding a lotus leaf, her robes embroidered with the swastika, signed *Stasuma yaki Nangakurei ga*, late 19th century, 37.2cm. high. (Christie's) £2,750

A small Satsuma dish decorated in various coloured enamels and gilt, the interior with the Takarabune laden with the Seven Gods and their attributes, the rim with overlapping fan design, made by Nakamura Baikei, late 19th century, 12cm. diameter. (Christie's) £2,200

A large Satsuma vase decorated in various coloured enamels and gilt with a profusion of chrysanthemums and other flowers and foliage, late 19th century, 46cm. high. (Christie's) £6,050

A small Satsuma lobed bowl, the exterior with a band containing seated figures praying, conversing, arguing, a lower band with various personal items, signed Kaizan sei, late 19th century, 11.1cm. diameter. (Christie's) £1,430

A Satsuma figure of Kannon, the seated divinity wearing an elaborate necklace and robes decorated with swirling cloud, mon and lozenge design, signed *Yasukyo saku*, late 19th century, 61.5cm. high. (Christie's) £4,400

A shallow Satsuma dish with foliate rim decorated in various coloured enamels and gilt the well depicting a cockerel and hen, signed *Kizan*, late 19th century, 15.9cm. diameter.
(Christie's) £770

A Satsuma koro and cover in the shape of a basket tied in a large bag decorated in various coloured enamels and gilt, signed *Kinkozan*, late 19th century, 9.9cm. high.
(Christie's) £2,860

A Satsuma rectangular box and cover decorated in various coloured enamels with a shaped panel depicting ladies and children in a lakeside landscape in Spring, signed *Ryozan*, late 19th century, 14cm. long.
(Christie's) £3,850

A Satsuma rectangular vase with panels alternately depicting chrysanthemums beneath bamboo beside a stream among brushwork fences and kimono stands, Satsuma mon, signed Satsuma yaki Tokozan, late 19th century, 24cm. high.
(Christie's) £3,300

A Satsuma shallow dish decorated with a scene of courtiers marvelling at the beauty of a lady's kimono within a circle of stylised fungus pattern, signed *Kinkozan zo*, Meiji period (1868–1912), 30.6cm. diameter.
(Christie's) £2,090

A fine and large Satsuma oviform jar and cover with three shaped panels depicting flowering shoots of peony and chrysanthemum, signed *Nihon Satsuma, Kinran Toki, Tokozan zo*, late 19th century, 52.5cm. high.
(Christie's) £35,200

A fine reticulated Satsuma vase with four leaf-shaped panels alternately depicting bijin with children in an extensive landscape and river scenes with cranes, blossom and other birds, Satsuma mon, signed Ryozan zo, late 19th century, 17.4cm. high.
(Christie's) £8,250

A pair of Satsuma vases decorated in various coloured enamels and gilt, the tapering cylindrical bodies with a continuous decoration of bijin and children strolling in an extensive landscape, signed *Seikozan zo*, late 19th century, 11.8cm. high.
(Christie's) £1,760

A Satsuma tripod koro, the body with three irregularly shaped panels depicting civic and military scenes on a ground of massed chrysanthemum heads and other flowers, signed *Hotado*, late 19th century, approx. 7.8cm. high.
(Christie's) £2,200

A Satsuma oviform vase decorated with shaped panels of a pair of stylised ho-o birds meeting and displaying their plumage, signed *Kozan ga,* late 19th century, 20cm. high. (Christie's London) £2,750

A pair of Satsuma baluster vases boldly decorated with two panels of courtiers and attendants beside a veranda and samurai beneath blossoming trees, late 19th century, 62.5cm. high. (Christie's London) £7,150

A Satsuma oviform vase decorated with a continuous pattern of sages and divines amongst rocky pools, late 19th century, 23cm. high. (Christie's London) £1,760

A Satsuma koro and cover of quatrefoil shape decorated with four rectangular panels depicting warriors, ladies and pastoral scenes, signed *Hoen Seizo,* late 19th century, 8.5cm high. (Christie's London) £990

A Satsuma deep bowl decorated with a bamboo grove, the stalks issuing from a central mass of peony, chrysanthemum and other flowers, late 19th century, 14cm. diam. (Christie's London) £4,400

A Satsuma koro and cover decorated with a continuous pattern of two sprays of flowers and grasses, signed *Shozan,* late 19th century, 14cm. high. (Christie's London) £2,970

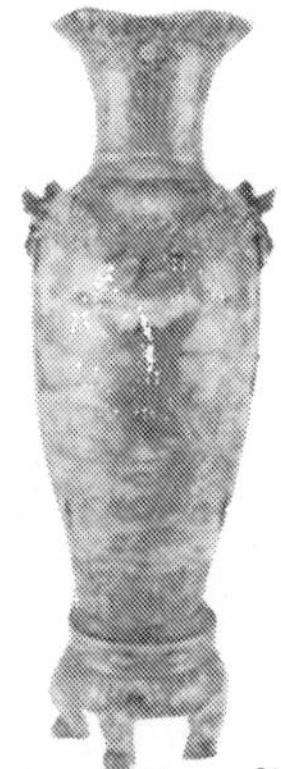

Satsuma pottery floor vase, late 19th century, one side decorated with samurai, the other with birds and an overall gilt moriage enamel ground, 59in. high. (Skinner Inc.) £5,000

A pair of tapering rectangular Satsuma vases decorated with four shaped panels surrounded by flowers and foliage, signed *Ryokuzan,* late 19th century, 24.5cm. high. (Christie's London) £3,850

A Satsuma moulded baluster vase decorated with various sages and scholars, oni and beasts under the boughs of a pine tree, signed *Satsuma yaki Tomonobu,* late 19th century, 45cm. high. (Christie's London) £3,740

Satsuma Lohan vase, Japan, late 19th century, of fine quality with excellent enamels, Shimazu crest and character marks, $6^1/_4$in. high.
(Skinner Inc) £230

Important pair of Satsuma vases, Japan, 19th century, one depicting a Japanese Kuan Yin, the companion vase with similar Kuan Yin figure riding an elephant, 22in. high.
(Skinner Inc) £2467

Satsuma koro and cover, Japan, c. 1890, with two raised handles and standing on three raised feet with moulded lion head masks, $12^3/_4$in. high.
(Skinner Inc) £625

Late 19th century Satsuma model of a caparisoned elephant decorated in coloured enamels and gilt, 31cm. high. (Christie's)
£1,650

Two Satsuma eggcups decorated in various coloured enamels and gilt with scenes of threshing, harvesting and other activities, signed *Kinkozan zo*, Meiji Period (1868–1912), 6.5cm. high.
(Christie's) £1,540

A Satsuma miniature teapot decorated in various coloured enamels and gilt with a continuous decoration of bijin and children walking in an extensive hilly landscape, signed *Seikozan*, late 19th century, 6.2cm. long.
(Christie's) £770

A Satsuma shallow dish, the interior depicting figures among household ornaments holding various objects, signed *Renmiken zo*, late 19th century, 23.6cm. diameter.
(Christie's) £660

Pair of late 19th century Kyo-Satsuma oviform vases, signed Mitsu, 25cm. high. (Christie's)
£1,155

A Satsuma teapot and cover, the upper surface with two rectangular panels depicting children playing by a lakeside, and a marriage procession crossing a river, signed *Kizan*, late 19th century, 7.1cm. high.
(Christie's) £880

SATURDAY EVENING GIRLS

This intriguing title (*SEG* is the usual mark) is found on the products of the Paul Revere Pottery, which was set up at the beginning of the 20th century for the purpose of training girls from poor immigrant families in Boston. The profits from the pottery were used to fund the girls' education in other subjects. The output mainly consisted of earthenware, nursery and breakfast bowls and dishes and these were decorated with birds, flowers or mottoes, often around the borders. The name Saturday Evening Girls Club is something of a misnomer, since the potters worked eight hours a day.

SAVONA

The Ligurian coast thrived as a pottery centre from the sixteenth century. Most commonly found today, however, are the wares marked with the arms of Savona or a crudely drawn lighthouse, dating from the seventeenth and eighteenth centuries. These tend to be heavily potted in a baroque style which imitates contemporary silver forms. The decoration is usually in blue, and in Ming style. Sometimes rather crudely painted polychrome pieces also appear.

One of the major workshops was that of Sebastian Falco, whose pieces bear a falcon mark. He specialised in a speckled manganese ground with tiny scenes in reserved panels.

The Borelli family too were making tin-glazed earthenware as early as 1735, in the Castelli style, and the family tradition was maintained into the early nineteenth century. They produced some figures, some painted and some in the biscuit state, and a pleasant butter-coloured creamware.

Saturday Evening Girls Pottery decorated motto pitcher. Boston, Massachusetts, early 20th century, 9¾in. high.
(Skinner Inc.) £1,143

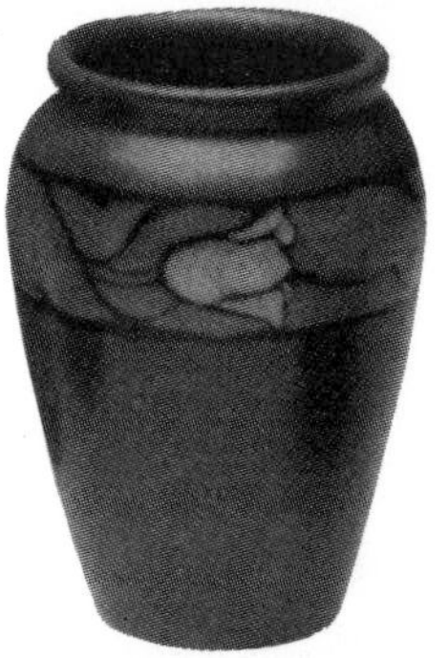

Saturday Evening Girl Pottery vase, Boston, Massachusetts, 1922, with incised and painted band of tulip decoration, 6¾in. high.
(Skinner Inc.) £169

A pair of Savona faience figures of a gardener leaning on a watering can, his companion with a hurdy-gurdy, circa 1760, 20cm. high. (Christie's London) £2,420

A Savona dated figure of Winter modelled as a bearded man clasping a fur-lined yellow cloak about his shoulders, incised with the date 1779, 33.5cm. high.
(Christie's) £1,980

A Savona blue and white fountain with loop-over handle, circa 1700, 59cm. high. (Christie's) £4,180

A large Savona charger painted in blue with a figure of Neptune in a shell-shaped chariot, 46cm., shield mark.
(Phillips) £1,700

SCRATCH BLUE

The term scratch blue is used to refer to a white salt glazed stoneware which is decorated with incised inscriptions in the form of stylized flowers, birds or rouletted patterns. These were filled in with a substance called zaffer before firing.

Zaffer, or sometimes zaffre, is a word of Arabic origin referring to an impure cobalt oxide which was obtained by fusing the mineral ore with sand. (Zaffer was also used, together with potassium carbonate and silica in the manufacture of smalt. This was a blue pigment which was imported into England from Saxony until native deposits of cobalt oxide were found. It was used as an enamel, as an underglaze colour for underglaze grounds and for tinting certain bodies.)

With zaffer a dark, impure blue was formed.

Scratch blue wares were made between 1724 and 1776 in Staffordshire and possibly too at Liverpool and elsewhere in England.

Doulton revived the technique in the 1870s, using black and brown pigments instead of blue. This was known as scratch brown ware.

A 'Scratch Blue' saltglaze sauceboat of silver shape, incised and coloured in blue with a simple flower spray on both sides, 15.5cm., circa 1750–60. (Phillips) £440

A 'scratch blue' saltglaze puzzle jug, the rim with three pinecone moulded spouts (two missing), 21.5cm. high. (Phillips) £2,800

A jug with incised scrolling brown foliage and applied white bead work, c.m., 1876, 6¾in. high. £110

A mid 18th century white saltglazed stoneware scratch blue short pedestal loving cup, all-over incised with flower heads and leaves, 19.5cm. high. (Spencer's) £550

A documentary Bovey Tracey saltglaze scratch-blue inscribed and dated rectangular tea-caddy, 1768, 11.5cm. high. (Christie's) £1,870

A Staffordshire saltglaze scratch-blue dated two-handled cup, each side incised with trailing flowering branches and with the initials *H:W.* above the date 1756, 30.5cm. wide. (Christie's) £12,100

An early jug, incised in a white ground with herons standing in water, o.m., 1874, 7½in. high. £200

SÈVRES

Porcelain production began at Sèvres in 1756 when the Vincennes factory was moved there, and the first 14 years of its output are considered by many to be unsurpassed.

At first, a soft paste porcelain was made, with silky glazes and richly ornate decoration. It was hugely expensive to make, however, and had the further disadvantage that it could not be moulded into complex shapes, which tended to fracture in the kiln. Nevertheless, it was dear to the heart of Louis XV, who was wholly responsible for funding the operation, and his mistress Mme de Pompadour. He assisted it further by issuing several decrees granting virtual monopolies in favour of Sèvres, and even acted as salesman in chief, holding annual exhibitions at Versailles and selling off the pieces to his court.

Sèvres products are remarkable for their brilliant ground colours and chemists were constantly at work developing new tones. Honey gilding, then a virtually new technique, was also widely used, while a host of flower and figure painters (Louis engaged fan painters for this) added their designs. With regard to form, tableware shapes largely followed those of the delicate lines of contemporary silver. Sèvres was also famous for its soft-paste biscuit models, notably in the period 1757-66, when Etienne Maurice Falconet was chief modeller.

By 1769, Sèvres was moving over to hard paste manufacture, and this period coincided with a change to more severe, neo-Classical forms, while decoration too became very much simpler. On many pieces, indeed, this was reduced to a simple ground colour with gilding.

A Sèvres saucer painted by Falot and gilded by Prevost, the centre painted with doves, date mark for 1781.
(Bearne's) £220

A Sèvres white porcelain group of Diana the huntress and two other figures on a rocky outcrop, 33cm. total height.
(Bearne's) £500

A pair of Sèvres style turquoise ground vases with pointed oviform bodies painted with figures of a lady and gentleman in 18th century costume, 29.5cm.
(Phillips) £500

A 19th century French giltwood occasional table set with a 'Sèvres' porcelain dish, the central oval panel painted with two lovers and a goat resting in a landscape signed *Boucher*, 1ft. 5in. wide.
(Spencer's) £400

A Sèvres Empire cabinet-cup and saucer painted with a portrait medallion of Darnalt on a silver ground with foliage swags, circa 1820.
(Christie's) £1,100

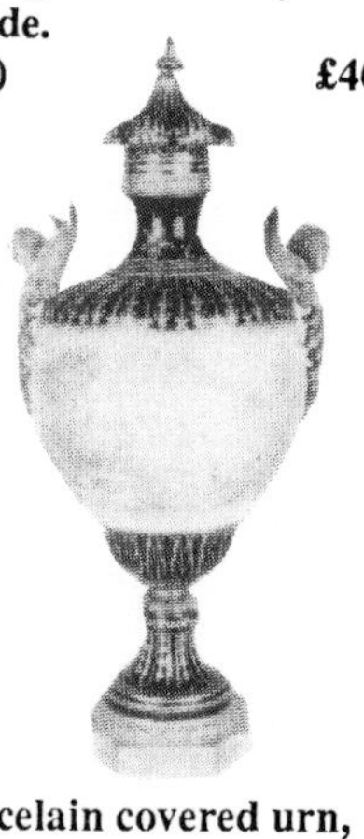

Sèvres porcelain covered urn, late 19th century, retailed by Bailey, Banks and Biddle, signed *"G. Poiterin"*, 22in. high.
(Skinner Inc.) £962

SÈVRES

Ground colours changed too, not always for the better. Nor did biscuit figures adapt very well, having a greyer cast in hard paste and becoming more classical in form. After the departure of Falconet for the Russian court, various sculptors were employed to produce reduced size copies of their own works, and they sought to reproduce in the new medium, the appearance of marble, but without surface glaze or shine.

On the abolition of the monarchy Sèvres was taken over by the State in 1793. Under Napoleon's appointee Brogniart, soft paste was finally abandoned (it was revived again in the late 1840s) in favour of a new hard paste formula which was particularly suitable for tableware.

Soft paste wares are clearly marked in blue enamel with the usual crossed *Ls* motif and a date letter (doubled after 1777). In hard paste, a crown is placed above the blue mark from 1769-79. After 1793 a date appears instead of the letter.

Fake Sèvres pieces abound, and it is important to be able to distinguish between hard and soft paste wares. This can be done by viewing obliquely so that the light penetrates both the ground colour and the painting. If it is soft paste, the transparency will be seen to be consistent throughout. On hard paste the painting will form a slight shadow against the close texture of the paste over which both glaze and colour form a thin coating.

Genuine Sèvres soft paste porcelain has a virtually clear glaze, not uneven as found in forgeries. On more recent forgeries too the colours are not blended with the glaze as was the case with the originals.

A Sevres bleu de roi ground tasse litron and saucer, reserved with garlands of pink roses, 1766. (Christie's Geneva) £858

A Sevres plate, painted with fishermen in two panels, with two others of fish and shellfish, 26.5cm. (Lawrence Fine Arts) £550

A Sevres vase hollandois and pierced stand painted en camaieu bleu with cottages and figures in rural landscapes, painter's mark script N to both pieces, 1757, 20cm. wide. (Christie's London) £6,050

Pair of Sevres ormolu mounted vases, 19th century, decorated with continuous landscape containing a maiden and putto, signed *Labarre,* 28½in. high. (Robt. W. Skinner Inc.) £1,463

A Sevres caisse a fleurs, the sides painted in colours with sprays of wild flowers within camieu bleu rose and trellis borders, date letter *G* for 1759, 17.5cm. (Christie's London) £3,850

A Sevres two handled seau a bouteille, painted in colours with large sprays of garden flowers, date letter *H* for 1760, painter's mark for Rosset, 19.5cm. high. (Christie's London) £3,520

A Sèvres rose-ground orange-tub, each side painted with trophies including a horn, hat, tambourine and peacock feathers, painter's mark for *Buteux*, circa 1758, 9cm. high.
(Christie's) £4,400

A Sèvres Republican coffee cup and saucer painted in colours with a garland of summer flowers and fruit intertwined with blue scrollwork.
(Phillips) £750

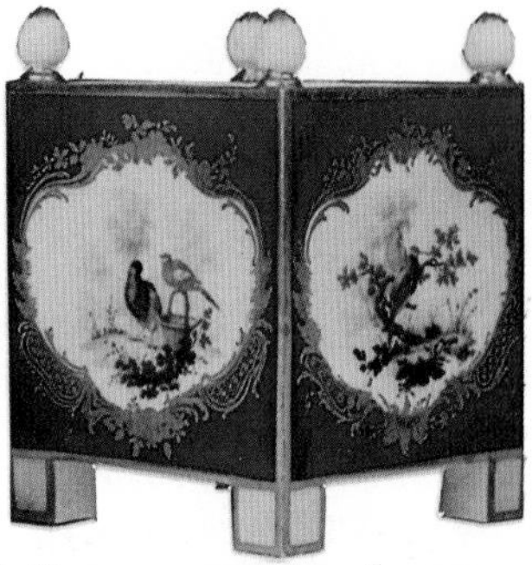

A Sèvres green-ground orange-tub (caisse à fleurs carrée) painted with birds among trees, shrubs and plants within shaped gilt quatrefoil scroll, date letter D for 1756, 14.5cm. high.
(Christie's) £8,800

A pair of Sèvres-pattern blue-ground ormolu-mounted vases and covers, the egg-shaped bodies enriched in gilding with a caillouté pattern, mid-19th century, $7\frac{3}{4}$in. high.
(Christie's S. Ken) £550

One of a pair of Sèvres-pattern dark-blue-ground slender oviform vases and covers with two gilt entwined double-serpent handles, mid-19th century, $15\frac{1}{2}$in. high.
(Christie's S. Ken) (Two) £880

A pair of Sèvres green-ground pots à fard painted with figures by buildings, strolling and fishing in wooded river landscapes within gilt scroll, date letter E for 1757, 9cm. high.
(Christie's) £9,350

A Sèvres green and blue-ground square tray (plateau carré) with flared sides, the centre painted with a bouquet within a circular gilt cartouche, date letter F for 1758, 11cm. wide.
(Christie's) £1,760

A Sèvres bleu lapis orange-tub with gilt vermiculé decoration, painted with bouquets of garden flowers within reserves, date letter H for 1760, painter's mark for Thévenet, 9cm. high.
(Christie's) £660

A large Sèvres porcelain vase, designed by Emile Decoeur, decorated by P. Gaucher, with a narrative frieze of mermaids, nereids and sea creatures in tones of blue and green, 50cm. high.
(Christie's) £6,050

One of a pair of Sèvres-pattern inverted baluster pot-pourri vases, the bleu celeste grounds each painted with a farm girl and boy feeding hens and goats, mid 19th century, 7½in. high.
(Christie's) (Two) £825

A Sèvres pink oeil-de-perdrix ground coffee-can and saucer painted with musical instruments and trophies in reserves, date letter R for 1770.
(Christie's) £1,540

A Sèvres-pattern bleu celeste-ground inverted baluster ewer painted with a gallant paying court to two ladies, circa 1860, 10in. high.
(Christie's) £440

A pair of 19th century ormolu mounted porcelain candlesticks, decorated in the Louis XVI Sèvres style, French, 19th century, 31.5cm. high.
(Duran, Madrid) £939

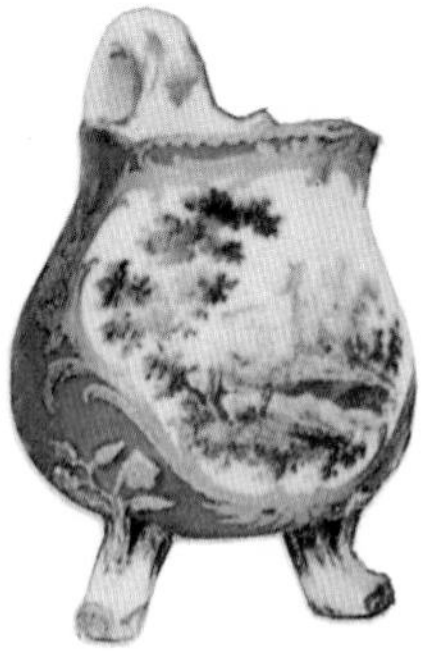

A Sèvres green-ground milk-jug (pot à lait à trois pieds), the gilt branch handle and three feet with gilt flower and foliage terminals, circa 1758, 8cm. high.
(Christie's) £715

An important pair of Sèvres Royal portrait vases of 'vase etrusque carafe' shape with double leaf scroll handles, 33cm.
(Phillips) £3,000

A Sèvres bleu celeste milk-jug painted with a bouquet of flowers and fruit reserved within a chased gilt line cartouche, date letter *J* for 1762, incised 4, 12cm. high.
(Christie's) £1,870

A fine Sèvres plate, the bleu lapis ground border with gilt bell-flower motifs, barbs and leaves, 23.5cm., painter's mark W. probably for Joseph-Leopold Weydinger.
(Phillips) £1,000

A Sèvres green-trellis-ground small sugar-bowl and cover (pot à sucre calabre) the gilt-edged green trellis ribbons joined by flowerheads, circa 1765, 6.5cm. diameter.
(Christie's) £1,430

A Sevres rose ground shaped oval tray, painted in colours with a watery landscape, a man fishing and another with a net, 29cm. wide. (Christie s London) £1,980

A Sevres fluted cup and saucer (tasse et soucoupe gaudrone), with radiating blue and white bands, date letter *K* for 1763, incised marks. (Christie's London) £264

A Sevres bleu nouveau two handled ecuelle, cover and quatrefoil stand painted with garlands of ribbon-tied flowers, the stand 26cm. wide. (Christie's) £2,530

A Sevres pattern turquoise ground circular tray, the centre reserved and painted by Paul Fortin, The village wedding by Greuze, interlaced L marks, late 19th century, 50cm. diam. (Christie's London) £1,650

A pair of Sèvres-pattern cylindrical jars and covers painted with narrow blue and gilt vertical stripes entwined with pink ribbon and gilt foliage divided by loose bouquets of flowers, late 19th century, 13.5cm. high. (Christie's) £418

A Sevres triangular tray (plateau triangle), the centre painted with sprays of colourful garden flowers, date letter *L* for 1764, painter's mark *X* for Xhrouet, 17cm. wide. (Christie's London) £3,300

A large pair of Sevres-pattern turquoise-ground baluster vases, painted with ladies and gentleman in 18th century dress at various pursuits, late 19th century, 98.5cm. high. (Christie's) £3,300

A Sevres plate from the Egyptian service painted with the Dyvan Militaire by Swebach, the centre in brown heightened with white, red printed mark *M. Imp. le de Sevres 1811,* 24cm. diam. (Christie's London) £26,400

A pair of Sevres pattern Napoleonic gilt metal mounted vases, decorated by Desprez, with continuous battle scenes including Napoleon Bonaparte on a white stallion, late 19th century, 100cm. high. (Christie's London) £13,200

A Sevres seau a demi-bouteille from the Duchesse du Barry service, date letters for 1771, and decorator's mark LB for Le Bel junior, 13cm. high. (Christie's) £5,280

A Sevres green-ground cup and saucer, interlaced L marks, date letters D for 1756 and R for 1770, decorators' marks L B and E. (Christie's) £550

A Sèvres oval tureen and cover with blue and gilt feuilles-de-choux decoration and sprays of flowers, the entwined handles and rims enriched with gilding, circa 1760, 15.5cm. wide. (Christie's) £550

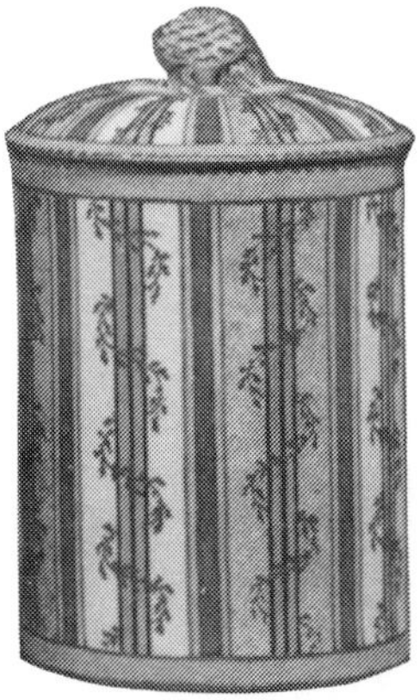

A Sevres pot a tabac and cover with rose finial painted in imitation of contemporary cloth with pink stripes on alternating bands of white and seeded pink, 14.5cm. high. (Christie's) £7,700

A pair of Sèvres-pattern turquoise-ground ormolu-mounted jardinieres painted with a gallant and two female companions in wooded landscapes, circa 1880, 30cm. high overall. (Christie's) £1,760

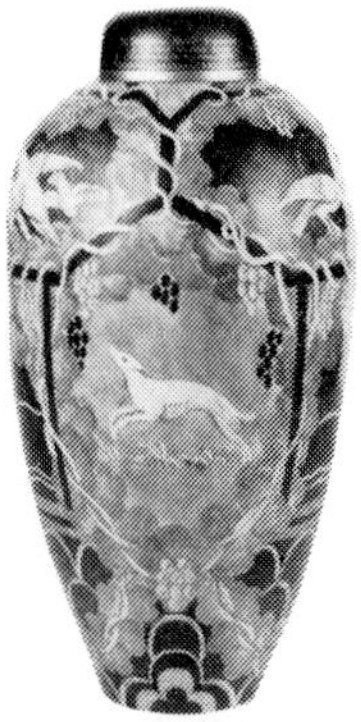

A Sevres porcelain urn and cover, painted in pale and dark amber and white with animals amidst vines and grapes, gilt borders, 47.5cm. high. (Christie's) £550

A pair of Sèvres-pattern gilt-metal mounted blue-ground oviform vases and covers with cast rope-twist, scroll and mask handles, painted by L. Bertion, circa 1900, 51.5cm. high. (Christie's) £1,650

A Sevres two-handled ecuelle, cover and stand, blue interlaced L marks, date letter for 1775, and blue decorator's mark for Thevenet, 25.5cm. wide. (Christie's) £990

A pair of assembled Sevres pattern gilt bronze mounted oviform vases, the bodies decorated after Fragonard, the bodies signed *Jeanne*, late 19th century, 98cm. high overall. (Christie's London) £11,000

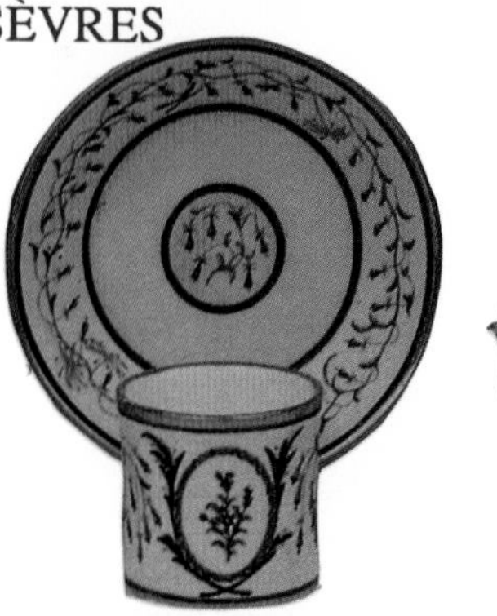

A Sèvres miniature yellow-ground coffee-can and saucer, painted with trailing blue and pink fuchsia, the cup with a sprig of cornflowers within a puce oval cartouche, 3.5cm. high.
(Christie's) £605

A pair of Sèvres style ormolu-mounted turquoise ground urns and covers, late 19th century, with ring in scroll handles headed by female herms, 16in. high.
(Christie's) £4,081

A Sèvres green-ground teacup and saucer with entwined gilt branch handle painted with trailing garlands of flowers from a cornucopia-shaped border, date letter *D* for 1756.
(Christie's) £3,080

Part of the Sèvres Louis Philippe hunting service, the border with *LP* monograms, oval cartouches of hunting trophies, vine and fruit reserved among scrolling flowers with birds and hounds, the centres with a radiating gilt patera, printed red marks for Château de Fontainebleau and various incised former's and painter's marks, 1838–48. (Christie's) £11,000

A Sèvres lime-green-ground coffee-can and saucer painted with bands of scrolling foliage, vases of flowers and oval medallions with puce landscapes.
(Christie's) £660

A Sèvres green and blue-ground square tray, blue interlaced *L* marks enclosing date letter *F* for 1758, 11cm. wide.
(Christie's) £1,540

A Sèvres ballooning coffee-can and saucer painted with landscape scenes, the saucer with figures watching an airborne balloon, enclosed by gilt, green and yellow bands with puce dashes.
(Christie's) £3,080

SÈVRES

A Sèvres green-trellis-ground small teacup, the gilt-edged green ovals joined by flowerheads, each compartment painted with a specimen flower, circa 1760.
(Christie's) £440

A pair of Sèvres style turquoise ground vases and covers, with gilt entwined serpent handles, the tapering forms painted with wide bands of court figures in classical landscapes, 19in. high.
(Christie's) £1,632

A Sèvres green-ground rectangular tea-caddy and cover with canted corners, each side painted with flowers within gilt oval cartouches, circa 1758, 7cm. high.
(Christie's) £6,050

A Sèvres gilt and white fluted tea-service, the narrow ribs interspersed with gilt lines beneath foliage bands and the handles, and interiors richly gilt, printed interlaced *L* marks enclosing a fleur-de-lys and date code for 1820 and 1821.
(Christie's) £4,180

A Sèvres green-ground coffee-cup and saucer with gilt edged ear-shaped handle painted with two birds in flight, one with a berried branch within gilt scroll, circa 1758.
(Christie's) £495

A pair of Sèvres style turquoise ground seaux, 19th century, with foliage scroll handles, the bucket shapes painted with reserves of court figures, 5$^{1}/_{2}$in. diameter.
(Christie's) £1,049

A Sèvres coffee-can and saucer with blue oeil-de-perdrix on a pale-pink-ground reserved with circular medallions painted with pink roses, circa 1765.
(Christie's) £770

SHELLEY

The Shelley Pottery grew out of the Foley factory in the 1920s. They produced very fine teawares in a strong Art Deco style, the cups sometimes in inverted conical shapes with triangular handles, or curved octagonal shapes. These were decorated with bold coloured motifs, such as geometric patterns, sunbursts or peacock tails. They also produced novelty pieces such as Humpty Dumpty teapots.

They later became Royal Albert and form part of the Doulton group.

A Shelley Intarsio teapot in the form of a caricature of Austin Chamberlain. (William H. Brown) £320

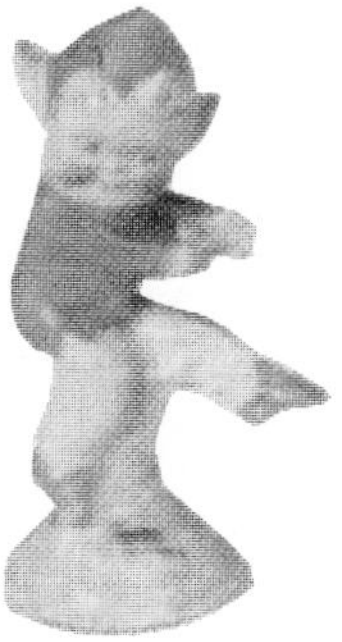

A Shelley bone china figure, designed by Mabel Lucie Attwell, of a pixie in green costume jumping over a log, 3in. high. (Christie's) £190

A Shelley Regent part coffee set printed and painted with sprays of primroses. (Christie's) £250

A Shelley 'Pixie' part tea set designed by Mabel Lucie Attwell, comprising pixie house teapot and cover, two toadstool sugar bowls and pixie mug, 5½in. high. (Christie's) £242

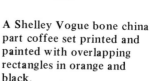

A Shelley Vogue bone china part coffee set printed and painted with overlapping rectangles in orange and black. (Christie's) £308

A Shelley 'Animal' teaset designed by Mabel Lucie Attwell modelled as duck, rabbit and chick in sailor costumes. (Christie's) £715

A Shelley nursery teapot by Hilda Cowham, modelled as a marquee and printed with two seated children reading, 5in. high. (Christie's S. Ken) £352

Part of a forty-piece Shelley white porcelain teaset in grey, black and yellow. £720

SICILIAN

Maiolica was produced in Sicily basically in imitation of the style of the North Italian centres such as Faenza, Venice and Tuscany, though the results tend to be cruder and more rustic than their prototypes. The areas of Caltagirone and Trapani were two major potting centres on the island.

As is often the case with a devolved art, Sicily went on producing this type of maiolica long after the vogue had passed in the north, and most examples date from the 17th century.

Marks are very rare: *SPQP* is occasionally found, indicating Palerman origin.

One of three 17th century Sicilian waisted albarelli, approx. 24cm. high. (Christie's) £550

One of two 17th century Sicilian drug jars with narrow necks, 23cm. high. (Christie's) £825

One of a pair of 17th century Sicilian wet-drug jars with scroll handles, 25cm. high. (Christie's) £1,430

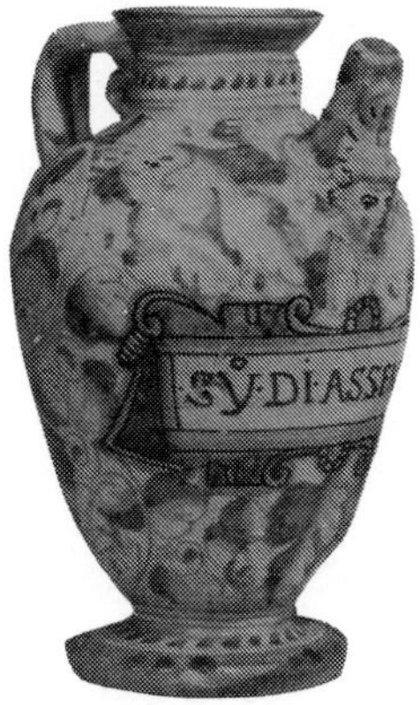

A Sicilian (Trapani) waisted armorial albarello painted in yellow, green and blue with an armorial device, circa 1620, 20.5cm. high. (Christie's) £880

A Sicilian oviform vase painted with a portrait of a helmeted soldier, dated 1662, 37cm. high. (Christie's) £605

One of three 17th century Sicilian waisted albarelli painted in yellow, green and blue, approx. 23cm. high. (Christie's) £935

A Sicilian Caltagirone albarello painted in colours with two portrait heads on yellow grounds, mid 17th century, 31.5cm. high. (Christie's London) £1,540

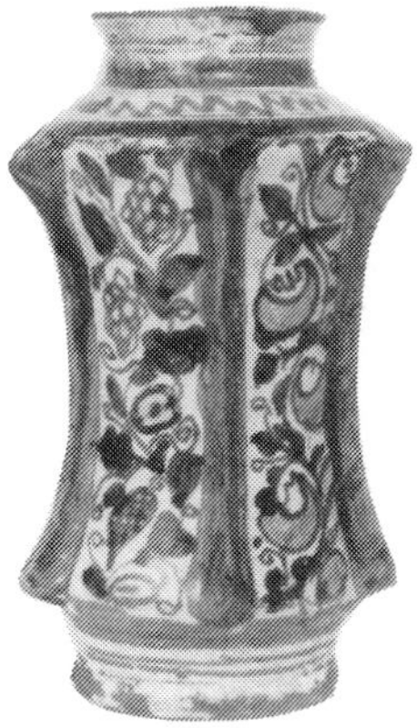

A Sicilian (Trapani) blue and white waisted albarello painted with stylised flowers, late 16th century, 21cm. high. (Christie's) £440

SIENA

The Tuscan town of Siena had a flourishing maiolica industry from the 13th century onwards, but reached its heyday from around the early 16th century, when apothecary pots, dishes depicting Biblical characters and tiles, many for the Petrucci palace, were produced in considerable numbers. These show a marked preference for an opaque dark orange tone.

In the 18th century dishes and panels were produced by Ferdinando Maria Campani and Bartolomeo Terchi, which lean towards Castelli in style. They feature principally buffs and light blues, and Terchi also makes use of a very dark brown.

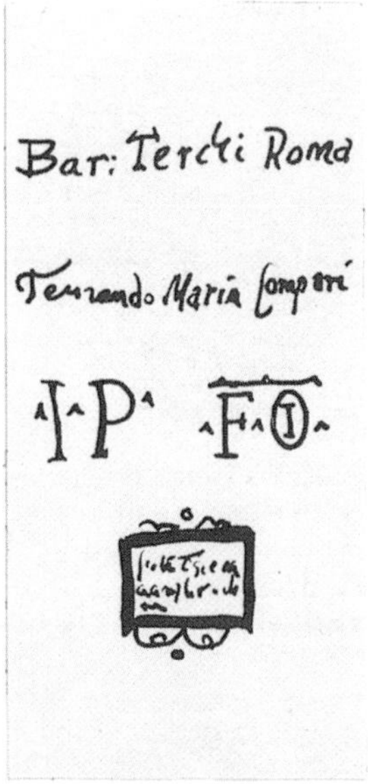

A pair of Siena wall-plaques, painted with an elephant and a porcupine in rocky wooded landscapes, Bartolomeo Terchi's factory, circa 1740, 28cm. high.
(Christie's) £1,760

A Siena wall-plaque painted in blue with buildings in a rocky wooded landscape, within an ochre and brown marbled pierced frame moulded with putti, circa 1740, 46.5cm. high.
(Christie's) £1,980

A pair of Siena massive campana-shaped ewers with moulded gilt-winged caryatid handles and an applied gilt foliate mask beneath the lip, the bodies painted with Bacchic fauns, circa 1730, 63cm. high.
(Christie's) £16,500

A pair of Siena wall-plaques, the centres painted with a snail and a turkey in rocky wooded landscapes with a town in the distance, Bartolomeo Terchi's factory, circa 1740, 28.5cm. high.
(Christie's) £3,300

SLIPWARE

Slipware is the earliest characteristically English earthenware, which gets its name from the creamy mixture of clay and water, known as slip, which was used for its decoration. Slip could either be painted on over large areas, trailed in lines or dots from a quill spouted pot, or combed into the surface of a piece. Many artists also used it to impart colour interest to a piece.

A slipware dish decorated with a black-coated hussar riding a cream-slip horse with brown spots, upper Austria, circa 1790, 31cm. diameter.
(Christie's) £1,320

A slipware dated dish decorated with a sgraffiato merhorse flanked by the initials *G.S.T.* and *M.S.T.*, probably upper Austria, 1790, 28.5cm. diameter.
(Christie's) £1,210

SONG

It was during the Song or Sung period, from 960–1279 AD, that potters became established as respected craftsmen on a par with the bronze worker and the jade carver, and the pieces they produced were strongly impressionistic and naturalistic in style.

Their wares were made in the simplest ways with little painting or embellishment. Most were wholly undecorated or enhanced by moulding, stamping, the application of clay reliefs or etching. All these processes were carried out while the clay was still unfired. The glaze was added and the whole was then subjected to a single firing.

Song glazes tend to be thick and hard, and any crackle is positive and well-defined. They consisted basically of two types, a thick, opalescent glaze of pale lavender or turquoise, and a smooth, translucent celadon glaze with a predominantly green tint. Varying colour effects were achieved by the use of different oxides, doubtless at first by accident, but they were soon obviously being achieved systematically.

A Cizhou painted pillow moulded from two parts as a lady recumbent, Song Dynasty, 33cm. wide. £9,180

A Ding type stem bowl, ivory white glaze, Northern Song Dynasty, 8.9cm. diam. £700

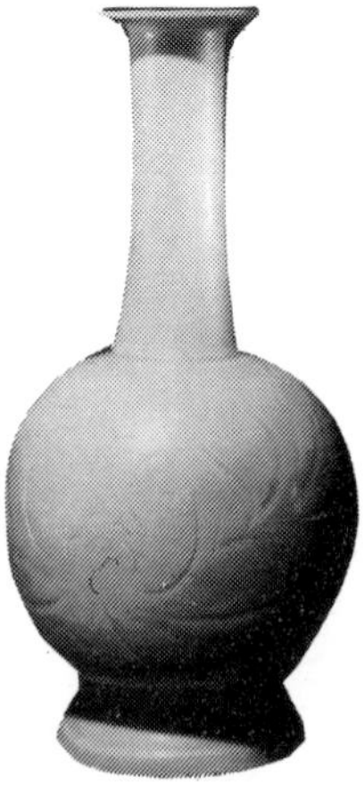

A Dingyao bottle potted in the form of a contemporary metal prototype, N. Song Dynasty, 25cm. high, fitted box. £66,000

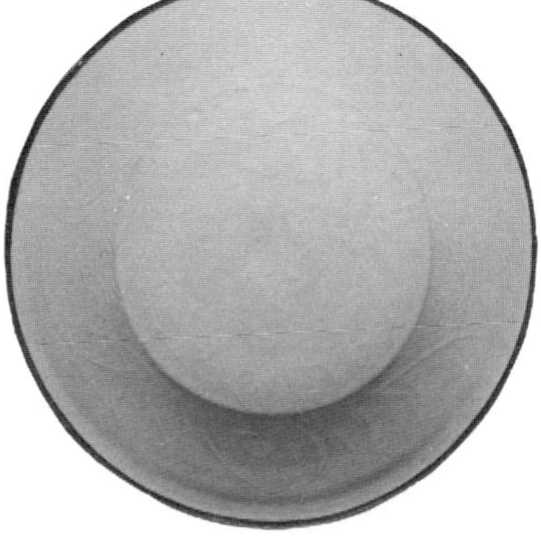

A Dingyao dish carved with a feathery lotus spray and scrolling leaves, N. Song Dynasty, 20.7cm. diam., fitted box. £16,500

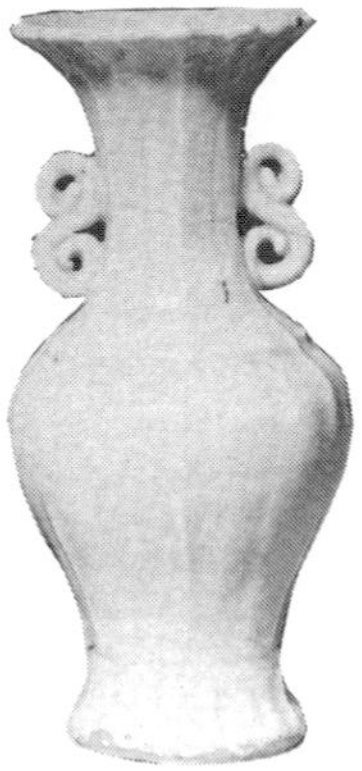

A Yingqing fluted baluster vase with S-scroll handles on the flaring neck, Song Dynasty, 17.2cm. high. £440

A Jun Yao bowl, the sides under a lightly-crackled lavender glaze, S. Song Dynasty, 11.3cm. diam. £2,750

A Henan black-glazed baluster vase, meiping, freely painted, Song Dynasty, 22cm. high. (Christie's) £3,080

A Northern celadon conical bowl moulded with two ladies reclining amongst clouds, Song Dynasty, 16.5cm. diam., fitted box. £6,480

A Jun Yao globular jar with two looped straight handles, Song Dynasty, 15cm. diam. £1,620

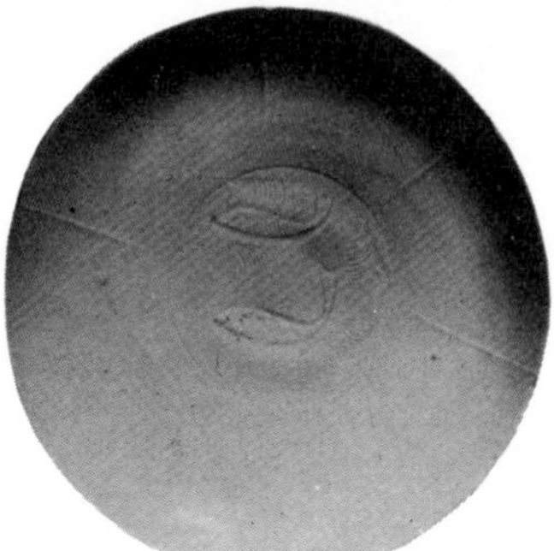

A Dingyao lobed hexafoil dish, clear ivory glaze thinning towards the unglazed rim, Song Dynasty, 17.8cm. diam. £1,080

A Cizhou carved oviform jar, Song Dynasty, 26cm. high, fitted box. £5,500

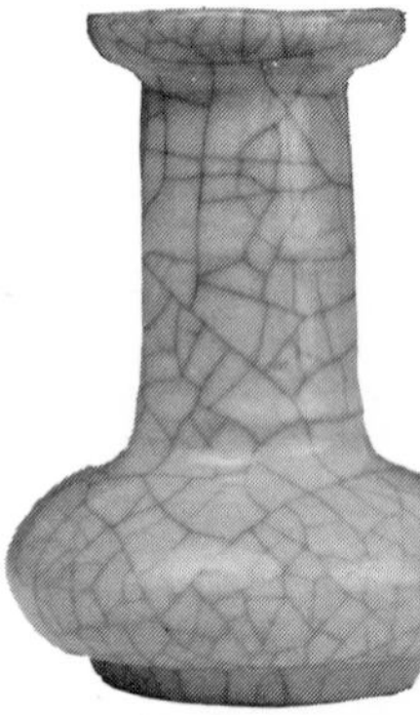

An important Jiaotan Guanyao bottle vase, southern Song Dynasty, with a rich pale grey-blue glaze with irregular light brown crackles, 4⅝in. high. (Christie's) £179,036

A Cizhou small baluster jar, Song Dynasty, 12.3cm. high, fitted box. £2,750

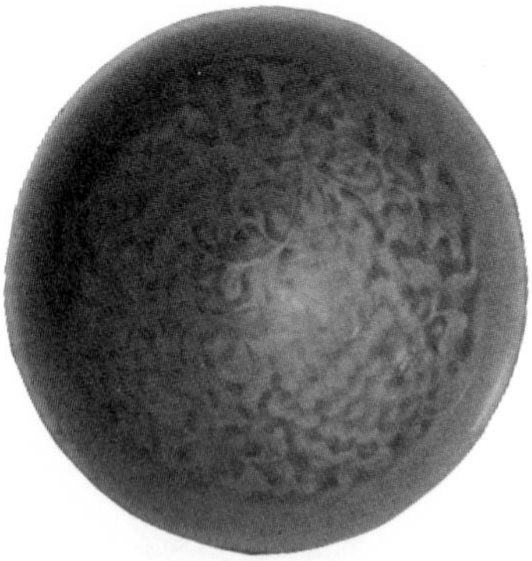

A Northern celadon conical bowl, Song Dynasty, 11.4cm. diam. £1,620

A Jun Yao tripod censer under a rich lavender glaze thinning to an olive translucency at the rim, Song Dynasty, 6.5cm. diam. £970

A large Northern Celadon bowl freely carved with a deer amongst scrolling foliage, Song Dynasty, 21cm. diam., fitted box. £3,780

SPODE

As early as 1762 Josiah Spode started developing his Staffordshire pottery, which, under his descendants, became the first in England to introduce bone china bodies at the end of the 18th century. Spode's shapes were mostly plain, with correspondingly simple but elegant decoration, or alternatively elaborate Japanese patterns. The bulk of the factory's production consisted of printed pottery and the porcelain was really only a sideline.

The company was bought in 1833 by Thomas Copeland (q.v.). From 1970, however, it has again traded as Spode Ltd.

Most pieces were marked *Spode*, with a pattern number in red. The earliest sometimes have impressed marks.

A Spode 'Beaded-Hoop' decorated with pattern no. 1106, circa 1810-20, 3½in. diam. £550

An attractive pair of Spode candle extinguishers on a small rectangular tray with loop handle, 12.5cm., impressed workman's mark. (Phillips) £480

A pair of Spode gold-ground flared cylindrical vases painted with groups of luxuriant fruit and flowers on the rich gold ground, between white beaded rims, one vase with red mark and pattern no. 711, circa 1815, 16.5cm. high. (Christie's London) £2,200

A Spode porcelain 'Beaded New Shape' jar and cover with gilt ball finial and loop handles, pattern No. 1166, 10½in. high. (Dacre, Son & Hartley) £3,900

A Spode two handled vase, painted in Imari palette with panels of flowers on a blue and gilded ground, 16cm. (Phillips London) £520

A Spode miniature teapot and cover with gilt spout, red mark and pattern no. 1166, circa 1820, 5cm. high. (Christie's) £440

An early 19th century iron-stone baluster jar and cover, possibly Spode, 46cm. high. £420

A Spode vase and pierced cover, finely painted with groups of flowers on a dark blue and gilt scale pattern ground, 24cm. (Lawrence Fine Arts) £902

A Spode blue and white rectangular octagonal meat dish printed with 'shooting a leopard in a tree' from the Indian Sporting Series, circa 1815, 20¼in. wide. (Christie's S. Ken) £330

A good Spode octagonal vase and cover by Abbeydale China commemorating Churchill's 90th birthday and Honorary Citizenship of the USA, 28cm. high. (Phillips) £110

An English porcelain tulip vase modelled as a red striped open yellow bloom, perhaps Spode, circa 1820, 15.5cm. high. (Christie's London) £1,980

Spode trio set finely painted in the Imari taste. (Prudential) £110

A Spode ironstone two-handled slender oviform vase with spreading neck and foot, 5½in. high. (Christie's) £198

One of a pair of Spode stone china oviform jugs with cylindrical necks and handles, printed and coloured in famille rose style, 12½in. high. (Christie's S. Ken.) £1,100

A Spode porcelain pastille burner in the form of a large house with two windows in the gable end. (Bearne's) £1,300

A Victorian Spode pottery pot-pourri vase, baluster shape with pierced domed cover having bud finial, 12in. high. (Hobbs & Chambers) £190

A Spode ironstone celadon-ground two-handled flared cylindrical bowl and cover painted in the famille rose palette, 8in. high, circa 1815. (Christie's S. Ken) £300

A Spode dog trough, printed in blue with the 'Queen Charlotte' pattern showing a chinoiserie landscape with two figures, 18cm. (Phillips) £300

An unusual ice pail, attributed to Spode, with two upright loop handles, printed in blue with the 'Greek' pattern, 23.5cm. (Phillips) £420

A Spode blue-ground two-handled oviform vase, painted with loose bouquets of luxuriant flowers and scattered flower-sprays on a dark-blue ground, circa 1820, 15.5cm. high. (Christie's) £1,045

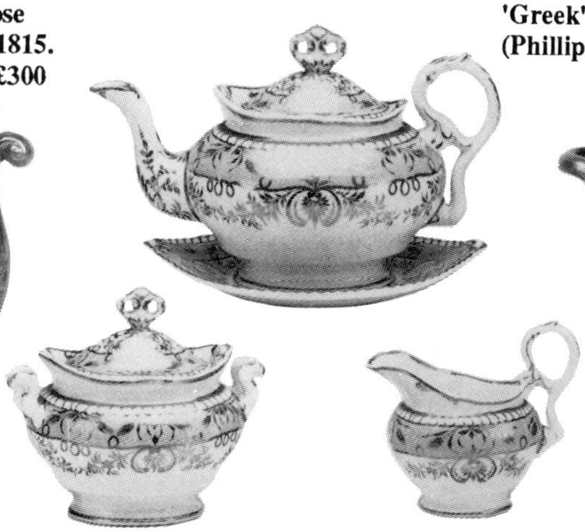

A Spode Felspar porcelain part tea and coffee service, each piece painted in gold with sprays of barley and garlands of flowers, early 19th century. (Bearne's) £580

A Spode blue-ground two-handled oviform vase with waisted neck and on a spreading circular foot, circa 1820, 15.5cm. high. (Christie's) £440

A pair of Spode two-handled pot-pourri vases, pierced covers and stands painted with loose bouquets of luxuriant flowers on dark-blue grounds, circa 1820, the stands 11cm. diameter. (Christie's) £1,980

A Spode flared spill-vase with white bead and gilt band borders, pattern no. 1166, 11cm. high. (Christie's) £385

A pair of Spode pedestal sauce tureens and covers, each piece brightly decorated with the 'Peacock' pattern within a spearhead border, 15cm. high, early 19th century. (Bearne's) £420

STAFFORDSHIRE

Devotees of Arnold Bennett's novels about the Five Towns will be aware of the names Fenton, Longton, Hanley, Burslem, Tunstall and Burmantofts – Bennett left one out – which were the centre of the great pottery industry of the 19th century. It was there that Staffordshire figures were produced in their thousands and bought with eagerness to adorn chest tops and mantlepieces in homes all over the country. At one time there were over 400 factories going full blast in the area around Stoke on Trent to satisfy the demand.

Staffordshire figures were unsophisticated in their modelling and cast in the shape of popular heroes or characters from stories, plays and poetry. There was an especially popular line in politicians and heroes like Wellington and Nelson. They were press moulded and decorated in underglaze blue and black with touches of colour in overglaze enamel and gilding. Early examples have closed bases or a small hole in the base while 20th century pieces are usually slip cast in Plaster of Paris moulds and are open ended.

A Staffordshire small green-glazed plate, with moulded diaper-pattern border, circa 1770, 19.5cm. diam. (Christie's) £385

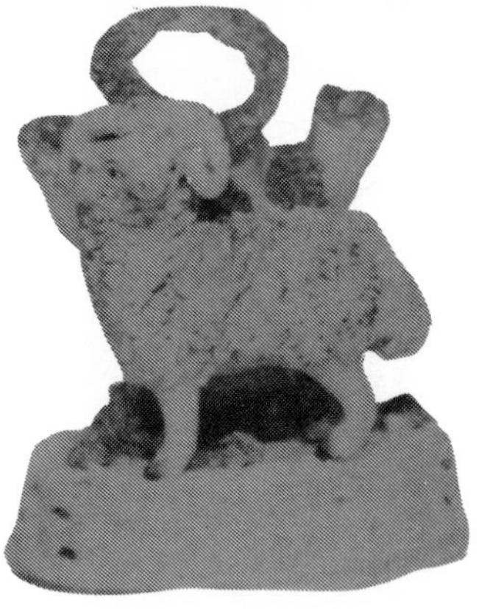

A Staffordshire spill-vase modelled as a ram, circa 1845, 4½in. high. (Christie's) £88

A Staffordshire jug, decorated with a band of silver lustre with a pattern of scrolling flower branches, 12cm. (Lawrence Fine Arts) £154

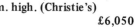

A Staffordshire solid-agate tapering hexagonal chocolate-pot and domed cover, (cover restored) circa 1750, 22.5cm. high. (Christie's) £6,050

A Staffordshire toby jug in the form of a man seated holding a jug of foaming ale, the base marked Walton, 10¼in. (Lawrence Fine Arts) £396

A pair of colourful Staffordshire pottery zebra vases, each animal with head held high, 27.5cm. high. (Bearne's) £500

A Staffordshire pottery figure of Andromache in a cream robe, leaning on an urn, circa 1790, 22.5cm. (Osmond Tricks) £85

A figure of a standing camel before a tree stump applied with foliage, painted in colours on a shaped oval base, 6½in. high.
(Christie's S. Ken) **£770**

Staffordshire pottery "Boxing" pitcher, England, circa 1825, titled below *Spring and Langan*, and with floral decorated rim and handle, 8½in. high.
(Skinner Inc.) **£202**

A colourful Staffordshire pottery group, the Prince of Wales and Princess Alexandra of Denmark, 26cm.
(Bearne's) **£200**

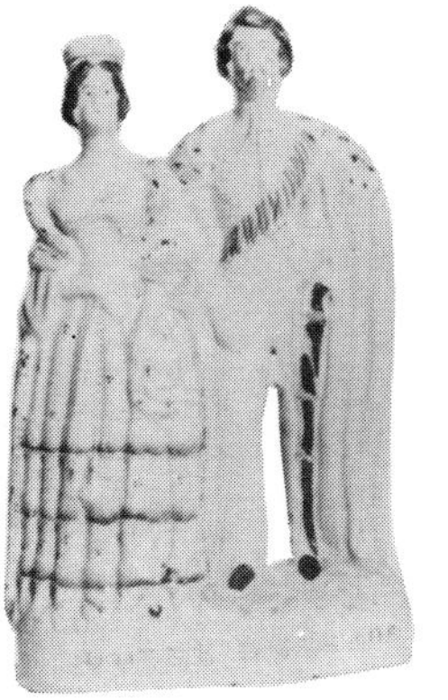

A group of the Queen and Emperor, painted in colours on shaped oval base, named in raised capitals and enriched in gilding, 11½in. high.
(Christie's S. Ken) **£242**

A Staffordshire pottery savings bank, in the form of a two chimneyed building, with three arched windows, 6in. high.
(Spencer's) **£400**

An early Staffordshire pottery group of a shepherd sitting on a rocky outcrop, playing a flute, his companion standing at his side, 25cm.
(Bearne's) **£340**

A Staffordshire octagonal plate with a portrait of Fred Archer, detailing various horse races which he won, 24cm.
(Phillips) **£220**

A Staffordshire figure of Wellington, seated in a large high-backed chair, with coloured face, 31cm.
(Phillips) **£340**

A 19th century Staffordshire pottery jug made to commemorate the Coronation of Queen Victoria, 17cm. high.
(Spencer's) **£350**

A bull-baiting group modelled as a bull with black-sponged markings and with a hound snapping at its lowered head, circa 1800, 5in. high.
(Christie's S. Ken) £330

A pair of Staffordshire pottery figures of a young man and woman, he with a monkey, she with a tambourine, 18cm.
(Bearne's) £95

A Staffordshire large blue printed meat dish, with a farmer's wife, surrounded by her children, offering food to a blind and lame traveller, 52cm.
(Phillips) £480

A large brown salt glazed stoneware spirit flask modelled as a standing figure of Sir Robert Peel, holding a scroll inscribed *'Bread for the Millions'*, 36cm.
(Phillips) £900

A pair of Staffordshire pottery groups each in the form of a cow by a stream with the farmer or the milkmaid, 21cm. high.
(Bearne's) £230

A Staffordshire figure of Gladstone shown standing, his hand resting on two books, well coloured, 30cm.
(Phillips) £280

A figure of Eliza Cook in brown jacket and green and pink dress, named in gilt indented capitals, circa 1849, 10in. high.
(Christie's S. Ken) £154

A pair of Salt pottery bocage figures, one inscribed *Sportsman*, his lady companion entitled *Archer*, 17.3cm.
(Bearne's) £540

A Staffordshire pottery group in the form of a young Welshman and woman, supporting a bucket on a milestone inscribed *Langolen 1 Mile*, 27cm.
(Bearne's) £300

Staffordshire creamware coffeepot and cover, England, circa 1780, black transfer decoration of "The Tea Party" to one side, 10in. high.
(Skinner Inc.) £123

A pair of early Staffordshire models of pumas with brown spotted coats, their tails arched over their backs, 9.5cm.
(Phillips) £1,200

A Staffordshire figure of R. Cobden, shown seated and well coloured, 18cm.
(Phillips) £180

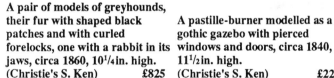

A brightly coloured Staffordshire porcelain figure of Nelson in dress uniform, 16.5cm.
(Bearne's) £85

A pair of models of greyhounds, their fur with shaped black patches and with curled forelocks, one with a rabbit in its jaws, circa 1860, 10$^{1}/_{4}$in. high.
(Christie's S. Ken) £825

A pastille-burner modelled as a gothic gazebo with pierced windows and doors, circa 1840, 11$^{1}/_{2}$in. high.
(Christie's S. Ken) £220

A Victorian Staffordshire group of Napoleon III and Albert shaking hands before crossed flags.
(Phillips) £120

An equestrian figure of Marshal Arnaud, 7$^{1}/_{2}$in. high, and an equestrian figure of the Sultan in similar colours, circa 1854.
(Christie's S. Ken) £330

A figure of a batsman at the wicket, probably Julius Caesar, painted in colours and enriched in gilding, circa 1865, 14$^{1}/_{4}$in. high.
(Christie's S. Ken) £715

A Staffordshire rectangular meat-dish printed with Oriental figures on a terrace before buildings in a river landscape, circa 1810, 20½in. wide. (Christie's S. Ken) £209

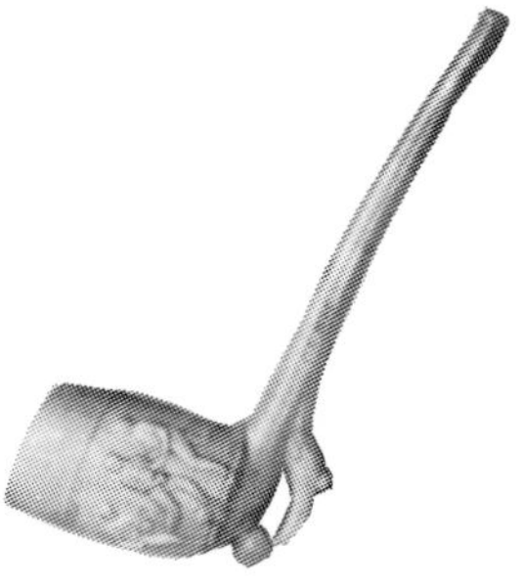

A Staffordshire pottery pipe modelled in relief with Rugby and Association footballers, 21.5cm. long. (Lawrence Fine Arts) £110

A large 19th century Staffordshire earthenware Masonic jug, circa 1831. (Phillips) £430

A Staffordshire group depicting 'Lady Hester Stanhope' riding on the back of a camel, circa 1860, 10½in. high. (Christie's S. Ken) £352

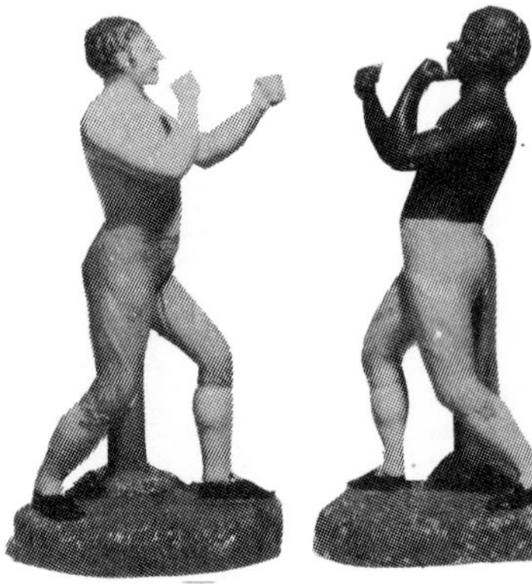

A pair of Staffordshire pugilist figures modelled as the boxers Mollineux and Cribb, circa 1810, 22cm. high. £2,050

A Staffordshire jug moulded as the head of 'Lord Rodney', the rim moulded with a flag and cannons, circa 1785, 6¼in. high. (Christie's S. Ken) £330

A rare Staffordshire figure of Jenny Lind as Marie in a green hat, dark blue bodice and pink skirt, circa 1847, 8in. high. (Christie's S. Ken) £308

A pair of Staffordshire lions facing to the left and right, painted in shades of brown, circa 1860, 6½in. high. (Christie's S. Ken) £880

A Staffordshire figure of a lady, carrying a basket of fruit on her head, wearing a floral sprigged dress, 15cm. (Phillips London) £280

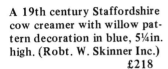

A 19th century Staffordshire cow creamer with willow pattern decoration in blue, 5¼in. high. (Robt. W. Skinner Inc.) £218

A pair of Staffordshire pottery figures of an old man and woman entitled 'Age', (restoration), 8¼in. high. (Christie's S. Ken) £165

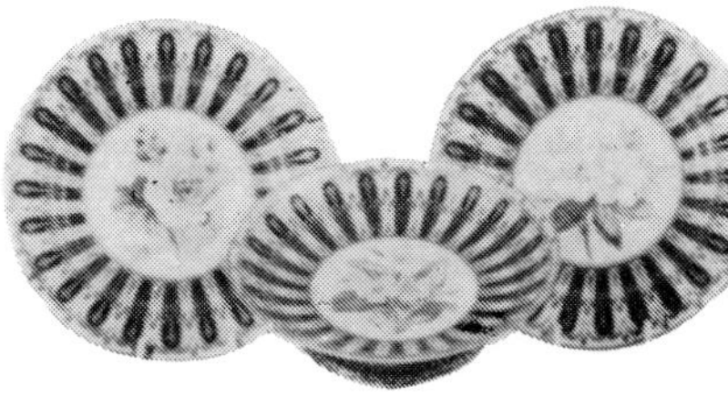

A Staffordshire porcelain part dessert-service, comprising two high comports, four low comports, and ten plates. (Christie's S. Ken.) £418

A Staffordshire pottery oviform jug, printed in puce with a busy portrait of Admiral Lord Nelson flanked by a map of the Battle of Trafalgar, (cracked), 5½in. high. (Christie's S. Ken) £187

19th century Staffordshire vase, decorated in the Mason manner with Oriental flowers, birds etc., with a recumbent lion finial, 18in. high. (G. A. Key) £570

A Staffordshire group of two seated spaniels, one chained to a barrel with iron-red fur markings, 9½in. high. (Christie's) £242

A Staffordshire figure of Dr Syntax in typical black costume seated between flowering branches reading a book, circa 1825, 5½in. high. (Christie's S. Ken) £385

A pair of Staffordshire seated figures of Queen Victoria and Prince Albert, both brightly coloured, circa 1845, 6in. high. (Christie's S. Ken) £209

A Staffordshire creamware equestrian group of Hudibras of Ralph Wood type, seated astride his bown-glazed horse, circa 1785, 30cm. high. (Christie's) £13,200

A Staffordshire stirrup cup, modelled as a hound's head, the ears and part of the head coloured brown, one ear repaired, 12.5cm. (Lawrence Fine Arts) £352

A Staffordshire silver resist lustre jug, decorated with birds standing in tubs among foliage branches, 14cm. diam. (Lawrence Fine Arts) £132

A Staffordshire white porcelain triple pastille burner, modelled as three Gothic pavilions, circa 1848. (Christie's) £495

A Staffordshire group of two greyhounds before a tree stump spill vase, 10½in. high. (vase chipped) (Christie's S. Ken) £105

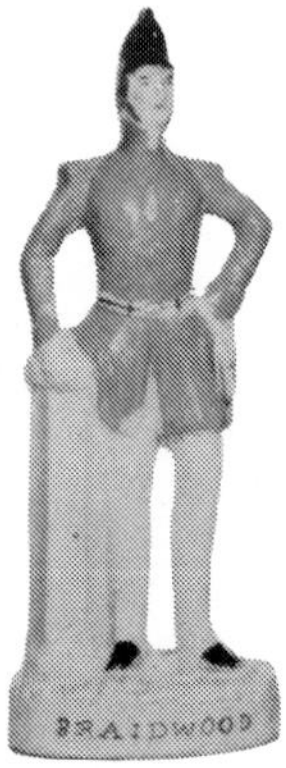

A rare Staffordshire figure of James Braidwood, with black helmet and iron red uniform, circa 1861, 15in. high. (Christie's S. Ken) £550

A Staffordshire gilt clock face, flanked by two seated spaniels and surmounted by a poodle, 9½in. high. (Christie's S. Ken) £176

An interesting Staffordshire hybrid porcelain figure of a hurdy-gurdy player, on mound base, late 18th century, perhaps Enoch Wood, 8¼in. high. (Tennants) £300

A pair of Walton type Staffordshire figures of a lady and gentleman playing a mandoline and a lute, 15.5cm. (Phillips London) £1,300

A Staffordshire creamware group of Venus and Cupid of Ralph Wood type, the goddess scantily draped in a green robe, circa 1785, 27cm. high. (Christie's London) £396

A Staffordshire tureen and cover modelled as a duck swimming in water, the base modelled with waves and painted in blue, 10¾in. long. (Christie's S. Ken) £495

A Staffordshire figure of a Turk wearing a brown coat, black fez and yellow turban, 13.5cm. (Phillips London) £150

A Staffordshire porcelain oval teapot and cover with feather moulded spout and painted in black with a windmill and cottage in a river landscape, perhaps Coalport, circa 1810, 10½in. wide. (Christie's S. Ken) £143

A Staffordshire figure of a lady, wearing a brown sprigged dress and sitting on a green glazed tree trunk, 12cm. (Phillips London) £90

A Staffordshire group of Victoria flanked bv Abdul-Medjid and Napoleon III, entitled 'Turkey, England, France', 11¾in. high. £170

A Staffordshire pastille burner, modelled as a cottage on a grassy mound with floral encrusted decoration, 7in. high. (Christie s S. Ken) £94

A Staffordshire jug, modelled in relief, with a stag, a faun and doe, 14.5cm. (Lawrence Fine Arts) £176

A pair of late Staffordshire cats, seated on rectangular cushion bases painted in green and pink, 7in. high. (Christie's S. Ken) £220

Staffordshire figure of Britannia on a rectangular base, polychrome decoration, 14in. high. (G. A. Key) £180

Large Staffordshire pottery meat plate, blue and white Canova pattern, probably by Godwin and Hewitt. (G. A. Key) £125

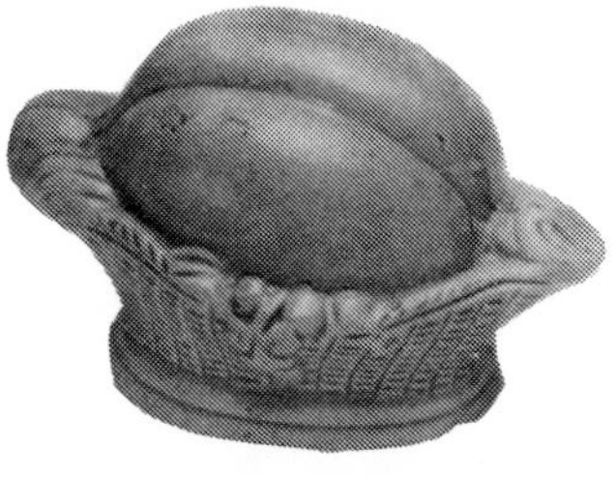

A Staffordshire model of a greengage, of Ralph Wood type, naturally modelled and resting on an oval basket, circa 1780, 8cm. wide. (Christie's) £418

A Staffordshire hexagonal meat-dish, printed with rustic figures before a cottage, 14¾in. wide. (Christie's S. Ken) £385

A Staffordshire figure of Gladstone shown standing by a fence, a flag by his head, partly coloured, 34cm. (Phillips) £340

A very attractive and rare set of three Staffordshire tea canisters, the sides with a continuous rural landscape with figures, 10cm. high. (Phillips) £3,000

A remarkable Staffordshire slipware owl jug and cover, the head lifting off to form a drinking cup, the body moulded in buff coloured clay, 23cm. (Phillips) £18,000

Staffordshire figure, Garibaldi, polychrome decorated with name plaque, 15in. high. (G. A. Key) £170

A pair of Staffordshire elephants coloured in a grey-brown, standing on oval bases heightened with green, 8.5cm. (Phillips) £240

Staffordshire figure of Shakespeare, polychrome decorated, named, 14in. high. (G. A. Key) £165

A Staffordshire character jug of Stanley Baldwin, shown seated with pipe in hand, 16.5cm.
(Phillips) £340

A Staffordshire pottery octagonal plate printed in black with a bust portrait of Charles Stuart Parnell, 24cm.
(Phillips) £320

A Staffordshire figure of Sir Robert Peel mounted on horseback, in black top hat, yellow waistcoat and brown jacket, 27cm.
(Phillips) £700

A rare Staffordshire arbour group of two musicians, the lady and gentleman seated on green stools and the lady playing a mandoline, the man a pipe, 16.5cm.
(Phillips) £1,700

A Staffordshire pearlware cow creamer and stopper with a pink lustred border, a milkmaid seated to one side, 14cm.
(Phillips) £480

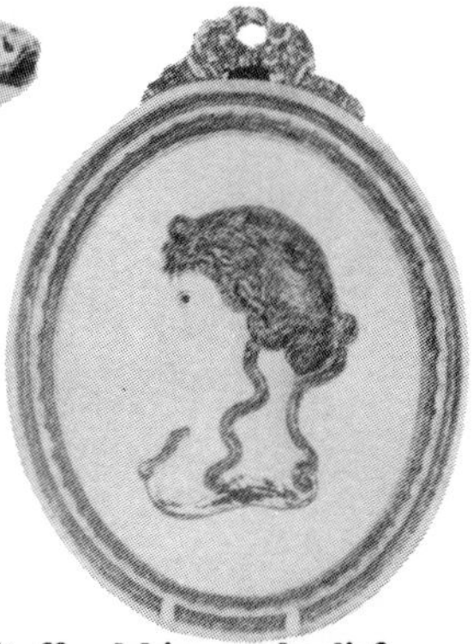

A Staffordshire oval relief moulded plaque with a bust portrait of a woman within a moulded frame, perhaps depicting Charlotte Corday, circa 1795, 10½in. high.
(Christie's S. Ken) £209

A Staffordshire pottery character jug formed as the head of Lord Kitchener, 18cm.
(Phillips) £110

A Staffordshire pottery Victorian coronation mug, printed in underglaze purple with the Swansea transfer of the young Queen and her dates, 9cm. high. (Spencer's) £900

Staffordshire figure of Admiral C. Napier, named, 12in. high. (G. A. Key)
£170

A Staffordshire hen on nest with chicks, probably by T. Randall, circa 1820, 9in. long. £620

A Staffordshire group, entitled 'The Allied Powers', 12¼in. high. £750

A Staffordshire saltglaze solid agate figure of a seated cat, circa 1755, 12.5cm. high. £1,025

A figure of Theobald Wolfe Tone holding two flags across his chest, the oval base named in gilt script, 13½in. high. £300

A pair of well modelled spaniels with brown markings, wearing gilt collars, 10¼in. high. £1,200

A figure of The Tichborne Claimant, holding a bird on his left hand, a rifle at his side, 14in. high. £280

A Staffordshire blue and white cylindrical mug printed with equestrian figures of The Duke of Wellington and Lord Hill, 4¾in. high. £200

One of a pair of late 18th century Staffordshire pottery cow creamers, 6¼in. long. £1,600

An Obadiah Sherratt group of Polito's menagerie, circa 1830, 29.5cm. high. £16,200

A Staffordshire pastille burner modelled as a house with four central chimneys, 11¼in. high overall. £1,200

A Staffordshire soup tureen and undertray, by R. Hall, circa 1825, 12in. high. £640

Mid 19th century tobacco jar and cover, modelled as the head of a spotted dog, 6¾in. high. £265

A group of Victoria standing with her arm around The Princess Royal, circa 1842, 10in. high. £95

A pair of figures of the Prince of Wales and Prince Alfred, circa 1858, 10¾in. high. £260

Titensor group of a shepherd and shepherdess, circa 1820, 7in. high. £375

A well modelled group of a lion with a recumbent lamb at it's feet, circa 1850, 7in. high. £280

An Obadiah Sherratt group, entitled 'Grecian and Daughter', 9in. high. £650

A Staffordshire equestrian figure of Sir Robert Peel, wearing a black top hat and dark blue riding jacket, 13½in. high. £3,500

A rare group of Mr Van Amburgh, the lion tamer, circa 1840, 5¾in. high. £3,100

A pastille burner modelled as a cottage with an iron-red doorway flanked by flowers and trees, on an oval shaped base, 6in. high. £260

A Shorthose tea bowl and saucer, printed in colours with the Tea Party, together with another. £175

Early 19th century English figure of Britannia with a lion at her side, 6¼in. high. £240

A pair of Staffordshire solid agate models of cats, seated upright, originally supporting candle nozzles, 12.5cm. (Phillips London) £2,000

A figure of George Parr, holding a cricket ball in his right hand, circa 1865, 14in. high. £550

A Staffordshire group, The Tithe Pig, on a green base, 15cm. high. £200

A Staffordshire model of Palmer's house, circa 1856. £240

A Staffordshire jug printed and coloured with an equestrian portrait of the Duke of Wellington. £170

STONEWARE

Salt glazed stoneware is a very old method of making pottery and there had been workshops producing this sort of ware at Lambeth in South London for many centuries when John Doulton started to work there in 1815. He made salt glazed domestic jars, bottles and barrels in brown with a slip glaze using the same methods as potters had used since the Middle Ages. John's son Henry realised the potential of stoneware when he followed his father into the business. He expanded the firm's operations into architectural stoneware and then the decorative stoneware which was to make the family fortune. In 1866 he encouraged students from the nearby Lambeth School of Art to come to work in a studio he attached to his pottery and allowed them complete licence to experiment and make everything they wanted. He was fortunate in having as protegés gifted people like the famous Barlow family, Frank Butler, George Tinworth and Eliza Simmance. Their work was shown abroad, particularly at Paris in the 1867 Exhibition, where it created a sensation that put Doulton's name on the international art map.

A stoneware jug by Thomas Samuel Haile, with strap handle, 19.9cm. high.
(Christie's) £330

A buff stoneware 'Gothic Windows' jug, possibly Charles Meigh, 9½in. high.
(Christie's S. Ken) £132

An Annaberg stoneware baluster jug moulded and coloured with a crowned king on horseback and holding his orb, with a coat-of-arms and the date 1689, 25.5cm. high.
(Christie's) £880

A Pierre Fondu stoneware amphora vase, covered in an olive-brown and blue crystalline glaze, 57.9cm. high.
(Christie's) £660

A Brameld light buff stoneware jug, decorated with a stag at bay and equestrian figures, having an entwined serpent handle, 7in. high. (Woolley & Wallis) £160

Important and unique stoneware crock with cobalt decoration of two deer flanking an eight-inch diameter pocket watch, 13in. high. (Eldred's) £22,628

A massive Kreussen armorial stoneware marriage Krug, moulded all over and painted in enamels, possibly 17th century, with pewter mount, 49cm. high. (Christie's) £990

A brown stoneware bust of Disraeli modelled by F. Mansfield, 1888, on waisted socle, 24cm.
(Phillips) £360

A Henri van de Velde stoneware two-handled vase, made for the firm of Reinhold Hanke, the rim extending into two curvilinear handles, 22.5cm. wide.
(Christie's) £7,700

A Derbyshire brown stoneware flask modelled as a bust of William IV, inscribed *'William IVth's Reform Cordial'*, 20cm.
(Phillips) £180

A Charles Vyse stoneware jug, inscribed *'Fishing's a dry job'* in a band around the rim, above a sceptical fish, 17cm. high.
(Phillips) £350

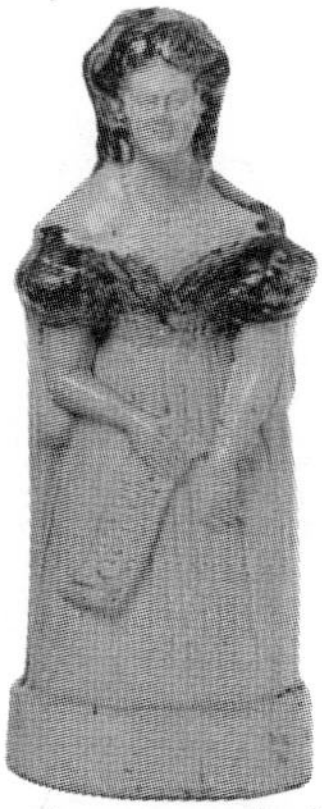

A brown stoneware flask modelled as a standing figure of 'Queen Alexandrina Victoria', 20cm.
(Phillips) £160

Cobalt decorated six-gallon stoneware crock, impressed *Riedinger & Caire Poughkeepsie NY*, circa 1850, 13in. high.
(Skinner Inc.) £620

A brown stoneware flask, modelled in relief on each side with a figure of Victoria, 26cm., impressed *S. Bedford.*
(Phillips) £300

A large brown stoneware jug flanked by portraits of Queen Victoria and the Duchess of Kent, 24cm.
(Phillips) £150

Cobalt decorated stoneware four-gallon crock, America, 19th century, 14in. high.
(Skinner Inc.) £168

A Yixing pale brown stoneware rectangular cylindrical teapot, circa 1750, 22.5cm. wide. £1,595

A Bottger brown stoneware cylindrical tankard and hinged cover, circa 1715, 21.5cm. high. (Christie's) £19,800

A Yixing brown stoneware globular teapot and domed cover, circa 1750, 19cm. wide. £1,420

A Bottger polished brown stoneware baluster coffee pot and domed cover, circa 1715, 17.5cm. high. £10,260

An Altenburg brown stoneware tankard applied in relief with dots forming the design of a hunter and his dog shooting a stag, first quarter of the 18th century, 20.5cm. high. (Christie's London) £1,320

A Nottingham stoneware carved mug with grooved loop handle, circa 1700, 10.5cm. high. £920

A Rhenish stoneware baluster tankard with English silver neck mount, circa 1700, 19cm. high. £385

A Nottingham type glazed red stoneware posset pot, dated 1791, 9½in. high. £1,145

A Nottingham stoneware puzzle-jug with a lustrous brown glaze, incised date 1715, 12cm. high. £2,420

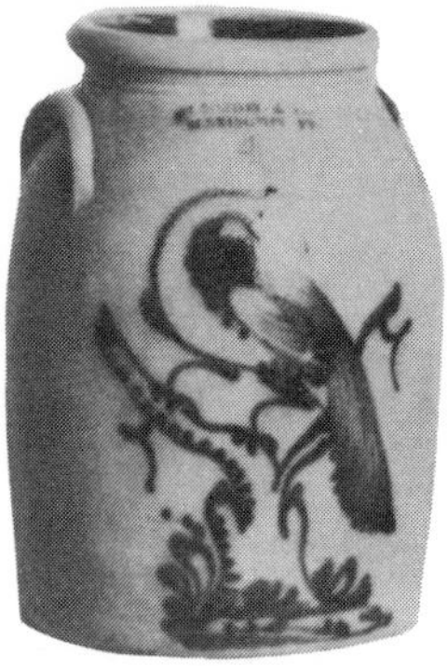

A stoneware four gallon crock, by J. Norton & Co., Vermont, circa 1880, 14in. high. £1,095

A one gallon crock, by A. O. Whittemore, Havana, N.Y., strong cobalt blue design of a house or houseboat. £220

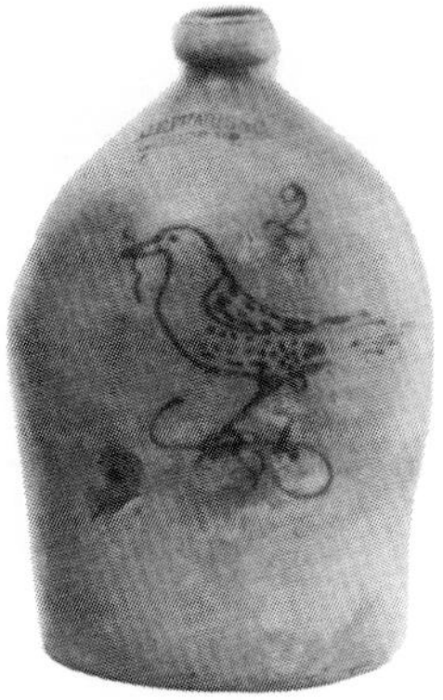

A two gallon jug, by C. E. Pharis & Co., Geddes, N.Y., cobalt blue bird holding worm in beak. £70

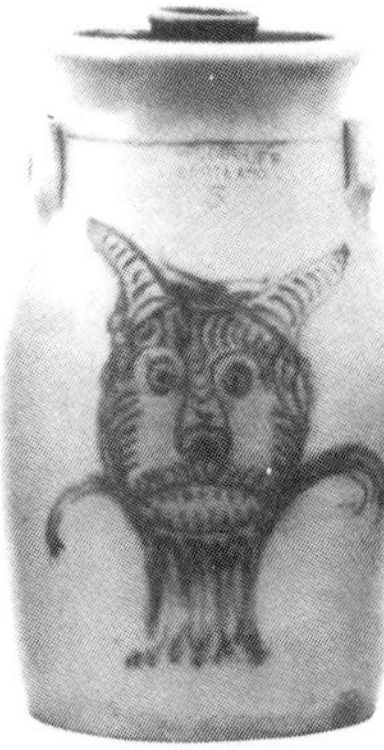

A five gallon churn by Woodruff, Cortland, large blue face, possibly tiger or devil head. £375

English saltglazed stoneware water closet. £150

A stoneware storage jar, approx. 20 gallons, by West Troy Pottery, 23in. tall. £9,525

A six gallon crock, by S. Hart, Fulton, cobalt blue lineal dog carrying a basket. £910

Stoneware butter churn, marked 'John Burger, Rochester', circa 1860, 19in. high. £20,280

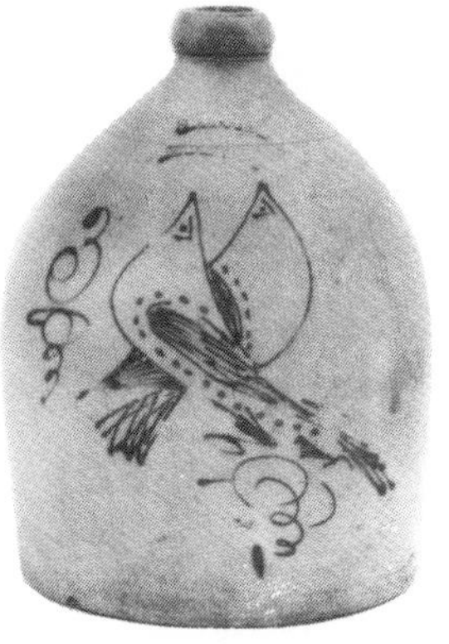

Mid 19th century three gallon stoneware jug, stamped 'S. Hart – Fulton', 13½in. high. £285

Incised and cobalt decorated stoneware crock, impressed *W. Lundy and Co., Troy,* New York, circa 1825, 11¼in., high. (Skinner Inc.) £2,914

Cobalt decorated stoneware jug, William H. Farrar & Company, Geddes, New York, 1841-1858 (flake at base), 11in. high. (Skinner Inc.) £2,025

A salt-glazed stoneware incised and decorated jug, 'Corlears Hook', New York, 1800–1815, with applied line-incised handle, 17in. high. (Christie's) £729

A saltglazed stoneware three-gallon jar, by Cowden & Wilcox, Penn., 1870-90, 12in. high. (Christie's) £235

A stoneware bread plate designed by A. W. N. Pugin, moulded decoration of stylised foliage and wheat ears, the rim inscribed *Waste not, want not,* circa 1850, 33.8cm. diam. (Christie's London) £1,210

A saltglazed stoneware two-gallon batter jug, by Cowden & Wilcox, Penn., 1870-90, 11in. high. (Christie's) £1,055

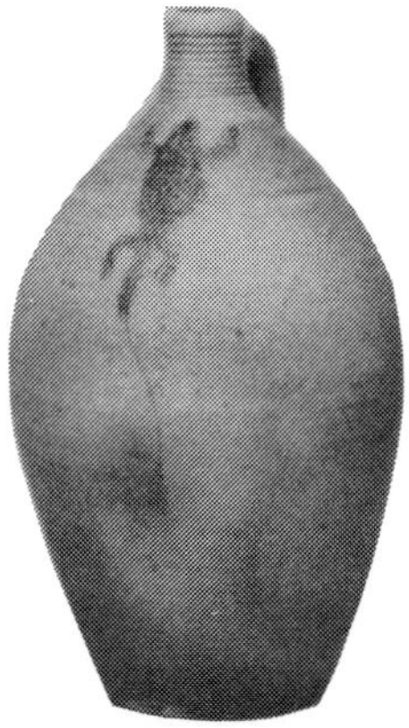

One of two 19th century salt-glazed stoneware jugs, N. Carolina, 8½in. and 10½in. high. (Christie's) £434

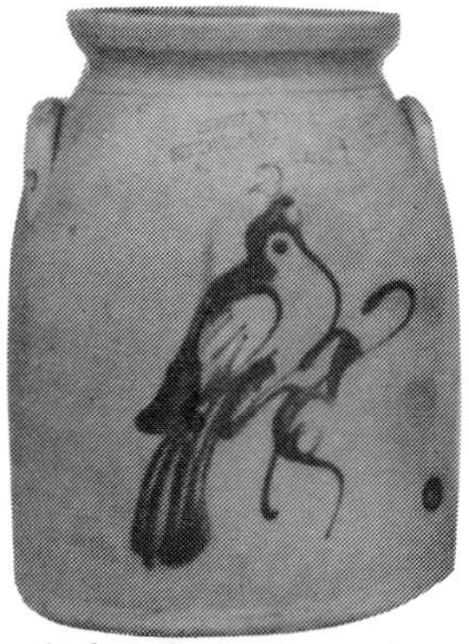

A saltglazed stoneware two-gallon jar, by G. A. Satterlee and M. Morey, 1861-85, and a two-gallon crock by P. Riedinger and A. Caire, 1857-78, 11½in. and 9½in. high. (Christie's) £217

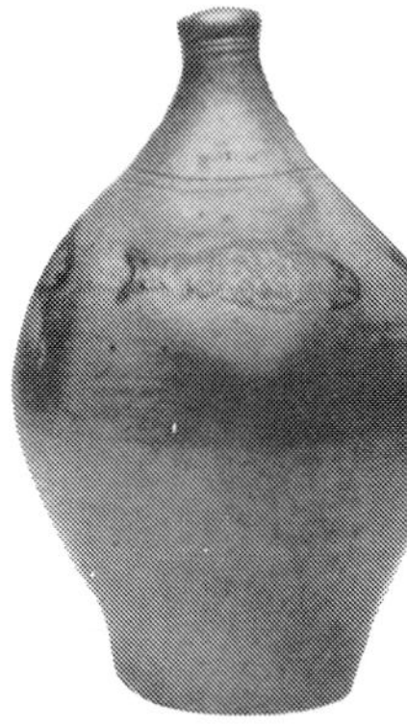

Cobalt decorated stoneware jug, Boston, early 19th century, cobalt decorated at shoulder with three fish, 14½in. high. (Skinner Inc.) £1,779

A stoneware footed vase, by Ewen Henderson, circa 1972, 27cm. high. £495

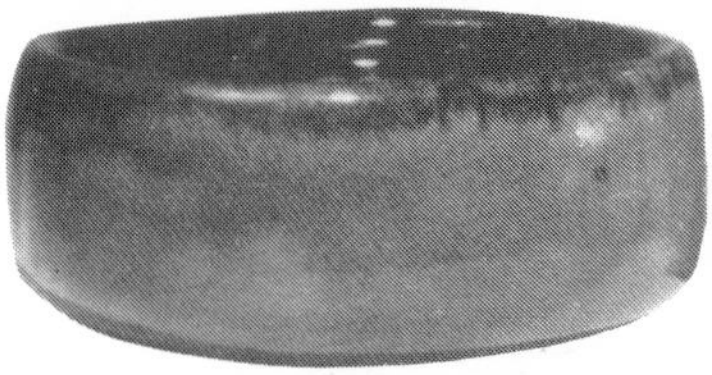

A stoneware rounded rectangular bowl, by Karl Scheid, dated 67, 19.5cm. wide. £325

A spherical stoneware bowl, by Val Barry, covered in a greenish-grey matt glaze, with brown speckling, 18.7cm. high. £150

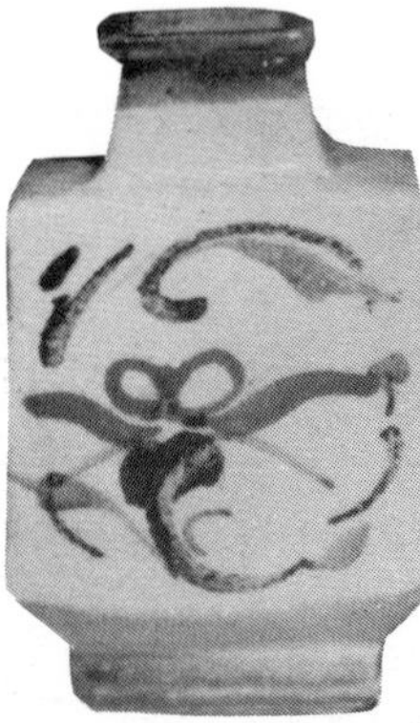

A stoneware press moulded rectangular bottle, by Kanjiro Kawai, covered in greyish-white glaze with khaki rims, circa 1952, 21.9cm. high. £755

A stoneware bowl, by Eric James Mellon, dated 1982, 33.2cm. diam. (Christie's) £286

A stoneware large grain jar and cover with two crescent shaped handles, by Audu Mugu Sokoto, circa 1960, 60.3cm. high. £280

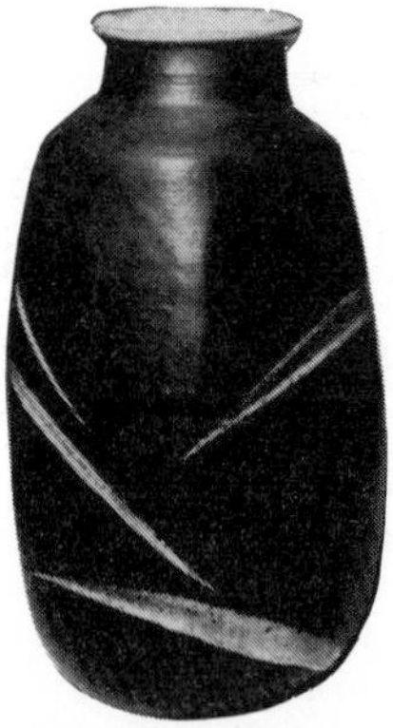

A black stoneware vase by Janet Leach, 1984, 27.3cm. high. £195

A massive stoneware asymmetrical vase, by Ewen Henderson, with everted rim, 56cm. high. £1,025

An English brown glazed stoneware wall mask, modelled as Comedy, 24in. high. £120

A stoneware plate, by Henry Hammond, covered in a grey pitted and fleck glaze with iron-brown brushwork, circa 1958, 26cm. diam. £140

A stoneware group of two nude dancers by E. J. Bachelet. £700

A stoneware globular vase by Ruth Duckworth, 30.5cm. high. £352

A Henri van de Velde stoneware amphora vase, covered in a sang-de-boeuf translucent glaze separating in parts to reveal beige-coloured body, 23.5cm. high. £6,050

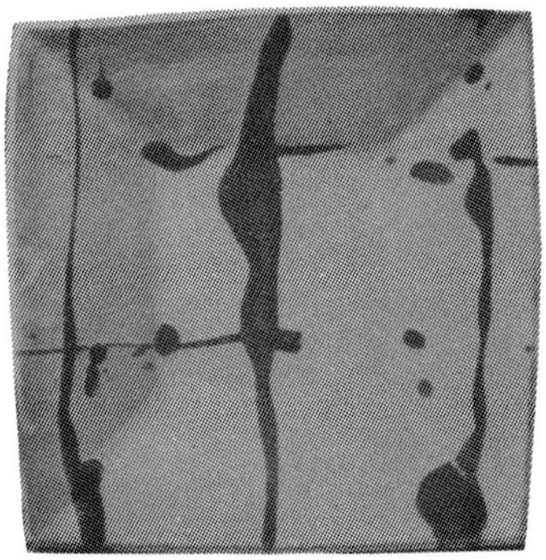

A stoneware press moulded rectangular dish by Wm. Marshall, impressed and incised WM, incised date 83, 31cm. wide. £50

An early handbuilt vase by Elizabeth Fritsch, circa 1970, 12.6cm. high. £1,295

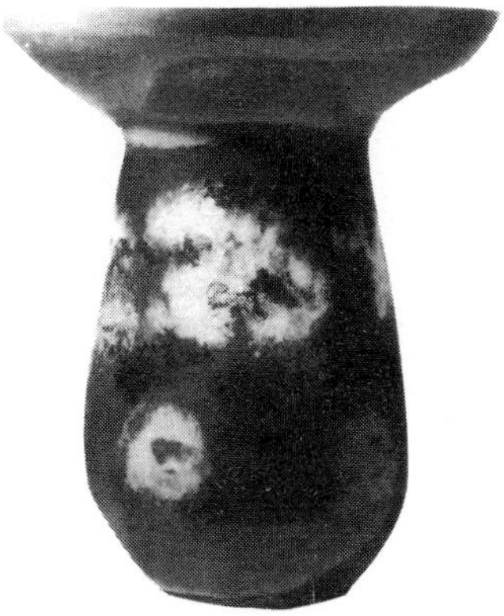

'Dark Sky with Clouds', a stoneware vase form, by Ivo Mosley, 40.4cm. high. £310

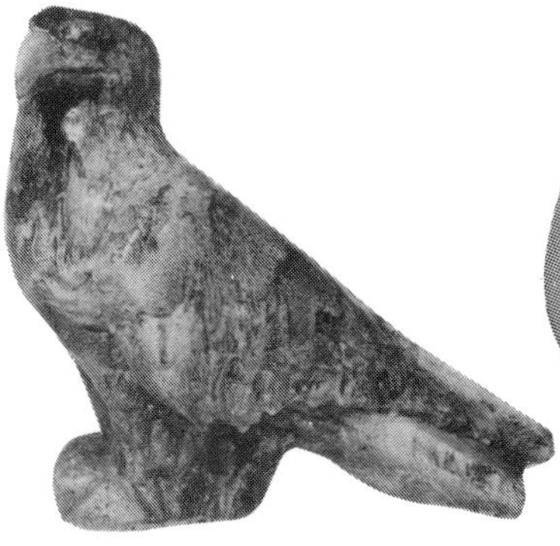

A stoneware figure of an eagle, inscribed M. Schilkin, Arabia, 44.2cm. high. £90

A porcelain flask form vase by Wm. Marshall, circa 1983, 26.2cm. high. £280

STONEWARE

ABUJA

It was Michael Cardew (q.v.) who established a training centre for potters at Abuja, northern Nigeria, in 1951, whilst working as Pottery Officer for the Nigerian government.

The forms follow traditional African designs, as does the decoration, which often takes the form of stylised animals, birds and fish. Ladi Kwali is one of the foremost potters working at Abuja today. Marks include the Abuja seal and often the potter's initials.

PLEYDELL BOUVERIE

Katherine Pleydell Bouverie (1895-1985) studied at the Central School of Arts & Crafts in London in the early 20s and then joined Bernard Leach at St Ives in 1924. Technically, her work was also much influenced by Matsubarjashi, the Japanese kiln expert.

In 1925 she set up her own kiln at Coleshill, Staffs. where she experimented with glazes obtained from wood and plant ashes. The results were high quality matt, in white or light grey, greens browns and blue. She also produced unglazed pots and bowls in grey-white or pink stoneware.

In 1946 she set up an oil fired kiln at Kilmington Manor near Warminster.

A stoneware water pot by Ladi Kwali, made at Abuja, circa 1960, 29cm. high. £200

A fine Abuja stoneware dish by Michael Cardew, with river pattern, the flared rim with vertical banding, glazed shiny olive and sage green, impressed twice with MC and Abuja seals, $15^{1}/_{4}$in. diameter. (Bonhams) £380

A stoneware bowl with rounded sides, by Katharine Pleydell-Bouverie, circa 1930, 18.5cm. diam. £700

A stoneware oviform vase, by Katharine Pleydell-Bouverie, covered in lavender blue glaze, with olive green glaze at the rim and shoulder, impressed *KPB* seal, 22.1cm. high. (Christie's London) £990

A stoneware 'Coleshill' bottle vase, by Katherine Pleydell Bouverie, covered in a rich streaked blue and green glaze, 17.1cm. high. (Phillips) £230

A stoneware mug, by Katharine Pleydell-Bouverie, impressed Cole, circa 1930, 11.5cm. high. £110

STONEWARE

WILLIAM STAITE MURRAY

William Staite Murray (1881–1962) trained originally as an engineer but began experimenting with pottery around 1912 in London, where he made earthenware with brushed decoration. After the Great War, he began making stoneware in Rotherhithe, producing vases and jars, mostly with an undecorated white body, though sometimes they were streaked or splashed. He moved to Brockley, Kent, where he patented a new high temperature oil-fired kiln. At this time too he came under the influence of the work of Hamada and began making yellow or red fired stoneware, often only part glazed, with brushed or scratched decoration.

Later works, dating from the 30s, show the influence of English earthenware, and his later work is also characterised by conspicuously modelled feet. In 1940 he emigrated to Rhodesia.

His marks usually consist of a *M* in a pentagon.

A William Staite Murray stoneware vase, 1930's, 43.5cm. high. £500

A William Staite Murray stoneware vase, 1930's, 31.5cm. high. £550

A stoneware pot by William Staite-Murray, incised with grey-blue floral designs, glazed grey with traces of pale yellow and brown areas, impressed M seal, 10in. high. (Bonhams) £600

A fine stoneware tall necked vase by William Staite-Murray, the body with incised bird and foliate decoration, covered with a crazed celadon glaze, impressed M seal, 12¾in. high. (Bonhams) £900

JAMES TOWER

James Tower was born in 1919 and began potting in 1947. He held his first exhibition in 1951 at Gimpel Fils, and exhibited regularly throughout the 50s and 60s, before becoming Head of Fine Arts at Brighton College of Arts.

His pieces were designed to express a sense of serenity and wonder at the beauty of the world, and he envisaged pottery as being of equal standing with painting.

In 1978 he exhibited again at Gimpel Fils and continued to do so until his death in 1988.

A large moulded stoneware vase of swelling rectangular section, incised James Tower 84, 54.3cm. high. £500

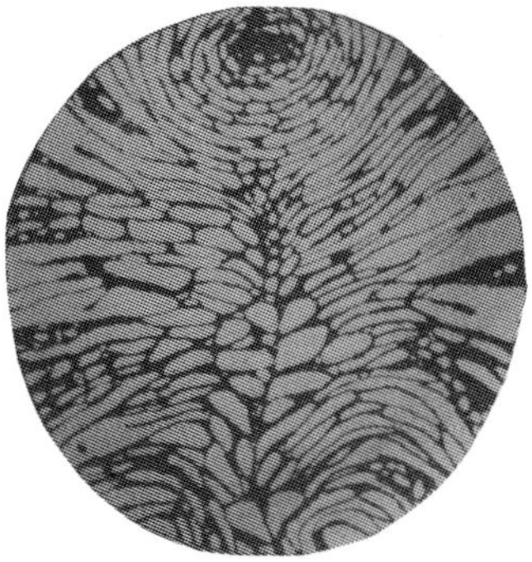

A large stoneware footed circular dish, incised James Tower 84 and with paper label inscribed James Tower No. 167 Reflections, 54.4cm. diam. £400

STRASBOURG

The Rococo style is seen at its best in the faience of Strasbourg, which was intended mostly for the German market.

The factory there was established in 1721 by Charles-François Hannong and its wares initially followed the Rouen style. In 1739 however Paul-Antoine Hannong became artistic director and he started making full use of the 'grand feu' colours, as well as gilding.

The arrival of several leading German painters in Strasbourg enabled Hannong by 1750 to become the first faience producer to decorate his wares in the full palette of enamel colours as used on porcelain. Perhaps the most striking of these was a rich crimson.

The monogram initials of Paul Hannong *(PH)* and Joseph Hannong *(JH)* are frequently seen on 19th century reproductions.

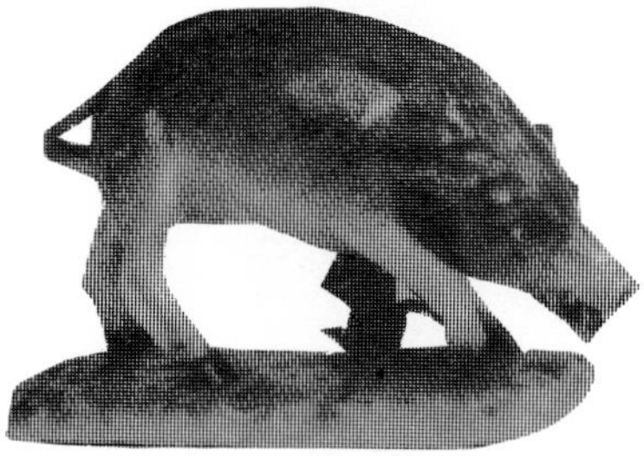

Mid 18th century Strasbourg figure of a wild boar. £7,000

A Strasbourg oval dish with pierced border, blue H/860 mark, circa 1770, 30cm. wide. (Christie's) £216

A large Strasbourg surtout-de-table, circa 1750, 52cm. high, the plateau 64cm. wide. £4,320

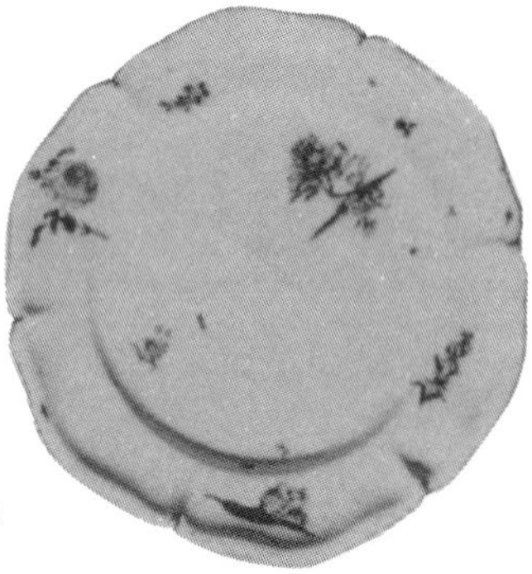

Strasbourg shaped circular dish painted with flowers, circa 1750, 47cm. diameter. £1,500

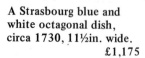

A Strasbourg blue and white octagonal dish, circa 1730, 11½in. wide. £1,175

Mid 18th century Strasbourg figure of a dog. £5,000

One of a pair of mid 18th century Strasbourg hexafoil plates, 24cm. diam. (Christie's) £495

SUNDERLAND

In the 19th century Sunderland became a popular pottery centre, where many factories specialised in producing commemorative wares and gifts for sailors. These consisted mainly of jugs, wall plaques and mugs, bearing some painted scene, a motto or doggerel, usually in a pink lustre frame, which was 'splashed' to give a blotched appearance.

The pictures which appeared on these are fairly limited in range, common themes being the Wearmouth Bridge, a balloon ascent and the 'Sailor's Return' or 'The Sailor's Farewell', or simply sailing ships.

Many other factories, from nearby Newcastle to far away Swansea, copied Sunderland lustre ware, and as most pieces are unmarked, it is often difficult to make a confident attribution, though many genuine Sunderland wares were made as presentation pieces, and the name and date on these can be very useful.

Genuine Sunderland commands a premium among lustre wares, and another criterion is the rarity of the scene or verse which appears on a piece. Some were used again and again, while others have survived on only a few pieces.

A rare Sunderland Reform mug, printed in black with green and pink lustre washes, with half length portrait of 'William the IV', 12cm. (Phillips) £380

Sunderland lustre pottery chamber pot with an applied frog and cartoon face in the interior. £320

Sunderland lustre jug, inscribed 'Francis & Betsy Taylor', circa 1845, 9¼in. high. £400

Early 19th century Sunderland lustre pottery jug, 4¾in. high. £175

A Sunderland lustre oviform jug, 9½in. high, circa 1830. (Christie's) £320

A Sunderland lustre jug decorated in colours with scenes and insignia relating to the Alliance of England and France, 17cm. (Phillips) £360

A Sunderland pink lustre jug printed in black with a portrait bust of Earl Grey and inscribed *'The Choice of the People and England's Glory'*, 19cm. (Phillips) £550

SWANSEA

The history of the Swansea pottery is closely bound up with that of Nantgarw, after the proprietor of the Cambrian pottery in Swansea, L W Dillwyn, brought William Billingsley and Samuel Walker from there in 1814.

Dillwyn, however, wanted a more reliable porcelain body than had been made at Nantgarw, and in response Walker was to produce three bodies for him. The first was a fine and light porcelain using bone ash, which had a duck-egg blue translucence. Whilst expensive to make, it found great favour in London. The second was a glassy looking porcelain using soaprock, and the third a lightly pitted glaze with a brown translucence. This was marked with a trident and is now known by that name, but it was not popular.

Like Nantgarw, Swansea styles show a strong French influence, but it is that of the Empire rather than Sèvres. There is less scroll and ribbon moulding and painting is often sparing, with plates often quite plain in shape.

The Swansea body was much stronger than that of Nantgarw, and thus many more upright shapes were produced. Swansea is in fact notable for its wide range of shapes. A few biscuit figures of sheep were even produced in 1817, together with biscuit plaques with applied flowers.

Like Nantgarw, distribution in 1816–7 was mainly through Mortlock in London, but a smaller proportion of pieces was put out for decoration. It was Billingsley who supervised in-house painting at Swansea, with a predilection for flowers and landscapes in very delicate colours. Other flower painters who worked with him there were David Evans, William Pollard and Henry Morris. Outside

A Swansea London-decorated flared cylindrical cabinet cup, painted with a continuous band of garden flowers, circa 1815, 9cm. high. (Christie's) £495

A Swansea oviform vase, painted with a wooded landscape vignette and a lakeland scene, circa 1815, 26cm. high. (Christie's) £3,960

A Swansea pot-pourri vase and pierced cover of campana shape, painted by David Evans, with a frieze of garden flowers, circa 1820, 13.5cm. high. (Christie's) £2,090

A Swansea porcelain plate from the Lysaght service, painted by Henry Morris, 24.3cm., early 19th century. (Bearne's) £400

A Swansea miniature cabinet cup and saucer painted by William Pollard with bands of wild flowers, circa 1815. (Christie's) £660

A Swansea oviform vase with flared neck and gilt eagle handles, painted by David Evans, red stencil mark, circa 1815, 15cm. high. (Christie's) £1,760

SWANSEA

decoration was also done in Swansea by Thomas Baxter, who was noted for his sentimental figure scenes and single birds in landscapes.

Swansea made wide use of formal patterns and transfer printing before 1817, but these are not found on the later Trident porcelain. Much decoration was carried out at Swansea between the end of production in 1816/7, when the factory was taken over by the Bevingtons, and the final dispersal sale in 1826, for although Billingsley had departed, Evans, Pollard and Morris were still there.

Swansea marks include *Swansea and Dillwyn & Co* on the duck egg china, or painted in cursive handwriting on the first two bodies. The third however has one or two tridents impressed, and *Swansea* also impressed.

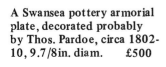

A Swansea cup and saucer painted with full-blown pink roses and green leaves, circa 1820. £275

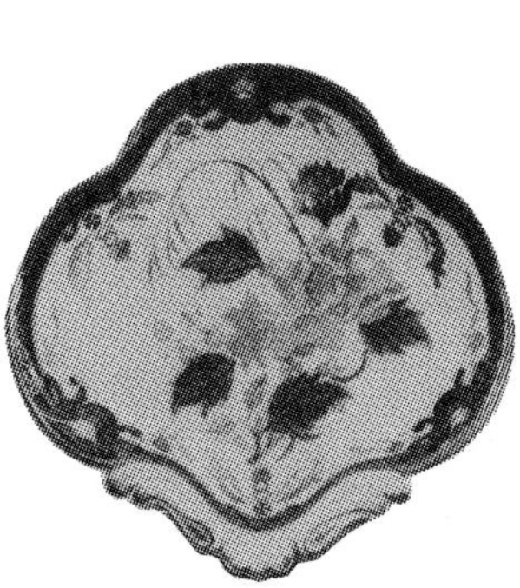

A Swansea pottery shell-shaped dish painted by Thos. Pardoe in an 'Imari' palette, circa 1800, 8¼in. £240

Part of a Swansea tea and coffee service of twenty-seven-pieces, circa 1814-22. £1,100

A documentary Swansea pottery jug with ovoid body, 5¼in., 1802. £600

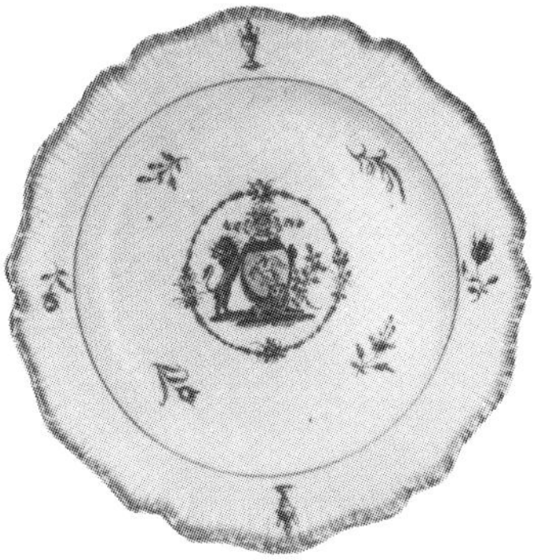

A Swansea pottery armorial plate, decorated probably by Thos. Pardoe, circa 1802-10, 9.7/8in. diam. £500

Pair of Swansea vases, each of elongated campana form, circa 1815, 10in. high. £2,500

A Swansea armorial plate, circa 1815-20, painted by Henry Morris, 8½in. diam. £1,100

TANG

The ancient custom of burying the dead alongside many of the items which surrounded them in life has contributed greatly to our understanding of earlier times, and most of the pottery which survives from the Tang period (618–906 AD) does in fact come from such burial sites.

These show that Tang potters were able to carve figures with skill and refinement from bodies ranging from soft earthenware to a hard porcelain-like stoneware, which varies in colour from light grey and rosy buff to white.

They are usually covered with a thin, finely crackled glaze, either pale yellow or green in colour, though some are more richly coated with amber brown or leaf green glazes. Splashing, streaking and mottling are all characteristics of Tang pieces, which presage the Staffordshire Whieldon and agate ware of 1000 years later. Marbling of the ware by blending light and dark clays in the body was also achieved, and again this was to be reproduced much later in the 'solid agate' ware of Staffordshire.

Of all the figures found in Tang pottery, the horse is conspicuous both for its frequency and for the spirit and character with which it is portrayed.

Some Western influences can be seen in Tang pottery, and certainly there were many contacts with the near East at the time. Typical examples are the egg-and-tongue and honeysuckle patterns to be found in border designs, which show clear Graeco-Roman influence.

唐

A fine blue glazed footed bowl, with thinly potted rounded sides, Tang Dynasty, 11cm. diam. (Christie's) £2,640

A red pottery figure of a mounted attendant, Tang Dynasty, 31.5cm. high. £1,190

A Sancai pottery figure of a horse, standing foresquare on a rectangular base, well modelled with strongly contoured flanks and facial features, Tang Dynasty, 50.5cm. high. (Christie's) £11,000

A Sancai buff pottery globular jar, Tang Dynasty, 16.8cm. high. £3,025

A rare blue-splashed Sancai tripod censer, Tang Dynasty, the body covered with blue, green, orchid and white splashes streaking toward the base, $7^{1}/_{2}$in. diameter. (Christie's) £7,878

An unglazed buff pottery figure of a seated lady musician, Tang Dynasty, 19.5cm. high. £1,295

A Sancai glazed buff pottery model of a boar standing four-square on a pierced rectangular base, Tang Dynasty, 20cm. long. (Christie's) £2,750

A fine Sancai glazed buff pottery shallow bowl, the exterior applied with quatrefoil florettes on a ground of slip-trailed diagonals, Tang Dynasty, 9.8cm. diam. (Christie's) £6,050

An ochre glazed buff pottery model of a ram standing four-square on a pierced rectangular base, (legs restored) Tang Dynasty, 20cm. long. (Christie's) £1,540

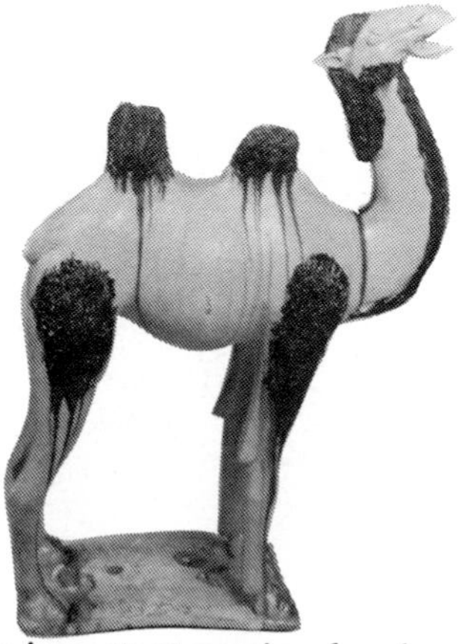

An important massive glazed buff pottery figure of a Bactrian camel, extremely well modelled standing four-square on a rectangular plinth, (restored, primarily to the legs) Tang Dynasty, 82cm. high. (Christie's) £154,000

Two painted red pottery figures of standing matrons, both with hands held before their chests, Tang Dynasty, both about 37cm. high. (Christie's) £13,200

A fine Sancai glazed buff pottery figure of a hound, standing four-square on an oval pedestal, Tang Dynasty, 17.2cm. high. (Christie's) £12,100

A massive Sancai glazed buff pottery figure of a caparisoned horse standing almost four-square on a trapezoidal base, Tang Dynasty, 76cm. high. (Christie's) £99,000

An amber-glazed shallow bowl, Tang Dynasty, the medallion on the underside with a large flower-head, 3⁷⁄₈in. diameter. (Christie's) £1,862

A Sancai glazed buff pottery figure of a camel standing four-square on a rectangular base, Tang Dynasty, 57.1cm. high. (Christie's) £9,900

TECO

The Teco pottery operated out of Terra Cotta Illinois in the early years of this century. Its output is characterised by matt green glazes which are frequently used on shapes based on natural forms.

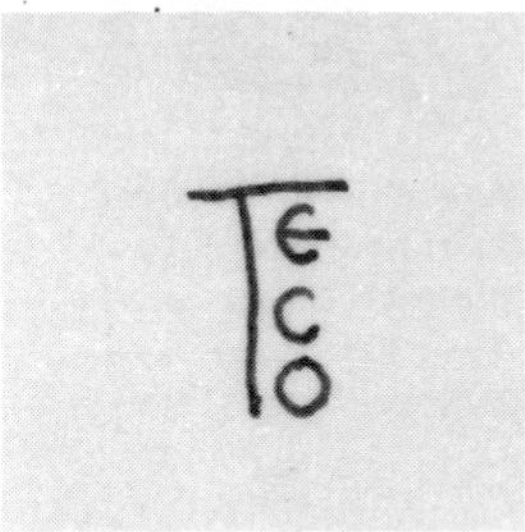

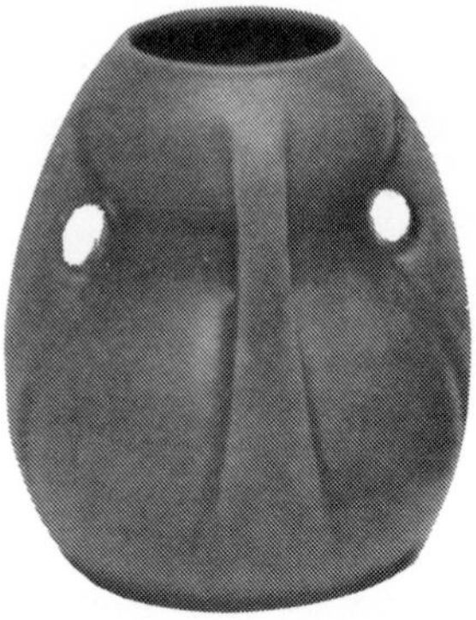

Teco pottery vase with four handles, Terra Cotta, Illinois, circa 1910, squat, impressed twice, 6½in. high. (Skinner Inc.) £802

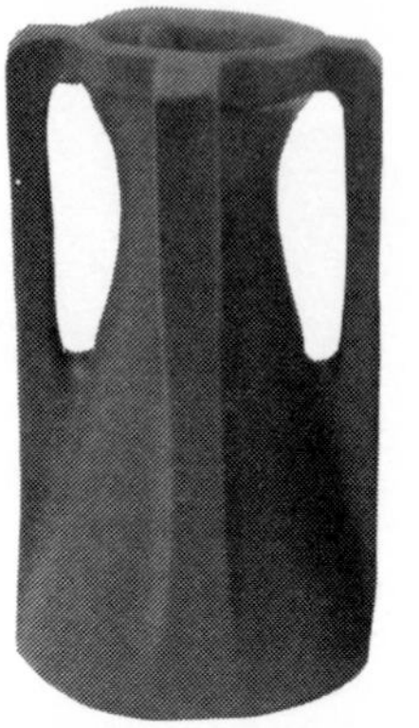

A Teco pottery four-handled vase, circa 1910, 7¼in. high. (Robt. W. Skinner Inc.) £386

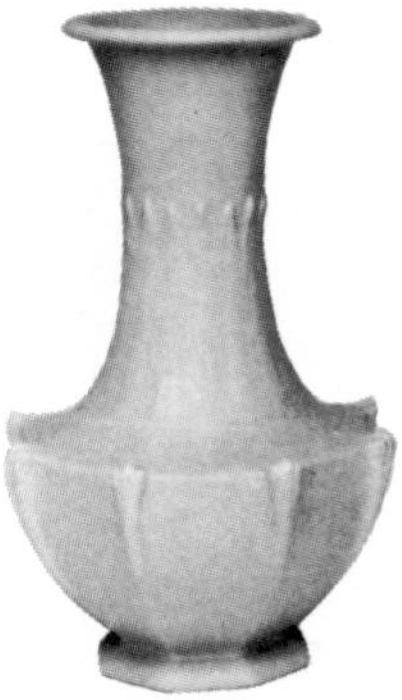

Teco pottery vase, Illinois, early 20th century, flared rim, in matte buff colour glaze, impressed Teco mark, 12¼in. high. (Skinner Inc.) £511

Early 20th century Teco pottery yellow bud vase, Illinois, 4½in. high. £234

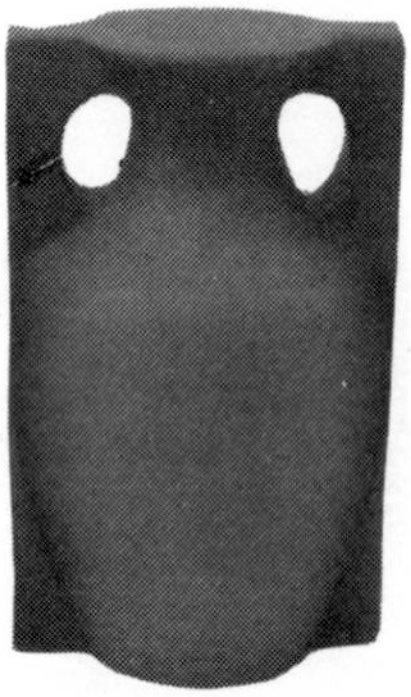

A Teco pottery double-handled vase, Illinois, circa 1910, 7in. high. (Robt. W. Skinner Inc.) £208

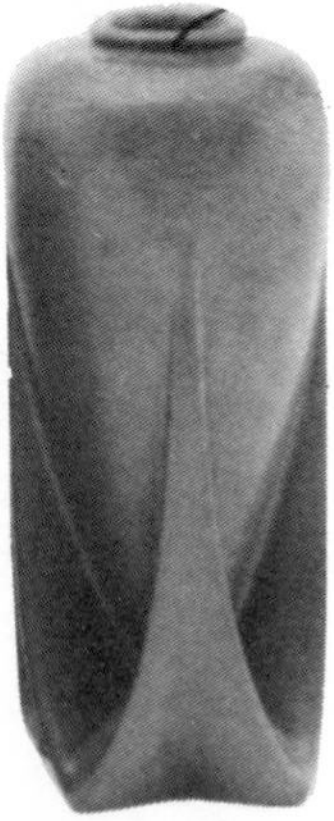

Teco pottery brown moulded vase, bullet shape on four elongated V feet, Illinois, 1909, 8½in. high. £1,260

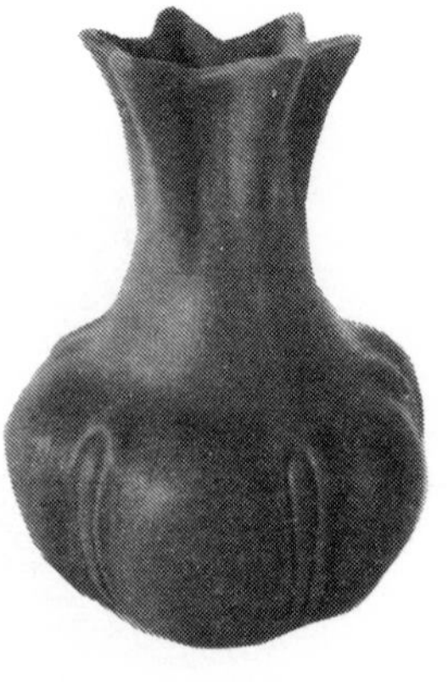

A Teco Art pottery fluted vase, Illinois, circa 1905, 10½in. high. (Robt. W. Skinner Inc.) £750

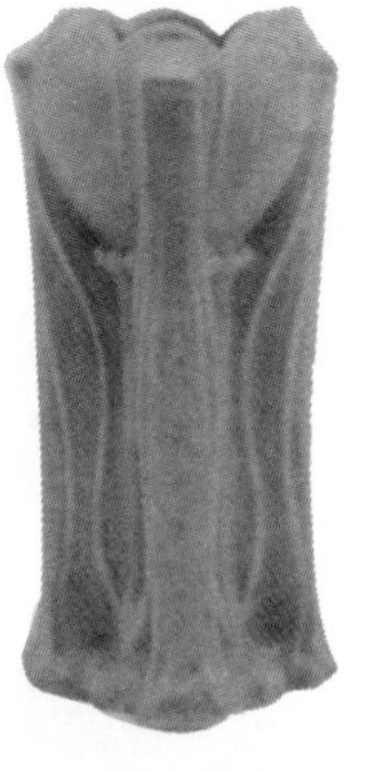

A Teco pottery moulded lotus flower vase, Chicago, circa 1905, designed by F. Moreau, 11½in. high. (Robt. W. Skinner Inc.) £1,621

TERRACOTTA

Terracotta is a red earthenware which has been used in many ages and civilisations for a wide variety of purposes. It is normally unglazed, though for domestic use a thin glaze has to be applied to inside surfaces, since it is slightly porous. Terracotta was very popular in the mid-late 19th century for garden ornaments, vases etc. as well as figures and tableware. English companies which included it in their range were the Minton factory, F & R Pratt, and Doulton, and notable examples of terracotta ware were designed by George Tinworth (Doulton) and Thomas Battam (Copeland).

A terracotta figure of Eros, 4th-3rd century B.C., Boetia, 7.5cm. high. (Phillips) £260

A terracotta figure of Eros, naked except for a drape across the shoulders, Boetia, 4th-3rd century B.C., 7cm. high. (Phillips) £200

A Cypro-geometric bowl raised on three looped supports, circa 1700 B.C., 15cm. high. (Phillips) £750

A late 19th century French terracotta statuette of the Art of Painting, by Alfred Drury, 39.5cm. high. (Christie's) £495

A Cypriot terracotta chariot drawn by two horses, 7th-6th century B.C., 13cm. long. (Phillips) £400

A Belgium terracotta face mask by L. Nosbusch modelled as Rudolf Valentino, 14in. high. (Christie's) £200

A late 19th century French terracotta group of two allegorical putti, by Albert Ernest Carrier-Belleuse, possibly representing Earth and Water, 36 x 65cm. (Christie's) £1,760

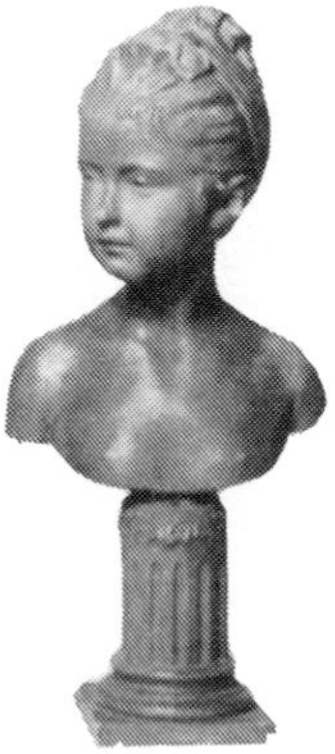

A 19th century French terracotta bust of Louise Brogniart, after Houdon, 50cm. high. (Christie's) £550

'Jean Cocteau', a terracotta bust by Arno Breker, signed, numbered 5/50, on a rectangular dark grey stone base, 35cm. high.
(Christie's) £1,980

A French terracotta relief of a leopard attacking an antelope, by Christopher Fratin, mid 19th century, $16^{3}/_{8}$ x 9in. without frame.
(Christie's) £990

An English terracotta model of a Hindu girl, by Joseph Gott, the maiden kneeling on the edge of a river, holding a tray with an oil lamp, first half 19th century, $13^{1}/_{2}$in. high.
(Christie's) £1,100

A terracotta plinth, the square top formed as a capital with acanthus leaf scrolls, the circular knopped shaft applied with trailing grapevine, 41in. high.
(Christie's) £990

A pair of terracotta garden ornaments in the form of seated greyhounds, each wearing a studded collar, 33in. high, 19th century.
(Bearne's) £3,800

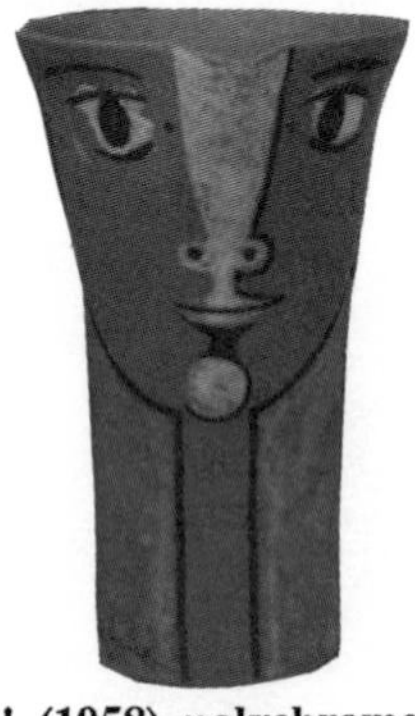

'Visage', (1958), polychrome enamelled terracotta jug, signed, inscribed on the base, *Edition Originale de Jean Cocteau Atelier Madeline-Jolly 30/30*, 26.5cm.
(Christie's) £2,750

A terracotta urn, decorated with acanthus, the fluted tapering with acanthus leaves to the lower part and circular spreading socle, 38in. high.
(Christie's) £605

An English terracotta group of a greyhound bitch with three puppies, by Joseph Gott, on black marble circular socle, first half 19th century, $5^{3}/_{8}$in. high.
(Christie's) £418

Continental terracotta figural fountain, late 19th century, the standard modelled as a naked winged mermaid figure with bifurcated tail, 4ft. 6in. high.
(Butterfield & Butterfield) £2,344

A late 19th century French terracotta bust of 'L'Esperance', signed J. B. Carpeaux 1874, 54cm. high. £990

Late 18th century Italian terracotta relief of Endymion, 15¼in. £1,430

A late 18th century French terracotta bust of a man wearing The Order of St. Esprit, in the style of Pajou, 20in. high. £1,980

A French terracotta bust of an 18th century lady with dressed hair, 16in. high. £1,730

A set of three black glazed terracotta jugs of graduated size, printed in yellow with portraits and vases of enamelled flowers. **£180**

A French terracotta bust of an 18th century boy, 18in. high. £2,270

A 19th century terracotta garden ornament, probably France, 25½in. diam., 25½in. high. £520

A pair of 19th century Continental terracotta figures of a peasant girl and a boy, 90cm. and 91cm. high. £1,800

A black glazed terracotta teapot and cover, printed in yellow and decorated in enamels and gilt, 16cm. high. £50

TOURNAI

The Tournai porcelain factory opened in 1751 when Joseph Peterinck was granted a patent by the Empress Maria Theresa. A soft paste porcelain was manufactured, at first with a slightly greyish hue, but after 1765 it became much creamier.

The decoration owed much to Meissen styles, and commonly depicted flowers, landscapes, castle scenes etc. Much of the finest bird and flower painting is attributed to Henri-Joseph Duvivier, who was chief painter at Tournai between 1763–71.

A blue enamel ground is common on Tournai pieces and later bird painting from Buffon's *Histoire Naturelle des Oiseaux* was done by Jean-Ghislain-Joseph Mayer, who became head painter in 1774.

Many English potters and painters were employed at Tournai during the early period and much of their output bears a strong resemblance to Derby, Worcester and Chelsea pieces of the period. Groups and figures were produced by Nicholas-Joseph Gavron and by Joseph Willems, a sculptor from the Chelsea factory, and, after his death in 1766, by Antoine Gillis and Nicholas Lecreux. Groups were often left white, but sometimes painted in strong enamels.

When Peterinck died his son took over for a short time, before leaving to establish his own factory in the town in 1800. The original factory was bought by the de Bettignies family who kept it until it was taken over by the Boch brothers in 1850. It was during the de Bettignies period that many flagrant forgeries of Sèvres, Chelsea and Worcester pieces were produced.

Early marks include a tower either in enamels or gold.

A porcelain snuff box mounted in England en cage in gold, possibly Tournai, circa 1765, 7.5cm. wide. £5,940

One of a pair of mid 18th century Tournai faience pug dogs, after the original Meissen models by J. J. Kaendler, 15.5cm. high. £7,560

A Tournai ornithological oviform jar and cover from the Duc d'Orleans service, circa 1787, 18.5cm. high. £1,025

A Tournai spirally-moulded plate painted by Henri Joseph Duvivier in puce camaieu with a coastal scene, a man on horseback urging his cattle towards a boat, circa 1765, 23cm. diameter. (Christie's) £1,650

A Tournai fable teacup and saucer painted in the manner of Duvivier with 'The Fox and The Crane', gilt castle marks, circa 1765. (Christie's) £1,100

One of a pair of Tournai two-handled seaux a glace covers and liners with moulded Ozier borders, circa 1770, 25cm. wide. £235

URBINO

Urbino, the capital of the Duchy of the same name, became a maiolica centre only in 1520, when "Guido da Castello Durante" established a workshop there. Guido was the son of Nicola Pellipario, who had worked at Castel Durante, and his father joined him at Urbino in 1527. It was Nicola Pellipario who popularised the istoriato style, with which Urbino came to be especially associated.

Their Fontana workshop produced many pieces, including large wine coolers, salvers, pilgrim bottles and stands, with a characteristic decoration of arabesques and grotesques painted in colour on a white ground edged in yellow and picked out in orange. Guido's son Orazio Fontana, started up his own workshop next door in 1565, and where pieces are unsigned, it is difficult to tell whose workmanship they are.

The work of the painter Francesco Xanto Avelli is fairly easy to distinguish, however, for he specialised in crowded scenes, almost like stage settings, featuring characters with very rounded limbs and his favourite tones were bright yellows and orange.

There are many recent imitations of the Urbino grotesque-arabesque style, but these can usually be distinguished by the pen-like draughtsmanship of the painting, which indicates that the white tin-glaze ground had been fired first to make painting easier. Beware too a pinkish purple tone which the 16th century artist did not possess.

An Urbino Istoriato dish painted in the Fontana workshop with Proserpine and her companions, circa 1570, 27.5cm. diam. (Christie's) £16,500

An Urbino istoriato plate painted with the Temptation of Adam, circa 1560, 23cm. diam. (Christie's) £3,520

An Urbino istoriato tazza painted with Marcus Curtius leaping into the abyss on a white stallion surrounded by soldiers before a tree, circa 1545, 25.5cm. diameter. (Christie's) £7,150

An Urbino maiolica accouchement bowl painted inside the deep bowl with an expectant mother and child, 15.5cm. diameter, Patanazzi workshop, last quarter 16th century. (Phillips) £1,500

An Urbino Istoriato dish painted with a figure of a bearded man, possibly intended for Hercules, 26cm. (Phillips) £1,700

A very spirited Urbino Istoriato plate painted by Francesco Durantino, showing the victorious Scipio, 29cm. (Phillips) £12,500

An Urbino dish painted in the Patanazzi workshop with Abraham sacrificing Isaac, circa 1580, 35cm. diam. (Christie's) £5,500

An Urbino Istoriato saucer dish painted in the Patanazzi workshop with the Menapians surrendering to Caesar, circa 1580, 27cm. diam. (Christie's) £19,800

An Urbino istoriato dish painted with the Death of Achilles, by Nicola Pellipario, circa 1535, 25.5cm. diam. (Christie's) £8,800

An Urbino istoriato dish painted with Galatea being borne across the waves riding on the back of a scaly dolphin accompanied by putti and Cupid holding his bow, circa 1560, 32cm. diam. (Christie's London) £55,000

An Urbino pilgrim flask painted in the Patanazzi workshop, in colours with Actaeon surprising Diana at her bath and with Paris judging the goddesses Juno, Minerva and Venus being restrained by Cupid, circa 1580, 38cm. high. (Christie's London) £6,050

An Urbino Istoriato charger painted in the Fontana workshop with the legend of Deucalion and Pyrrha, circa 1560, 40.5cm. diam. (Christie's) £18,700

An Urbino istoriato tazza painted in colours in the style of Francesco Xanto Avelli with Marcus Curtius on horseback, circa 1545, 26.5cm. diam. (Christie's) £9,900

An Urbino small albarello, workshop of Orazio Fontana, circa 1665-70, 15cm. high. (Phillips) £2,600

A fine Urbino istoriato shallow tazza, painted with Aeneas setting off in a ship in his search for Italy, 26cm., mid-16th century. (Phillips London) £29,000

VAN BRIGGLE

Artus van Briggle was born in Felicity, Ohio in 1869. He studied painting in Cincinnati, where he also worked as a decorator of dolls' heads and vases. Around 1887 he became Director of the Rookwood Pottery, where he decorated vases with flowers in underglaze colours. It was part of Rookwood's enlightened philosophy to send talented decorators on scholarships abroad, and van Briggle benefited under this scheme with a period at the Académie Julien in Paris in 1893. On his return to Cincinnati he continued at Rookwood, while experimenting at home with the production of Chinese matt glazes.

He fell ill with tuberculosis and moved to Colorado in 1895, where he established the van Briggle Pottery Co in 1902. There he produced vases and plates decorated with stylized animal and flower forms in the Art Nouveau style. These were often relief decorated and covered in soft-coloured glazes. Until his death in 1904, the pieces were entirely glazed, but later only partial glazing was introduced.

VENICE: VEZZI

The first hard-paste porcelain factory was established in Venice in 1720 by Francesco Vezzi (1651–1740), a wealthy goldsmith. In this he enlisted the assistance of the dubious Christoph Konrad Hunger, who had already deserted Meissen in 1717, claiming to be able to help duPaquier in Vienna. He had at least learned enough there to enable him to help Vezzi produce true porcelain, but he then reverted to type and quit Venice for Meissen again in 1727. He promptly disclosed that Vezzi was reliant on Saxon clays, whereupon their export was promptly banned, forcing the factory to close.

A Rookwood pottery basket, by artist Artus Van Briggle, decorated in slip underglaze with blossoms, berries and leaves, 6½in. high. (Robt. W. Skinner Inc.) £414

One of two 20th century Van Briggle pottery vases, Colorado, one 2¾in. high, the other 5½in. high. (Robt. W. Skinner Inc.) £225

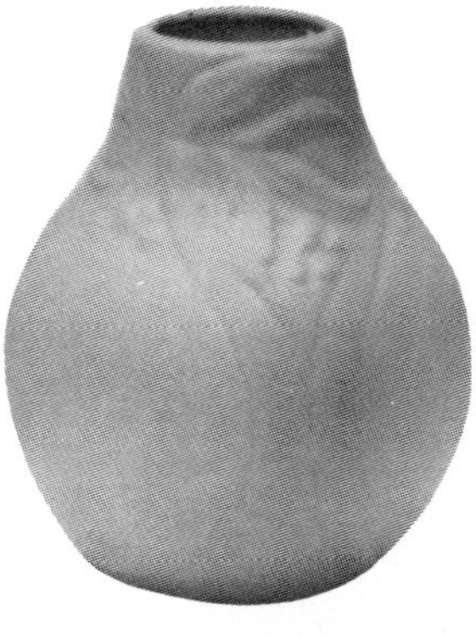

Van Briggle Pottery vase, Colorado Springs, circa 1904, with moulded floral design, yellow and ochre semi-matte glaze, 8½in. high. (Skinner Inc.) £442

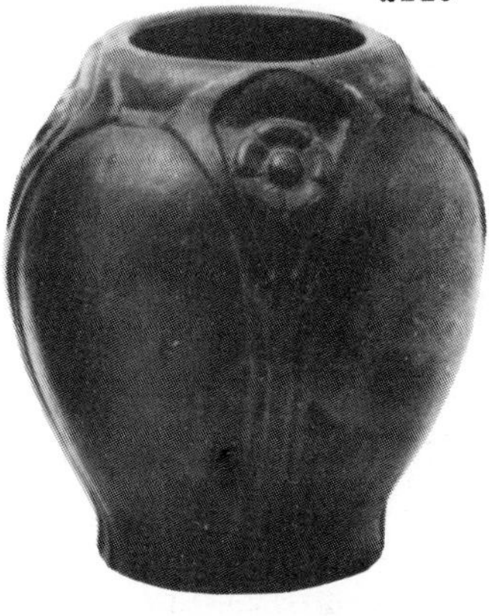

Van Briggle pottery copper clad vase, Colorado, 5½in. high. £840

A Venice (Vezzi) blue and white teabowl painted in a grey-blue with two birds in flight among plants and flowering shrubs flanked by buildings between blue line rims, circa 1725, 7.3cm. diameter. (Christie's) £6,050

A Venice (Vezzi) teapot and a cover with coloured chinoiserie figures in panels at various pursuits including swinging on a rope, playing a horn and carrying a snail, incised Z mark circa 1725, 16.5cm. wide. (Christie's) £11,550

VENICE

Though some pieces of Venetian faience can be dated back to 1520, production did not begin in any quantity until the middle of the century. As a major trading port, Venice was obviously open to Middle and Far Eastern influences and this is reflected in the pottery which was produced there.

Ground colours are often stained to a lavender blue, with the decoration painted in strong cobalt, relieved only occasionally with a little opaque white or yellow.

A Venice plate painted in colours with the Children of Venus, 23.5cm. diam. (Christie's) £1,650

One of a pair of mid 16th century Venetian vasi a palli, 33cm. high. (Christie's) £13,200

A Venice istoriato dish of shallow cardinal's hat form, painted with the story of Jacob and the Angel, workshop of Domenico da Venezia, circa 1560, 30cm. diameter. (Christie's) £5,500

A large Venetian Berretino albarello, painted with an elaborate scroll inscribed with the name of the contents *Mo Franda F,* 17th century, 34cm. high. (Christie's London) £2,860

A Venice vaso a palla with the portrait heads of two saints in cartouches, circa 1550, 28cm. high. (Christie's) £5,500

A Venetian drug bottle painted with portraits of a Turk and a soldier, second half of 16th century, 23cm. high. (Christie's) £2,640

A Venice Istoriato saucer dish painted with Apollo slaying the children of Niobe, circa 1560, 29.5cm. diam. (Christie's) £17,600

An attractive Venice albarello of cylindrical form, painted in colours with bands of convolvulus on a scrolling blue ground, 14.5cm. (Phillips) £1,100

VIENNA

The porcelain factory of Claude Innocent Du Paquier was established in Vienna during the early years of the 18th century. Though it received no state patronage, the Emperor granted it many privileges and it became the second factory in Europe to commence hard paste porcelain manufacture, following the defection of the Meissen arcanist Stölzel in 1719 and Böttger's half-brother, Tiemann who brought the kiln designs from that factory.

Early Vienna porcelain can be distinguished from Meissen by the flatness of the glaze, which becomes greenish when thickly applied, and footrims tend to be rough and unglazed. Like Meissen, the early designs owe much to silver shapes,

Apart from adopting architectural features in their forms, such as gadrooning and fluting, Viennese designers also borrowed shapes from Dutch delftware. Three features which became highly characteristic of Viennese decoration were plastic decoration, baroque scrollwork and Japanese 'sprigs'.

There was some copying of figures from Meissen originals, and many fine pieces were made as gifts for the Russian court. By 1725 iron red, green, purple, pink, yellow and blue enamels were being used, and these were softer in tone than the brilliance of their Meissen counterparts. Schwarzlot, black enamel painting with a brush or point, was much in evidence to depict putti, animals, mythological or hunting scenes. Tableware bearing this last decoration are known as Jagd services.

The factory's output was set firmly in the Baroque tradition, as reflected in the Laub and Bandelwerk (scroll and foliage) and naturalistic

A Vienna (Dupaquier) rectangular casket and liner, circa 1728, in a contemporary fitted leather box, 16.5 x 12cm. (Christie's) £22,000

A Vienna (Dupaquier) two-handled, double-lipped baroque moulded sauceboat painted in the Imari style, circa 1740, 24.5cm. wide. (Christie's) £4,950

One of a set of six 'Vienna' porcelain plates, signed Wagner, 9½in. diam. (Capes Dunn) £1,700

A Vienna porcelain snuff box, the interior of the lid finely painted with two gentlemen seated out-of-doors at a table, drinking wine, 9cm. (Phillips London) £850

A Vienna Commedia dell'Arte group of Scaramouche and Pulchinella, circa 1750, 14.5cm. high. (Christie's) £8,800

A Vienna (Dupaquier) cream-pot and cover painted by Johann P. Dannhoffer, circa 1725. (Christie's) £3,300

VIENNA

deutsche Blumen decorations which are much used. The period ends with Du Paquier offering the factory to the archduchess Maria Theresa, who bought it in 1744. Du Paquier continued as director, but retired the same year and died in 1751.

During the state-owned period from 1744 there was a noticeable improvement in the quality of the colour of the clay, which became whiter. Pieces were decorated now rather in Rococo style and many decorators were persuaded to come from Meissen, among them the flower painters Johann Klinger and J G Richter. From about 1760 there was a large output of Meissen-type figures, under the direction of the chief modeller from 1747–1784, J J Niedermayer. The bases of these assist in their dating, beginning as a mound with a little scrollwork, before becoming more like a flat slab and finally adopting a Neo Classical high base with vertical edging with moulded and gilt designs.

The factory was again in difficulties in 1784, when a successful wool merchant, Konrad von Sorgenthal, took over as manager. The restoration of its fortunes which he brought about lasted well into the 19th century, and it did not close until 1866.

In the Sorgenthal period, neo-Classicism asserted itself, as the pieces tried to recapture the forms of classical antiquity in much the same way as Wedgwood did in England, though sometimes the decoration could become too elaborate.

A useful guide to dating post 1783 Vienna is that, in addition to the impressed shield, two or three numbers are also impressed as date marks, eg. 89 = 1789, 808 = 1808.

A 'Vienna' puce ground plate, the centre painted with a scantily draped nymph standing beside a flaming altar, imitation blue beehive mark, circa 1880, 25.5cm. diam. (Christie's London) £495

A Vienna style vase, the claret lustrous ground reserved with a shaped panel of two maidens in a garden, signed *Legles,* 14¾in. high. (Christie's S. Ken) £385

A pair of Vienna vases and covers, decorated with groups of classical figures in oval panels, signed *Cauffmann,* 32cm. (Lawrence Fine Arts) £396

A Vienna figure of a pretzel seller standing beside a tree stump, a wicker basket slung over his left arm, holding a pretzel, circa 1760, 19.5cm. high. (Christie's London) £2,420

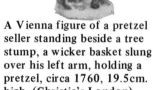

A Vienna style rectangular porcelain plaque with 'Fruhling' painted by Bauer, with two maidens accompanied by children, with blue beehive mark and inscription, circa 1880, 11 x 8½in. (Christie's S. Ken) £660

A 'Vienna' circular dish, painted by Falera with the head and shoulders of a young woman, inscribed *Coquetterie,* imitation blue beehive mark, circa 1900, 34cm. diam. (Christie's London) £528

A Vienna style silver-mounted snuff box of canted rectangular form, painted in colours with a hunting scene, 8.5cm.
(Phillips) £520

A Vienna purple-ground coffee-can and saucer, the saucer painted with scantily clad maidens with fruit and flowers and the cup painted with a nymph being helped onto the back of a satyr.
(Christie's) £462

A Vienna cabaret painted in purple camaïeu with peasants at various pursuits in wooded landscape vignettes within lime-green borders, circa 1775, the tray 31.5cm. wide.
(Christie's) £1,100

A Vienna porcelain cabinet plate, of dished circular form, the central circular panel painted by F. Pauli with 'Theseus'.
(Spencer's) £180

A pair of Vienna vases and covers, painted with nymphs, satyrs and putti in landscapes, 21cm.
(Lawrence Fine Art) £2,750

A Vienna porcelain cabinet plate, the central circular panel painted by Wagner with 'Psyche Am Wasserspiegel', within a gilt and blue border.
(Spencer's) £600

A Vienna powdered-claret-ground baluster mug and stepped domed cover, with entwined branch handle and dahlia finial, circa 1780, 8cm. high.
(Christie's) £198

An attractively painted Vienna style plate with a portrait of Amalie von Shintling after the portrait by F. Stieler, signed indistinctly, 24cm.
(Phillips) £1,100

A Vienna dated gold-ground urn-shaped vase and cover with ormolu entwined serpent handles, the sides painted with Julius Caesar standing on a pedestal addressing five soldiers, date code for 1817, 81cm. high.
(Christie's) £16,500

A Vienna plate painted in the Oriental style the centre with an exotic bird, incised *N*, circa 1735, 22.5cm. diam.
(Christie's London) £935

A Vienna (Dupaquier) two handled double lipped baroque moulded sauce boat painted in the Imari style, circa 1740.
(Christie's London) £1,650

A Vienna large circular dish, painted with Amor auf Reisen, signed *A. Becher,* 36cm.
(Lawrence Fine Arts) £880

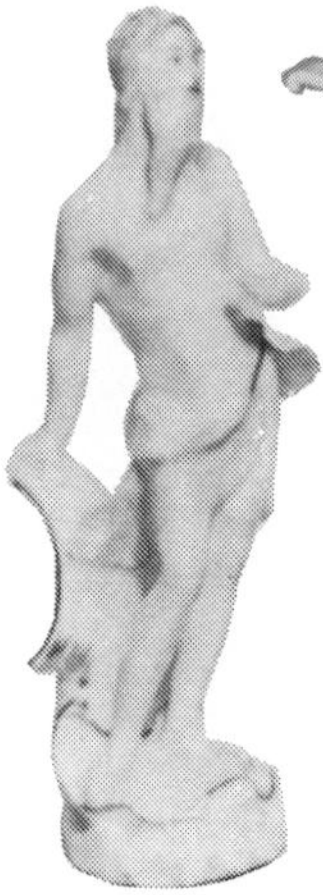

A Vienna figure of Neptune standing scantily clad with a puce cloak tied around his waist, circa 1760, 15.5cm. high.
(Christie's London) £198

A pair of Vienna baluster wine-coolers on stepped circular feet with high scroll handles, the broad waists painted in an Imari palette, circa 1770, 23.5cm. high.
(Christie's London) £2420

A Vienna group after a model by Anton Grassi, depicting a man and woman in 18th century costume, 29cm. high.
(Bearne's) £900

A pair of Vienna putti dressed for the Commedia dell'Arte, in multi-coloured chequered harlequin dress and carrying their slapsticks, circa 1745, 10cm. high. (Christie's London)
£2,860

A Vienna-style cylindrical cup, cover and stand, the apple-green ground reserved with an oval panel enclosing a cherub, circa 1880.
(Christie's S. Ken) £308

An impressive pair of Vienna style ewers, both colourfully painted with continuous Classical scenes, with high square plinth bases, 57cm.
(Phillips London) £2,600

VINCENNES

Vincennes may be said to be the birthplace of the famous Sèvres factory, whither it was removed in 1756 on the orders of King Louis XV.

The entire operation began however at Vincennes between 1738–40, when two financiers, Orry de Vignory and Orry de Fulvy were granted a permit by Louis to use the chateau there for experiments in porcelain manufacture. Their first managers, the brothers Dubois, proved unreliable and were sacked in 1741. Their assistant, François Gravant, took over and his efforts were more successful.

In 1745, with the king increasingly interested, a group of prominent figures was brought together to run the factory with the Orrys and Gravant, its capital was greatly increased, it received a 'privilege' from the king, and the period of its true greatness really began. Vincennes was something of an anachronism in that it set out only to produce soft paste porcelain. Perhaps its backers were wedded to the French traditions that had served well enough at Rouen, Chantilly and Mennecy, or perhaps it just lacked adequate supplies of kaolin, but the result was that it remained hampered by a process that was both costly and increasingly obsolete.

No such conservatism was seen in its decoration however. A new range of colours were developed, with an original range of forms and much use of gilding. Vincennes set out to compete with Meissen, but unlike Meissen pieces, the colours in the Vincennes palette were absorbed into the glaze, which on the usual white ground gave a wonderfully jewel like effect. By 1753 coloured grounds were becoming increasingly popular and this led to many

A Vincennes miniature campana vase, painted in colours with sprays of heartsease, gilt rims, 6cm., interlaced L's marks. (Phillips) £420

A Vincennes circular baluster sugar-bowl and cover painted with sprays of flowers including pink roses, date letter for 1754, 8cm. diameter. (Christie's) £495

A Vincennes bleu celeste teacup and saucer (gobelet Hébert) with gilt entwined branch handle, painted with trailing flowers from cornucopia-shaped bleu celeste borders, date letter B for 1754. (Christie's) £2,640

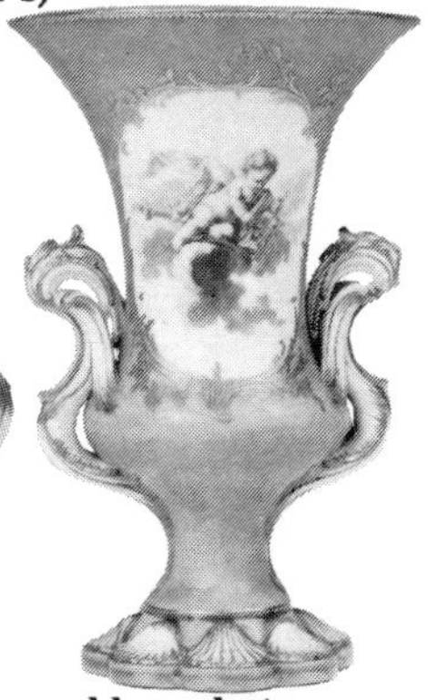

A Vincennes bleu celeste vase duplessis of flared trumpet shape, painted in puce camaieu with Cupid among clouds within gilt scroll and flower cartouches beneath a gilt dentil rim, date letter C for 1755, 19.5cm. high. (Christie's) £6,600

A Vincennes blue celeste sugar-bowl and cover (pot à sucre du roy) painted with figures walking by buildings in wooded landscapes, date letter B for 1754, 8.5cm. diameter. (Christie's) £3,520

A Vincennes bleu lapis coffee-cup and saucer (gobelet à la reine) with loop handle, each side of the cup and the centre of the saucer painted with two birds. (Christie's) £1,760

pieces being covered in lapis blue, jonquil yellow and apple green. These grounds were often supplied with white reserves, which were embellished with superb miniature paintings of landscapes, dallying couples, birds, and an abundance of floral motifs. Gilding was lavish, sometimes enhanced with engraving or, in some cases, two tones of gold were used to give an even richer effect.

While much of the production consisted of tableware, Vincennes, being so closely involved with the Crown, had to maintain French international prestige, and many highly ornamental pieces, vases, urns, jardinières etc. were also produced and these were often used as Royal gifts.

Vincennes also set out to rival Meissen's figure production, and some wonderfully refined sculptures were made. Most were left in the white, but what made the essential difference was a decision in 1749 not to glaze them. The resulting biscuit had a texture akin to the finest marble and immediately became immensely popular.

After the death of the Orrys in the early 1750s, some reorganisation was urgently necessary. The King more or less took over and decreed in 1754 that the factory should remove to Sèvres. It did so in 1756, bringing the Vincennes period to a close.

Dating early Vincennes is extremely difficult. Some pieces are unmarked, others carry only crossed *Ls*. From 1753 an alphabetical date code was introduced with *A* for 1753 and so on. These dates were usually placed within the crossed *Ls*.

A Vincennes goblet litron, 7cm. high, crossed LL mark in blue enamel. £460

A Vincennes bleu lapis conical teapot, blue interlaced L marks and painter's mark of Thevenet, circa 1753, 11cm. high. £1,210

A Vincennes blue lapis teacup and saucer (gobelet calabre) with indented loop handle painted in puce camaieu with Cupid holding a torch and a putto with a bunch of grapes and a spear, date letter A for 1753. (Christie's) £2,640

A Vincennes circular bowl, blue crowned interlaced Ls enclosing the Bourbon fleur-de-lys, circa 1752, 32.5cm. diam. £8,250

One of a pair of Vincennes two-handled small seaux in the Meissen style, blue interlaced L marks enclosing dots, circa 1752, 13.5cm. wide. £10,450

A Vincennes partly glazed white biscuit figure of a sleeping putto resting on a bale of hay, circa 1753, 11cm. high. £970

VYSE

Charles Vyse was an English sculptor and potter who studied at Hanley Art School before moving to London where he opened his studio in Chelsea in 1919. With his wife Nell, he experimented with wood ash glazes on stoneware, and also during the 1920s successfully reproduced Chinese Sung vases.

His figure groups, realistically modelled and sometimes coloured, are very sought after. His work is usually marked with initials or a signature. Charles Vyse died in 1968.

A Charles Vyse figure of a Shire horse, on rectangular base, 28.5cm. high. £300

A Charles Vyse figure of a ribbon seller on a square plinth, circa 1925, 30.5cm. high, including plinth. £650

A Charles Vyse pottery figure of The Piccadilly Rose Woman, modelled as a plump lady, 10in. high. £550

A stoneware oviform jar by Charles Vyse, 1928, 17cm. high. (Christie's) £165

A Charles Vyse group in the form of Pan kneeling on the ground with lambs in his arms, his companion leapfrogging over his shoulders, 33cm. (Bearne's) £620

A stoneware globular vase by Charles Vyse, covered in a lustrous mottled khaki and brown glaze with areas of crimson, incised *CV 1933,* 13cm. high. (Christie's London) £484

'Fantasy', a Charles Vyse pottery group, of a woman seated cross-legged on a grassy base, scantily clad with a turquoise and mauve robe, 21.50cm. high. (Phillips) £360

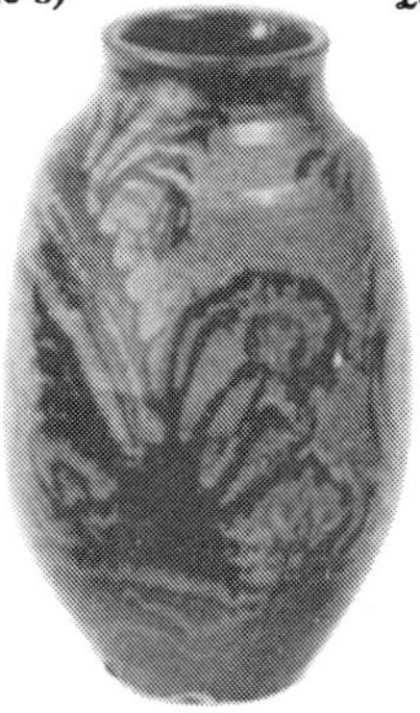

A Charles Vyse oviform, stoneware vase decorated with tenmoku-brown and yellow-green tree forms, 29cm. high. (Phillips) £170

WAIN

Louis Wain (1860–1931) was an English illustrator and designer who is best remembered for his illustrations of cats engaged in human pursuits. In the early 1900s he designed series of postcards, the A-Mewsing Write-away Series, on this theme for Raphael Tuck. Between 1910–20 he also designed pottery figures of cats in the Cubist style and brightly coloured in eg. green, orange and black. His work became increasingly eccentric, however, and he died in an asylum in 1931.

A Louis Wain porcelain Bulldog vase, decorated in cream, yellow, green, russet and black enamels, 14.5cm. long. (Christie's) £935

A Louis Wain porcelain vase, decorated in blue, green, yellow and russet enamels, with painted marks Louis Wain, Made in England, 14.5cm. high. (Christie's) £352

A Louis Wain porcelain lion vase, decorated in black, yellow, green and russet enamels, 11.8cm. high. (Christie's) £935

A Louis Wain porcelain animal vase, the stylised figure of a dog bearing a shield, with shaped aperture on its back, 14.2cm. high. (Christie's) £990

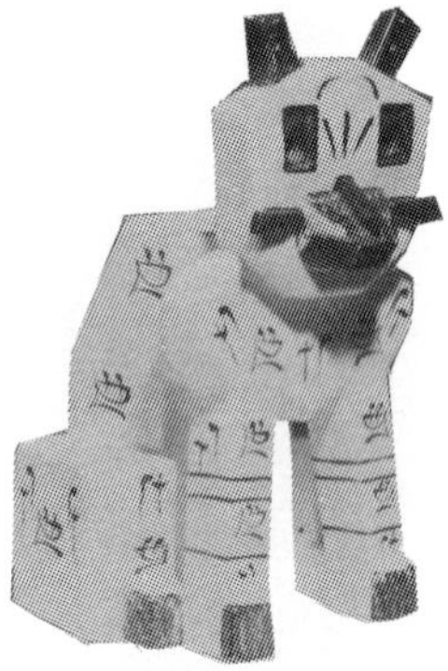

A large Louis Wain pottery vase, modelled as a seated cat, 25.4cm. high. £1,190

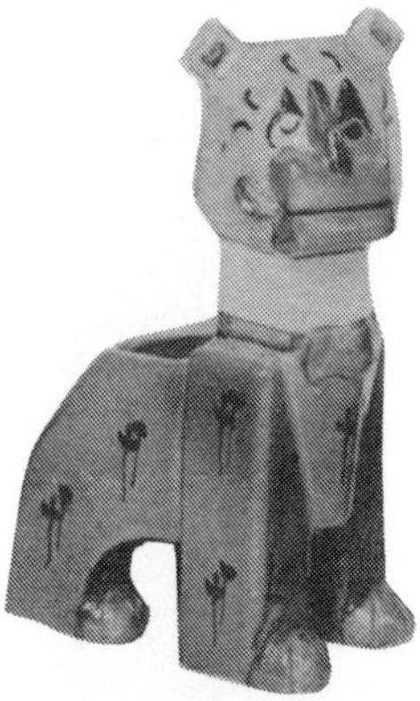

A Louis Wain ceramic animal model of a stylised dog with squared geometric features, coloured in green, red, black and blue, 13cm. high. (Phillips London) £440

A Louis Wain porcelain cat vase, decorated in white, green, russet and black enamels, with impressed and painted marks, 15.5cm. high. (Christie's) £1,540

A Louis Wain porcelain pig vase, decorated in green, yellow, russet and black enamels, with impressed and painted marks, 12.4cm. high. (Christie's) £1,540

WALLEY ART

The Walley Pottery flourished around the turn of the century in the town of Sterling, Massachusetts.

Its output consisted mainly of simple forms, vases, mugs etc, designed in equally simple shapes. Decoration was often confined to the glazes, which could be mottled or streaked, and used in combinations of colour such as a green drip on a brown ground. Occasionally pieces were simply moulded with stylized plant and leaf forms. Grotesque mugs with moulded mask faces were also produced.

Walley pottery basket-shaped vase, Massachusetts, circa 1910, 8¼in. diameter. £250

A small Walley Pottery vase, early 20th century 6½ins high. £300

An early 20th century Walley Art pottery moulded vase, 6¾in. high. £435

Walley Pottery vase, Sterling, Massachusetts, early 20th century, in green drip glaze on brown ground, 9½in. high. (Skinner Inc.) £360

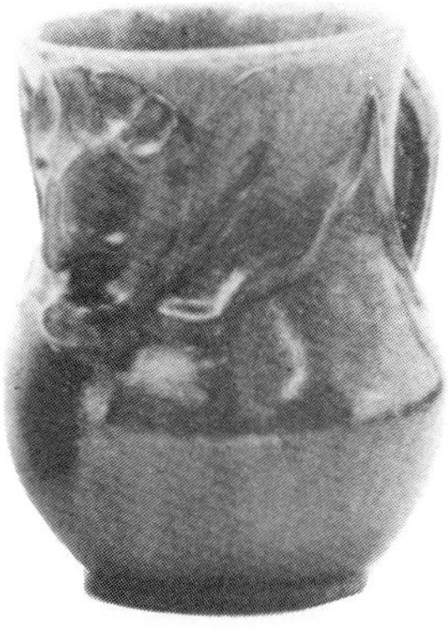

Late 19th century Walley pottery 'Devil' mug, impressed WJW, 5½in. high, 4in. diam. £245

WALRATH

Frederick Walrath (c1880–c1920) was an American artist potter who studied under Charles Binns. He also taught at Rochester and Columbia University, New York. His production consisted of earthenware vases and jars, decorated with linear motifs and stylized plant forms, covered in matt glazes. He exhibited in 1904 at the St Louis World Fair, and in later life worked for two years at the Newcomb College Pottery (q.v.), New Orleans. His mark consists of *Walrath Pottery*, incised, with a device of four arrows.

A Walrath pottery pitcher and five mugs, circa 1910, pitcher 6½in. high £900

A Walrath floral decorated vase, circa 1910, 7in. high. £1,040

WEDGWOOD

Josiah Wedgwood founded his pottery at Burslem in 1759. It operated there until 1774, by which time he had already opened his Etruria factory, and the business continues in the family until the present day.

Wedgwood products were noted from the first for their high quality, and the company was always in the forefront of pioneering new techniques. One of their early successes, achieved as early as 1761, was the cream coloured earthenware, durable and reasonably priced, which was known as creamware. In 1765 came a commission to supply a 60-piece tea service to Queen Charlotte, and this met with such royal satisfaction, that Wedgwood was allowed to call his recent invention Queensware, which name it has borne ever since.

In response to a call for a whiter earthenware, Wedgwood set to work again to develop pearlware, which contained more white clay and flint and was fired at a higher temperature to give a bluish white body. This again proved hugely popular and sold in great quantities between 1790-1820. Production continued until 1846.

Bone porcelain production was attempted from 1812 and successfully resumed in 1878. With Copeland and Minton, Wedgwood was in the vanguard of parian production and parian ware, notably portrait busts, were being produced from 1848 onwards.

Majolica was produced between 1860–1910 for such items as umbrella stands, plaques, comports etc., often using émaux ombrants for decoration. Tiles were also made, and usually transfer printed.

In the 1870s came other developments, such as

A Wedgwood Fairyland lustre malfrey pot and cover designed by Daisy Makeig-Jones and decorated with pixies and elves, 1920's, 22cm. diam. (Christie's) £5,500

19th century blue and white Jasperware Stilton cheese dish and cover, possibly Wedgwood. (G. A. Key) £110

'Sun & Wind', a Wedgwood green and white Jasper plaque designed by Anna Katrina Zinkeisen, 12.5cm. diam. (Phillips) £299

A pair of mid 19th century Wedgwood black basalt triton candlesticks of conventional type, 28cm. high. (Christie's) £880

A Wedgwood creamware punch pot and cover, transfer printed in black with two oval panels of Aurora in chariots representing day and night, 25cm. (Phillips London) £1,000

A Wedgwood flame Fairyland lustre tapering oviform vase with flared neck designed by Daisy Makeig-Jones, 1920's, 30cm. high. (Christie's) £990

WEDGWOOD

Victoria ware, with a body midway between bone porcelain and Queensware. From 1880, decoration with printed and painted landscapes and commemorative wares, often at first for the American market, began.

Jasperware had been in Wedgwood's range from the beginning. In the early years of the 20th century it began to be relief decorated not only now in lilac and green but also olive, crimson, buff, black and turquoise. At this time too lustre ware production began, notably the Dragon and Fairyland lustre series designed by Daisy Makeig-Jones.

Traditional designs continued – particularly at the end of the 19th century there was much harking back to earlier styles – but innovations were, at the same time, constantly being introduced. In 1940 the factory moved to Barlaston.

Marks include *Wedgwood*, and from 1891 *Made in England*. Bone porcelain from 1878 is marked with a replica of the Portland Vase. Various designers also signed their works.

A rare Wedgwood creamware teapot and cover, depicting on one side the Jeremiah Meyer portrait of George III reversed with the Thomas Frye portrait of Queen Charlotte, height 4½in. (Bonhams) £4,200

A good Wedgwood Fairyland lustre bowl, decorated with numerous figures on a waterside, printed mark in brown, circa 1920, 8¾in. diam. (Tennants) £1,200

Two Wedgwood black basalt miniature busts of Homer and Aristophanes, circa 1785, 11cm. and 10cm. high. (Christie's) £1,430

A rare Ralph Wedgwood & Co. creamware ovoid jug, printed in black with the full arms of the Cordwainers Company, 18cm. (Phillips London) £320

A Wedgwood creamware oval sauce tureen, cover and pierced stand, painted in the manner of James Bakewell, circa 1770, the stand 26.5cm. wide. (Christie's) £2,200

A Wedgwood pottery charger designed by Keith Murray, covered in a matt straw yellow glaze, printed facsimile signature *Keith Murray,* and *Wedgwood, Made in England,* 35.5cm. diam. (Christie's London) £506

A Wedgwood Boat Race cup designed by Eric Ravilious, decorated with three oval coloured panels showing scenes associated with the Boat Race, 25.5cm. high. (Phillips London) £2,400

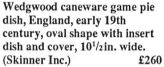

Wedgwood caneware game pie dish, England, early 19th century, oval shape with insert dish and cover, 10½in. wide.
(Skinner Inc.) £260

A rare Wedgwood drabware coffee biggin, the olive body with a blue sprigged band of fruiting vines, 18.5cm.
(Phillips) £220

A Wedgwood caneware rectangular bough-pot on scroll feet, the shaped front applied with Classical figures at various pursuits in a landscape on a blue ground, circa 1790, 19.5cm. wide.
(Christie's) £605

A Wedgwood black basalt encaustic-decorated oviform vase and cover, the shoulder with upright loop handles, painted with Classical figures at various pursuits, circa 1820, 24cm. high.
(Christie's) £715

A pair of Wedgwood pearlware snake-handled vases, the oviform bodies painted by John Holloway with continuous seascapes depicting figures on a quay attempting to rescue a ship, circa 1876, 37.5cm. high.
(Christie's) £1,980

A Wedgwood Fairyland lustre ovoid vase decorated in purple, green, black, yellow and gilt, with the 'Candlemas' pattern, 18.5cm.
(Phillips) £1,700

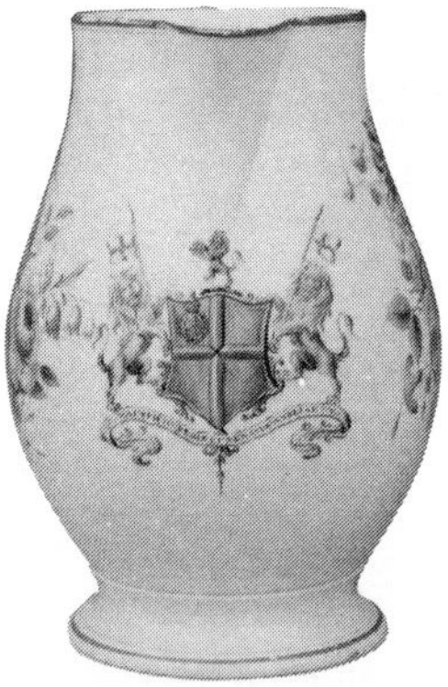

A Wedgwood baluster jug, painted on the front with the Arms of the Company in blue, the supporters bearing banners with red crosses, 21.5cm.
(Lawrence Fine Art) £1,100

A Wedgwood blue and white jasper 'ruined column' vase, the white fluted columns moulded with lichen supported on a solid-blue rectangular base, circa 1795, 21cm. wide.
(Christie's) £5,500

A large Wedgwood blue jasperware dip two-handled campana-shaped pot-pourri jar, 41.5cm.
(Bearne's) £380

A blue and white pottery supper set, probably by Ralph Wedgwood, each piece printed with a Chinese landscape featuring an elephant with a howdah, 60cm. wide.
(Bearne's) £440

A Wedgwood rosso antico teapot and cover of boat shape with crabstock handle, spout and finial, 12cm.
(Phillips) £360

Wedgwood dark blue jasper Stilton cheese dish and cover, England, late 19th century, with continuous classical scene, 11⅝in. diameter.
(Skinner Inc.) £202

A Wedgwood Fairyland lustre vase decorated with the 'Imps on a Bridge' pattern, with the brown boy and blue Rock bird, 23cm.
(Bearne's) £1,400

A pair of Wedgwood Fairyland lustre square vases decorated with panels of the 'Dana' pattern, 19.5cm.
(Phillips) £2,700

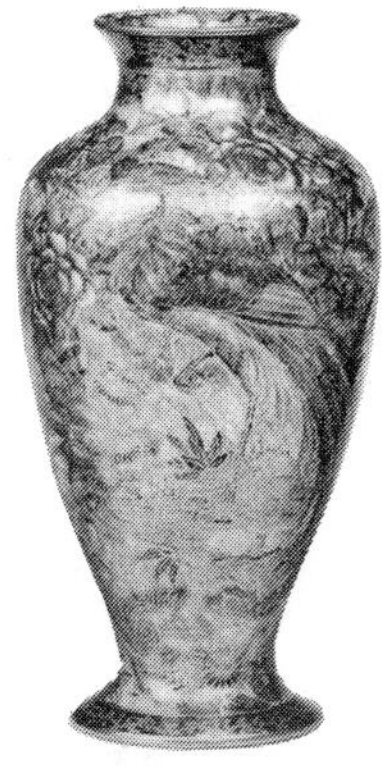

A Wedgwood 'Argus Pheasant' lustre vase, decorated in red and gold with two long tailed birds on a blue mottled ground, 23cm.
(Phillips) £1,300

A Wedgwood Fairyland lustre punch bowl, the interior decorated with The Woodland Bridge pattern, 28.5cm. diameter.
(Bearne's) £1,700

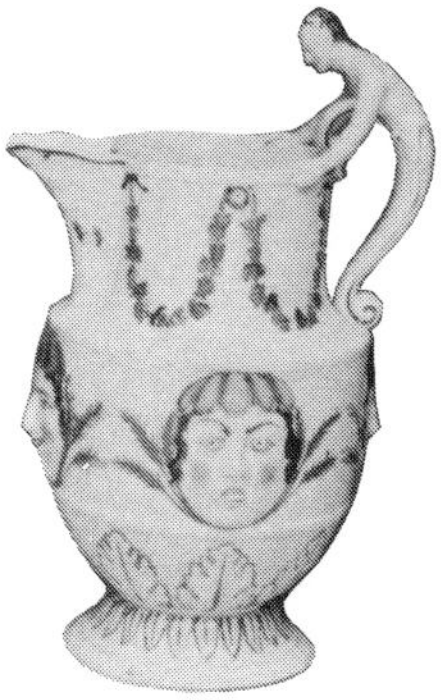

Rare Wedgwood and Company Prattware "Faces" pitcher, England, circa 1795, central band with four moulded faces showing various emotional expressions, 12¾in. high.
(Skinner Inc.) £513

A Wedgwood ceramic ewer and basin designed by George Logan, covered in a lilac glaze and decorated with stylised yellow floral designs, 29.6cm. height of ewer. (Christie's)
£770

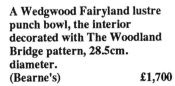

'Bison', a Wedgwood earthenware cream glazed sculpture from a model by John Skeaping, 9in. high. (Christie's) £352

A Wedgwood earthenware fluted centre-dish with entwined double serpent handles, painted by Emile Lessore with Youthful Architects studying a Plan, circa 1865, 32cm. wide. (Christie's London) £660

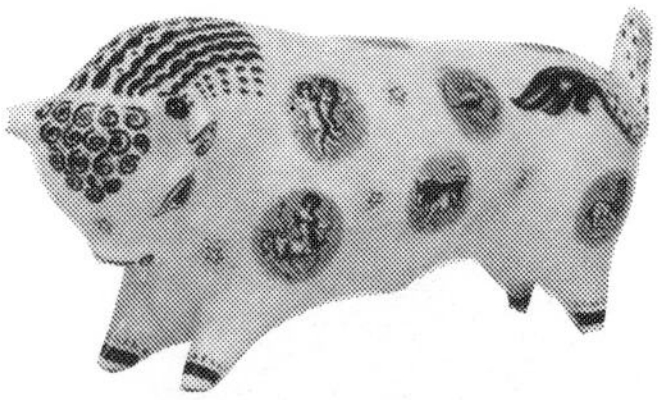

Zodiac Bull, a Wedgwood porcelain bull, designed by Arnold Machin, the cream glazed body with brown painted features, stars and signs of the Zodiac, circa 1945, 40.5cm. long. (Christie's London) £605

A fine Wedgwood basalt figure group of Eros and Euphrosyne modelled by Thomas Woolner, the winged putto seated on her shoulder, 53cm. (Phillips London) £1,600

A garniture of four Wedgwood white stoneware vases, each applied with lilac pilasters terminating in lions heads, 18cm. and 13.3cm. (Bearne's) £860

A Wedgwood black basalt vase designed by Keith Murray, of flaring cylindrical form with everted rim, 8in. high. (Christie's) £1,980

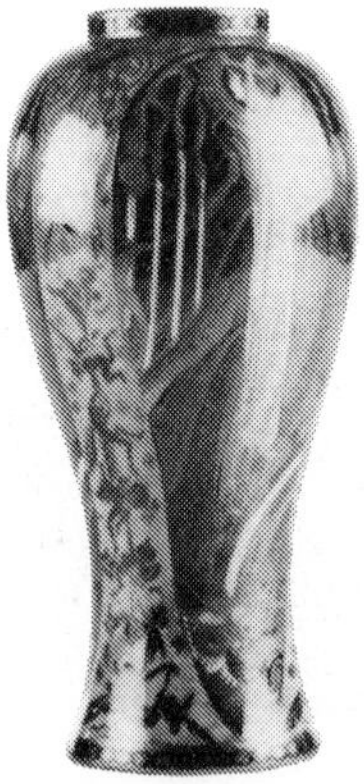

Wedgwood Fairyland lustre 'Candlemas' vase, decorated with panels of heads and candles, 9½in. high.(Prudential) £500

Wedgwood pottery mug commemorating the Coronation of Queen Elizabeth II, designed by Eric Ravilious. (G.A.Key) £120

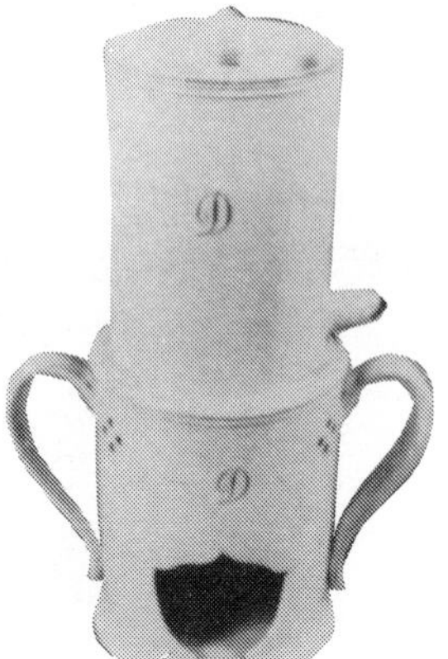

An interesting Wedgwood creamware veilleuse, the upper section containing an inverted cone, with two spouts, 43cm. high. (Henry Spencer) £330

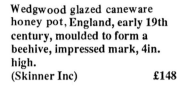

Wedgwood glazed caneware honey pot, England, early 19th century, moulded to form a beehive, impressed mark, 4in. high.
(Skinner Inc) £148

A Wedgwood majolica-ware three-piece strawberry set, 24.5cm., impressed Wedgwood, registration mark and GBX.
(Phillips) £320

A Wedgwood, Greatbatch red-ware teapot and cover moulded in relief with Chinese ladies and children, 12cm. (Phillips London) £2,200

Two of four Wedgwood black basalt column candlesticks, carved in gilt with stiff leaves to the tops and spiralling bands of foliage, circa 1900, $11\frac{1}{2}$in. high.
(Christie's S. Ken) £3,190

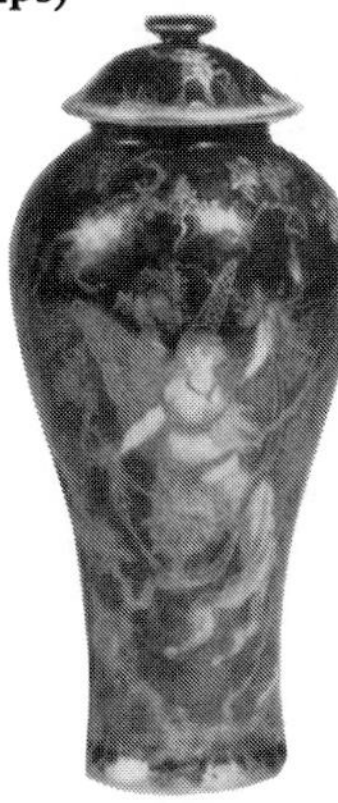

A Wedgwood Fairyland lustre slender baluster vase and cover, the iridescent black ground printed in gold and coloured with three fairies, 1920s, 21.5cm. high. (Christie's London) £2,420

A pair of early 19th century Wedgwood three colour Jasper baluster vases and covers with gilt metal pine-cone finials, female mask handles and bases, $11\frac{1}{2}$in. high.
(Christie's S. Ken) £1,540

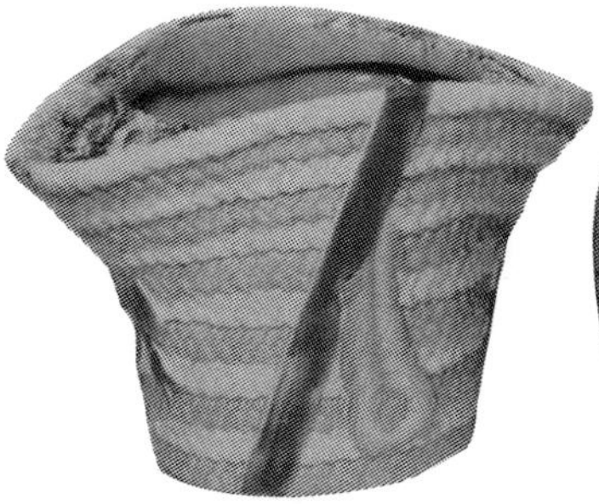

A Wedgwood majolica-ware 'Kate Greenaway' jardiniere, modelled as a lady's straw bonnet, 16.5cm., impressed Wedgwood and moulded registration mark. (Phillips) £230

A rare and important Wedgwood Sydney Cove medallion, titled below Etruria 1789, the reverse impressed, 5.7cm. overall diam. (Phillips) £15,000

A Wedgwood Fairyland lustre 'Malfrey Pot' and cover, 18cm. high, 26cm. diam., Portland Vase mark, Z5257, incised shape number 2308. (Phillips) £550

A Wedgwood creamware globular teapot and cover, 5$\frac{3}{4}$in. high, circa 1770.
(Dreweatt Neate) £1,800

Wedgwood Queensware gilt and bronzed vase, England, late 19th century, moulded floral and leafy decorations surrounded by fields of hand painted dot and floral designs, 5$\frac{1}{2}$in. high.
(Skinner Inc.) £356

A Wedgwood creamware teapot and cover of globular form, printed in black, by Sadler, with 'La Bonne Aventure', 15cm.
(Phillips) £600

A Wedgwood Fairyland lustre vase decorated with the 'Imps on a Bridge' pattern, this version with the brown boy and green Rock bird, 26.3cm.
(Bearne's) £2,100

A Wedgwood Fairyland lustre footed bowl decorated inside with a 'Picnic by a River' around a central panel of a mermaid, 27.5cm.
(Phillips) £1,100

A Wedgwood Fairyland lustre vase decorated with the Ghostly Wood pattern, 35cm.
(Bearne's) £8,500

A Wedgwood pottery mug, designed by Keith Murray, the rim inscribed *Edward VIII Coronation 1937*, height 4$\frac{3}{4}$in.
(Bonhams) £180

An encaustic basalt vase, probably Wedgwood, of baluster shape, decorated with rosso antico anthemion and key fret bands, 15cm.
(Phillips) £130

A Wedgwood Fairyland lustre plate decorated with 'Boys on a Bridge', with a green bat above a boy in a boat below the bridge, 27cm.
(Phillips) £1,250

WEDGWOOD & BENTLEY

In around 1770 Josiah Wedgwood arranged with Thomas Bentley for the latter to open a workshop in Cheyne Row Chelsea, where painters would be engaged in decorating creamware. Their partnership lasted for a number of years, and their catalogue of 1779 shows that they were producing biscuit ware, jasperware and pearlware.

A Wedgwood & Bentley black basalt teapot and cover of globular shape with a curved collar and reeded handle, 21.5cm. wide. (Phillips London) £1,200

A Wedgwood & Bentley black basalt cylindrical ink-well, circa 1775, 7.5cm. diam. (Christie's) £286

A Wedgwood & Bentley black basalt encaustic-decorated circular sugar bowl and cover, circa 1775, 11.5cm. diam. (Christie's) £1,760

A pair of Wedgwood & Bentley black basalt griffin candlesticks, seated on their haunches, their wings raised towards the fluted nozzles, circa 1775, 33cm. high. (Christie's) £4,400

A Wedgwood & Bentley cream-ware large flower pot and stand, circa 1775, the stand 27cm. diam. (Christie's) £990

A Wedgwood and Bentley black basalt oval portrait medallion of Minerva in high relief, circa 1775, 20cm. high. (Christie's) £660

A Wedgwood & Bentley black basalt oval portrait medal-lion of Oldenbarneveld in high relief, circa 1780, 7cm. high. (Christie's London) £176

A Wedgwood & Bentley black basalt oval portrait medallion of Solon in high relief, circa 1775, 16cm. high. (Christie's) £330

One of a pair of Wedgwood & Bentley black basalt oviform two-handled vases and covers, circa 1775, 38cm. high. £7,700

A Wedgwood & Bentley black basalt hare's head stirrup cup, circa 1775, 16cm. high. £9,180

A Wedgwood & Bentley black basalt miniature bust of Ariadne, circa 1775, 10.5cm. high. £1,190

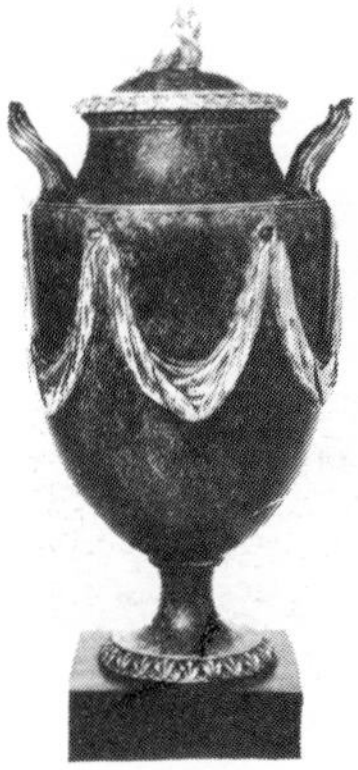

A Wedgwood & Bentley 'porphyry' vase and cover, the shield-shaped body applied with gilt mounting, 47.5cm. high. £4,200

A pair of Wedgwood & Bentley black basalt oval portrait plaques of Vespasian and Nero, circa 1777, 20cm. high. £1,945

One of a pair of Wedgwood & Bentley black basalt oviform ewers, circa 1775, 31cm. high. £700

A Wedgwood & Bentley black basalt compressed globular vase and cover, circa 1775, 16.5cm. high. £810

A Wedgwood & Bentley black basalt miniature bust of Aristophanes, circa 1775, 11cm. high. £1,405

A Wedgwood & Bentley black basalt oviform two-handled vase and cover, circa 1775, 40cm. high. £1,980

WEDGWOOD WHIELDON

Thomas Whieldon (1719-95) was perhaps the last and greatest of the traditional Staffordshire potters using traditional potting methods. He also had an eye for talent and in 1754 took as his apprentice and then partner Josiah Wedgwood. Together they developed earthenware figures characterised by their dripping coloured glazes. Whieldon is particularly associated with a tortoiseshell glaze, made by the use of a limited range of high temperature oxides. The partnership lasted until 1759, when Wedgwood struck out on his own.

A Wedgwood/Whieldon teapot and cover, with crabstock handle, circa 1765, 6in. high. £1,815

A Wedgwood/Whieldon hexagonal teapot and cover in chinoiserie style, 16cm. high. £1,500

A mid-18th century Wedgwood Wheildon type cauliflower moulded coffee pot and cover, 24.5cm. high. (Spencer's) £1500

A Wedgwood/Whieldon cauliflower teapot and cover in shaded green colours. (A. J. Cobern) £750

A Wedgwood/Whieldon cauliflower moulded coffee pot and domed cover, of pear shape, 25.5cm. (Phillips London) £1,500

A Wedgwood/Whieldon cauliflower teapot and cover, 11.6cm. high. £600

A creamware double rectangular tea caddy of Wedgwood/Whieldon type, circa 1760, 14.5cm. wide. (Christie's) £1,650

A Wedgwood/Whieldon lobed hexagonal teapot and cover with scrolling handle, in green with ochre streaks, 12cm. (Phillips London) £1,800

WELLER

Samuel Weller (1851–1925) acquired the Lonhuda pottery at Steubenville, Ohio in the early 1890s, and moved production to his own pottery which he had established in 1882 at Zanesville. There, he continued to produce pottery in the Lonhuda style, which was now called Louwelsa. This was very like Rookwood Standard ware in appearance, and Weller continued to imitate subsequent Rookwood innovations.

A French potter, Jacques Sicard, joined the business in 1901 and produced Sicardo ware, on which a lustre decoration was applied to an iridescent ground in shades of purple, green and brown. Later, a variation, Lasa ware, was introduced with landscape decoration.

Weller worked too in imitation of French Art Nouveau styles, with relief decorations of flowers, foliage and female figures. Aurelia ware was introduced by 1904, having a brushed ground, also Jap Birdimal, with stylised natural forms as decoration.

At its height the business employed some 600 workers and by 1925 Weller owned three factories producing art pottery, garden and kitchen wares. He was succeeded by his nephew Herbert, who died in 1932, and the factory finally closed in 1949.

Marks include impressed *Weller* with the name of the style, and incised *Weller Faience*.

Weller pottery Indian portrait mug, circa 1920, 6in. high. £300

Louwelsa Weller cider pitcher with Indian portrait, Ohio, circa 1910, 12½in. high. £400

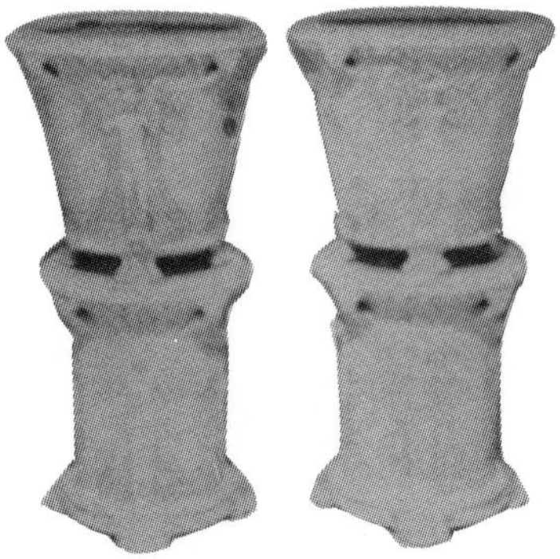

Pair of Weller 'Ivory Ware' jardinieres on stands, Zanesville, Ohio, circa 1915, 35in. high, 18in. diam. (Robt. W. Skinner Inc.) £1,657

Louwelsa Weller pottery Indian portrait vase, Ohio, circa 1915, 10¾in. high. (Robt. W. Skinner Inc.) £296

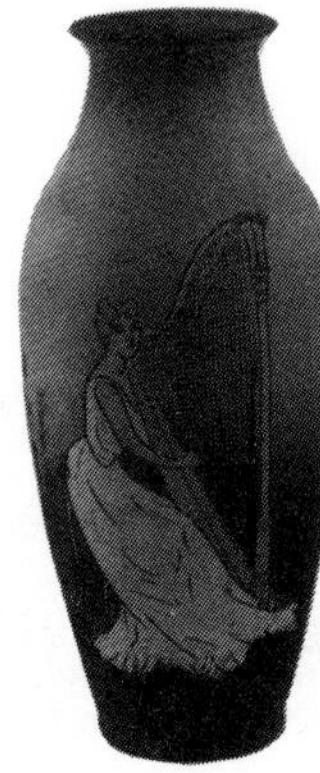

A Weller Dickensware vase, circa 1900, 16in. high. £225

A Weller Sicard twisted pottery vase, iridescent purples and greens with snails in the design, circa 1907, unsigned, 7½in. high. (Robt. W. Skinner Inc.) £324

WEMYSS

Wemyss Ware is the most distinctive product of the Scottish potteries. Its trademarks are free flowing designs on white of roses, cherries and apples.

The pottery of Robert Heron & Sons was based at Kirkcaldy in Fife and its fame really began when a young Bohemian decorator called Karl Nekola joined the staff in 1883. He became Art Director and by the time he died in 1915 he had made Wemyss Ware famous. The name was taken from nearby Wemyss Castle, the home of the Grosvenor family who did much to popularise the pottery with their upper class friends in London. Thomas Goode and Co, the Mayfair china shop, became the sole outlet for Wemyss Ware in London and sent up special orders for individual customers.

Nekola trained other artists and also his own two sons in the work of ceramic decoration and though no pieces were signed, it is possible to identify different artists by their style. Wemyss was produced in a vast range of shapes and sizes from buttons to garden seats and the washstand sets were particularly well designed, especially the squat jug with its generous mouth.

A Wemyss character jug modelled as the Fair Maid of Perth and painted with a floral sprigged yellow dress, 21.5cm. (Phillips London) £380

A Wemyss cream jug, decorated with cockerels, and inscribed *Bonjour*, impressed mark and *T. Goode and Co.* stamp, 7cm. high. (D.M. Nesbit) £170

A pair of Wemyss pottery candlesticks, painted with roses in colours and edged in green, 18cm. high. (Henry Spencer) £320

A Wemyss vase of panelled baluster form, the shoulders with eight pierced circular panels, 38cm. (Lawrence Fine Arts) £814

A late Wemyss model of a pig of small size, the body painted in green with scattered shamrock, 16cm. high. (Phillips) £820

A rare signed Karel Nekola Wemyss comb tray, painted with mallards and ducks by reed pond, 29.5cm. long. (Phillips) £2,600

A Wemyss sauce boat or flower holder modelled as a goose, with green neck, yellow beak, purple and blue breast. (Phillips London) £750

A Wemyss 1902 Coronation twin handled cup, the lid with thistle finial, the exterior with all-over decoration, $8^{3}/_{4}$in. high.
(David Lay) £600

A Wemyss dog's bowl, impressed mark, $6^{3}/_{4}$in. diameter.
(Dreweatt Neate) £360

A Wemyss (Bovey Tracey) large pig, made for Jan Plicha, painted with pink and green thistles, 41.5cm. long.
(Phillips) £460

Wemyss ware plant pot decorated with branches of cherries, green borders, spiral fluted body, $8^{1}/_{2}$in. x 7in.
(Barbers Auctions) £380

A Wemyss Plichta cat signed *Nekola*.
(R.K. Lucas) £570

An unusual Wemyss pottery part toilet set, painted in colours with pink carnations within typical sea green borders.
(Spencer's) £740

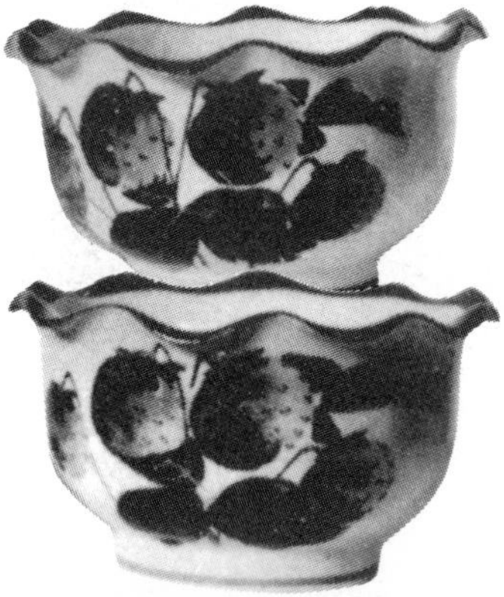

Pair of Wemyss fruit bowls, decorated with strawberry pattern, green borders, 5in. diameter.
(G.A. Key) £130

An attractive Wemyss (Bovey Tracey) model of a pig in the usual squatting pose, with ears pricked, painted all over the back and ears with sprays of flowering clover, 46cm.
(Phillips) £1,900

A Wemyss pottery preserve jar and cover painted with strawberries.
(Bearne's) £150

WESTERWALD

The Westerwald was one of the great stoneware centres of Germany, though little of value is recorded until the late 16th century. Jugs and Krugs were made in great numbers, often with initials and small decorations such as rosettes, lion masks and angel heads until the late 17th century. Thereafter, greater use was made of incised and combed lines which acted as barriers to contain the cobalt blue and manganese purple colours. Production of these wares continues to the present day.

A German Westerwald stoneware jug, circa 1750, 22cm. high. £3,900

Late 17th century Westerwald stoneware square flask, 22.5cm. high. (Christie's) £440

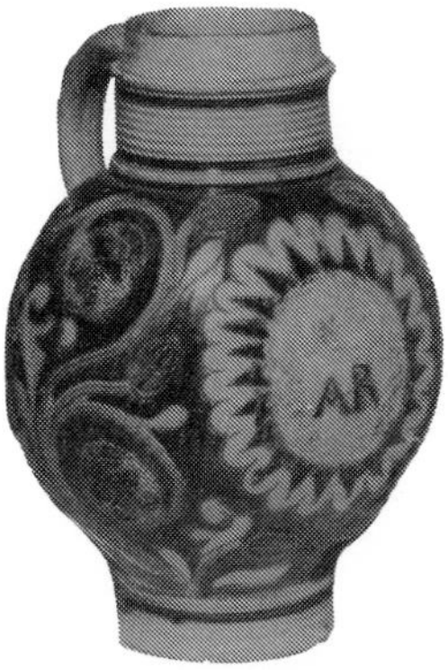

Early 18th century Westerwald oviform tankard (Birnkrug) painted in blue and manganese on the gray body, 24cm. high. (Christie's) £330

A Westerwald stoneware inverted baluster kanne moulded allover with relief rosettes on a blue-ground, 32cm. high. (Christie's) £352

A German Westerwald stoneware baluster jug with horizontally ribbed neck and pewter cover and mount, 17th century, 8in. high. (Christie's S. Ken) £418

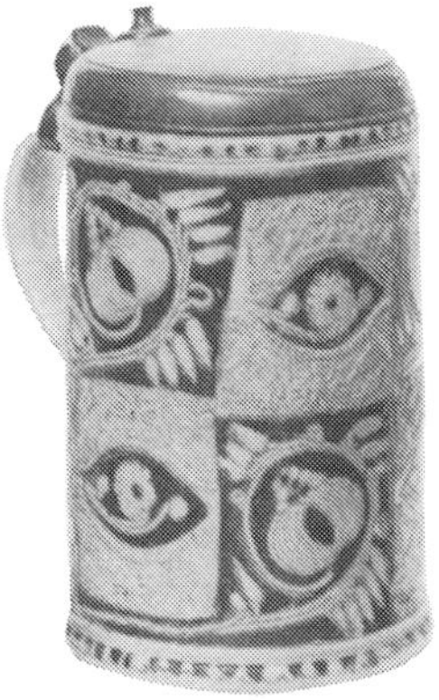

A Westerwald tankard of cylindrical shape, the body with two bands of square panels incised and moulded in relief with floral motifs, 19.5cm. (Phillips London) £340

A Westerwald stoneware Sternkanne, the oviform body impressed with a starburst enclosing a heart within a circular cartouche, circa 1700, 30cm. high. (Christie's) £880

A Westerwald buff stoneware jug of large globular shape with cylindrical grooved neck and loop handle, circa 1700, 22cm. high. (Christie's London) £495

Westerwald stoneware flagon, with portrait mask, 18th century.
(Auktionshaus Arnold) £384

A Westerwald stoneware cylindrical mug with loop handle, incised with four interlocking oval cartouches of prancing horses, early 18th century, 22.5cm. high.
(Christie's) £242

A Westerwald stoneware jug with loop handle and short flared neck applied with a mask, the shoulder with alternating panels of rouletting and fleurs-de-lys, late 17th century, 18.5cm. high. (Christie's) £440

A German Westerwald grey stoneware globular jug, enriched in blue and manganese and moulded in relief with three oblong-octagonal medallions of the Crucifixion, early 18th century, 7¼in. high.
(Christie's S. Ken) £132

A Westerwald stoneware globular jug with loop handle, applied with an octagonal portrait medallion of William III flanked by scrolling flowers enriched in manganese and with incised stems, on a blue ground beneath a ribbed manganese neck, late 17th century, 13.5cm. high. (Christie's) £495

An unusual Westerwald William III Krug with ovoid body, cylindrical neck molded with horizontal ribbing and a ribbed loop handle, 18.55cm., end 17th century.
(Phillips) £440

A German Westerwald grey stoneware globular jug, the body enriched in blue and stamped with bands of flowerheads enriched in manganese, late 17th century, 10½in. high.
(Christie's S. Ken) £176

Westerwald-type stoneware jug, Northern Europe, 18th century, globular shape underglazed blue scrolls and highlighting, 8½in. high.
(Skinner Inc.) £148

A German Westerwald stoneware globular GR jug, enriched in blue and incised with five horizontal bands of interlaced scrolls, 18th century, 13in. high.
(Christie's S. Ken) £275

WHIELDON

Thomas Whieldon (1719–95) was an English potter working out of Fenton Low, or Little Fenton, in Staffordshire. He gave his name to the distinctive earthenware which he produced and which is notable for its range of colours. He was in partnership with Josiah Wedgwood from 1754–79.

No marks were used.

A 7in. 18th century Whieldon pottery study of a ram on naturalistic base. (Riddetts) £1220

A Whieldon style teapot and cover, the portrait of Flora moulded on either side with flowing hair, 14cm. high. (Bearne's) £4,200

A creamware cauliflower-moulded baluster coffee-pot and cover of Whieldon type, the upper part with cream florettes and the lower part with crisply moulded overlapping green leaves, circa 1765, 24.5cm. high. (Christie's) £4,400

A pair of creamware Arbour figures of Whieldon type, modelled as a musician playing the fiddle in streaked grey topcoat and yellow waistcoat, his companion in a green splashed crinoline and holding a pug dog on her lap, circa 1750, 15cm. high. (Christie's) £35200

A Staffordshire creamware tea caddy of Whieldon type, the moulded panelled sides framed by ropetwist pattern, circa 1760, 9.5cm. high. (Christie's) £495

A Whieldon cauliflower moulded teapot and cover with green scrolling handle, the oviform body naturalistically modelled with green glazed leaves, 11cm. (Phillips) £950

A Whieldon green-ground cornucopia wall-pocket of spirally moulded form, circa 1750, 26.5cm. high. £920

A rare and small Whieldon 'pear' teapot and cover, 8.5cm. high. (Phillips) £6,200

A Whieldon cow creamer and cover, circa 1760, 6½in. high. £1,435

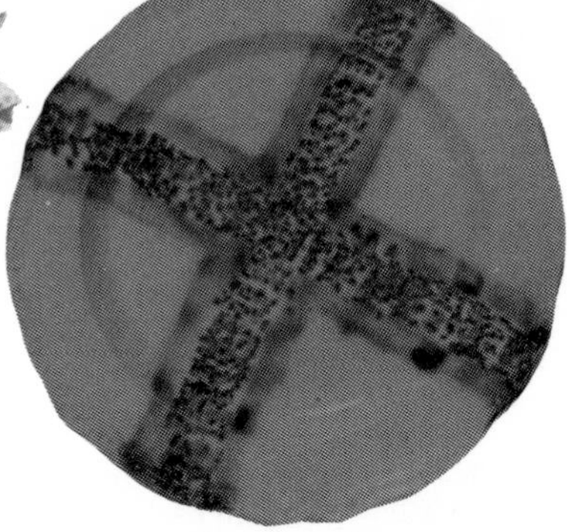

A creamware plate of Whieldon type, circa 1770, 24.5cm. diam. (Christie's) £990

A Whieldon type figure of a horse, circa 1770, 7in. long. £2,705

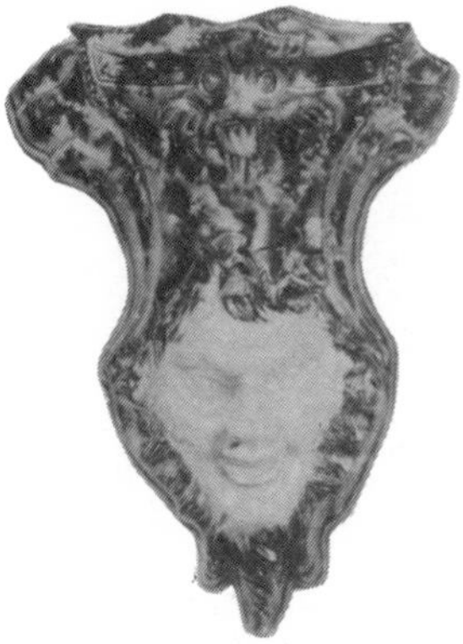

A Whieldon wall pocket of waisted form moulded with bearded mask beneath a manganese glaze, circa 1760, 22.5cm. high. £1,100

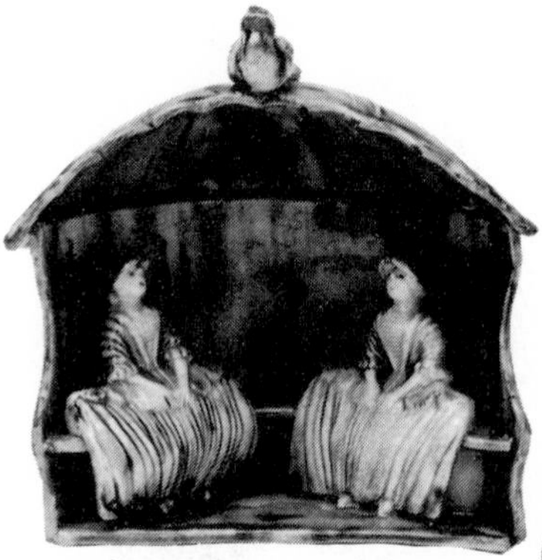

A creamware arbour group of Whieldon type, modelled as a garden shelter of semi-circular form, a woman in a crinoline sitting on either side of the curved seat, 14.5cm. high. (Bearne's) £32,000

A Whieldon group of lovers embracing and seated on rockwork, circa 1750, 12cm. wide. £8,640

A creamware globular teapot and cover of Whieldon type, with entwined strap handle and foliage-moulded spout, circa 1765, 10cm. high. (Christie's) £418

An important Whieldon figure of a bagpiper, the gentleman dressed in short coat, buttoned waistcoat and striped breeches, 19cm. (Phillips) £9,500

A Whieldon solid agate pecten shell teapot and cover moulded in the form of a shell and marbled in grey, brown and a clear lead glaze, 13.5cm. (Phillips) £1,700

WOOD

The Wood family of Burslem are famous to collectors because of their high quality pottery figures made by two, if not by three, generations of Ralph Woods. Ralph Wood Senior, who died in 1772, and his brother Aaron developed an individual style for their productions which they passed onto their respective sons. Ralph's son, also named Ralph, lived between 1748 and 1795, and worked as a potter of model figures in Burslem with his cousin Enoch (died 1840). Their products were particularly noted for delicate colouring. Ralph Wood III succeeded his father Ralph but died at the early age of 27 in 1801. Some earthenware figures that bear the name mark *Ra Wood* may have been his handiwork as may also be porcelain examples. Enoch Wood started his own factory in 1784 and in 1790 went into partnership with James Caldwell, making tableware marked *Wood & Caldwell* which was shipped to America in vast quantities.

An Enoch Wood model of a lion painted in shades of dark brown with his forepaw resting on a ball, 12in. wide. (Christie's) £660

A Ralph Wood figure of a harvester, circa 1775, 20cm. high. (Christie's) £1,870

A pair of creamware figures of Ralph Wood type, each modelled as a youth in translucent blue, yellow and manganese clothes, circa 1780, 12.5cm. and 12cm. high. (Christie's) £418

A Ralph Wood white pearlware group of Roman Charity, the veiled woman suckling a child at her breast, circa 1790, 20cm. high. (Christie's) £600

A Ralph Wood pearlware figure of St. Peter standing holding a crucifix and a Bible under his right arm, wearing puce-lined green robe and turquoise trousers, circa 1800, 36cm. high. (Christie's) £715

A creamware model of a fox of Ralph Wood type, naturally modelled to the right with brown coat, a bird beneath his right forepaw, circa 1780, 9.5cm. high. (Christie's) £1650

A Staffordshire pearlware figure of a gentleman of Ralph Wood type, wearing a black hat, his grey-lined pale-green cloak tied with a blue ribbon, circa 1785, 25cm. high. (Christie's) £1,430

A Ralph Wood Bacchus mask jug, circa 1775, 23.5cm. high. £410

A Ralph Wood figure of a recumbent ram, on an oval green rockwork base moulded with foliage, circa 1770, 18.5cm. wide. £2,640

A Ralph Wood triple spill vase modelled as two entwined dolphins, circa 1775, 20cm. high. £1,190

A well modelled and brightly glazed Enoch Wood bust of Wesley, the head and hair in white, 32cm. (Phillips London) £1,100

A pair of rare Ralph Wood models of a stag and a doe both at lodge, on green glazed bases, 16cm. and 17cm. (Phillips London) £3,200

A documentary self portrait bust by Enoch Wood, in white smear glazed stoneware, cast in 1899 by Macintyre & Co., 56cm. high. (Phillips London) £180

A Ralph Wood Toby jug of conventional type, circa 1770, 25.5cm. high. £1,870

A Ralph Wood oval plaque portrait of a woman, perhaps Charlotte Corday, circa 1780, 20cm. high. £595

A Ralph Wood group of the Vicar and Moses of conventional type, circa 1770, 21.5cm. high. £455

WORCESTER

The history of porcelain making in Worcester is a complex one, involving a number of principal factories. The process began around 1751, when the Worcester Tonquin Manufactory was set up by a consortium of 15 local businessmen. The leading figures in the group were a local surgeon, John Wall, and an apothecary, William Davis. During this earliest, or 'Dr Wall' period, a soaprock body was perfected from experiments at Bristol. The wares were decorated both in blue and white and a colourful polychrome, in a manner which amalgamated both oriental and European influences to form a highly distinctive style of their own. The shapes of these were graceful and the painting very fine.

During the ten years from 1755, decoration became increasingly subtle, derived mainly from Meissen or Chinese ideas, and while oriental figure painting was fairly naive, flower painting reached surprising heights of sophistication.

No factory marks were used until after 1765. Between then and 1776, which is generally seen as the end of the First Period, there was an enormous output of all the standard forms in a huge range of patterns. Both potting and painting continued to be of a high standard.

Between 1757-76 transfer printing in overglaze jet black became common and took the form of either European scenes or commemorative prints, of which the most common is Frederick of Prussia. Most were engraved by Robert Hancock.

Wall retired in 1775, and Davis struggled to keep the factory going in the face of increasing competition, in particular from the Caughley

A Worcester blue-scale porcelain lobed circular plate, circa 1770, 19.5cm. diam. (Christie's) £825

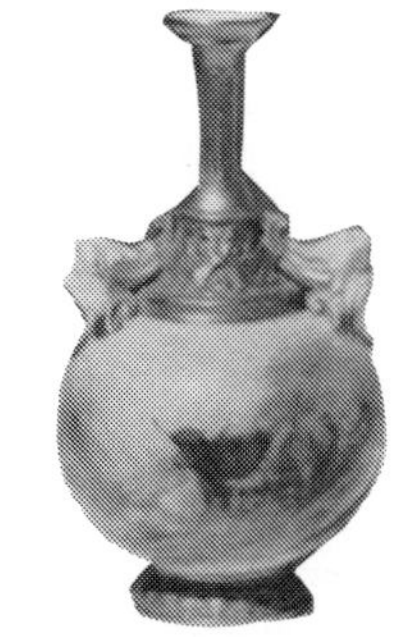

A Worcester vase, painted with two Highland cattle on a misty mountainside, signed *H. Stinton,* 16.5cm., date code for 1911. (Phillips London) £650

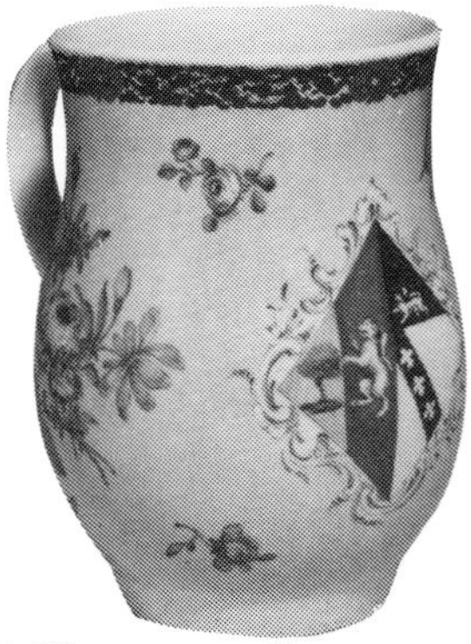

A Worcester yellow ground armorial baluster mug with grooved loop handle, circa 1770, 12cm. high. (Christie's London) £8,250

A very rare Worcester wine funnel, painted in famille-rose enamels with flowering paeony branches, 9.8cm., 1753–1755. (Phillips) £12,000

A wide trophy-shaped vase, on a fluted circular base, the body painted with yellow and white roses, signed *J. Lander*, 19cm., date code for 1909. (Phillips) £550

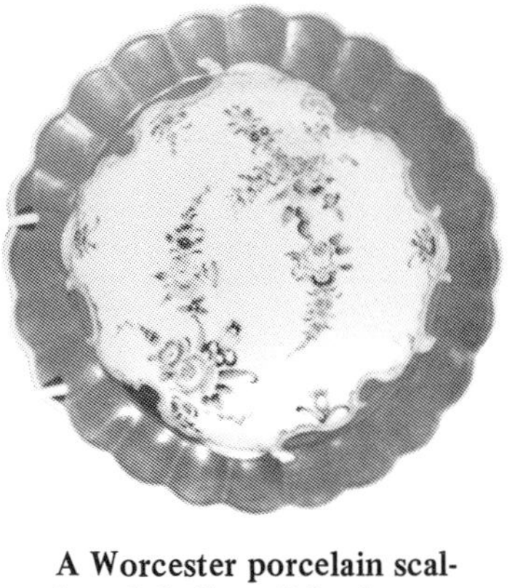

A Worcester porcelain scalloped shallow dish, the centre painted with sprays of flowers, 8¼in. wide. (From the Marchioness of Huntly service) circa 1770. (Dacre, Son & Hartley) £440

WORCESTER

factory, which, under Thomas Turner, had by then more or less cornered the market for blue and white.

In 1783, Davis was joined by John Flight, and after that they managed to produce some blue and white to compete with Caughley, but most was by now of an inferior quality. By the time a further new partner, Martin Barr, joined in 1793, blue and white production had ceased.

The factory had received a further blow in 1787, when Turner had persuaded Flight's chief decorators, Robert and Humphrey Chamberlain, to set up on their own as painters and decorators. The partners now decided to concentrate their efforts of producing high quality, though not always very expensive pieces, for the top end of the market. Flight improved the soaprock body, with the result that tea services were now of unsurpassed thinness and translucence. They also rediscovered fine gilding.

By 1790 Chamberlain's had severed their links with the Caughley factory and were now making their own products. Because of their common backgrounds perhaps, the products which they and Flight's turned out over the next decade were very similar. Both, for example produced tea services in spiral, fluted shapes, decorated in underglaze blue with gold, or simple gold sprigs. Flight's however continued to play more for the upper end of the market, and their quality was unsurpassed.

They did, however, have to find new painters. Of these, John Pennington was the only one capable of reproducing the cabinet pieces of Sèvres. Zachariah Boreman and Joseph Hill specialised in landscapes. Between 1808–13, William

An ovoid vase, the body well painted with two Highland cattle, signed H. Stinton, 21cm. high, shape no. 1762, date code for 1910. (Phillips) £580

A Worcester porcelain two handled pot pourri vase and cover, painted with a horizontal band of landscape within moulded bands of beads, 5½in. high. (Christie's S. Ken) **£160**

A Barr, Flight & Barr inkwell painted with a shell attributed to Samuel Smith, painted with a whelk-type shell and seaweed, 7cm. (Phillips) £3,100

A Worcester large bulbous mug printed with three flowers and four butterflies, 6in. high. (G.A.Property Services) £300

An early Worcester fluted coffee cup with scrolling handle, painted in famille-rose palette with trailing flower sprays, 5cm. (Phillips) £1,500

A Worcester blue and white baluster flaring vase painted with two tall Chinese maidens, circa 1765, 8in. high. (Christie's S. Ken) £308

Billingsley, the greatest flower painter of the age, also worked for Flight before leaving for Swansea and Nantgarw.

By now a third Worcester factory had been opened by Thomas Grainger, who had been a manager at Chamberlains. For the next 80 years Graingers were to rival the two main factories, for while their wares were generally cheaper and aimed at the more modest end of the market, at their best they could produce pieces quite equal in quality to Flights and Chamberlains.

After the Neo-Classical period of the early 1800s, the 1820s and 30s saw a revival of a fussier, almost neo-rococo taste. Richness and extravagance were called for both in terms of shapes and decoration. Graingers and Chamberlains both answered this demand with hundreds of different, complicated designs, with each fancy border available in a selection of coordinating colours. Flights, however, failed to adjust and this failure ended in their near bankruptcy and merger with Chamberlains in 1840, when the company became known as Chamberlain & Co.

Times were getting harder for everyone, however, and the new company was failing to compete with the bigger Staffordshire factories. It was bought by Kerr & Binns in 1851 and became the Worcester Royal Porcelain Co in 1862.

The popularity of parian had prompted a renewed interest in figure making, and Worcester became the most important maker of coloured figures when these became popular in the 1870s and 80s. Their success was due in no small measure to the modelling skills of James Hadley, who though largely untutored, was able to design

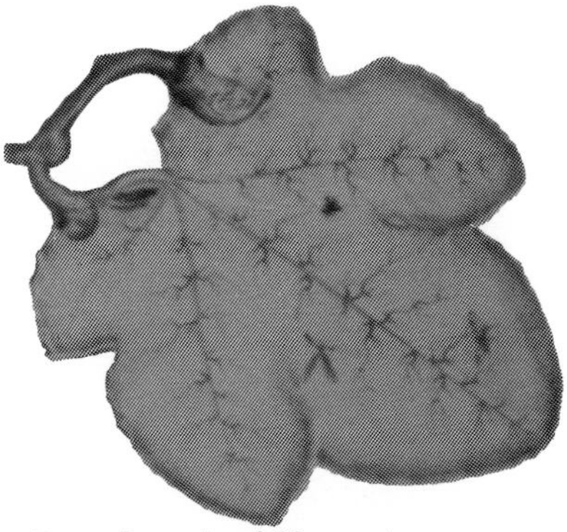

One of a pair of Worcester leaf dishes with green stalk handles, circa 1760, approx. 18cm. wide.(Christie's) £2,090

A Dr. Wall Worcester quart mug with strap handle, circa 1770, 6.1/8in. high. (Robt. W. Skinner Inc.) £163

A remarkable globular pot-pourri vase and cover with scroll handles, painted with brilliant specimens of Easter cacti, signed *W Hale*, 20.5cm., date code for 1905. (Phillips) £1,700

A Worcester partridge-tureen and cover, the bird on an oval nest to the right, its plumage enriched in shades of brown, the edge of the cover with stylised entwined straw, circa 1765, 17.5cm. long. (Christie's) £7,700

A Worcester flared cylindrical mug with strap handle, painted in a typical famille rose palette with The Beckoning Chinaman Pattern, circa 1758, 11.5cm. high. (Christie's London) £660

A Worcester hunting jug, painted in the manner of John Wood, with two dogs stalking a capercaillie, a horseman approaching, 18.7cm. (Phillips London) £800

and model in any required style. Also very popular at the time were ivory carvings which were being brought over from Japan and India. Most porcelain factories tried to reproduce these tones, but Worcester was by far the most successful with their 'Old Ivory' and 'Blush Ivory' bodies, which were widely copied and used on most of Hadley's figures, as well as vases and teawares.

After the death of their director R W Binns in 1900 and Hadley in 1903, the Worcester factory, which had bought out Graingers in 1889, continued to rely on the popularity of their designs, and little new or very exciting was produced for the next twenty years.

During the later first period a crescent or square mark was used on pieces decorated with underglaze blue, then incised *B* marks were used from 1792 till 1800. Thereafter the name of the factory usually appears, with date codes below the factory mark from 1862.

A Worcester finger bowl stand, painted in colours with sprays of flowers, 14.5cm., and a saucer en suite, 13cm.
(Phillips) (Two) £580

A Worcester blue and white faceted baluster cream jug, painted with The Root Pattern, circa 1758, 9cm. high.
(Christie's) £825

A pair of Kerr and Binns reticulated perfume bottles and stoppers with jewelled panels, 16cm., 1862. (Phillips London) £750

A very fine large Worcester mug of bell shape with a plain handle, painted in bright Chinese style enamels with the 'Beckoning Chinaman' pattern, 14cm., circa 1754–56.
(Phillips) £4,200

A Kerr & Binns vase in Limoges enamel style, by Thomas Bott Snr., signed and dated 1862, 24cm., shield mark and signature. (Phillips London) £260

A Worcester leaf dish with a butterfly hovering above flowering branches, circa 1758, 18.5cm. wide. (Christie's) £550

A small Worcester vase, painted with festoons of pink and yellow roses, signed *Chair,* below the fine arabesque piercing by George Owen, 10.8cm.
(Phillips London) £2,000

Worcester porcelain teapot, printed in a blue and white pattern of fence and tram-line design, circa 1770, 5½in. high.
(G. A. Key) £350

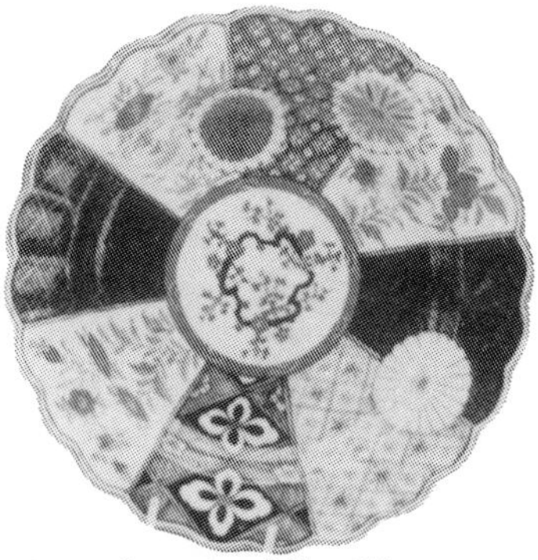

One of a pair of fine Worcester polychrome plates, each painted with the 'Old Mosaic Japan' pattern, 21.5cm., late 18th century. (Bearne's)
Two £800

A Worcester group of shells and coral forming a mound, on circular base modelled and gilt with scrolls, 12cm. diam.
(Lawrence Fine Arts) £495

A good James Hadley & Sons Worcester earthenware bottle vase painted with three japanesque cranes, circa 1896–97, 10in. high.
(Tennants) £150

A pair of pot-pourri vases, covers and inner covers of spreading baluster shape with foliate scroll handles, 25.5cm.
(Phillips) £1,000

A fine early Worcester coffee cup of quatrelobed shape, painted in stronger than usual colours with a Long Eliza figure, circa 1752-53, 7cm.
(Phillips London) £3,500

James Stinton, a tall cylindrical vase with flared rim and foot shaded in bright gold, painted with a brace of pheasant, 22.5cm., date code for 1923.
(Phillips) £550

A Worcester plate from The Duke of Gloucester Service, gold crescent mark, circa 1775, 22.5cm. diam.
(Christie's) £14,300

An early Worcester cream jug of pear shape with large sparrow-beak lip and scroll handle, 7cm. high, circa 1752-53. (Phillips)
£1,800

A large 'bow' vase, signed John Stinton, 30.5cm. high, shape no. 1428, date code for 1908. (Phillips) £2,600

A pair of Worcester Hogarth comports modelled as a girl and boy leaning on tree trunks, in the style of Kate Greenaway, 21cm., date codes for 1886. (Phillips London) £750

One of a pair of Worcester blue-scale tapering hexagonal vases and covers, circa 1768, 28cm. and 29.5cm. high. (Christie's) £14,300

One of a pair of ice pails, liners and covers, painted by P. Bradley, circa 1830, 33cm. £8,800

A Worcester oblong-shaped basket with pierced cover, painted with flowers, 14.5cm. (Lawrence Fine Arts) £1,100

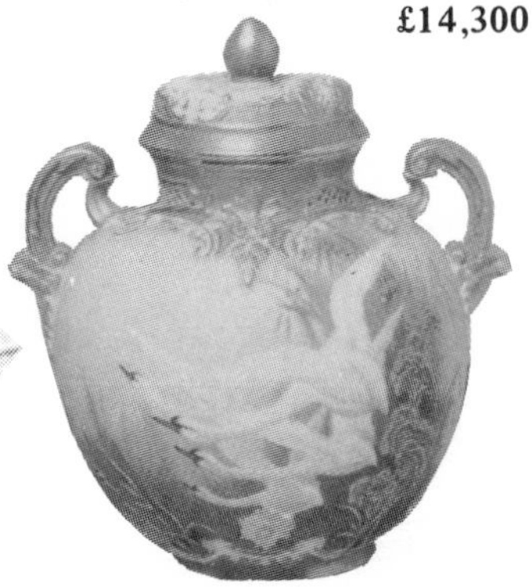

A globular pot-pourri vase and cover, painted on a matt sky-blue ground with a flock of four swans emerging from raised gold plants, signed *G. Johnson*, 15cm. (Phillips) £1,600

An unrecorded Worcester plate painted in blue with a high handled basket containing prunus, chrysanthemums and paeonies, 21cm. (Phillips) £520

A tall tear-shaped vase and cover with a ribbed neck, the body painted with pink and yellow roses, signed *Hood*, 24.5cm. (Phillips) £460

A Worcester 'blind earl' sweetmeat dish, painted in deep underglaze blue and with scattered insects, 15cm. long, crescent mark, circa 1765. (Phillips) £2,050

Singing Monk, a very rare Kerr and Binns extinguisher in unglazed Parian, 11.5cm. (Phillips) £750

A Worcester taper stick, painted with flower sprays on a royal blue ground, 10cm. (Lawrence Fine Arts) £220

Worcester porcelain jug, the blush ivory ground with hand-painted floral sprigs, circa 1902, 7in. high. (G. A. Key) £210

A fine early Worcester cylindrical mug, painted in deep mauve monochrome with overgrown Classical ruins in a gentle landscape, 8.5cm. (Phillips) £4,300

A pair of Worcester shagreen-ground Imari pattern tapering hexagonal vases and domed covers, painted with fabulous winged beasts sinuously entwined about flowering shrubs, circa 1770, 30.5cm. high. (Christie's) £26,400

An early Worcester baluster tankard with a spurred loop handle and scroll terminal, the body painted in colours with Oriental flowering peony, 9.5cm. (Phillips) £3,000

A large Worcester porter mug, printed in blue with a rare print of The Temple Bells, circa 1780, 15cm. (Phillips London) £750

A Worcester porcelain coffee cup and saucer painted by 'The Spotted Fruit Painter', saucer 5¼in. wide. (Dacre, Son & Hartley) £440

A Worcester sparrow-beak cream jug of pear shape, painted with the 'Arcade' pattern, 10cm. high, circa 1765-70. (Phillips) £440

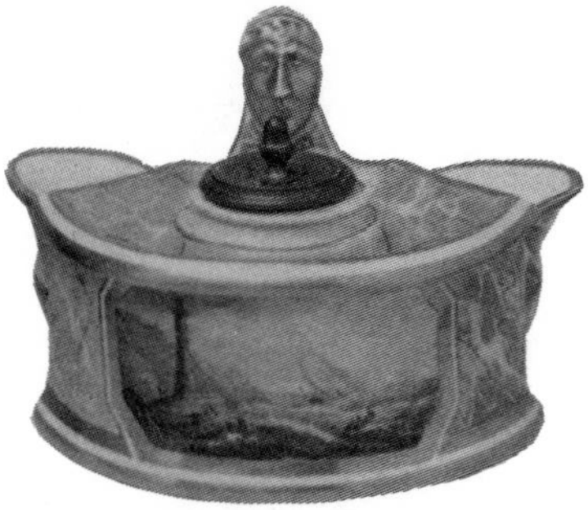

A Barr, Flight & Barr inkstand with two ear-shaped holders at the side flanking a loop handle with gilt mask, 14cm. (Phillips) £700

A rare Worcester eye bath of boat shape on a slender stem with a spreading foot, painted in blue, 4.5cm. (Phillips) £1,700

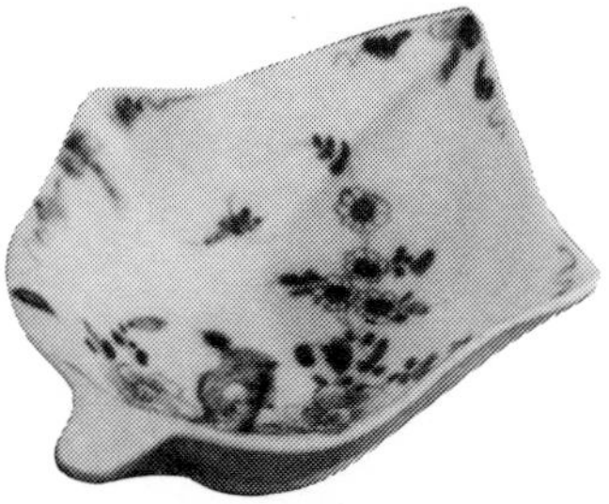

A rare early Worcester leaf-shaped pickle dish, decorated in underglaze blue with flowers and a moth in Oriental style, circa 1752, 4 x 3in. (Woolley & Wallis) £400

A Worcester teapot and cover, circa 1758, 12.5cm. high. (Phillips) £1,300

A Barr, Flight & Barr porcelain circular tureen and stand, the painted panel attributed to Thos. Baxter, 7in. high, 7½in. wide overall, circa 1810-15. (Dacre, Son & Hartley) £4,200

A rare Worcester teapot and cover of early fluted silver shape, painted in blue with the Prunus Root pattern, 12.5cm. (Phillips London) £3,300

A good Worcester transfer printed mug, crisply printed in black with the Whitton Anglers, circa 1765, 5¾in. high. (Tennants) £800

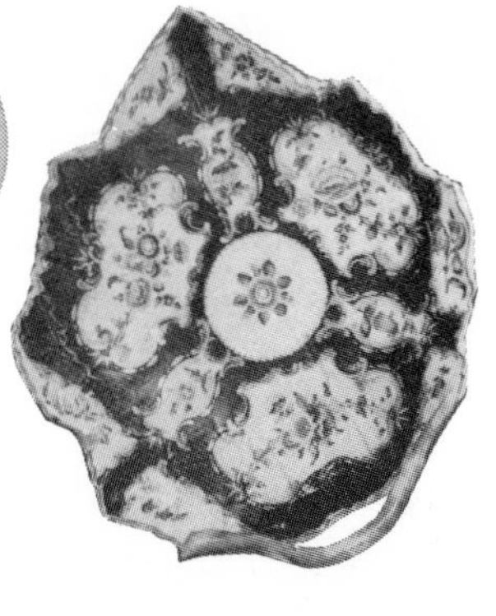

A Worcester leaf shaped dish with gilt serrated rim and green twig handle, painted in colours with festoons of flowers, 22cm. (Phillips) £850

An attractive Worcester sucrier and cover, richly decorated in the Sèvres style with rococo shaped turquoise panels edged in gold, 12.5cm. (Phillips) £2,600

Early 19th century Chamberlain's Worcester honeypot and cover, 4¼in. £460

A Chamberlain's Worcester watch stand modelled as Apollo holding his lyre and draped in a gilt flowered robe, circa 1795, 23cm. high. (Christie's London) £462

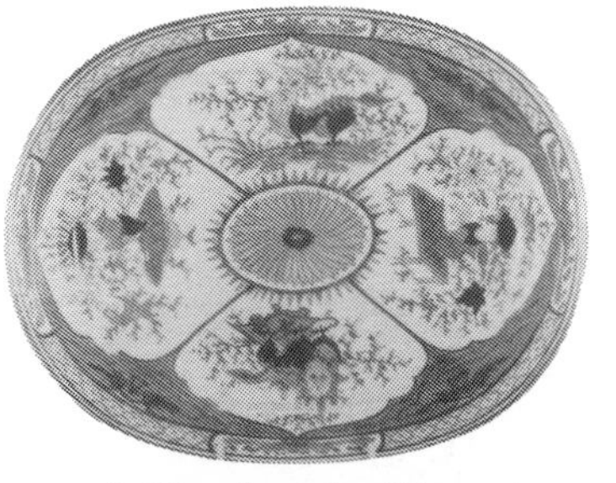

A Chamberlains Worcester porcelain oval dish painted and gilded with 'Kylin' or 'Dragons in Compartments' pattern, 12½in. long, 9½in. wide. (Dacre, Son & Hartley) £680

A large Chamberlain jug, finely gilt with bands of hops and foliage on alternating blue and white grounds, 19.5cm. (Phillips) £850

A Chamberlains Worcester porcelain cup and saucer with a painted scene of a castle framed in gilt and inscribed '*Sherbourn*', saucer 5½in. wide, circa 1815. (Dacre, Son & Hartley) £1,500

A Chamberlains Worcester beaker inscribed '*Peace*' possibly commemorating the battle of the Nile, painted in the manner of John Wood, chipped. (Phillips) £750

A Chamberlain's Worcester armorial plate, decorated with the Arms of Allan, 9¼in. diam. £240

A Chamberlains Worcester spill vase, with an elongated panel depicting Cardinal Wolsey, 8cm. (Lawrence Fine Arts) £880

A Chamberlain's Worcester yellow ground reticulated two handled cup and saucer pierced with gilt hexagons, script marks, circa 1830. (Christie's London) £660

A First Period Worcester saucer, crossed swords mark and 9 in underglaze blue. £330

A First Period Worcester leaf-shaped dish with raised ribs, 21.7cm. wide. £305

A First Period Worcester apple-green teacup and saucer, crossed swords mark and 9 in underglaze blue. £395

A First Period Worcester coffee cup and saucer, painted in an orange Japan pattern. (Lawrence Fine Arts) £209

A First Period Worcester apple-green teapoy and cover with floral knop, 16.5cm. high. £770

A First Period Worcester sweetmeat stand with three scallop shaped dishes, painted with flowers in underglaze blue, 9in. (Lawrence Fine Arts) £1,100

A First Period Worcester globular teapot and cover, polychrome enamel decorated with sprays of flowers, 13.5cm. (Osmond Tricks) £320

A Worcester First Period cream jug, with sparrow-beak spout, 9.5cm.,square seal mark. £305

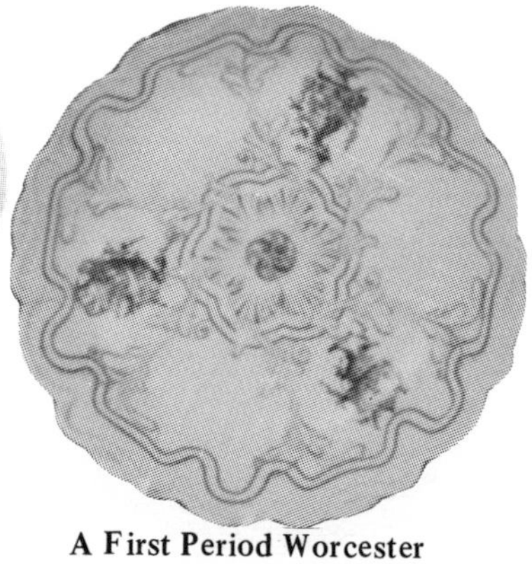

A First Period Worcester junket dish, painted with three classical vases adorned with flower branches, 23cm., cracked. (Lawrence Fine Arts) £253

A Worcester, Flight & Barr goblet, script mark and incised B, circa 1805, 12cm. high. £970

A Worcester, Flight & Barr inkstand. £400

An early Flight and Barr yellow ground bough pot and cover, the central panel painted with convolvulus, roses, poppies and stocks.
(Phillips) £2,200

A Worcester Flight & Barr oviform jug, with central medallion painted by John Pennington in grisaille with a portrait of King George III, height 6½in., circa 1790.
(Bonhams) £1,700

A Worcester jardiniere by Flight & Barr, painted with a mountain finch perched on a rock. (Lawrence Fine Arts) £2,750

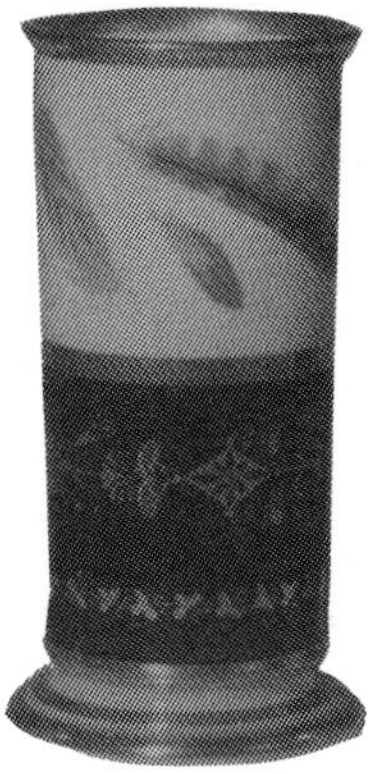

A Worcester, Flight & Barr blue ground spill vase, circa 1805, 12cm. high. £380

A Worcester, Flight & Barr, canary-yellow ground flared flower pot with fixed gilt ring handles, circa 1805, 16cm. high. (Christie's) £1,404

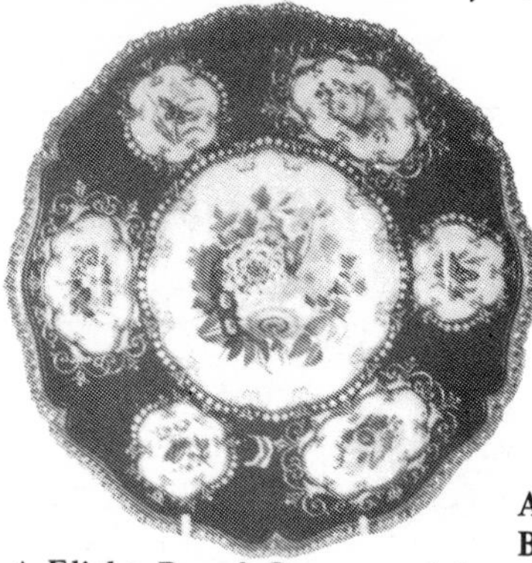

A Flight, Barr & Barr porcelain dessert dish with paintings of flowers and butterflies, attributed to Henry Stinton, circa 1825, 10in. wide. (Dacre, Son & Hartley) £2,600

A Worcester vase, by Flight Barr & Barr, painted in ancient Greek style with figures of Cadmus and Actaeon in flesh colour. (Lawrence Fine Arts) £660

A Worcester oblong tray, by Flight Barr & Barr, painted with a group of blackcurrants, cherries and gooseberries arranged on a cabbage leaf, 13cm. (Lawrence Fine Arts) £550

Part of a one hundred and fifty-two piece Worcester dinner service, by Flight, Barr & Barr, the borders painted with flowers in underglaze blue, overglaze iron-red and pink, circa 1815. £34,560

A Worcester, Flight, Barr & Barr urn-shaped two-handled vase and cover, circa 1820, 46cm. high. £1,650

One of a pair of Flight, Barr & Barr porcelain shallow circular dishes with gros bleu borders, in the manner of J.Barker; 7¾in. wide. (Dacre, Son & Hartley) Two £620

A Flight, Barr & Barr Worcester armorial vase and cover, attributed to Thos. Baxter, 19cm. high. £3,200

A Grainger's Worcester porcelain tankard with boldy gilded borders, scrolling and handle, 5¼in. high, circa 1812-20. (Dacre, Son & Hartley) £1,200

A very fine Grainger Lee and Co wall plaque, painted with a view of Worcester from the North West, 27.5cm., marked *Grainger Lee and Co. Worcester.* (Phillips London) £2,100

One of a pair of Grainger Worcester mugs with single spur handles, titled below painted panels, 'Drawing Cover' and 'The Death', 11.5cm. high. (Phillips) £6,600

A Grainger, Lee & Co. Worcester tea service, painted in bright Imari style with panels of fences and foliage on blue and red grounds with zig-zag bands and flowerheads, pattern no. 575, some pieces with script marks. (Phillips) £900

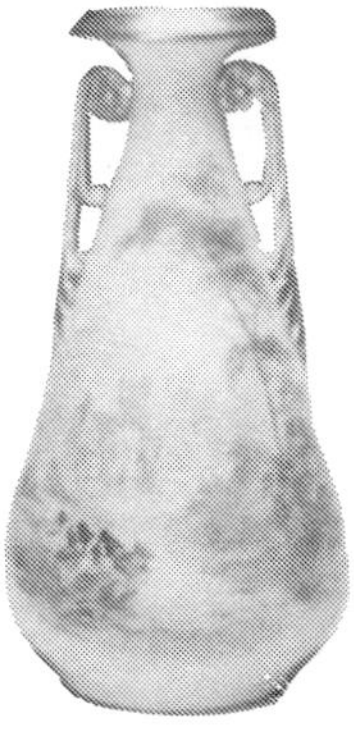

One of a pair of Grainger Worcester vases, painted by John Stinton, with views of Melrose Abbey and Stratford on Avon, 26.5cm. (Lawrence Fine Arts) Two £726

A set of three Worcester vases by Grainger, painted with flowers in panels, 24cm. and 20cm. (Lawrence Fine Arts) £352

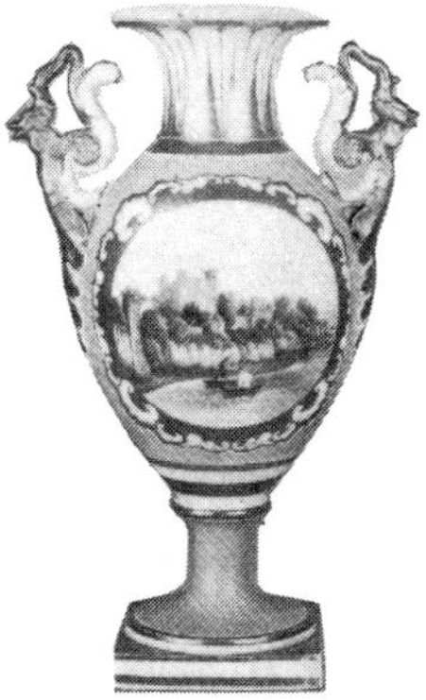

One of a pair of late 19th century Worcester porcelain vases, Grainger period, 9.3/8in. high. (Christie's) £358

A Royal Worcester porcelain jardiniere by John Stinton, with painted highland cattle watering in a mountainous lakeland landscape, 25cm. diam. (Henry Spencer) £2,200

A Royal Worcester figure of a negro man dressed in trousers and shirt and wearing a hat, 1882. (Greenslades) £352

A Worcester (Flight) Royal armorial sauce tureen and cover from the service made to the order of the Duke of Clarence, circa 1789, 17.5cm. wide. (Christie's London) £770

A fine Royal Worcester porcelain two handled vase by Harry Davis, the handles moulded with grotesque mythical beasts heads, 1899, 32cm. high. (Henry Spencer) £2,050

A pair of Royal Worcester figures in the form of Eastern water carriers, each on one knee pouring the contents from a large jar, 25.5cm., printed mark, circa 1891. (Bearne's) £860

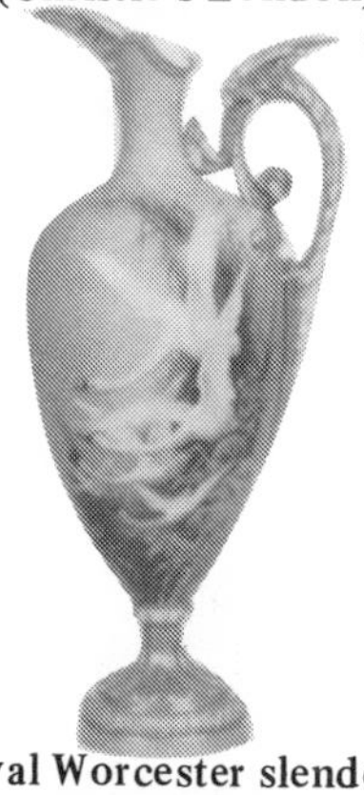

A Royal Worcester slender oviform ewer, painted by C. Baldwyn with swans in flight among brown reeds and richly gilt foliage, date code for 1902, 35cm. high. (Christie's London) £4,180

A rare Royal Worcester porcelain 'Persian' pierced vase modelled by James Hadley, with gilded decoration by Samuel Ranford, of birds amongst scrolling foliage, 7in. high. (Spencer's) £1,000

A pair of Royal Worcester figures of Joy and Sorrow modelled by James Hadley, modelled as maidens standing on waisted circular bases, date code for circa 1933, 9½in. high. (Christie's S. Ken) £462

Royal Worcester plate, signed James Stinton, puce mark, 1922, 10in. diam. (Giles Haywood) £130

A Royal Worcester shallow vase with twin leaf moulded handles the spirally moulded body painted by Jarman, date code for circa 1911, 12in. across. (Christie's S. Ken) £495

A Royal Worcester cabaret set moulded in relief with scrolls and foliage in green and flutes in ivory and peach, printed mark for 1886. (Christie's S. Ken) £500

A Royal Worcester chamber candlestick modelled as a mouse nibbling at the sconce, 15cm., date code for 1912. (Phillips London) £260

A late 19th century Royal Worcester porcelain figure of a Yankee resting against a post, date letter for 1881, 18cm. high. (Henry Spencer) £160

A Royal Worcester blue-ground three-piece garniture, decorated by Thomas Bott, the largest with TB monogram and 63, gilded by Josiah Davis, the largest 16in. high. (Christie's) £4,714

A Royal Worcester figure of a woman on a swing, entitled 'Alice', from the series of Victorian figures by Ronald Van Ruyckevelt. (Bearne's) £230

A Royal Worcester two-handled footed bulbous vase, by John Stinton, model no. 1428, puce mark, 1930, 12in. high. (Giles Haywood) £4,400

A pair of Royal Worcester porcelain 'Miniature Cairo' water carriers, both standing wearing robes and carrying amphoras, 1913 and 1916, 9 and 10in. high. (Spencer's) £500

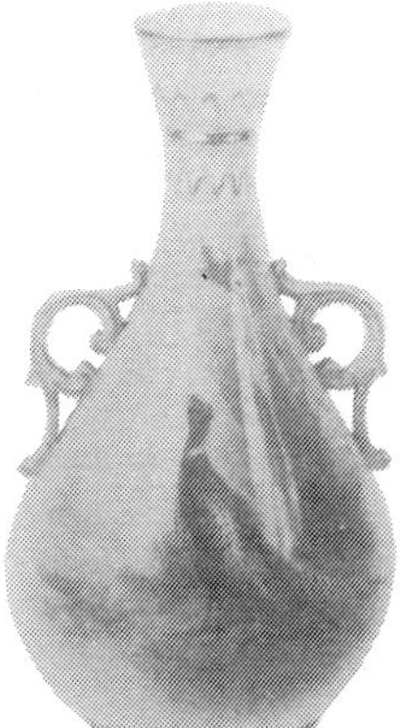

Royal Worcester china vase painted by Jas. Stinton, 5.75in. high, date code for 1909 and pattern no. 995. (Prudential Fine Art) £250

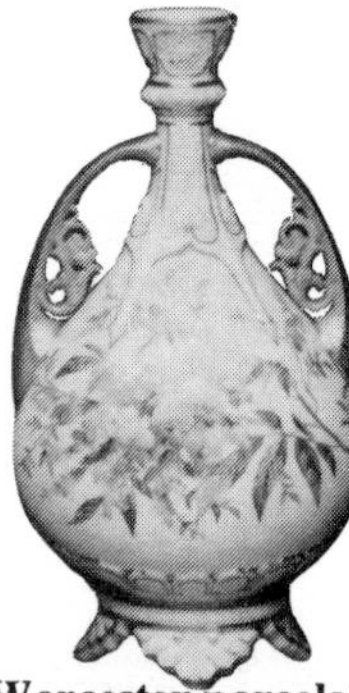

Royal Worcester porcelain double-handled vase, England, late 19th century, matte ivory enamel decorated flowers surrounded by gilt leaves, 13in. high.
(Skinner Inc.) £499

A 19th century Royal Worcester porcelain figure of an elephant, wearing a blanket and howdah, 7½in. high. £275

A Royal Worcester vase, by George Owen, shape no. 1527, date code for 1922, 11cm. high. £2,000

A Royal Worcester green ground oviform vase, painted by Jas Stinton with a continuous frieze of pheasants in a woodland and a misty river landscape, date code for 1897, 33cm. high. (Christie's London) £1,870

Three Royal Worcester 'Ivory' figures from The Countries of the World series after James Hadley, modelled as a Yankee, John Bull and an Irishman, date codes for 1881, 1889 and 1897, about 17.5cm. high.
(Christie's) £715

One of a pair of Royal Worcester tapering vases with tall slender tapering necks and gilt ring and scroll handles, date code for circa 1892, 11½in. high. (Christie's S. Ken)
Two £605

A Royal Worcester footed pot-pourri, model no. 1286, black mark, signed R. Lewis, 10in. high. (Giles Haywood) £320

Pair of Royal Worcester Cairo water carriers, England, 1883, enamel and gilt accenting over an ivory body, modelled by James Hadley, 21in. high.
(Skinner Inc.) £810

Royal Worcester two-handled footed bulbous vase, signed W. Hale, 1919, model no. 1428, 12in. high. (Giles Haywood) £3,100

A Royal Worcester pepper pot modelled as an owl perched on a barrel, 10cm., date code for 1908. (Phillips London) £130

A pair of Royal Worcester figures modelled as a lady and gentleman, 14in. high, circa 1887. £1,000

A Royal Worcester 'ivory' mermaid and nautilus centre-piece, decorated by Callow-hill, circa 1878. £970

A Royal Worcester two-handled vase, the body painted by N. Roberts, signed, blue painted marks and date code for 1899, no. 2007, 49cm. high. (Christie's) £1,430

A pair of Royal Worcester figures of seated musicians, he playing a pipe, his companion playing a guitar, 4in. high. (Christie's S. Ken) £200

A Royal Worcester two handled slender oviform vase, the sides painted by Sedgley, date code for 1914, 36.5cm. high. (Christie's London) £660

One of a pair of Royal Worcester vases, date code for 1914, 10½in. high. (Reeds Rains) £359

An attractive pair of Royal Worcester porcelain vases painted by John Stinton, with scenes of a pair of highland cattle watering and a pair of cattle grazing, 31cm. high. (Henry Spencer) £2,500

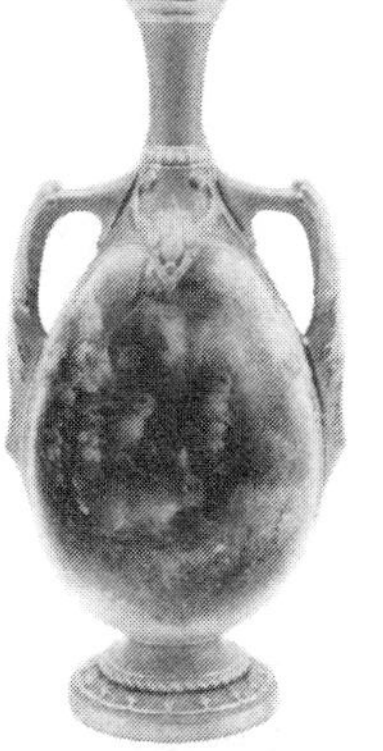

A rare Royal Worcester vase painted with rabbits by C.H.C. Baldwyn, signed, the handles in pale metallic green, cream and gold, 10¾in. high. (Tennants) £1,900

ZSOLNAY

The Zsolnay earthenware pottery was established in 1862 at Pécs in Hungary by Vilmos Zsolnay, with the aim of shaping a characteristic national style.

Most of the output consisted of practical ware for everyday use, though some ornamental pieces were produced, often with Persian inspired motifs. Vases and bowls were made in Art Nouveau style with boldly coloured glazes and lustre decoration. These were the achievements of an experimental workshop under the direction of Vinsce Wartha which was operational around the turn of the century. Around that time too, vases with painted decoration designed by Josef Rippl-Rónai, also in Art Nouveau style, were produced.

The marks consist of versions of five churches with *Zsolnay*, and sometimes also with *Pécs*.

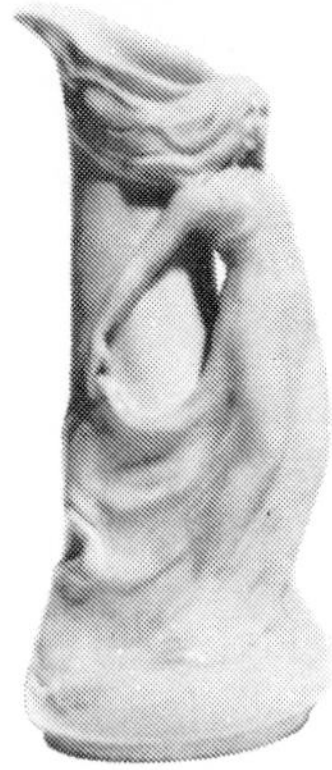

A Zsolnay ceramic jug, the handle formed as an Art Nouveau maiden with flowing hair and dress, 22.8cm. high.
(Christie's) £220

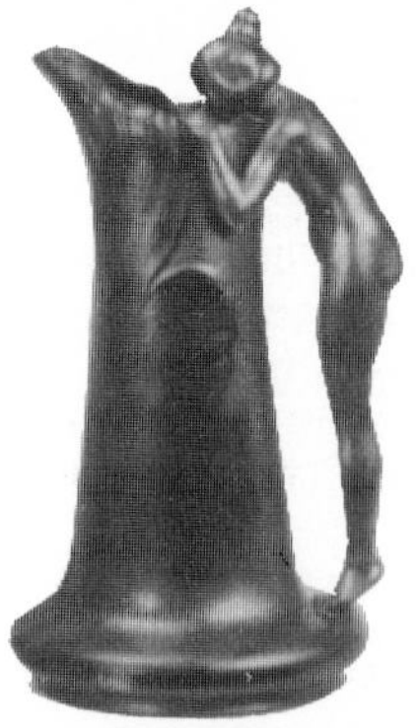

A Zsolnay Pecs green lustre jug, the handle modelled as a nude maiden gazing over rim, 16in. high.
(Christie's S. Ken) £715

A Zsolnay Pecs lustre group, modelled as two polar bears on a large rock in a green and blue golden lustre, 4½in. high.
(Christie's) £250

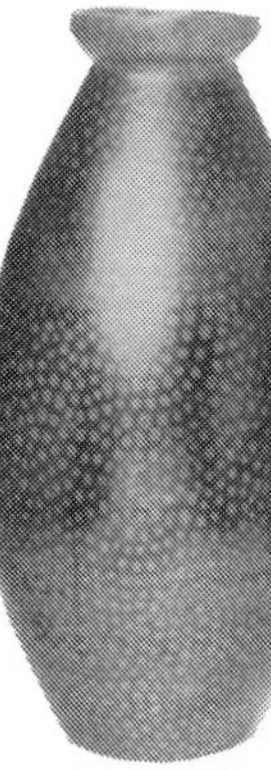

A large Zsolnay lustre vase, covered with a violet/plum lustre glaze with random spots of gold/green/amber hues, 45.5cm. high. (Phillips London) £680

A small Zsolnay figural lustre vase decorated on the shoulders with the partially clad Orpheus with his lyre beside him and an amorous mermaid, 13cm. high.
(Phillips) £680

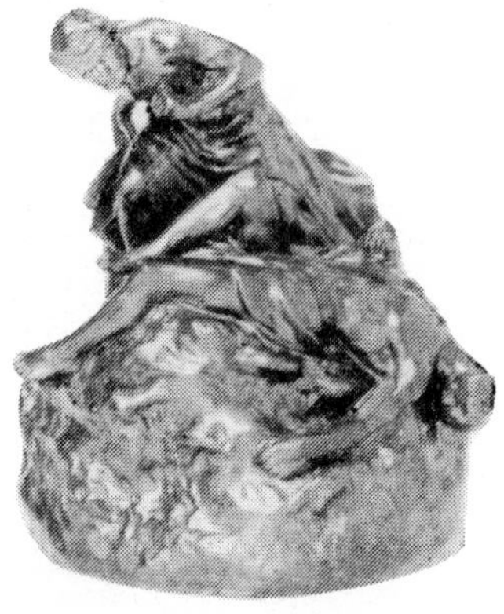

A large Zsolnay lustre group, of two men possibly Cain and Abel, one lying prostrate on a domed rocky base with the other towering above him, 37.5cm. high. (Phillips) £550

A Zsolnay lustre figural ewer possibly designed by Lajos Mack moulded around its circumference with three sinuous Art Nouveau maidens, 35cm. high. (Phillips) £360

ZURICH

The Zurich porcelain factory was begun by a group of business men in 1763, under the direction of Adam Spengler, a skilled faiencier. At first, soft paste porcelain was produced, but later production changed to hard paste, using clays from near Limoges.

The early years were very productive, with a thriving export trade. Small individual pieces of table ware were made, as well as great services. From about 1780 vases in the Sèvres style were produced in simple forms with painted rural scenes, often inspired by Nilson engravings.

1775–9 saw the finest period of figure production. Many of these were by Johann Valentin Sonnenschein, whose work followed German models, depicting peasants, soldiers etc. in contemporary dress. Towards the end of his career he also designed some larger table centrepieces. Spengler's son, John James, also spent a short while making figures at Zürich before going to Derby.

The smoky brown hue of Zürich porcelain can often look rather like Ludwigsburg, and there was little originality of form. The best known painter at the factory was the poet Salomon Gessner, who signed his work, and specialised in rather tedious Swiss landscapes.

After Spengler's death in 1790 porcelain production ceased, and faience only was produced thereafter.

The usual mark is a Z with a stroke through it, in underglaze blue.

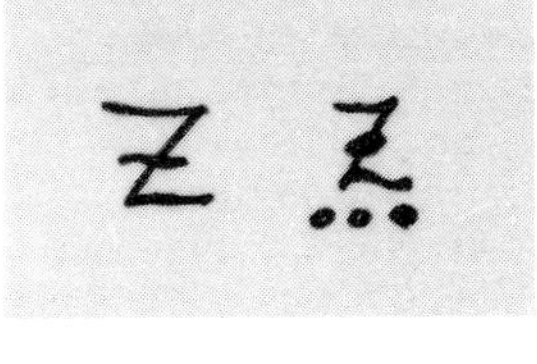

A Zurich figure of a shepherd, modelled by J. J. Meyer, 20cm. high, incised mark N I. (Phillips) £4,400

A Zurich figure of a young girl feeding chickens, her long skirt with alternating bands of cornflowers and berried foliage, circa 1775, 11.5cm. high. (Christie's London) £935

A Zurich ornithological teapot and a cover of bullet shape, painted in colours, one side with an owl and a woodpecker, the other with an eagle and a snipe, circa 1770, 17cm. wide. (Christie's Geneva) £1,900

Zurich sugar bowl and cover with gilt fruit knop and floral decoration, circa 1765, 10cm. high. £1,500

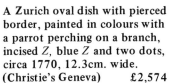

A Zurich oval dish with pierced border, painted in colours with a parrot perching on a branch, incised *Z*, blue *Z* and two dots, circa 1770, 12.3cm. wide. (Christie's Geneva) £2,574

A Zurich figure of a sportswoman, a duck in her left hand, a rifle in her right, with a spaniel at her side, circa 1770, 20.5cm. high. (Christie's Geneva) £1,073

INDEX